GREAT EVENTS
FROM
HISTORY II

GREAT EVENTS FROM HISTORY II

Science
and
Technology
Series

Volume 3
1931-1952

Edited by

FRANK N. MAGILL

SALEM PRESS

Pasadena, California   Englewood Cliffs, New Jersey

Library of Congress Cataloging-in-Publication Data
Great events from history II. Science and technology
series / edited by Frank N. Magill.
    p.   cm.
    Includes bibliographical references and index.
    1. Science—History—20th century. 2. Technology—
History—20th century. I. Magill, Frank Northen, 1907-

Q125.G825 1991
509'.04—dc20
ISBN 0-89356-637-3 (set)   91-23313
ISBN 0-89356-640-3 (volume 3)   CIP

PRINTED IN THE UNITED STATES OF AMERICA

92-0373

LIST OF EVENTS IN VOLUME III

GREAT EVENTS
FROM
HISTORY II

LAWRENCE DEVELOPS THE CYCLOTRON

Category of event: Physics
Time: January 2, 1931
Locale: Berkeley, California

Lawrence developed the first successful magnetic resonance accelerator for protons, giving rise to the modern era of particle accelerators

Principal personages:

ERNEST ORLANDO LAWRENCE (1901-1958), an American nuclear physicist who was awarded the 1939 Nobel Prize in Physics

M. STANLEY LIVINGSTON (1905-1986), an American nuclear physicist who was the coinventor of the cyclotron with Lawrence

NIELS EDLEFSEN (1893-   ), an American physicist who worked with Lawrence on the cyclotron

DAVID SLOAN (1905-   ), an American physicist and electrical engineer who developed a resonance linear accelerator with Lawrence

Summary of Event

The invention of the cyclotron by Ernest Orlando Lawrence marks the beginning of the modern era of high-energy physics. Although the energies have increased steadily, the principles incorporated in the cyclotron have been fundamental to succeeding generations of accelerators, many of which were also developed in Lawrence's laboratory. The care and support for such machines have also given rise to "big science": the massing of scientists, money, and machines in support of experiments to discover the nature of the atom and its constituents.

Lawrence received his undergraduate degree in physics at the University of South Dakota and studied under W. F. G. Swann, an expert in electromagnetic theory and experiment at the Universities of Minnesota and Chicago and at Yale University, where he received his Ph.D. in 1925. He was an assistant professor until 1928, when he was lured to the University of California by an associate professorship, the opportunity to teach more graduate courses, and the new physics research laboratory.

At the University of California, Lawrence took an interest in the new physics of the atomic nucleus, which had been developed by Ernest Rutherford and his followers in England, and which was attracting more attention as the development of quantum mechanics seemed to offer an explanation of the problems of atomic physics that had long preoccupied physicists.

In order to explore the nucleus of the atom, however, suitable probes were required. Rutherford had used alpha particles ejected from radioactive substances to make his early studies, but these were not energetic enough to penetrate the nuclei of most atoms. An artificial means of accelerating ions to high energies was needed. During the late 1920's, a variety of means were tried to accelerate alpha particles protons (hydrogen ions), and electrons, but none had been successful in causing a nuclear transformation when Lawrence entered the field. The high voltages required stressed the resources available to physicists. It was believed that more than a million volts would be required to accelerate an ion to sufficient energies to penetrate even the lightest atomic nuclei. At such voltages, insulators broke down, releasing sparks across great distances. European researchers even attempted to harness lightning to the task, with fatal results.

Early in April, 1929, Lawrence chanced on an article in *Archiv für Electrotechnik* by Rolf Wideroe, a German electrical engineer, describing a linear accelerator of ions that worked by passing an ion through two sets of electrodes, each of which carried the same voltage and increased the energy of the ions correspondingly. By spacing the electrodes appropriately and using an alternating electrical field, this "resonance acceleration" of ions could speed subatomic particles up to many multiples of the energy applied in each step, overcoming the problems presented when one tried to apply a single charge to an ion all at once. Unfortunately, the spacing of the electrodes would have to be increased as the ions were accelerated, since they would travel farther between each alternation of the phase of the accelerating charge, making an accelerator impractically long in those days of small-scale physics.

Lawrence knew that a magnetic field would cause the ions to be deflected and form a curved path. If the electrodes were placed across the diameter of the circle formed by the ions' path, they should spiral out as they were accelerated, staying in phase with the accelerating charge until they reached the periphery of the magnetic field. This, it seemed to him, afforded a means of producing indefinitely high voltages without using high voltages by recycling the accelerated ions through the same electrodes. Many doubted that such a method would be effective. No mechanism was known that would keep the circulating ions in sufficiently tight orbits to avoid collisions with the walls of the accelerating chamber. Others tried to use resonance acceleration without success. Lawrence waited nearly a year before encouragement from Otto Stern, a visitor in the University of California physics department from the University of Hamburg, persuaded him to try the method.

In the spring of 1930, Lawrence put one of his graduate students, Niels Edlefsen, to work on reducing his idea to practice. Edlefsen used glass flasks coated with silver or copper with a diametrical gap to serve as their electrodes. A filament introduced through one aperture in the flask produced protons from hydrogen introduced through another. When the flask was placed between the poles of a 10-centimeter electromagnet and radio frequency current was applied to the metallic electrodes, Edlefsen thought he saw evidence of particle acceleration. Unfortunately, he left Berkeley before this could be confirmed.

Another graduate student, M. Stanley Livingston, took up the project. He decided quickly that resonance could not be achieved with Edlefsen's apparatus. For his dissertation project, he used a brass cylinder 10 centimeters in diameter sealed with wax to hold a vacuum, a half-pillbox of copper mounted on an insulated stem to serve as the electrode, and a Hartley radio frequency oscillator producing 10 watts.

The shape resembled the letter D. The box itself constituted the other electrode: A brass bar was placed across it parallel to the straight side of the D with slots corresponding to those in the D. The hydrogen molecular ions were produced by a thermionic cathode mounted near the center of the apparatus from hydrogen gas admitted through an aperture in the side of the cylinder after a vacuum had been produced by a pump. Once formed, the oscillating electrical field drew them out and accelerated them as they passed through the gap between the bar and the D. The accelerated ions spiraled out in a magnetic field produced by a 10-centimeter electromagnet to a collector. By November, 1930, Livingston observed peaks in the collector current as he tuned the magnetic field through the value calculated to produce acceleration.

Borrowing a stronger magnet and tuning his radio frequency oscillator appropriately, Livingston produced 80,000 electronvolt ions at his collector on January 2, 1931, thus demonstrating the principle of magnetic resonance acceleration.

Impact of Event

Demonstration of the principle led to a succession of large cyclotrons, beginning with a 25-centimeter cyclotron developed in the spring and summer of 1931, which produced million electronvolt protons. Lawrence succeeded in winning support for his device from Frederick Cottrell's Research Corporation and the Chemical Foundation, which were interested in its applications to the production of high-voltage X rays. Lawrence also developed a linear accelerator for heavy ions with the help of David Sloan, another of his graduate students. Sloan built a million volt X-ray tube as well. With the support of the Research Corporation, Lawrence was able to secure a large electromagnet that had been developed for radio transmission and a disused Civil Engineering Laboratory to house it. This was the Radiation Laboratory. The 69-centimeter cyclotron built with the magnet was used to explore nuclear physics. Rather than ordinary hydrogen ions, it accelerated deuterons, ions of heavy water or deuterium that contain, in addition to the proton, the neutron, which was discovered by Sir James Chadwick in 1932. The accelerated deuteron, which injected neutrons into target atoms, was used to produce a wide variety of artificial radioisotopes, which had been discovered by Frédéric Joliot and Irène Joliot-Curie. Many of these, like technetium and carbon 14, were discovered with the cyclotron and found applications in medicine and tracer research.

The 69-centimeter cyclotron was enlarged to 94 centimeters in diameter in 1937. By 1939, Lawrence had built a 152-centimeter cyclotron for medical uses, including therapy with neutron beams. In that year, he won the Nobel Prize in Physics for the invention of the cyclotron and the production of radioisotopes. He also received $1.15 million from the Rockefeller Foundation in 1940 to build a 467-centimeter cyclotron, designed to produce 200 million electronvolt deuterons. World War II interrupted this effort, and Lawrence and the members of his Radiation Laboratory developed electromagnetic separation of uranium ions to produce the uranium-235 required for the atomic bomb. After the war, the 467-centimeter cyclotron was completed as a synchrocyclotron, which modulated the frequency of the accelerating fields to compensate for the increase of mass of ions as they approached the speed of light. The principle of synchronous acceleration, invented by Lawrence's associate Edwin Mattison McMillan, became fundamental to proton and electron synchrotrons, just as the linear accelerator was developed by another member of the Radiation Laboratory staff, Luis W. Alvarez.

The cyclotron and the Radiation Laboratory were the center of accelerator physics throughout the 1930's and well into the postwar era. The invention of the cyclotron not only provided a new tool for probing the nucleus but also gave rise to new forms of organizing scientific work and to applications in nuclear medicine and nuclear chemistry. Cyclotrons were built in many laboratories in the United States, Europe, and Japan, and became a standard tool of nuclear physics.

Bibliography

Childs, Herbert. *An American Genius: The Life of Ernest Orlando Lawrence, Father of the Cyclotron*. New York: E. P. Dutton, 1968. Anecdotally details the life of the cyclotron's inventor, relying heavily on interviews with his colleagues. Illustrated with a bibliography and index.

Heilbron, J. L., and Robert W. Seidel. *Lawrence and His Laboratory: A History of the Lawrence Berkeley Laboratory*. Berkeley: University of California Press, 1989. Describes in detail the development of accelerator technology in the 1920's and 1930's and the impact of these developments on nuclear physics up to World War II. Illustrated, with a bibliography and index.

Livingston, M. Stanley, ed. *The Development of High-Energy Accelerators*. New York: Dover, 1966. Twenty-eight classic articles and an introduction written by the coinventor of the cyclotron depict the evolution of direct voltage, resonance, linear, synchronous, and strong-focusing accelerators. Illustrated, with an index.

_____. *Particle Accelerators: A Brief History*. Cambridge, Mass.: Harvard University Press, 1969. Describes for the general reader the early attempts to produce high voltages for nuclear physics, the invention of the cyclotron and the electrostatic generator, the development of the betatron, and the origin and growth of the principles of synchronous acceleration and alternating gradient focusing. Illustrated, with references and an index.

Livingston, M. Stanley, and John P. Blewett. *Particle Accelerators*. New York: McGraw-Hill, 1962. The classic technical reference on particle accelerators and a comparative critical analysis of the capabilities of various types of accelerators as well as a brief historical essay on each. Illustrated, with references and indexes.

Mann, Wilfred Basil. *The Cyclotron*. 3d ed. London: Methuen, 1948. Written for university students, this monograph describes the cyclotron's history and development, contains an introduction by Lawrence, and is well illustrated, with sketches of the components of cyclotrons. Contains references and an index.

Robert W. Seidel

Cross-References

Cottrell Invents the Electrostatic Precipitation Process (1906), p. 320; Rutherford Presents His Theory of the Atom (1912), p. 527; Rutherford Discovers the Proton (1914), p. 590; Chadwick Discovers the Neutron (1932), p. 973; Cockcroft and Walton Split the Atom with a Particle Accelerator (1932), p. 978; Frédéric Joliot and Irène Joliot-Curie Develop the First Artificial Radioactive Element (1933), p. 987; Segrè Identifies the First Artificial Element, Technetium (1937), p. 1101; Libby Introduces the Carbon-14 Method of Dating Ancient Objects (1940's), p. 1160; Seaborg and McMillan Make Element 94, Plutonium (1941), p. 1181; The Tevatron Particle Accelerator Begins Operation at Fermilab (1985), p. 2301; The Superconducting Supercollider Is Under Construction in Texas (1988), p. 2372.

RUSKA CREATES THE FIRST ELECTRON MICROSCOPE

Categories of event: Physics and applied science
Time: April, 1931
Locale: The Berlin Institute of Technology, Berlin, Germany

Replacing light rays and optical lenses, respectively, with electron beams and "electron lenses," a group of German engineers pioneered electron microscopy

Principal personages:
ERNST RUSKA (1906-1988), a German engineer, researcher, and inventor who was a cowinner of the 1986 Nobel Prize in Physics
HANS BUSCH (1884-1973), a German physicist who founded a new science, electron optics
MAX KNOLL (1897-1969), a German engineer and professor who was Ruska's adviser and collaborator in building the first electron microscope
LOUIS DE BROGLIE (1892-1987), a French physicist who made the startling prediction of the "matter wave" and was awarded the 1929 Nobel Prize in Physics
REINHOLD RÜDENBERG (1883-1961), a German engineer and administrator who applied for a patent in electron microscopy in May, 1931

Summary of Event

A number of the most important inventions of the twentieth century had scattered origin, as did the first electron microscope constructed by Ernst Ruska and Max Knoll in 1931. Its history can be traced along three lines: motivation, theory, and technology. Scientists who look into the microcosmic world always demand microscopes of higher and higher resolution, or resolving power, that is, the ability of an optical instrument to distinguish closely spaced objects. As early as 1834, George Airy, the eminent British astronomer, theorized that there should be a natural limit to the resolution of (optical) microscopes. In 1873, two Germans, Ernst Abbe, cofounder of the Karl Zeiss Optical Works at Jena, and Hermann von Helmholtz, the famous physicist and philosopher, independently published papers on this issue. Both arrived at the same conclusion as Airy.

When it was proved that the wavelength of the light is the ultimate obstacle in raising the resolving power of the microscope, scientists and engineers began to consider electromagnetic radiations of shorter and shorter wavelengths. At the beginning of the twentieth century, Joseph Edwin Barnard experimented on microscopes using ultraviolet light. Such instruments, however, only modestly improved the resolution. In 1912, Max von Laue considered trying X rays. At the time, however, it was hard to turn "X-ray microscopy" into a physical reality. The wavelengths of X rays were exceedingly short; but they mostly penetrated material objects. Thus, it was made clear in the early 1920's that, in terms of resolving power, the optical microscope was approaching its limit. In a new microscopy, light—even electromagnetic radiation in general—as the traditional medium that carries image information, had to be replaced by a new medium. At the same time, progress in physics—theoretical as well as experimental—began to offer a prospective medium. In 1924, the French theoretical physicist Louis de Broglie advanced a startling hypothesis. His insight into the analogues between dynamic and optical phenomena and their mathematical formalities—a profound analogy first disclosed by William Rowan Hamilton in the 1830's—led him to state that there was something of a wave nature associated with material particles, particularly light microcosmic particles, such as electrons. His quantitative conclusions included a formula relating the particle's motion—more exactly, momentum—to the wavelength of the particle's associated wave. The faster the particle moves, the shorter the wavelength is.

Before the first electron microscope had been built, the technological possibility of electron microscopy occurred to some theoreticians along the line of the "matter wave." According to Dennis Gabor, in 1928 Leo Szilard suggested to him that an electron microscope should be made. Gabor, however, dismissed the idea with a forceful, yet hypothetical statement: "Everything under the electron beam would burn to a cinder!" The electron microscope is another case of technological breakthrough that illustrates an interesting historical theme: Those who knew too much theory did not make the thing; those who made it were not aware of the latest theory. When Knoll and Ruska built the first electron microscope in 1931, they had never heard about de Broglie's "matter wave." Ruska recollected that when, in 1932, he and Knoll first learned about de Broglie's idea, he became "extremely disappointed," and then "was immediately heartened," because he realized that those matter "waves must be around five orders of magnitude shorter in wavelength than light waves." It was based on two other lines of physical study—oscillography and electron optics—that Knoll and Ruska accomplished their invention. The core component of the two new subjects was the electron beam, or the "cathode ray," as it was usually called then. Although for a long time the physical nature of the beam was not clear, some nineteenth century physicists succeeded in controlling and focusing it. As early as 1858, the mathematician and physicist Julius Plücker noticed that magnetic fields could deflect the "electric glow discharge." Later, in 1869, Johann Wilhelm Hittorf performed more and better experiments in controlling the cathode rays. In 1891, Eduard Riecke, using Hittorf's results and carrying out his own calculations, conjectured about the ultimate corpuscular nature of the phenomena involved. Five years later, in 1896, Olaf Kristian Birkeland, a Norwegian physicist, after experimenting with axially symmetric magnetic fields, arrived at a very encouraging conclusion: "Parallel light rays are not concentrated better to the focal point by a lens than are cathode rays by a magnet."

From around 1910, the German physicist Hans Busch was the leading researcher in this field. In 1926, he published his theory on the trajectories of electrons in magnetic fields. His conclusion was that magnetic or electric fields possessing axial symmetry act as lenses for electrons or other charged particles. In 1927, he conducted experiments verifying his own theory with a magnetic lens. With these contributions, Busch has been recognized as the founder of a new field later known as electron optics. His theoretical study showed, *inter alia*, the exactness of the analogy between light rays and optical lenses on one side and electron beams and electromagnetic lenses on the other. Thus, one logical consequence should be the feasibility of electron microscopy. Busch's experimental verification, however, was not a complete success. Ruska noticed that there existed an "order-of-magnitude discrepancy between the size of cathode image that he [Busch] found experimentally and that required by the imaging equation," in short, between theory and measurement.

From 1928, Ruska, as a graduate student at The Berlin Institute of Technology, belonged to a group engaged in studying and building cathode ray oscilloscopes, an instrument much in demand in the industry of electric power. Knoll and Ruska worked hard to find the physical laws of focusing electron beams by magnetic or electric fields. Ruska's first project was the "bundling" of electron rays in the coaxial magnetic field of the short coil. On the one hand, he had to find a method of calculation for the optimal design; on the other hand, he tried to build "powerful and compactly built oscillographs." Because of this task, he was concerned with the discrepancies in Busch's result. At this juncture, the difficulty of Busch became Ruska's motivational force. Ruska carried out accurate measurements, especially with regard to "the lens theory of the short coil." By doing so, he identified the major problem in Busch's work, that is, the nonuniformity of the energy of the electrons in the beam. Beginning with certain nonuniformity, everything thereafter became increasingly diffused.

Knoll and Ruska's effort ended in a series of successes: verification of Busch's theory, design and materialization of a concentrated electron "writing spot," and the actual construction of the electron microscope. By April, 1931, they established a technological landmark with the "first constructional realization of an electron microscope," although when Knoll lectured about their work in June, he avoided the term electron microscope "for fear of being accused of showmanship."

Impact of Event

The world's first electron microscope, which took its first photographic record on April 7, 1931, was rudimentary. Its two-stage total magnification was only sixteen times. Galileo's first astronomical telescope, however, was also rudimentary and so were the Wright brothers' first airplanes. Since Ruska and Knoll's creation, progress in electron microscopy has been spectacular. It is one of the prominent examples that illustrate the historically unprecedented pace of science and technology in the twentieth century. One comparison in the field of microscopy is that it took centuries for the simple magnifier, or the "burning glass," to become the compound microscope, but the equivalent transition in the transmission electron microscope took only two years.

Ruska and Knoll's achievement immediately motivated others to study further and experiment, although electron microscopes with better-than-light-microscope resolution seemed in 1932, according to many experts at the time, a pipe dream. Ruska had set his goal to create an electron microscope that would have a resolution better than that of the best optical microscope and that could observe every kind of specimen that had been observed previously in the light microscope. After Knoll left the team to work on the developing technology of television, Ruska found new coworkers and stimulated more. Reinhold Rüdenberg was then the chief of the scientific department of the Siemens-Schuckent-Werke. At the end of May, 1931, he applied for a patent in electron microscopy; later, after Knoll and Ruska's first paper was published in 1932, he stated that similar work had been on-going for some time at Siemens. According to Ruska, Rüdenberg could not substantiate such claims with actual results.

In 1935, for the first time the electron microscope surpassed the optical microscope in resolution. The problem of damaging the specimen by the heating effects of the electron beam proved to be more difficult to resolve. In 1937, a team at the University of Toronto constructed the first generally usable electron microscope. In 1942, an RCA group headed by James Hillier produced its commercial transmission electron microscopes. From 1939 and 1940, research papers on electron microscopes began to appear in Sweden, Canada, the United States, and Japan; from 1944 to 1947, papers appeared in Switzerland, France, the Soviet Union, The Netherlands, and England. Following research work in laboratories, commercial transmission electron microscopes using magnetic lenses with short focal lengths also appeared in these countries.

Despite some priority disputes, Ruska's personal contribution has been generally recognized. In 1960, Ruska and Hillier were jointly presented the Albert Lasker Award in Medical Research for "their major contribution to the design, construction, development and perfection of the electron microscope, which led to the creation of an unique and much used research instrument." In 1986, Ruska received the Nobel Prize in Physics with Gerd Binnig and Heinrich Rohrer, two IBM physicist-engineers, for inventing the scanning tunneling microscope in the early 1980's. Although the scanning tunneling microscope is a different microscope from Ruska's transmission electron microscope, both types use the quantum-mechanical characteristics of the electron beam.

The long-range impact of the electron microscope on science and engineering is self-evident. It is justifiably described as one of the most important inventions of the twentieth century. On Ruska's 1931 invention, John Reisner of RCA stated: "While electron-optics people knew of the idea after the work by Busch on electron trajectories, Ruska did it. It was tough technology, and his was the step that got everyone going."

Bibliography

Bradbury, S. *The Evolution of the Microscope.* Oxford, England: Pergamon Press, 1967. This relatively detailed book treats the evolution of microscopy as a whole and ends with a history of the electron microscope.

Bradbury, S., and G.L'E. Turner, eds. *Historical Aspects of Microscopy*. Cambridge, England: W. Heffer, 1967. A collection of papers read at a conference held by The Royal Microscopical Society at Oxford in March, 1966. Contains a paper by Thomas Mulvey "The History of the Electron Microscope" that is worth reading. A clear presentation.

Burton, E. F., and W. H. Kohl. *The Electron Microscope*. New York: Reinhold, 1942. This book, though dated, succeeded in explaining physics and technology to lay readers. Chapters 9 and 13 "The Dual Theory of the Electron" and "The History of the Electron Microscope," respectively, are useful. Intellectually beneficial and enjoyable.

Hawkes, Peter W., ed. *The Beginnings of Electron Microscopy*. Orlando, Fla.: Academic Press, 1985. Prefaced by Ruska and published one year before he was awarded the Nobel Prize, this is a substantial anthology of the history of electron microscopy. Most of the contributions are about the development in various nations, fields, and laboratories.

Marton, Ladislas. *Early History of the Electron Microscope*. San Francisco: San Francisco Press, 1968. A good, brief historical introduction by another original contributor in the development of electron microscopy. Dennis Gabor, the major constructor of the first electron lens and oscilloscope, wrote the preface with pertinent philosophizing.

_____. "History of Electron Optics." In *The Encyclopedia of Microscopy*, edited by George L. Clark. New York: Reinhold, 1961. Lucid chronological summary. A long and compact list of names, dates, and contributions.

Ruska, Ernst. *The Early Development of Electron Lenses and Electron Microscopy*. Translated by Thomas Mulvey. Stuttgart, Germany: S. Hirzel, 1980. Historical introduction by the acknowledged inventor himself. Beginning from the ancestry of the optical microscope. Aware of his own special position in the overall development, Ruska acknowledges other researchers' contributions. The account extends to around 1940, when Ruska's major contributions (magnetic lens with short focal lengths and the prototype transmission electron microscopes) still exerted a significant influence.

Wyckoff, Ralph W. G. *Electron Microscopy*. New York: Interscience Publishers, 1949. Although this book is dated, the first two chapters consist of a historical introduction about the technique and the applications.

Wen-yuan Qian

Cross-References

Zsigmondy Invents the Ultramicroscope (1902), p. 159; Müller Invents the Field Emission Microscope (1936), p. 1070; Müller Develops the Field Ion Microscope (1952), p. 1434; Rohrer and Binnig Invent the Scanning Tunneling Microscope (1978), p. 2093.

PICCARD TRAVELS TO THE STRATOSPHERE
BY BALLOON

Category of event: Space and aviation
Time: May 27, 1931
Locale: Augsburg, Germany to Ober-Gurgl, Austria

Piccard piloted his balloon through an extended ascent into the stratosphere, presaging the space age in his pioneering use of a controlled-environment cabin

Principal personages:
AUGUSTE PICCARD (1884-1962), a Swiss physicist, aeronaut, and engineer who was nominated for a Nobel Prize in Physics in 1932 and 1933
PAUL KIPFER (1905-   ), a Swiss physicist and assistant to Piccard who accompanied Piccard on the first successful balloon flight into the stratosphere

Summary of Event

In the early 1930's, the last of Earth's physical frontiers were slowly being understood and conquered. Stories of humankind pushing its limits regularly qualified for the front page of major newspapers. When Auguste Piccard and Paul Kipfer ascended to 15,781 meters to break the world altitude record in a balloon of Piccard's own design, the world was enthralled and the scientific community gained new venues for exploration.

The stratosphere remained as one physical barrier that had been touched previously only barely. Léon Teisserenc de Bort, in 1902, discovered the stratosphere, a layer in the atmosphere above the troposphere. There, the temperature does not decrease with altitude but is approximately constant at −55 degrees Celsius. The altitude of the lower boundary of the stratosphere varies greatly; a useful average is 12 kilometers. Since barometric pressure decreases with altitude, the ambient pressure at such an altitude is about one-sixth that at the surface of the earth; at 16 kilometers, the fraction is only about one-tenth.

Prior to 1931, only two humans had been able to penetrate beyond 12 kilometers, and neither had available to them technology that would sustain life for extended periods of time. In 1927, U.S. Army Captain Hawthorne Gray made two flights to 12.7 kilometers, utilizing an open gondola. Neither flight, however, set an official altitude mark; the first ended in a bailout, the second, in his death from lack of oxygen. In 1930, U.S. Navy Lieutenant Apollo Soucek flew successfully to the lower reaches of the stratosphere in an airplane with the aid of heated goggles, gloves, and oxygen mask, setting a record of 13.16 kilometers.

In the two decades preceding Piccard's flight in 1931, the realm of high-energy physics saw unexpected developments. Victor Franz Hess of Austria made a scientific balloon flight in 1912, in which he discovered a source of ionizing radiation that increased with altitude. Robert Andrews Millikan of the California Institute of Technology named the radiation "cosmic rays," although it had not been generally agreed yet that these rays were celestial in origin. Into this setting entered Auguste Piccard. Piccard, a native of Switzerland, was trained in mechanical engineering and became a professor of physics at the University of Brussels. His scientific interests included radioactivity and electricity in both laboratory and natural environments. He also actively pursued an interest in aeronautics, first learning his practical ballooning skills in the Swiss Aero-Club, and later serving in the Swiss Army Observation Balloon Corps. His complement of skills and interests led him, as early as 1926, to work on a balloon envelope and gondola capable of ascending to extremely high altitudes. He saw the balloon as a platform from which he could conduct cosmic ray research far away from the radioactive elements of the earth, which would otherwise bias any measurements.

The balloon Piccard designed incorporated several innovative features. Most notably, the gondola was to be sealed and airtight, so that air pressure inside the gondola would not be lost as the balloon ascended to regions of lower and lower pressure. Piccard chose to construct the gondola out of aluminum, a material that had been under development only recently. Because the flight would be many hours long and the gondola relatively small, there needed to be a source of oxygen as well as a way of detoxifying exhaled air. For these purposes, Piccard imported technology used in German submarines, a filtering system known as a Draeger apparatus. It utilized alkaline compounds to absorb unwanted gases. The oxygen supply was stored in liquid form, restoring the cabin air as it slowly vaporized.

The balloon envelope was spherical, as was usual for hydrogen-filled balloons. The constraints of a high-altitude flight, however, dictated some adjustment. To prevent the lightweight rubberized cotton balloon from bursting as it ascended into the low pressures of the stratosphere, the balloon was only partially inflated at take off. The balloon, which was pleated for storage, would unfold and expand of its own accord as it ascended. To ensure that the fabric unfolded safely, Piccard devised a way to hang the gondola to the envelope from points on a horizontal band attached to the envelope, rather than from a net that enclosed the envelope.

Piccard applied for funding from the Belgian science agency, the Fonds National de Recherches Scientifique (FNRS), founded by King Albert I. King Albert, being eager to promote Belgium's reputation as a leading nation in scientific and industrial endeavors, and being a balloon enthusiast himself, was happy to provide the necessary funds. The craft, named the FNRS, was ready in the fall of 1930. Piccard scheduled an ascent for September 14, from Augsburg, Germany. The weather changed, however, and Piccard reluctantly called off the flight at the last moment. Weather conditions were not suitable again until the next spring. An ascent was finally planned for 5:30 A.M. on May 27, 1931. During the night, the wind began to rise; in anticipation of worsening weather, the crew prepared for a hastened launch. Suddenly, at 3:57 A.M., the ground crew somehow let go of the ropes without communicating the designated warning signal. Piccard and his assistant Kipfer found themselves in the air and rising quickly. A few minutes later, Piccard discovered a leak in the gondola, caused by a seal that was broken when the gondola was accidentally dropped during take-off procedures. A supply of vaseline mixed with fibers, which Piccard had prepared for just such accidents, then proved its worth.

As the day progressed, Piccard and Kipfer discovered a problem with the gas exhaust valve. This was the valve with which they were to let gas out of the balloon, a principal component of their altitude control. Their eventual landing would be problematic if they could not control the valve. The only way to proceed was to wait until sundown, when the lower temperature would cause the balloon envelope to shrink, thereby reducing the lift sufficiently for a landing. Piccard and Kipfer tied down the instruments in anticipation of a difficult landing. Hours passed, and the balloon drifted southward over Bavaria and into Tyrol. Finally, around 9 P.M., the gondola touched ground on a glacier in the Tyrolean Alps, in the region of Ober-Gurgl. The two aeronauts spent the night on the glacier, and the next morning hiked toward the village of Gurgl. A patrol sent up from the valley met them around noon and led them to safety.

Piccard had planned several scientific activities for the ascent of the FNRS. The quick rate of ascent, the emergency leak that had to be taken care of, and the uncertain landing all conspired to prevent any measurements from being made while the balloon was at any other but top altitude. Thus, Piccard and Kipfer lost their opportunity to obtain much useful data, such as cosmic ray altitude-intensity curves. One approximate observation was made, however, which suggested that cosmic rays were indeed more intense in the stratosphere than below it; this, in turn, lent support to the theory that cosmic rays are in fact extraterrestrial.

For their achievements, Piccard and Kipfer were knighted by the King of Belgium, and Piccard received nominations for the Nobel Prize in Physics in both 1932 and 1933. Their altitude record of 15,781 meters stood for more than a year, until it was surpassed by Piccard and Max Cosyns.

Impact of Event

The flight of the FNRS made its mark on a wide cross section of the scientific world, not so much by resolving scientific controversies as by preparing the way for further exploration. The data obtained on the flight was encouraging. Piccard and Kipfer measured cosmic radiation apparently 2.5 times more intense at 16 kilometers than that measured by Werner Kolhörster at 9 kilometers. The data point was only marginally useful, though; because only one measurement was taken, it could not be calibrated with data from previous flights at lower altitudes, and its accuracy was not absolutely certain.

Nevertheless, this first flight gave future balloonists a resource of experience and technology from which to draw. In fact, the next stratospheric ascent, with Piccard and Cosyns piloting the FNRS in August, 1932, was quite successful scientifically as well as logistically, bringing back data to fill in the Hess-Kolhörster cosmic ray altitude-intensity curve between 9 and 16 kilometers. A 1934 flight in Explorer II by Americans Albert Stevens and Orvil Anderson returned cosmic ray data that physicists Robert Andrews Millikan and his rival Arthur Holly Compton both considered useful for their respective theories. In addition, their flight carried interesting experiments in other branches of science. For example, they measured ozone distribution in the atmosphere, photographed the earth from very high altitudes, and demonstrated an increased mutation rate in *Drosophila* fruit flies. Thus, Piccard's vision of the balloon as a platform from which to conduct scientific research did prove moderately fruitful.

Ascents subsequent to those of the FNRS retained many of Piccard's innovations. For example, United States balloons such as Explorer used bands also rather than nets to attach the gondola. Most significant, though, was the sealed gondola. As late as 1956, balloons such as Stratolab were still using a gondola of essentially the same design as that of 1931.

The flights of the FNRS preceded the space age by only three decades. During those decades, stratospheric ballooning evolved from a matter of rising in open-air baskets to one of orbiting the earth in space capsules. Pressurized passenger airplane cabins and modern-day space capsules trace their ancestry to the sealed cabin that Piccard devised for his FNRS. Though the impact of Piccard and Kipfer's ascent into the stratosphere reaches beyond the glory that their achievement brought, the glory itself was instrumental in promoting ballooning to the public and to policymakers. Proponents of aeronautic exploration in the United States in the following decades pointed to the flights of the FNRS to convince major funding agencies that research in high-altitude flight was feasible and that the symbolic value of accomplishing such flights was worth the expense. Both technologically and sociologically, it was only a small step between the Stratolab 5 balloon flight in 1961 and the Mercury, Gemini, and Apollo space missions of the same period. To those who came after Piccard, the witness of his flights stood as vital inspiration and encouragement.

Bibliography

DeVorkin, David H. *Race to the Stratosphere: Manned Scientific Ballooning in America*. New York: Springer-Verlag, 1989. Although this history and analysis of science policy focuses on ballooning in the United States, Piccard and his twin brother, Jean-Felix, figure prominently in the story. By the curator of the Smithsonian Institution's National Air and Space Museum, this intensely researched volume is annotated throughout with reference notes and includes an extensive bibliography. An exemplary work of highly readable scholarship.

Piccard, Auguste. "Ballooning in the Stratosphere." *National Geographic* 63 (March, 1933): 353-384. Consistent with its calling to promote exploration, the National Geographic Society supported scientific ballooning from the start. One of the ways in which it accomplished this was to publish, in its popular magazine, reports of projects in which it was interested. Piccard's article is an example of the

National Geographic Society's efforts to bring science to the public.

_____. *Earth, Sky, and Sea.* Translated by Christina Stead. New York: Oxford University Press, 1956. A first-person account by Piccard of his voyages into the stratosphere and later, in a bathyscaphe, into the depths of the sea. Another work of his, *Entre terre et ciel* (1946; *Between Earth and Sky*, 1950) is devoted entirely to the science, technology, and history of scientific ballooning. Both volumes inform while also providing a personal perspective. Among his works are *Auf 16,000 Meter* (1933), in German, and *Au-dessus des nuages* (1933), in French.

Sekido, Yataro, and Harry Elliot, eds. *Early History of Cosmic Ray Studies.* Boston: D. Reidel, 1985. An anthology of reminiscences by leading cosmic ray researchers. The depiction of the birth of the field is balanced and thorough. Sekido and Elliot acknowledge and describe the roles of manned and unmanned balloons, of underwater observations, and of developments in theory. Often technical, but written with the general science reader in mind. A moderate background in physics is suggested.

Stehling, Kurt R., and William Beller. *Skyhooks.* Garden City, N.Y.: Doubleday, 1962. A very accessible volume detailing the stories of fifteen historic balloon flights, extending from the birth of ballooning in 1783 to the publication date in the early 1960's. Also includes a chronology of important ascents. The chapter on the flight of the FNRS contains some minor inaccuracies.

Joyce Tang

Cross-References

Teisserenc de Bort Discovers the Stratosphere and the Troposphere (1898), p. 26; Zeppelin Constructs the First Dirigible That Flies (1900), p. 78; Tsiolkovsky Proposes That Liquid Oxygen Be Used for Space Travel (1903), p. 189; The First German U-Boat Submarine Is Launched (1906), p. 350; Hess Discovers Cosmic Rays Through High-Altitude Ionizations (1912) p. 532; Millikan Names Cosmic Rays and Investigates Their Absorption (1920), p. 694; Shepard Is the First United States Astronaut in Space (1961), p. 1698.

DOMAGK DISCOVERS THAT
A SULFONAMIDE CAN SAVE LIVES

Category of event: Medicine
Time: 1932-1935
Locale: Elberfeld, Germany

Domagk developed the experimental procedures for testing the effectiveness of drugs and discovered that sulfonamides were effective in curing a large number of diseases caused by bacteria

Principal personages:
GERHARD DOMAGK (1895-1964), a German physician who was awarded the 1939 Nobel Prize in Physiology or Medicine
PAUL EHRLICH (1854-1915), a German chemist and bacteriologist who was known as the father of chemotherapy and was the cowinner of the 1908 Nobel Prize in Physiology or Medicine

Summary of Event

Quinine was used to treat malaria for hundreds of years and had been purified by the French chemists Pierre Joseph Pelletier and Joseph Bienaimé Caventou around 1820. Nevertheless, Paul Ehrlich is usually designated as the father of modern chemotherapy because he was responsible for discovering a number of useful drugs. Ehrlich was familiar with dyes used to stain microorganisms and suspected that some of them might specifically poison the microorganisms responsible for disease but not hurt the patient. Ehrlich began a search of dyes for "magic bullets" that would destroy microorganisms and cure diseases. Ehrlich tested compounds from 1906 to 1910 that had been developed by the German dye industry. He eventually found that a number of complex trypan dyes would inhibit the protozoans that caused African sleeping sickness.

Ehrlich and his coworkers also synthesized hundreds of organic compounds that contained arsenic. In 1910, he found one of these compounds, called Salvarsan, was useful in curing syphilis, a disease caused by the bacterium *Treponema*. This was an important discovery because the disease killed between 6 and 10 percent of Europeans each year. Unfortunately, Salvarsan was very toxic to patients. The reason it was so toxic was that it had to be taken in large doses for one to two years to effect a cure. Ehrlich found a less toxic arsenic compound called neosalvarsan and it replaced Salvarsan in 1912.

In 1915, tartar emetic (a compound containing the metal antimony) was found to be useful in treating kala-azar, which was caused by a protozoan. Kala-azar affected millions of people in Africa, India, and Asia, causing much suffering and many deaths each year. Two years later, it was discovered that injection of tartar emetic into the blood of persons suffering from bilharziasis killed the flat worms infecting the bladder, liver, and spleen. In 1920, suramin, a colorless compound developed from trypan red, was introduced to treat African sleeping sickness. It was much less toxic to the patient than any of the drugs Ehrlich had developed, and a single dose would give protection for more than a month. From the dye methylene blue, chemists made mepacrine (also called Atabrine and quinacrine) that was effective against the protozoan that causes malaria. This chemical was introduced in 1933 and used during World War II. Its drawback was that it caused the skin to become yellow.

Gerhard Domagk had been trained in medicine but turned to research in an attempt to discover chemicals that would inhibit or kill microorganisms. He became Director of Experimental Pathology and Bacteriology at the Elberfeld laboratories of the German chemical firm I. G. Farbenindustrie in 1927. Ehrlich's discovery that trypan dyes selectively poisoned microorganisms suggested to Domagk that he look for antimicrobials in a new group of chemicals known as azo dyes. A number of these dyes were synthesized from sulfonamides and purified by Fritz Mietzsch and Josef Klarer. Domagk found that many of these dyes protected mice infected with the bacteria *Streptococcus pyogenes*. In 1932, he discovered that one of these dyes was much more effective than any tested previously. This red azo dye containing a sulfonamide was named prontosil rubrum.

From 1932 to 1935, Domagk began a rigorous testing program to determine the effectiveness and dangers of prontosil at different doses in animals. Since all chemicals injected into animals or humans are potentially dangerous, Domagk determined the doses that harmed or killed. In addition, he worked out the lowest doses that would eliminate the pathogen. The ratio of the smallest amount of drug that kills the patient to the minimum amount of drug that eliminates the pathogen is called the therapeutic ratio of the drug. Chemicals with low therapeutic ratios (near one) are not very useful, while those with high therapeutic ratios (greater than ten) are usually the safest and the most effective drugs. The firm supplied samples of the drug to a select number of physicians to carry out clinical trials on humans. Animal experimentation can give only an indication of which chemicals might be useful in humans and which doses are required.

The synthesis and purification of a drug, its testing in animals, and then its testing in humans require the involvement of many scientists and technicians as well as expensive and appropriate facilities. Clearly, the discovery of a new group of useful drugs does not result from the discovery and work of a single person. The chemists, the animal researcher, and the physicians at clinics all contribute to the final conclusions.

From drug testing in animals, Domagk learned which doses were effective and safe. This knowledge saved his daughter's life. One day while knitting, Domagk's daughter punctured her finger with the needle and infected herself with virulent bacteria. The bacteria quickly multiplied and spread from the wound into neighboring tissue. In an attempt to alleviate the swelling, the infected area was lanced and allow to drain. This did not stop the infection that was spreading into her lymph and blood. The child became critically ill because of the developing septicemia (blood poisoning). In those days, more than 75 percent of those who acquired blood infections died. Domagk realized that the chances for his daughter's survival were very poor. In desperation, he obtained some of the powdered prontosil that had worked so well on infected animals. He extrapolated from his animal experiments how much to give his daughter so that the bacteria would be killed but his daughter would not be poisoned. Within hours of the first treatment, her fever dropped. Complete recovery followed repeated oral doses of prontosil. Domagk's daughter was saved because of prontosil.

In 1935, Domagk published his results demonstrating that prontosil was useful in treating streptococcal infections in animals. German physicians, who had extensively tested prontosil on humans, reported that it was also extremely effective in treating streptococcal infections in humans. This announcement was an important first step in the battle against diseases caused by bacteria. Different strains of *Streptococcus pyogenes* are responsible for strep-throat (tonsillitis), rheumatic fever, scarlet fever, erysipelas (spreading skin infection), cellulitis (localized skin infection), puerperal sepsis (childbed fever), and septicemia. During the 1920's, puerperal sepsis, rheumatic fever, scarlet fever, and septicemia killed thousands of women, babies, and children every year.

The use of sulfonamides lowered the death rate of a number of diseases very quickly. Before 1935, the death rate for puerperal sepsis in England was 175 per 100,000 births. In 1937 and 1938, the death rate fell to eighty. The use of sulfanilamides saved the lives of more than one thousand English mothers in only two years.

Impact of Event

The publication of Domagk's 1935 paper stimulated extensive research in Germany, France, and England. French researchers found that the active portion of the azo dye prontosil was the colorless sulfonamide called sulfanilamide. Much later, it was discovered that bacteria are sensitive to prontosil if they are able to cleave the azo dye and release sulfanilamide. Sulfanilamide as well as other sulfonamides blocks the synthesis of a coenzyme bacteria needed to grow. The discovery that sulfanilamide was the actual antimicrobial agent spurred scientists to synthesize new classes of sulfonamides and test their effectiveness on other pathogenic bacteria.

Domagk demonstrated that some sulfonamides called ulirons were effective against the bacteria that caused gonorrhea. The ulirons were the first drugs used in Germany to treat gonorrhea because prontosils were not effective. Soon after the introduction of ulirons, it was found that gonorrhea could be treated more effectively with a number of newly synthesized sulfonamides. By 1938, English researchers and physicians demonstrated that sulfapyridine was effective against a number of bacterial pathogens. It was used to treat gonorrhea, pneumonia, meningitis, and wound infections. Another sulfonamide called sulfathiazole was even more effective against these organisms. Because of its rapid excretion, sulfathiazole was replaced by sulfadiazine and sulfadimidine.

Research on the many different sulfonamides and their effectiveness on bacterial infections showed that bacterial species varied significantly in their sensitivity to a particular sulfanilamide. For example, some gonococci (bacteria that cause gonorrhea) were sensitive and effectively inhibited by low concentrations of a sulfonamide. Other bacteria of the same species were extremely resistant and would grow even when subjected to very high concentrations of the sulfonamide. It was found that a particular bacterium was not inhibited equally by all the different sulfonamides. Sulfathiazole, for example, might be more effective than sulfapyridine, which in turn, might be more effective than uliron. Experiments showed that a particular sulfonamide was not equally effective when tested on different genera. For gonococcal infection, sulfathiazole was found to be the best sulfonamide. Nevertheless, sulfapyrimidines and sulfones were discovered to be more effective for streptococcal infections.

In 1940, Domagk observed that sulfathiazole and sulfathiodiazole inhibited the bacterium *Mycobacterium tuberculosis* that causes tuberculosis. In 1946, Domagk and the chemists working with him reported the development of a new group of compounds called thiosemicarbazones that were also effective against the mycobacteria that caused tuberculosis. Treatment of tuberculosis with the semicarbazones required more than one hundred days at a dose of one gram a day. The use of sulfonamides and semicarbazones beginning in 1945 caused a dramatic decline in the number of cases and deaths caused by tuberculosis. Because mycobacteria frequently develops resistance if treated with only one drug, tuberculosis is now treated with a combination of drugs that include streptomycin (1947), para-aminosalicylic acid (1950), isoniazid (1952), and rifampin (1963). Dapsone, a sulfone studied by Domagk, is used to treat leprosy. Leprosy is caused by *Mycobacterium leprae*.

Domagk's work also showed that sulfonamides were effective in treating gas gangrene caused by the anaerobic bacteria *Clostridium septicum, C. perfringens,* and *C. novyi.* Sulfonamides were not very useful in treating tetanus even though *Clostridium tetani* was inhibited. This results from the fact that the disease is caused by a toxin that binds to nerve cells. Killing the bacteria with sulfonamides after the toxin has caused its damage is like closing the barn door after the horses have escaped. A new sulfonamide, resembling sulfanilamide, was shown to be more effective on the clostridia than sulfanilamide, uliron, or sulfathiazole.

Sulfonamides spread on wounds and taken orally saved thousands of lives during World War II. For example, the U.S. army lost 8.25 percent of its wounded in World War I but cut this to 4.5 percent during World War II through the use of sulfonamides. The number of fatal cases resulting from operations on perforated appendices fell from 14 percent to 1 percent when sulfonamides were used.

Although Domagk was awarded the 1939 Nobel Prize, he was unable to accept the prize money or give the Nobel lecture because Europe had entered World War II. His Nobel lecture was postponed until after the war and was given on December 12, 1947. His lecture was entitled "Further Progress in Chemotherapy of Bacterial Infections." Much of the lecture concerned the relative effectiveness of the various sulfonamides, semicarbazones, and sulfones.

Bibliography

Brock, Thomas D. *Milestones in Microbiology.* Englewood Cliffs, N.J.: Prentice-Hall, 1961. This book contains a collection of original papers by scientists that contributed to the development of microbiology. The foreign language papers are translated into English. Part 5 is concerned with chemotherapy. Papers by Ehrlich, Sir Alexander Fleming, and Domagk are worthwhile reading.

Edwards, David I. *Antimicrobial Drug Action.* Baltimore: University Park Press, 1980. For those interested in antimicrobial drugs, this is a concise, clearly written book. There is a short history of antimicrobial chemotherapy but most of the book is devoted to how the drugs inhibit and kill microorganisms as well as how microorganisms become resistant to drugs. There is also a section on chemotherapeutic agents used to treat some cancers.

Franklin, T. J., and G. A. Snow. *Biochemistry of Antimicrobial Action.* 2d ed. New York: John Wiley & Sons, 1975. This book contains a concise history of the discovery of antimicrobial agents. The mechanism of action of the sulfonamides is discussed in chapter 6.

Riedman, Sarah R., and Elton T. Gustafson. *Portraits of Nobel Laureates in Medicine and Physiology.* New York: Abelard-Schuman, 1963. This book contains a short biography of Alfred Nobel and concise accounts of most of the Nobel Prize winners and their achievements. There is a good section on the synthesis of drugs by the chemists at I. G. Farbenindustrie. A well-written section describes Domagk's research with the drugs to determine if any of them were effective in combating bacterial infections.

Taylor, F. Sherwood. *The Conquest of Bacteria: From Salvarsan to Sulphapyridine.* New York: Philosophical Library, 1942. This book, written for the layperson, presents a history of drug development before antibiotics were developed in the 1940's. The book concentrates on the discoveries showing that different sulfonamides were effective on a variety of pathogenic bacteria. The roles played by Domagk and other researchers in discovering the effectiveness of the sulfonamides are made clear.

Jaime S. Colome

Cross-References

Ehrlich Introduces Salvarsan as a Cure for Syphilis (1910), p. 476; Fleming Discovers Penicillin in Molds (1928), p. 873; Florey and Chain Develop Penicillin as an Antibiotic (1940), p. 1171; Waksman Discovers the Antibiotic Streptomycin (1943), p. 1224; Duggar Discovers Aureomycin, the First of the Tetracyclines (1945), p. 1255.

CHADWICK DISCOVERS THE NEUTRON

Category of event: Physics
Time: February, 1932
Locale: Cavendish Laboratory, Cambridge, England

Chadwick discovered that there was a fundamental particle in the atom that had no electrical charge and had a mass approximately equal to that of the proton

Principal personages:

JAMES CHADWICK (1891-1974), a British physicist who discovered the neutron, in 1932, at the Cavendish Laboratory in Cambridge, England, and was awarded the 1935 Nobel Prize in Physics

SIR JOSEPH JOHN THOMSON (1856-1940), an English physicist who identified the electron, in 1897, as a particle with a negative electrical charge

ERNEST RUTHERFORD (1871-1937), an English physicist who, in 1911, proposed the nuclear model of the atom

FRÉDÉRIC JOLIOT (1900-1958), a French physicist who, along with his wife, Irène, produced artificial (or induced) radioactivity in 1934 and was awarded the 1935 Nobel Prize in Chemistry

IRÈNE JOLIOT-CURIE (1897-1956), a French physicist who, with her husband, Frédéric, produced artificial radioactivity and was awarded the 1935 Nobel Prize in Chemistry

WALTHER BOTHE (1891-1957), a German physicist who, in 1930, discovered the neutron but was unable to identify it

Summary of Event

Although the word "atom" actually means "indivisible," discoveries that began in the late nineteenth century indicate that the atom has a very complex structure. The first discovery that indicated that the atom has parts was the discovery, in 1895, of X rays by Wilhelm Conrad Röntgen; the second was the discovery of radioactivity by Antoine-Henri Becquerel in 1896; the third was the discovery of the electron by Joseph John Thomson at the Cavendish Laboratory in Cambridge, England, in 1897. About a decade later, Ernest Rutherford began a series of experiments with alpha particles, known to be identical with a helium atom that has lost two electrons. Rutherford studied the scattering of these alpha particles when they bombarded a thin sheet of gold foil. He concluded that the type of scattering produced would be possible only if nearly all the mass of the atom and all the positive electrical charge were concentrated in an extremely small part of the atom, which he named the "nucleus." Rutherford estimated the diameter of the nucleus to be one ten-thousandth of the diameter of the atom; consequently, the electrons associated with the atom occupy a much larger volume than the nucleus. The nuclear model of the atom came to be universally accepted and confirmed by the work of Niels Bohr (1885-1962) on atomic spectra. In 1914, Ernest Rutherford proposed that the positive electrical charge in the atom was carried by another elementary particle, which he named "proton" ("first" in Greek).

At this point, then, there were two elementary particles: the proton, with a positive charge, and the electron, with a negative electrical charge of the same magnitude as that of the proton. The atom, therefore, had to be built up with only these two particles. Helium, for example, would have two protons and two electrons. Yet, since the mass of the helium atom was known to be four times that of the mass of the hydrogen atom, the nucleus of the helium atom needed two more protons to produce the appropriate mass. In order to keep the electrical charge of the nucleus equal to that of two protons, it was suggested that there were also two electrons in the nucleus, which neutralized the charge of the additional two protons. This theory of the nucleus came to be known as the proton-electron theory.

As early as 1920, however, Rutherford speculated that there may be another elementary particle with about the same mass as the proton, but with no charge, if it were in some way produced by the combination of a proton and an electron. In 1921, an American chemist, William Draper Harkins (1873-1951), named this hypothetical particle the neutron, because it was electrically neutral. Despite Rutherford's prediction of the neutron, the proton-electron theory was supported in the next ten years by many physicists. Serious doubts concerning its validity arose in the minds of many scientists because of new developments in theoretical physics. Consequently, there were also physicists in the 1920's who searched for Rutherford's hypothetical particle. It was at this stage of atomic research that James Chadwick began his work at the Cavendish Laboratory in Cambridge, England, under the guidance of Rutherford.

James Chadwick's career in physics began in 1910 at the University of Manchester, England, where he became one of Rutherford's pupils and performed experiments under his direction. He also became familiar with Hans Geiger and Ernest Marsden, two notable German physicists. In 1913, Chadwick was awarded a scholarship to work with Geiger in Berlin. When World War I began the following year, he was immediately interned in a prisoner-of-war camp in Ruheleben, Germany. He used the time in camp to set up a crude laboratory and perform scientific experiments. Returning to England in 1918, he rejoined Rutherford in Manchester and then followed him to Cambridge the following year.

Two projects that immediately drew Chadwick's attention and efforts were the search for the neutron, which Rutherford had predicted, and the attempt to produce artificial radioactivity. Yet, Chadwick's persistent search for the elusive particle was not rewarded. Other physicists were pursuing the same search; in 1930, Walther Bothe of Germany found that when the light elements of beryllium and boron were bombarded by high-energy alpha particles, radiation with no electrical charge but with great penetrating power was produced. Only two years later, Irène Joliot-Curie and Frédéric Joliot reported that this radiation could cause protons to be ejected from paraffin. These scientists concluded that the radiation was a type of gamma ray, that is, electromagnetic energy of very high frequency.

When Chadwick read the account of these experiments performed by the French scientists, he immediately decided to examine this phenomenon further. He found that when boron and beryllium were bombarded by alpha particles from polonium, the mysterious radiation from these two substances could eject protons from any materials that contained hydrogen. He also discovered, from calculating the energy acquired by nitrogen atoms bombarded by the unknown radiation, that the radiation could not be gamma rays, as Frédéric Joliot and Irène Joliot-Curie had reported.

Chadwick then showed that his experimental results were completely consistent with the assumption that each proton ejected from the paraffin had undergone a collision with a particle of approximately equal mass (very much like what happens when billiard balls collide head on). When Chadwick was unable to deflect this particle in a magnetic field, he concluded that it had no electric charge. Since it did not correspond to any previously known particle, it must be the long-sought-after neutron hypothetically proposed by Rutherford in 1920.

Impact of Event

With the discovery of the neutron came a much clearer understanding of atomic structure, specifically the structure of the nucleus. For this reason, it marked a turning point in the development of nuclear physics. The German physicist Werner Heisenberg proposed that by constructing the nucleus of an atom out of neutrons and protons, a number of previous difficulties were resolved.

First, it became evident how an atom of helium could have an atomic number of two (two protons in the nucleus and two electrons associated with it) while having a mass number of four. The additional mass of the nucleus was ascribed to the presence of two neutrons. As a result, physicists no longer had to deal with the inconsistencies presented by the proton-electron theory of nuclear structure. The existence of isotopes—atoms of the same element having different atomic masses—is readily explained by the proton-neutron theory as well: The additional mass is caused by the presence of more neutrons in the nucleus.

The discovery of the neutron, in 1932, marked the beginning of nuclear physics, that is, the study of the nuclear structure of the atom. It was readily seen that, since nuclei of most elements are extremely stable, there are forces of attraction hitherto unknown between the nucleons (the word coined to designate the particles in the nucleus). Until the discovery of the neutron, the only known forces in physics were those as a result of gravity, electricity, and magnetism. After 1932, it was necessary to speak of a new kind of force: the nuclear force.

When it was seen that the neutron was a very penetrating particle because it was electrically neutral, scientists realized that it could be used to bombard stable nuclei and produce transmutation of elements—a modern kind of alchemy. Neutrons were used to change many stable nuclei into radioactive nuclei; in this way, the number of radioactive elements was increased and medicine was, in time, furnished with an abundance of radioisotopes for use in radiation therapy. It was also seen that bombarding nuclei of heavy elements with neutrons could also produce new elements with atomic masses greater than that of uranium—the transuranium elements.

This experimentation with neutrons continued at a rapid pace in the 1930's and led to the discovery, in 1939, by Lise Meitner, Otto Hahn, and Fritz Strassmann that when uranium atoms were bombarded by neutrons, the uranium atoms underwent fission, that is, they broke into two parts, each part being an element with a mass much less than that of the original uranium atom. Shortly thereafter, using Albert Einstein's theory of relativity, physicists showed that this fission would take place with the release of considerable energy. When it was also discovered that the fission process produced additional neutrons, scientists realized that a chain reaction was possible. Consequently, the discovery of the neutron ushered in the atomic age—the use of atomic energy for weapons as well as for peaceful uses.

Bibliography

Asimov, Isaac. *Mass and Energy: The Neutron. The Structure of the Nucleus.* Vol. 2 in *Worlds Within Worlds: The Story of Nuclear Energy.* Washington, D.C.: United States Atomic Energy Commission, Office of Information Services, 1972. This renowned science writer presents a brief discussion on the history of atomic energy. He begins with the theory of relativity and brings the reader up to the use of neutrons to bombard uranium. It is nonmathematical and nontechnical, with many fine illustrations and photographs.

Crowther, J. G. *The Cavendish Laboratory, 1874-1974.* New York: Science History Publications, 1974. For readers interested in the historical context in which the development of atomic theory took place, Crowther provides an excellent account. He describes how close Chadwick's contemporaries in France and Germany came to discovering the neutron.

Goldhaber, Maurice. "With Chadwick at the Cavendish." *The Bulletin of the Atomic Scientists* 13 (December, 1982): 12-13. Goldhaber, a distinguished German physicist who worked with Chadwick, gives a lively, though brief, account of Chadwick and some of his coworkers at the Cavendish Laboratory. Readers interested in the personal side of scientific activity will enjoy this article, as it shows how scientific ideas arise and how scientists are motivated and influenced by one another.

Hughes, Donald J. *The Neutron Story.* Garden City, N.Y.: Doubleday, 1959. Since the author was directly acquainted with some of the physicists associated with the development of nuclear physics, he gives an excellent historical perspective to the subject. The physics is presented in nontechnical language without passing over significant details; it includes an index.

Oliphant, Mark. "The Beginning: Chadwick and the Neutron." *The Bulletin of the Atomic Scientists* 15 (December, 1982): 14-18. Oliphant, a close associate of Chadwick at Cavendish Laboratory, describes some of the scientific activity. His observations show that scientists work closely with others concerned with a common problem.

Smyth, Henry De Wolf. *Atomic Energy for Military Purposes.* Princeton, N.J.: Princeton University Press, 1945. This is the first published account of the Manhattan Project—the story of the development of the atomic bomb in World War II. Since the bomb's production depended on the possibility of a chain reaction, the role of the neutron was crucial to the success of the project. Contains numerous helpful appendices and an index.

Wilfred Theisen

Cross-References

Frédéric Joliot and Irène Joliot-Curie Develop the First Artificial Radioactive Element (1933), p. 987; Segrè Identifies the First Artificial Element, Technetium (1937), p. 1101; Fermi Creates the First Controlled Nuclear Fission Chain Reaction (1942), p. 1198; Hofstadter Discovers That Protons and Neutrons Each Have a Structure (1951), p. 1384; The World's First Breeder Reactor Produces Electricity While Generating New Fuel (1951), p. 1419.

COCKCROFT AND WALTON SPLIT THE ATOM WITH A PARTICLE ACCELERATOR

Category of event: Physics
Time: April, 1932
Locale: Cavendish Laboratory, Cambridge, England

Cockcroft and Walton bombarded a lithium atom with protons, producing the first artificial nuclear disintegration with accelerated particles

Principal personages:

T. E. ALLIBONE (1903-   ), an English electrical engineer who developed early accelerators and served as liaison to the Metropolitan Vickers Company in the development of the Cockcroft-Walton accelerator

SIR JOHN DOUGLAS COCKCROFT (1897-1967), an English physicist and electrical engineer who was a corecipient of the Nobel Prize in Physics in 1951 with Walton

MARCUS LAURENCE OLIPHANT (1901-   ), an Australian nuclear physicist who worked on alternate means of accelerating protons

ERNEST RUTHERFORD (1871-1937), an English nuclear physicist and the 1908 Nobel laureate in chemistry, who inspired the successful disintegration of lithium by Cockcroft and Walton

ERNEST THOMAS SINTON WALTON (1903-   ) an Irish physicist who was the cowinner with Cockcroft of the 1951 Nobel Prize in Physics

Summary of Event

Sir John Douglas Cockcroft and Ernest Thomas Sinton Walton opened a new era in physics in 1932 when they successfully split the lithium nucleus using 500-kilovolt protons accelerated in a voltage multiplier. Modern nuclear and particle physics depends upon subatomic particle accelerators for sources of probes to investigate the behavior of nuclei of atoms, their constituent particles, and the forces that influence them. Their achievement made the heart of the atom accessible for nuclear physicists.

Following Ernest Rutherford's discovery of the atomic nucleus in 1910, his transformation of nitrogen into radioactive oxygen using natural radioactive substances in 1917, and his assumption of the directorship of the Cavendish Laboratory at the University of Cambridge in 1918, the importance of the atomic nucleus as a field of physical inquiry was well established. Yet, the nature of the nucleus could not be explored adequately with the projectiles placed at scientists' disposal by nature: alpha particles, electrons, and gamma rays. An artificial means of producing high-energy particles was required to disintegrate the atomic nucleus; this was supplied first by Cockcroft and Walton.

Cockcroft was educated in physics at the Universities of Manchester and of Cambridge, and in electrical engineering at the Manchester College of Technology. At Metropolitan Vickers Company, one of the engineers, T. E. Allibone, had made the first attempts to produce nuclear disintegration with accelerated electrons produced by a modified tesla coil in 1927, thus inspiring Rutherford's call "for a copious supply of atoms and electrons which have an individual energy far transcending that of the alpha- and beta-particles from radioactive bodies."

Walton had earned his doctorate in physics at the University of Cambridge by investigating a variety of means of accelerating subatomic particles: electrons in a circular magnetic field similar to the one later successfully used by Ernest Orlando Lawrence in his cyclotron and by Donald Kerst in his betatron, and positive ions of the heavier elements in a linear accelerator.

Late in 1928, Cockcroft became aware of a theory propounded by Soviet theoretical physicist George Gamow. Using the wave mechanics developed by Erwin Schrödinger, Gamow had proposed that alpha particles escaped their parent atoms occasionally, not by attaining sufficient energy to overcome the potential barrier that surrounded the nuclei but by "tunneling" through it. The reverse process, Gamow argued, could account for a particle penetrating the nucleus with smaller energies than those of its potential barrier.

Cockcroft realized that several million-volt subatomic particles were not required to penetrate the nucleus. Yet, given enough subatomic particles, about six in one thousand particles with energies of about 300,000 volts should penetrate a boron nucleus. Cockcroft informed Rutherford of this prospect and immediately began to build an accelerator to test this hypothesis. Rutherford assigned Walton to assist Cockcroft in building a source of protons (positive hydrogen ions) and a vacuum tube to withstand several hundred kilovolts to accelerate them. Rutherford then arranged for the team to receive a grant to purchase a transformer and rectifiers to produce steady direct-current voltage for the experiments; these were provided by the Metropolitan Vickers Company. The 350-kilovolt transformer was custom-built to fit the room in which it was housed by B. L. Goodlet and was installed in December, 1928. The rectifiers were designed by Allibone to produce steady direct currents to accelerate ions from the transformer's alternating current. When the transformer failed in August, Cockcroft determined a new means of producing higher voltages than the 280 kilovolts they had achieved.

Cockcroft reinvented the "voltage multiplying" circuit in which condensers, which store electric charges like a battery, were linked alternately in parallel with rectifying diodes. The voltage was divided from the transformer, which had been applied to the first condenser in the series between it and the others, then separating the condensers as the first was charged up again, and reconnecting them so that it was possible to build up a charge equivalent to three times that of the source. With the 200-kilovolt transformer, four rectifiers, and four condensers, 800 kilovolts could be built up in this way.

Cockcroft and Walton also built an accelerating tube strong enough to bear this high voltage, basing their design upon that of a high-voltage X-ray tube invented by W. D. Coolidge of General Electric in the United States. The particles to be accelerated were generated in a small glass chamber at its top, to which 60 kilovolts were applied. Then, they entered two evacuated glass tubes placed end to end in which the electrodes, supported by a steel plate to withstand the stresses induced by the high voltages applied to them, supplied the energy to accelerate the tubes to 710 kilovolts.

At this point, Cockcroft and Walton's experiments were interrupted by the demands of the laboratory in which they had built their apparatus. They moved the apparatus to a larger laboratory in May of 1931 and resumed their experiments. By early 1932, 710-kilovolt protons had been produced by the tube. The two researchers, however, interrupted these studies to look for gamma rays which they expected to be produced when alpha particles struck beryllium, as Irène Joliot-Curie and Frédéric Joliot had observed in Paris. Although it had yet to be revealed by their colleague James Chadwick, these "gamma rays" were in fact neutrons, which Rutherford had predicted should exist in the nucleus ten years earlier.

After a fruitless search, Cockcroft and Walton returned to accelerating protons and measured their magnetic deflection in order to determine their energies. At this point, Rutherford intervened, and reminded them of the fundamental technique for detecting alpha particles that had been developed by the Cavendish Laboratory: the use of a fluorescent screen, a paper, or card coated with zinc sulfide. He was convinced that when protons bombarded lithium, alpha particles must be produced. Rutherford believed they should give up their search for gamma rays to hunt them. On April 14, 1932, they inserted a lithium target in the tube, and Walton climbed into a darkened cabin built at its base to look for fluorescence. He saw them immediately, and summoned Rutherford, who confirmed that the fluorescence was produced by alpha particles. This was the first man-made artificial disintegration of any atom: The proton had united with lithium and broken it up into two atoms of helium, releasing 17 million electronvolts of energy. This energy conformed to the difference between the masses of the lithium and hydrogen before the disintegration and the helium afterward. Mass had been converted to energy according to the formula $E = mc^2$, exactly as predicted by Albert Einstein's theory of special relativity.

Impact of Event

The disintegration of the lithium atom by Cockcroft and Walton unleashed the power of particle accelerators on the nucleus and led to the rapid development of the field of nuclear physics in the succeeding decades. Rutherford and Marcus Laurence Oliphant, who came to Cavendish in 1927 from Australia, developed a low-energy accelerator of protons to follow up the experiments of Cockcroft and Walton with 200-kilovolt protons in order to examine the thresholds of proton-induced nuclear reactions. They succeeded in producing the disintegration of lithium with only 100-kilovolt protons by February, 1933, and subsequently found that 20-kilovolt protons would suffice; boron required only 60-kilovolt protons.

Other accelerator developers, such as Lawrence at the University of California's

Radiation Laboratory in Berkeley, Robert J. Van de Graaff at Princeton University, and Charles C. Lauritsen at the Kellogg High-Voltage Laboratory at the California Institute of Technology, quickly entered the field with more powerful particle accelerators. They had not paused to look for disintegration of atoms at the energies Cockcroft and Walton used because they were not as familiar with nuclear theory. Once they had developed the appropriate detectors, they were able to surpass the Cambridge experimenters, whose machine was not capable of much higher energies. Indeed, Cockcroft built a cyclotron at the Cavendish in 1937, after trying and failing to develop a larger machine of their design in collaboration with a physicist in The Netherlands. Lawrence's cyclotron easily out-paced direct current accelerators in energy, although very significant scientific work was done with the accelerators developed at Cambridge in the mid-1930's.

The voltage multiplier remained, however, a very successful source of potentials around 1 million volts and has been used extensively as the first stage of many larger accelerators. Cockcroft and Walton received the Nobel Prize in Physics in 1951 for their pioneering work with this accelerator. By demonstrating that it was possible to disintegrate nuclei with artificially accelerated particles, they had opened up the new field of accelerator physics and demonstrated conclusively the conversion of mass to energy in nuclear processes.

Their achievement also reflected the new constellation of interests which was to give rise to modern science. The involvement of industrial firms such as Metropolitan Vickers and General Electric with the Cavendish Laboratory in the investigation of nuclear physics presaged the industrial scale of the particle accelerators that were to be developed in the twentieth century. Allibone and Cockcroft's engineering skills were required, along with training in physics, to accomplish the goal of artificially accelerating protons to energies sufficient to split the atom. The state of the art in high-voltage engineering had to be advanced to do this; therefore, industry benefited from the quest to understand the nucleus just as did physics. Such early collaborations have engendered the gigantic efforts of the 1990's, such as the Superconducting Supercollider currently under construction in Texas.

Bibliography

Cockburn, Stewart, and David Ellyard. *Oliphant*. Adelaide, Australia: Axiom Books, 1981. This biography of Rutherford's associate chronicles aspects of Cambridge nuclear physics during Oliphant's tenure there from 1927 to 1936 and his work with Rutherford in following up the Cockcroft and Walton experiment. It is well illustrated, with bibliography and index.

Crowther, J. G. *The Cavendish Laboratory, 1874-1974*. New York: Science History Publications, 1974. This anecdotal history of the Cavendish Laboratory is a well-illustrated introduction to its work with references and index but is rather imposing and unorganized.

Hartcup, Guy, and T. E. Allibone. *Cockcroft and the Atom*. Bristol, England: Adam Hilger, 1984. This biography of Cockcroft, written in part by Allibone, who was a participant in the work, is an authoritative source of information on Cockcroft's life and work, illustrated with appendices, bibliography, and index.

Hendry, John, ed. *Cambridge Physics in the Thirties.* Bristol, England: Adam Hilger, 1984. This collection of retrospective accounts interspersed with historical commentary places the achievements of the 1930's in a broad context and illuminates many of the more obscure technical developments that ensured its leadership in the field. It includes a number of illustrations, a select bibliography, and a name index.

Oliphant, Mark. *Rutherford: Recollections of Cambridge Days.* New York: Elsevier, 1972. This anecdotal account for a wide audience includes a chapter on the work of Cockcroft and Walton by a participant who knew them and is illustrated with contemporary photographs.

Rutherford, Lord Ernest. *The Newer Alchemy.* New York: Macmillan, 1937. A brief discussion of nuclear physics by its founder. Written for a general audience.

Wilson, David. *Rutherford: Simple Genius.* Cambridge, Mass.: MIT Press, 1983. This massive biography of the founder of nuclear physics summarizes what has been said in about twenty-one existing volumes on the "force of nature" who led the Cavendish Laboratory at the time of this experiment. Illustrated, with bibliography and an index.

Robert W. Seidel

Cross-References

Rutherford Presents His Theory of the Atom (1912), p. 527; Rutherford Discovers the Proton (1914), p. 590; Lawrence Develops the Cyclotron (1931), p. 953; The Tevatron Particle Accelerator Begins Operation at Fermilab (1985), p. 2301; The Superconducting Supercollider Is Under Construction in Texas (1988), p. 2372.

ANDERSON DISCOVERS THE POSITRON

Category of event: Physics
Time: September, 1932
Locale: California Institute of Technology, Pasadena, California

Anderson discovered a positively charged particle with the same mass as that of the electron, thus identifying the first antiparticle

> *Principal personages:*
> CARL DAVID ANDERSON (1905-   ), a physicist and professor at the California Institute of Technology who was a corecipient of the 1936 Nobel Prize in Physics
> PAUL ADRIEN MAURICE DIRAC (1902-1984), a physicist who first formulated relativistic quantum mechanics to predict the existence of the antiparticle
> ROBERT ANDREWS MILLIKAN (1868-1953), an experimental physicist who measured the electronic charge; winner of the 1923 Nobel Prize in Physics

Summary of Event

The first three decades of the twentieth century is perhaps the period that saw the most radical change in the concepts of physics, especially at subatomic levels. To this period belong the theoretical discoveries of the quantum of energy (Max Planck), the quantum of light and the theory of relativity (Albert Einstein), the theory of atomic structure (Ernest Rutherford and Niels Bohr), the uncertainty principle (Werner Heisenberg), quantum mechanics (Erwin Schrödinger), and relativistic quantum mechanics (Paul Adrien Maurice Dirac). It was also a period of great experimental discoveries, particularly of hitherto unknown constituents of matter. The electronic charge was measured by Robert Andrews Millikan and the charge-to-mass ratio by Sir Joseph John Thomson. The alpha particle was discovered by Ernest Rutherford, and the neutron was discovered by James Chadwick. It seemed like the basic structure of matter was completely unveiled and physics had discovered a way to describe subatomic matter completely in terms of Schrödinger's and Heisenberg's quantum mechanical theories.

Thus, by the mid-1920's, it had been established that matter consists primarily of heavy particles called protons, with a positive electric charge, and very light, negatively charged particles called electrons. The neutron—an electrically neutral particle, now known to be the third primary constituent of matter found on Earth—had not been discovered yet. The neutron was discovered in 1932 by Chadwick.

Dirac, physicist at St. John's College, Cambridge, was convinced that the quantum theory and theory of relativity needed to be combined. It was combined to formulate a relativistic quantum theory in 1928. This mathematically elegant theory led to the conclusion that every particle known had to have an antiparticle—a counterpart that was oppositely charged and with an opposite "spin." The spin is a property of every particle that is difficult to measure. This means that there should be a positive electron and a negative proton. There should even be an antineutron which, like the neutron, has no charge but has a spin opposite to that of the neutron. Thus, Dirac's relativistic quantum mechanics predicted the existence of "antimatter." Such particles had not been observed until then.

In 1927, Carl David Anderson, a physicist at the California Institute of Technology in Pasadena, California, started his study of elementary particles by investigating cosmic radiation. Cosmic radiation is the continuous stream of radiation into the earth's atmosphere, originating from nuclear reactions on the sun and elsewhere. It was not clear if these "rays" contained both particles and high-energy radiation. Early experiments could not detect any particles. Anderson had begun his work at the Norman Bridge Laboratory of Physics under Millikan, who first measured the charge on an electron. Their research goal was to find the nature of cosmic radiation. As Millikan's junior research colleague, Anderson was first given the job of planning and direction of the research.

The equipment was ready for operation in the summer of 1931. The technique they used was to send up balloons containing instruments called cloud chambers. When charged particles entered these chambers containing water vapor, they left a track. By studying the track, the mass and charge of the particle that caused the track were calculated. In addition, if a magnet was placed in the chamber so that the track was made in the presence of a magnetic field, the way the track curves shows whether the particle had a positive or negative charge.

The equipment took photographs every fifteen seconds. A very strong electromagnet was incorporated into the chamber. The photographs showed several tracks of particles with very high energies. There seemed to be as many positive as negative particles in cosmic radiation. A special feature that Anderson noted, and which he described in his 1936 Nobel lecture, was: " . . . [I]n many cases several positive and negative particles were found to be projected simultaneously from a single centre. The presence of positively charged particles and the occurrence of 'showers' of several particles showed clearly that the absorption of cosmic rays in material substances is due primarily to a nuclear phenomenon of a new type."

The first explanation was that the positive particles whose tracks were observed must be protons, and the negative ones must be electrons. Nevertheless, the experimental results seemed to show that the positive particle in the cosmic radiation showers had a mass close or equal to that of an electron. (A proton has 1,835 times the mass of the electron.) Anderson stated in his Nobel lecture that the assumption that the positive particles had electronic mass "appeared very radical at the time." Further refined experiments showed that the only possible conclusion was that the positive particle had to be a light particle like the electron rather than the heavier proton. Anderson published a paper in September, 1932, announcing the existence of positive electrons, or positrons.

Experiments by Patrick M. S. Blackett and Giuseppe Occhialini at the University of Cambridge confirmed Anderson's findings in 1933. Blackett and his coworkers suggested that the positive particle they had found was the antiparticle of the electron that Dirac's theory had predicted. This discovery was the first evidence of the existence of antimatter. Dirac received the 1933 Nobel Prize in Physics (with Schrödinger) for his experimental confirmation of the theory. Anderson received the Nobel Prize in Physics in 1936 (with Victor Franz Hess) for his work on the positron. Anderson went on to win many other awards for his efforts, such as the Gold Medal of the American Institute of the City of New York (1935), the Elliot Cresson Medal of the Franklin Institute (1937), and the Presidential Certificate of Merit (1945).

The "showers" or collection of positive and negative particles Anderson had found in the photographs now had an explanation. Some of the energy in the cosmic radiation actually was changing into particles, forming an electron-positron pair, which then took off in opposite directions under the magnetic field. This was the first observation of what is known as "pair creation" (or, pair production). Also, it was an example of the conversion of energy into matter, as predicted by Einstein's famous equation $E = mc^2$. The opposite of pair creation is annihilation. When equal amounts of matter and antimatter collide, they annihilate each other, with their mass being turned into pure energy.

Some of the theories of the early history of the universe involve the conversion of energy into matter through pair creation. According to the big bang theory of creation of the universe 15 billion years ago, a gigantic explosion took place which created substance from energy. This means that as many particles as antiparticles were created at that moment. The question arises why Earth's part of the universe is predominantly composed of one type of particles (proton, electron, and neutron) that is called matter to the exclusion of antimatter. It is not known yet if there are far away galaxies that are predominantly composed of antimatter. Anderson's discovery was the first evidence that this is a possibility.

Impact of Event

The discovery of the positron—the first antiparticle to be discovered—was a direct proof of Dirac's theory of the existence of antimatter. Since antimatter is scarce on Earth, scientists began to produce antimatter under laboratory conditions. These experiments need particles at very high energies. At these energies, it was found that many new kinds of reactions occur and new kinds of particles are produced.

The entire field of "high-energy physics," for which the big Superconducting Supercollider particle accelerator is being constructed in Texas, thus, can be considered to have started with Anderson's discovery of the positron. His discovery gave physicists a clearer understanding of elementary particles. Further, this branch of physics has led to the unveiling of a very complex set of particles and of new forces that operate in the subnuclear realm.

Bibliography

Guillemin, Victor. *The Story of Quantum Mechanics.* New York: Charles Scribner's Sons, 1968. A general textbook discussion on the history of the development of quantum mechanics.

Heathcote, Niels H. de V. *Nobel Prize Winners in Physics, 1901-1950.* New York: Henry Schuman, 1953. Each year's entry contains the details of the discoveries for which the Nobel Prizes were awarded and gives lengthy extracts from the Nobel lectures.

Inman, Fred W., and Carl E. Miller. *Contemporary Physics.* New York: Macmillan, 1975. A modern survey of physics, this book divides physics into the classical and modern eras. The discoveries of the modern era, including that of the positron, are described.

Kim, S. K. *Physics: The Fabric of Reality.* New York: Macmillan, 1975. Starting with the idea of absolute and relative motion, this book attempts to give a simple description of the central concepts of modern physics, including Dirac's relativistic quantum theory for the nonspecialist.

Trefil, James S. *The Moment of Creation, Big Bang Physics from Before the First Millisecond to the Present Universe.* New York: Charles Scribner's Sons, 1983. This book is a description of the theories of the starting point and development of the universe and includes a lengthy discussion of the role of matter and antimatter in this development.

Indira Nair

Cross-References

Thomson Wins the Nobel Prize for the Discovery of the Electron (1906), p. 356; Rutherford Discovers the Proton (1914), p. 590; Millikan Names Cosmic Rays and Investigates Their Absorption (1920), p. 694.

FRÉDÉRIC JOLIOT AND IRÈNE JOLIOT-CURIE DEVELOP THE FIRST ARTIFICIAL RADIOACTIVE ELEMENT

Category of event: Physics
Time: 1933-1934
Locale: Radium Institute, Paris, France

Frédéric Joliot and Irène Joliot-Curie used alpha particles from polonium to bombard aluminum and create phosphorus 30, an artificial nucleus that was radioactive

Principal personages:

IRÈNE JOLIOT-CURIE (1897-1956), a French physicist, the wife of Frédéric Joliot and half of the team who discovered artificial radioactivity, for which she was awarded the Nobel Prize in Chemistry in 1935

FRÉDÉRIC JOLIOT (1900-1958), a French physicist and the other half of the husband-wife team who discovered artificial radioactivity and received the 1935 Nobel Prize in Chemistry

MARIE CURIE (1867-1934), a Polish/French physicist and Nobel laureate in both physics and chemistry who was director of the Radium Institute, the mother of Irène, and the mentor of both Frédéric Joliot and Irène Joliot-Curie

Summary of Event

Although they frequently published as collaborators, Frédéric Joliot and Irène Joliot-Curie had separately carved out scientific careers for themselves. Irène Curie was the daughter of the legendary Marie Curie, who was twice the winner of the Nobel Prize, and a member of the French scientific elite by birth as well as a brilliant physicist in her own right. As a teenager, she had worked alongside her mother using X-ray equipment to treat soldiers wounded during World War I and published her first paper in physics in 1921. In 1932, she succeeded her mother as director of the Radium Institute.

Frédéric Joliot grew up in a middle-class family and attended the École de Physique et de Chimie Industrielle de la Ville de Paris rather than one of the prestigious French universities. Because of his unquestionable ability as an experimenter, he was recommended to Marie Curie as an assistant by her close friend, Paul Langevin. He joined the laboratory at the end of 1924 and gradually acquired the necessary degrees. Because of his background, he found it difficult to break into the inner circle of French science, despite his personal charm and undoubted ability.

Surprisingly, the outgoing, charming, handsome Frédéric Joliot fell in love with quiet, capable, socially awkward Irène Curie. In 1926, they were wed, beginning a very happy marriage and an extremely successful scientific collaboration. The Joliot-Curies had an enormous advantage over their scientific competitors because they had access to the supply of radioactive materials owned by the Radium Institute, which was directed by Marie Curie. All experiments in nuclear physics depended on using naturally emitted radioactive particles to probe nuclei. In addition, the Joliot-Curies were careful technicians who built the finest equipment in Europe for their experiments. During the first four years of the 1930's, they embarked upon a remarkable series of experiments in nuclear physics.

In 1930, a German team reported that beryllium bombarded by alpha particles emitted a new sort of penetrating radiation. The Joliot-Curies confirmed the German results and showed that the new radiation ejected protons from a paraffin screen placed in front of the source. The new radiation also produced proton tracks in a cloud chamber, which started at varying spots in the cloud chamber. The new radiation must have been bumping into protons and accelerating them, but it did not produce tracks in a cloud chamber so that it must have been uncharged. The French group proposed that the new radiation was very high-energy gamma radiation. The British researcher James Chadwick read their published results and guessed that the new radiation must be the uncharged particle known to share the atomic nucleus with the proton: the neutron. He established the existence of a particle with no charge and the mass of the proton and won a Nobel Prize in Physics for doing so. The Joliot-Curies had come very close to a major discovery.

Similarly, in 1932, the Joliot-Curies studied cosmic radiation in the high Alps. They concluded that neutrons were not an important constituent of cosmic radiation. They were puzzled that some of the electron tracks in their cloud chamber curved backward as if the electrons had a positive charge but did not follow up their observation. That same year, an American physicist Carl David Anderson identified the positron, the antiparticle of the electron with identical mass and a positive charge, from photographs of cosmic-ray tracks in a Wilson cloud chamber similar to that used by the Joliot-Curies. Although the French physicists must have been disappointed narrowly to miss making a critical discovery in nuclear physics once again, they reportedly enjoyed good skiing and were able to produce the first cloud chamber photograph showing the creation of an electron-positron pair by the annihilation of a gamma ray.

Returning to Paris, they began to study positrons in the laboratory, in particular their interaction with various absorbing materials. (Irène was forced to slow the pace of her work as she bore her second child during this period, but Frédéric carried on the experiments.) By early 1933, they were using alpha particles produced from polonium to bombard boron, beryllium, fluorine, aluminum, and sodium. After the bombardment, these elements emitted neutrons and both positrons and electrons. The experiments on beryllium showed a great difference in the kinetic energies of positrons and electrons from those of the other elements. The Joliot-Curies were able to show that in beryllium, the positrons and electrons were produced directly from high-energy gamma radiation. In the other elements, there were two different types of nuclear reactions that produced the same final nucleus: Either the alpha particle knocked a proton out of the nucleus or it knocked out a neutron and a positron. They also measured the mass of the neutron and found it to be slightly larger than that of the proton.

In October, 1933, they presented their recent results at the Seventh Solvay Conference, attended by most of the major physicists in Europe. Their studies produced a storm of controversy, including some severe questions of the accuracy of their results, led by the German physicist, Lise Meitner. Fortunately, they also received some encouragement to continue their work. They returned to Paris with damaged pride, determined to show that neutrons and positrons were emitted simultaneously from the targets when they were irradiated.

To conduct the necessary experiments measuring emission times, they were forced to modify their experimental apparatus. Heretofore, the Geiger counter, which detected radioactivity, was automatically turned off when the irradiating source was removed. In the new arrangement, it could be left on after the source was removed. In observing emission times, they noted that aluminum did not emit neutrons when the alpha source was removed but that positrons continued to be emitted for some time. Ever cautious, Frédéric Joliot asked a young assistant to check the electronics on the Geiger counter and its attendant amplifier. The electronics proved to be in perfect working order, so the aluminum target had been made artificially radioactive by bombardment with alpha particles.

The Joliot-Curies were certain, as physicists, that they had produced artificial radioactivity. In order to place their discovery beyond doubt, they were obligated to separate chemically the source of the new radioactivity and to demonstrate that it was not the original aluminum. On January 15, 1934, friends, including Marie Curie, received frantic telephone calls from the young experimenters and rushed to the laboratory. From makeshift apparatus scattered in apparent disarray over several tables, the Joliot-Curies bombarded aluminum with alpha particles and separated from the irradiated samples an isotope of phosphorus with a half-life of only three minutes and fifteen seconds. Marie Curie, who was dying of the leukemia produced by her lifetime of work with radioactivity, was handed a tiny tube containing the first sample of artificially produced radioactivity. Her face lighted with joy and excitement. Other colleagues filled the room with excited comments.

The Joliot-Curies soon repeated their experiments with boron and magnesium, producing still other sources of artificial radioactivity. They promptly sent off a report of their discovery to the scientific press. Its publication opened a floodgate of new experiments on the transmutation of nuclei, which led directly to the discovery of nuclear fission five years later.

Impact of Event

The report of the discovery of artificial radioactivity was published early in 1934 and earned the husband and wife a shared Nobel Prize in 1935. The scientific community almost immediately recognized the discovery as equal to that of the neutron or the positron. Laboratories around Europe and in the United States attempted to repeat and amplify the Joliot-Curies' work with a variety of chemical elements.

Once artificial radioactivity had been produced, it was obvious that the number of chemical elements that could be made radioactive had been enormously increased. This opened the door to the use of radioactive elements as tracers to study the movement of atoms in chemical reactions or through biological systems. The particular isotope of phosphorus that the Curies produced was of less importance than the technique for producing artificial radioactive species.

Enrico Fermi and his group in Rome quickly noted that neutrons were more effective in producing artificial radioactivity than the alpha particles used in the original experiments. The entire community, including the Joliot-Curies, began to study artificial radioactivity produced by bombarding different elements with neutrons. Studies on uranium in Rome, then in Berlin and Paris, led to confusing results, which were finally interpreted as nuclear fission in 1939. The Joliot-Curies continued to conduct important experiments on artificial radioactivity during this period, but Irène increasingly took control of the laboratory. Frédéric assumed a greater administrative load. Both continued to teach, work closely with students, and lead a rich family life hampered only by poor health caused, in Irène's case, by her early work with large amounts of radioactivity.

Frédéric Joliot was now accepted as a member of the French scientific elite and not an upstart who had married Madame Curie's daughter. He rapidly became involved in public science and defense work with access to the highest officials in the French government. As World War II loomed on the horizon, Frédéric was drafted into the military. Recognizing the possibility of a nuclear fission bomb, he took steps to secure uranium for France and began negotiations for a large supply of heavy water located in Norway. With the Nazis closing in, he and his colleagues smuggled the heavy water to Britain and hid the uranium in Morocco just ahead of Adolf Hitler's advancing troops. During the war, Joliot used the prestige of his Nobel Prize to conceal his activities in support of the Resistance.

After the war, the Joliot-Curies returned to Paris. Irène went back to experiments in the laboratory, but her husband assumed a leading role in restructuring French science. He headed the French equivalent of the Atomic Energy Commission. Joliot had become a communist during the war and was removed from his posts as the Cold War began. He suffered from his disgrace but continued to work for excellence in French science and world peace until his early death. In addition to being a major scientific contribution in its own right, the discovery of artificial radioactivity allowed Joliot to become one of the shapers of modern European science.

Bibliography

Biquard, Pierre. *Frédéric Joliot-Curie: The Man and His Theories.* Translated by Geoffrey Strachan. New York: Paul S. Eriksson, 1966. A biography by a scientific colleague who was an eyewitness to the discovery of artificial radioactivity, this account is marred by an extremely sentimental attachment to Frédéric Joliot.

Goldsmith, Maurice. *Frédéric Joliot-Curie.* London: Lawrence and Wishart, 1976. The most readable biography of Joliot by a colleague. It provides a clear account of the physics of the situation but tends to idealize Joliot. The discussion of Joliot's role in World War II reads like a spy novel.

Jungk, Robert. "An Unexpected Discovery." In *Brighter Than a Thousand Suns*, translated by James Cleugh. New York: Harcourt Brace, 1958. This chapter provides a history of the discovery of artificial radioactivity in the context of the time during which it was made. The volume is oriented toward a history of the Manhattan Project but provides solid background on the physics of the day.

Opfell, Olga S. "Irène Joliot-Curie." In *The Lady Laureates: Women Who Have Won the Nobel Prize*. Metuchen, N.J.: Scarecrow Press, 1978. This readable account is written from the point of view of Irène Joliot-Curie and provides a readable view of the vital role she played in the discovery of artificial radioactivity. It emphasizes her life as the mother of a family and daughter of a Nobel laureate.

Rhodes, Richard. "Stirring and Digging." In *The Making of the Atomic Bomb*. New York: Simon & Schuster, 1986. A lively description of the discovery of artificial radioactivity set in the context of the physics community and the political events surrounding it, this chapter lives up to the high standards of this excellent history of early twentieth century physics.

Ruth H. Howes

Cross-References

Chadwick Discovers the Neutron (1932), p. 973; Cockcroft and Walton Split the Atom with a Particle Accelerator (1932), p. 978; Segrè Identifies the First Artificial Element, Technetium (1937), p. 1101; Hahn Splits an Atom of Uranium (1938), p. 1135; Seaborg and McMillan Make Element 94, Plutonium (1941), p. 1181; Fermi Creates the First Controlled Nuclear Fission Chain Reaction (1942), p. 1198.

FERMI PROPOSES THE NEUTRINO THEORY
OF BETA DECAY

Category of event: Physics
Time: November-December, 1933
Locale: Rome, Italy

Fermi used quantum mechanics to derive a theory of radioactive beta decay involving the neutrino and a new weak force of nuclear interactions, which led to many new elementary particle discoveries

Principal personages:

ENRICO FERMI (1901-1954), an Italian-American nuclear physicist who won the 1938 Nobel Prize in Physics for his work with neutrons and later built the first nuclear reactor

WOLFGANG PAULI (1900-1958), an Austrian-American theoretical physicist who won the 1945 Nobel Prize in Physics for his work in quantum theory

PAUL ADRIEN MAURICE DIRAC (1902-1984), a British-American theoretical physicist who shared the 1933 Nobel Prize in Physics with Erwin Schrödinger for their work in quantum field theory and antimatter prediction

ANTOINE-HENRI BECQUEREL (1852-1908), a French physicist who shared the 1903 Nobel Prize in Physics with Pierre Curie and Marie Curie for their discovery of radioactivity

HIDEKI YUKAWA (1907-1981), a Japanese theoretical physicist who won the 1949 Nobel Prize in Physics for his meson theory

Summary of Event

Enrico Fermi's theory of beta decay solved one of the most puzzling problems of radioactivity and provided strong evidence for the existence of the neutrino and of a new type of weak force in nuclear interactions. Radioactivity was discovered by Antoine-Henri Becquerel in 1896 in the form of spontaneous and continuous radiation from various compounds of uranium that could penetrate layers of black paper to expose a photographic plate. Additional radioactive elements were discovered by Marie Curie and others in the next few years. More than one type of radiation from these materials was demonstrated by Ernest Rutherford in 1898 at the Cavendish Laboratory in Cambridge. He showed that one component could be absorbed by a single piece of paper while another component was about one hundred times more penetrating. He called the short-range radiation alpha rays and the penetrating radiation beta rays.

By the end of 1899, Becquerel and several other researchers had shown that beta rays are deflected by a magnetic field in the same direction as cathode rays (electrons) and thus consist of negatively charged particles. In 1900, Paul Villard in France discovered an even more penetrating radiation that was not deflected by a magnetic field. These rays were eventually called gamma rays and were shown to be electromagnetic waves like X rays but with higher frequencies. Meanwhile, Becquerel showed that the deflection of beta particles was consistent with the behavior of electrons, with some of them ejected at speeds of up to about half the speed of light.

By 1903, Rutherford succeeded in observing a much smaller magnetic deflection of alpha rays in the direction of positively charged particles and by 1909 had identified them as positive helium ions (helium atoms that have lost their two electrons). Other differences between alpha and beta particles soon became evident. The deflection of alpha particles was found to be well collimated, while beta-particle deflections formed a diffuse and extended image on a photographic plate. Thus, alpha decay seemed to produce particles of a single velocity compared to beta particles with a variety of energies. By the end of 1903, at McGill University in Montreal, Rutherford and Frederick Soddy proposed that alpha and beta decay result from a transmutation of the atoms of one element into another. Eventually, it was shown that alpha decay produces a new element with atomic number (of nuclear protons) reduced by two and atomic mass number (protons and neutrons) reduced by four, corresponding to the charge and mass of the helium nucleus. Beta decay increases the atomic number by one with no change in atomic mass number.

The spontaneous energy associated with radioactive decay was at first a mystery that seemed to contradict the law of conservation of energy. This mystery was partially resolved with Albert Einstein's theory of relativity in 1905, which showed the equivalence of mass and energy and could account for radioactive energy from the decrease in mass between the parent and product nuclei. The energy of alpha particles was found to agree closely with this change in mass, but beta particles did not fit as well. By 1914, James Chadwick confirmed the continuous distribution of beta-particle energies, in addition to some definite energies associated with so-called conversion electrons ejected from their orbits around the nucleus by gamma rays. The continuous beta-energy spectrum was found to vary from small energies up to a maximum value that corresponded to the decrease in mass in the nuclear transmutation.

For several years, the problem of the continuous distribution of energies among beta particles perplexed physicists. Calorimeter measurements by Lise Meitner and others showed that the average energy of beta decay was only about one-third the value expected from the difference in masses of the parent and product nuclei. In his Faraday lecture of 1931, Niels Bohr suggested that energy conservation might not apply to beta decay. Additional problems arose with the quantum concept of particle spin, indicating that angular momentum might not be conserved in the beta decay of an electron with spin.

One way to save the conservation principles was suggested by Wolfgang Pauli at a meeting of the American Physical Society in Pasadena, California, in June, 1931.

He suggested that the beta-decay electrons might be accompanied by light neutral particles too penetrating to be observed or have any effect on a calorimeter experiment. The beta particle and the neutral particle would share the available energy so that their sum would be equal to the mass-energy difference between parent and product nuclei. Such a particle would have zero or near zero rest mass, since some beta electrons were at or near the maximum possible energy. It would be neutral to conserve charge and have spin equal to the electron spin but possibly in the opposite direction to conserve angular momentum. In Rome, Pauli's light neutral particle was called the neutrino (Italian diminutive for neutron) to distinguish it from the neutron, which was discovered by Chadwick in 1932 and shown to have a mass slightly greater than the proton. Pauli's neutrino hypothesis was first published in a report on discussions at the Solvay Conference on physics held in Brussels in October of 1933. After returning from the Conference, Fermi began to develop a quantitative theory for the role of the neutrino in beta decay from the equations of quantum mechanics. He followed the same approach that Paul Adrien Maurice Dirac used in his 1928 relativistic quantum theory of photon emission and pair creation (particle and antiparticle). He postulated the simultaneous creation of an electron and an antineutrino (same as a neutrino except for spin) when a nuclear neutron converts into a proton during beta decay. In doing this, Fermi introduced a new weak force of much shorter range than the familiar gravitational and electromagnetic forces. The equation he derived for the probability of beta emission contained a coupling constant for the weak interaction that was determined from beta-decay data to be 100 billion times smaller than the corresponding coupling constant in Dirac's theory of electromagnetic interactions. The weakness of this interaction is one factor in the relatively long half-life for beta decay.

Fermi sent his findings to the British journal *Nature* at the end of 1933, but it was promptly rejected. It was then accepted for publication in the German journal *Zeitschrift für Physik* in January, 1934.

Fermi's theory successfully explained the exact form of the beta-decay energy spectrum, the decay half-life, and its relation to beta-particle energies, and other characteristics of beta decay. After the 1934 discovery of artificial radioactivity with positron emission (positive electrons), Fermi's theory was found also to fit this positive beta decay in which nuclear protons convert to neutrons by the emission of a positron and neutrino. The discovery of electron capture in 1937, in which a nuclear proton converts to a neutron by capturing one of its atomic electrons, could also be explained with Fermi's theory by assuming the emission of a neutrino. The beta-decay theory was Fermi's theoretical masterpiece and the foundation for many new discoveries.

Impact of Event

Fermi's beta-decay theory led to the development of new concepts of nuclear interactions and the discovery of new elementary particles. In 1935, Hideki Yukawa used the theories of Fermi and Dirac (for weak and electromagnetic interactions) as models for his theory of the strong nuclear force that holds protons and neutrons together in the nucleus. His theory included the prediction of the meson as the field quantum to transmit the strong interaction, and he also proposed a field quantum to mediate weak interactions in beta decay instead of the direct coupling used by Fermi. Yukawa showed that the meson would have mass equal to about two hundred electron masses; his theory implied a much larger mass for the field quantum to transmit weak interactions, now called the W-particle because of its much shorter range.

In 1937, a 207-electron-mass particle was discovered in cosmic rays, but this so-called muon was shown by Fermi and his associates to interact with matter by the weak force. A 273-electron-mass particle was discovered in 1947, now called the pion, which interacted by the strong force and matched the properties of Yukawa's meson. The neutrino was more difficult to detect since it passes readily through matter. In 1956, C. L. Cowan and Frederick Reines confirmed the effects of neutrinos near a nuclear reactor, where enough were produced for a few to interact with protons to yield nearly simultaneous neutrons and positrons, easily detected in this so-called reversed beta decay. By 1961, experiments revealed a difference between the electron neutrino of ordinary beta decay and the muon neutrino produced when pions decay into muons. Theories predicting a large production of neutrinos when stars explode were confirmed by the supernova of February, 1987, when about ten neutrino events were recorded in a Japanese detector.

The most important result of Fermi's beta-decay theory was the development of a unified electroweak theory in 1967 by Steven Weinberg and independently by Abdus Salam. They showed that the electromagnetic and weak interactions are different aspects of a single electroweak force requiring three new massive field quanta. The electroweak theory was dramatically confirmed in 1983 when a 135-member team led by Carlo Rubbia used proton collisions in a giant accelerator in Geneva to produce positive and negative W-particles with mass about eighty-five times the proton mass, and neutral Z-particles with about ninety-seven proton masses, in exact agreement with the Weinberg-Salam theory.

Bibliography

Beyer, Robert T., ed. *Foundations of Nuclear Physics.* New York: Dover, 1949. This volume contains facsimile copies of a dozen foundational articles, including Fermi's original 1934 beta-decay article in German, the 1932 article by Chadwick on the existence and mass of the neutron, and Yukawa's 1935 article on the meson theory of the strong nuclear force and beta decay. The second half of the book is a 120-page bibliography of the most important early articles on nuclear physics.

Eisberg, Robert, and Robert Resnick. *Quantum Physics of Atoms, Molecules, Solids, Nuclei, and Particles.* 2d ed. New York: John Wiley & Sons, 1985. An intermediate-level college physics textbook with good sections on beta decay, Fermi's theory of weak interactions, and the electroweak theory. Theoretical results are discussed with equations, graphs, and diagrams, but without lengthy mathematical derivations.

Evans, Robley D. *The Atomic Nucleus.* New York: McGraw-Hill, 1955. A classic graduate-level textbook on nuclear physics with excellent historical documentation, with more than thirty pages of bibliography. A chapter on beta-ray spectra gives a good outline of experimental data and a twenty-page sketch of the mathematical details of Fermi's beta-decay theory.

Glasstone, Samuel. *Sourcebook on Atomic Energy.* 3d ed. Princeton, N.J.: D. Van Nostrand, 1967. A well-organized introduction to atomic and nuclear physics with good historical detail. Chapters on radioactivity, nuclear radiations, and elementary particles provide good background on the discovery of beta decay, Fermi's theory, and the neutrino.

Segrè, Emilio. *From X-Rays to Quarks: Modern Physicists and Their Discoveries.* San Francisco: W. H. Freeman, 1980. A very readable historical account of modern physics and of the personalities involved in it. A chapter on radioactivity and a brief treatment of Fermi's beta-decay theory provide personal details by an early associate of Fermi. Many interesting historical photographs and diagrams are included.

Strachan, Charles. *The Theory of Beta-Decay.* Elmsford, N.Y.: Pergamon Press, 1969. An introduction to the theory of beta decay, the neutrino, and weak interactions is given in part 1. In part 2, several original articles are reprinted, including an English translation of Fermi's 1934 article on beta decay.

Joseph L. Spradley

Cross-References

Becquerel Wins the Nobel Prize for the Discovery of Natural Radioactivity (1903), p. 199; Einstein States His Theory of Special Relativity: $E = mc^2$ (1905), p. 297; Rutherford Presents His Theory of the Atom (1912), p. 527; Chadwick Discovers the Neutron (1932), p. 973; Anderson Discovers the Positron (1932), p. 983; Frédéric Joliot and Irène Joliot-Curie Develop the First Artificial Radioactive Element (1933), p. 987; Rubbia and van der Meer Isolate the Intermediate Vector Bosons (1983), p. 2230.

BENEDICT PUBLISHES *PATTERNS OF CULTURE*

Category of event: Anthropology
Time: 1934
Locale: New York

Benedict published Patterns of Culture, *a classic work which contributes to new directions in anthropological theory, methodology, and philosophy*

> *Principal personages:*
> RUTH BENEDICT (1887-1948), an American anthropologist whose ideas and writings profoundly influenced anthropological theory and contributed to popularizing the discipline
> FRANZ BOAS (1858-1942), the father of American anthropology and founder of the relativistic and culture-centered anthropology that dominated the field in the early twentieth century

Summary of Event

The field of anthropology began to develop new concerns and methods in the beginning of the twentieth century. Having its origins in the nineteenth century, it focused originally on the concerns of that period—classification and development of human races, languages, and societies. Charles Darwin's *On the Origin of Species* (1859), with the general concept of evolution, strongly influenced the thinking of the time so that by the end of the nineteenth century, studies classified societies on a hierarchical scale to determine the phases, stages, and states through which all human groups passed. Karl Marx and Friedrich Engels added to this evolutionary perspective by stressing the causes of human evolution and argued that the mode of production was the prime force upon which political, judicial, and ideological superstructures were based. The evolutionary perspective, however, assumed that there was a universal "human nature" and did not consider the different meanings and functions similar traits can have when in different contexts.

It was in this context that Franz Boas, a German-born American and the father of American anthropology, joined the staff of the American Museum of Natural History and Columbia University. He scorned the sweeping generalizations of many evolutionists because they were selective in the facts they used and their ideas did not account for the more sophisticated observations of cultural variability. Boas emphasized field work and firsthand observation. He founded the culture history school; the title is misleading because Boas tended to favor the functionalist approach which considered societies as likened to organisms where the parts are interdependent. Boas argued that cultures should be considered as a whole. He emphasized the importance of life histories and drew attention to the relationship of culture and personality.

Boas inspired a number of students who became prominent anthropologists, one of whom was Ruth Benedict. Her humanistic ideas led her not only to challenge the rigid scientific methodology (considered by some to be essential in anthropological research) but also to argue that anthropology belonged with the humanities and not the social sciences. After the age of thirty, she discovered anthropology and believed that the discipline enabled her to contrast different peoples and different historical periods. She was a student at the New School for Social Research, where she was greatly influenced by Franz Boas. She affectionately referred to him as "Papa Franz." She was also influenced by Robert Lowie and was directed in her field work among the Serrano Indians by Alfred Kroeber. She completed her doctoral dissertation in 1923 and was appointed an assistant to Boas. In 1927, she studied the Pima Indians and was struck by the contrast between them and the Pueblo Indians. The Pueblo emphasized harmony, while the Pima emphasized extremism. During this time, Benedict began to view culture as a total configuration, not merely as a matrix in which personalities develop, but as being like a personality on a large scale. This view of culture being like a personality developed into the theoretical framework for *Patterns of Culture* and was presented at the Twenty-third Congress of Americanists in 1928; however, the book was not written until 1931.

After Boas' retirement, Benedict became chair of the anthropology department at Columbia University and edited the *Journal of American Folklore*, directed field trips, and continued to write poetry. World War II opened up new avenues, and Benedict received a research posting in Washington, where she applied anthropological thought to contemporary societies. After returning to Columbia University in 1946, she completed *The Chrysanthemum and the Sword*, a book about Japan which some consider to be her masterpiece and which continues to remain unique in the annals of anthropology.

Patterns of Culture, however, remains Benedict's most popular work and the central event in her life. The work was not only a culmination of her questioning in the 1920's but also the fulfillment of a sense of social responsibility and a desire to lead our society to new values and goals. It was a course given at Columbia University by Kroeber, however, that triggered the effort. At the insistence of Boas, Kroeber acquiesced to give a series of lectures on the cultures of Highland South America. Benedict thought that Kroeber's lectures and contributions were dry. Out of exasperation, she made the impulsive decision to write her own book, which became *Patterns of Culture*. In *Patterns of Culture*, Benedict argues that every culture is an integrated whole, a "personality writ large." As her friend Margaret Mead explained, Benedict showed that "each historical culture represents a many-generational process of paring, sifting, adapting, and elaborating on an available 'areal forma,' and that each culture, in turn, shapes the choices of those born and living within it." Benedict recognized that hereditary factors contributed to differences in behavior, but those who did not conform to the culture found difficulty living within it.

To support her argument, Benedict analyzed and compared the cultures of three peoples: the Kwakiutl of western Canada, the Zuni of the southwestern United States, and the Dobuans of Melanesia. She chose them because she considered the data of each culture viable. She had studied the Zuni, was familiar with the literature concerning them, and could also draw on Ruth Bunzel's field materials. Boas had studied and written extensively on the Kwakiutl, and she had full access to his published and unpublished materials, as well as spending many hours discussing the Kwakiutl with him. Benedict had a high regard for Reo Fortune's work on the Dobuans and got permission from him to use his material.

Building on her earlier work, she used Friedrich Wilhelm Nietzsche's terms Apollonian and Dionysian as classification terms, but used the psychological term paranoid for her third category. Also, she had become acquainted with Gestalt psychology, an approach that agreed with her insights. Thus, she used the Gestalt framework in her analysis. She compared the three cultures. The Kwakiutl were "Dionysian" because she viewed them as egocentric, individualistic, and ecstatic in their rituals. Located on a narrow strip of the Alaskan coast, the Kwakiutl were wealthy, living off the products of the sea. Technologically, they were superior; they worked wood without metal tools, built houses, ceremonial halls, and raised great totem poles. In spite of this wealth, however, they were Dionysian in their ecstatic dancing. Often, a dance leader foamed at the mouth, seemed mad, and sometimes even threw himself on burning coals. Wealth was for display, not use. They would lend out etched sheets of copper, blankets, and canoes with obligatory interest, which often began with the children. The potlatch was a ritual competition where gifts were heaped on a rival who could not repay or a contest of wild destruction while reciting hymns of self-glorification. If the guest could not destroy an equal amount, he was shamed. The same contest was performed at a wedding, where the bridegroom's party might try to overpower the father of the bride with heaps of gifts. During other forms of revenge, innocent parties were killed to avenge natural deaths. A boy struck by his father was shamed into committing suicide; similarly, a wife heaped with accusations of adultery was sent home to take her own life eventually. The ideal character among the Kwakiutl was to strive constantly to escape limitations, to achieve excesses, and to break into the order of experience. Thus, they valued drugs and alcohol, fasted, and used self-torture and frenzy.

The Zuni's were "Apollonian" because they were restrained—they did not condone excessive or disruptive psychological states. They preferred noncompetitive, gentle, peace-loving, and middle-of-the-road existence. In fact, it was forbidden for a serving priest even to feel anger. They emphasized the ceremony, the perfection of ritual, and had hierarchies of kachinas, or masked gods, some of which were impersonated in dances. Marriage was a personal affair with little ceremony attached to it, and divorce was easy. The society was matrilineal, and when a wife became tired of her husband, she merely laid his belongings on the doorstep and he went home to his mother. Dreams and hallucinatory experiences were avoided, but there were hour-long prayers that were repeated without a mistake. Aggressive, ambitious individuals were frowned upon and suspected of sorcery. The ideal person was easygoing, socially poised, and made others feel comfortable.

The Dobuans, on the other hand, were considered paranoid because they emphasized magic, and everyone feared and hated everyone else. The Dobuans were of Melanesia and part of the kula ring studied by Bronisław Malinowski. Unlike Malinowski's Trobrianders, the Dobuans displayed antagonisms and hostility. In their yam crops, they used charms to defend their crops against competitors. If there was a problem, it was ascribed to evil magic. They saw life being dominated by treacherous rivalry, with adultery being common and violent jealous outbursts being frequent. Dobuans used incantations to cause disease in those they disliked and all had antidotal spells. Charms were to protect them and their property as well as infect trespassers and thieves. Death was always attributed to magic, with women being particularly suspect. Often on the death of a spouse, the survivor was suspected of magical murder. The Dobuans disapproved of laughter and believed that laughter during gardening prevented yams from growing. The ideal person cheated, stole, charmed, and poisoned his way to eminence.

Impact of Event

When *Patterns of Culture* was published, it initially received acclaim. *The New York Times* said it was "expertly conceived and brilliantly developed." Kroeber, in the *American Anthropologist*, called it "an important contribution," but hoped Benedict's configuration approach would be further developed to give anthropology "new stimuli and insights." In spite of the initial favorable reaction and its popularity among nonanthropologists, the approach has been abandoned because it is considered impressionistic, reductionist, and not susceptible to replication. It explained behavior by focusing on cultural patterns, and did not account for the variation within a particular group. Also, some of the data have been challenged by other studies.

In spite of these limitations, however, *Patterns of Culture* had a significant impact for both anthropologists and nonanthropologists alike. Like many great works, they may not be perfect in hindsight; and, as knowledge develops, concepts go beyond them. Nevertheless, *Patterns of Culture* made a significant contribution at a crucial time. It raised philosophical and theoretical issues, while building and developing existing concepts. Some of the criticisms were exactly what Benedict had argued against. For twenty years, many had tried to discredit subjectivity in anthropology. Benedict, with her humanistic orientation, reintroduced subjectivity into analysis, but it was subjectivity based on verifiable facts. This marked a clear split between what Kroeber termed "scientific" and "historical" anthropology. A debate within the discipline of anthropology concerning the merits and validity of each approach followed. Benedict defined anthropology as a discipline that studied differences between cultural traditions so that the concern would be what particular cultures do to people. Second, she presented "culture" as an integrated whole made by humans, which meant that every culture is integrated and implied that a culture is more than the sum of its parts.

By studying whole cultures and seeing culture as a total configuration, Benedict adopted Boas' emphasis on the collection of information and took it further by integrating data around a concept, in her case, it was the cultural configuration. This gave impetus to cultural relativism, which argued that whole cultures should be studied rather than cultural traits or culture as a general concept. Also, she brought forth the issue concerning the relationship of the individual and society. She showed that the culture provided stimulus to certain behavioral patterns and individuals influenced their culture; influence flowed both ways. Thus, people who did not fit into a society did not necessarily have to blame themselves. In fact, Benedict showed that even though our culture evaluated behaviors (such as homosexuality) as abnormal, other cultures provided an environment where people practicing such traits functioned well. These revelations gave impetus to the culture and personality focus in anthropology.

For the nonanthropologist, as well as the anthropologist, Benedict set forth a concept of culture and showed the importance it had on everyday life, even in modern society. She challenged the biological deterministic position dominating the thinking of the time and replaced biology with culture as a prime determinant in human behavior. Also, the concept of cultural relativity was communicated to the public where people would be more open to evaluating others on their terms rather than from the outsiders' ethnocentric bias. This set forth the basis for reevaluation of cultural practices, such as sex roles. One ramification was that women did not have to be seen as innately weaker or inferior because in other cultures they held a dominant position.

Patterns of Culture is still a popular book, and much of the philosophy and concepts it sets forth are as relevant today as the time it was published. It was one of the steps in building an understanding of human behavior which is part of the foundation of our knowledge, but also a step that has now been passed.

Bibliography

Benedict, Ruth. *Patterns of Culture*. Boston: Houghton Mifflin, 1934. A classic work setting forth Ruth Benedict's philosophical and theoretical views concerning the analysis of human behavior.

Bohannan, Paul, and Mark Glazer, eds. "Ruth Fulton Benedict." In *High Points in Anthropology*. New York: Alfred A. Knopf, 1973. This work briefly sets forth some of Ruth Benedict's contributions to anthropology as well as criticisms of her ideas. It also includes the original writings so the reader can judge the ideas by reading the primary source.

Caffrey, Margaret. *Ruth Benedict: Stranger in This Land*. Austin: University of Texas Press, 1989. A highly acclaimed, well-researched, and insightful portrayal of Ruth Benedict and her works.

Harris, Marvin. *The Rise of Anthropological Theory: A History of Theories of Culture*. New York: Thomas Y. Crowell, 1968. An analysis of anthropological theories from the cultural materialist perspective.

Hays, H. R. *From Ape to Angel*. New York: Alfred A. Knopf, 1958. An account of the development of anthropology from a literary perspective.

Honigmann, John J. *The Development of Anthropological Ideas*. Homewood, Ill.:

Dorsey Press, 1976. The development of anthropology from a cultural perspective of the American school.

Mead, Margaret. *Ruth Benedict*. New York: Columbia University Press, 1974. A portrayal of Ruth Benedict by a close friend and scholar who had access to much of her correspondence.

Modell, Judith Schachter. *Ruth Benedict: Patterns of a Life*. Philadelphia: University of Pennsylvania Press, 1983. An insightful biography and analysis of Ruth Benedict's life and works.

Arthur W. Helweg

Cross-References

Boas Publishes *The Mind of Primitive Man* (1911), p. 481; Mead Publishes *Coming of Age in Samoa* (1928), p. 869; Ardrey's *The Territorial Imperative* Argues That Humans Are Naturally Territorial (1966), p. 1808.

CHERENKOV DISCOVERS THE CHERENKOV EFFECT

Category of event: Physics
Time: 1934
Locale: Soviet Academy of Science, Moscow, Soviet Union

Cherenkov undertook a detailed study of the properties of the faint blue light emitted by charged particles moving through a material faster than the speed of light in that material

Principal personages:
PAVEL ALEKSEYEVICH CHERENKOV (1904-   ), a Soviet physicist who discovered the light emission by particles traveling faster than the speed of light in a medium; cowinner of the 1958 Nobel Prize in Physics
ILYA MIKHAILOVICH FRANK (1908-   ), a Soviet physicist who, with Tamm, formulated a theoretical explanation for Cherenkov radiation and cowinner of the 1958 Nobel Prize in Physics
IGOR YEVGENYEVICH TAMM (1895-1971), a Soviet physicist who, with Frank, formulated a theoretical explanation for Cherenkov radiation and cowinner of the 1958 Nobel Prize in Physics

Summary of Event

In the early twentieth century, many scientists noticed that transparent materials placed near intense radioactive sources emitted a very faint blue light. Pierre Curie, codiscoverer of the radioactive element radium, is recorded by his biographers to have fascinated dinner guests by producing from his pocket a tube of radium salt which illuminated the dinner table with a mysterious blue glow visible in the fading evening light. At the time, however, scientists were interested in the isolation and identification of new chemical elements, and little or no effort went to understanding the origin of the bluish glow. The first systematic attempt to understand this emission of blue light was made by Lucien Mallet from 1926 to 1929. He found that the light emitted from a wide variety of different transparent materials placed next to radioactive sources always had the same bluish-white color and that its spectrum was continuous. This later observation was very important because it distinguished this light from the fluorescent light emission, which occurred in narrow, discrete color bands, also observed when materials were bombarded with the rays from radioactive sources. Mallet, however, completed his work without attempting to offer any explanation for the mechanism that produced the light.

In 1934, Pavel Alekseyevich Cherenkov, working at the Institute of Physics of the Soviet Academy of Science in Moscow, undertook an exhaustive series of experiments to characterize the properties of the blue emission. Cherenkov had been studying the problem of fluorescent emission from materials exposed to radiation. Apparently unaware of Mallet's earlier efforts, Cherenkov noticed the very weak emission of visible light from liquids exposed to "gamma rays," high-energy light invisible to the human eye. In his first experiment to determine the nature of this emission, Cherenkov inserted a vial containing about 100 milligrams of radium into a wooden block. The wood absorbed all the radiation from the decaying radium except the gamma rays. A container of liquid was then placed above the radioactive source and an optical microscope system was used to observe the intensity and color of the light emitted by the liquid. Sixteen different pure liquids including distilled water, paraffin, and various alcohols were examined. Cherenkov concluded that the intensity of the emission varied little when one liquid was substituted for another, that the emission was mainly in the blue and violet regions of the color spectrum, and that the color of the emission did not change significantly when a different liquid was substituted. These properties of the emission were quite different from what would be expected from the fluorescence emission process. In addition, when Cherenkov added compounds such as potassium iodide or silver nitrate (known to inhibit the fluorescence process) into the liquids, the intensity of the emitted light did not decrease.

By the early 1930's, the mechanism for the fluorescent emission from materials bombarded with the rays from radioactive sources was well understood. Soviet scientists, who were the first to become aware of Cherenkov's observations, took up the challenge of attempting to explain the mechanism for this new emission process. In 1934, Sergei Ivanovich Vavilov proposed the emission might be caused by the energy lost as electrons produced by the passage of the gamma rays through the liquid slowed down, a process known as bremsstrahlung. Cherenkov undertook a second series of experiments in 1936 to understand better the mechanism of the emission process. He investigated the influence of a magnetic field on the emitted light and concluded that the emission must be from electrons produced in the liquid by the gamma rays, not directly from the gamma rays themselves, but that the process was inconsistent with bremsstrahlung. In 1937, two other Soviet physicists, Ilya Mikhailovich Frank and Igor Yevgenyevich Tamm, developed a theory to explain the emission process. Frank and Tamm recognized that the speed of light in solids, liquids, and gases is slower than in a vacuum. According to Albert Einstein's theory of special relativity, no particle can travel faster than the speed of light in a vacuum, but it is possible for a particle to travel faster than the speed of light in the medium through which it is moving. Applying what was known about electricity and magnetism, Frank and Tamm concluded that when a charged particle travels faster than the speed of light in the medium through which it is moving, it will give off light directed in a cone oriented along its direction of motion. This emission is analogous to the bow wave produced by a boat moving through water or the sonic boom produced by an airplane moving through air faster than the speed of sound in the medium. The theory predicted that the angle of the cone of emitted light would depend on the speed of the charged particle as well as the properties of the medium. Their theory also predicted the distribution of colors to be expected in the emitted light.

Cherenkov, as well as two American physicists George B. Collins and Victor G.

Reiling, undertook a series of experiments to test the new theory. Cherenkov succeeded in photographing the emission in 1937, and showed that it had a shape crudely consistent with the cone predicted by the theory. In 1938, Cherenkov improved his apparatus and was able to verify that the angle the cone of emitted light made with the path of the particle varied in a manner consistent with the theory of Frank and Tamm. In addition, Cherenkov confirmed that the intensity of the emitted light as well as its color distribution were consistent with the theory. Independently, in 1938, Collins and Reiling published results on the intensity and angle of the emitted light, generally referred to as the "Cherenkov effect." Their observations were also consistent with Frank and Tamm's theory.

These early experiments were all performed by examining the Cherenkov radiation from an intense beam of particles. The emission from a single particle, however, was so faint that it could not be seen in the 1930's. The development of the "photomultiplier tube," an extremely sensitive light detector, provided the hope that the Cherenkov radiation from a single particle passing through a liquid or solid could be detected. After several unsuccessful attempts by a number of researchers, John V. Jelley, in 1951, succeeded in detecting the Cherenkov emission from a single, fast-moving charged particle passing through distilled water. Almost immediately, other scientists succeeded in using Cherenkov radiation for the direct measurement of particle velocities. By the mid-1950's, Cherenkov detectors were being employed by particle physicists worldwide to detect unusual atomic particles at accelerators and in the cosmic rays. For their efforts in characterizing the properties of the radiation and developing a theory to explain its emission mechanism Cherenkov, Frank, and Tamm were jointly awarded the 1958 Nobel Prize in Physics.

Impact of Event

Although initially regarded as little more than a scientific curiosity, the distinctive Cherenkov effect has found widespread applications in the fields of particle physics, astronomy, and chemistry. In 1955, Emilio Gino Segrè and his colleagues set up an apparatus at the Bevatron particle accelerator, located in Berkeley, California, to search for the antiproton. They expected only a few antiprotons in a background of many other particles called pions. Their experiment was set up in a way that the pions would be moving more rapidly than the antiprotons, so they built a Cherenkov detector filled with a particular organic liquid in which the speed of light was faster than the expected antiproton speed but slower than the pion speed. This detector provided a signal when a pion went through but none from the antiproton. They used a second detector sensitive to both types of particles, so a comparison of the two outputs allowed identification of the antiprotons. On September 21, 1955, they obtained their first evidence for the antiproton using detectors based on Cherenkov radiation.

Cherenkov detectors have been employed in the investigation of the stability of the proton. Although the proton was once believed to be a stable particle, certain theories predict that eventually the proton will decay. Its lifetime must be very long;

therefore, to see a decay, scientists would have to watch a single proton for billions and billions of years or watch a large number of protons for a shorter time. Cherenkov radiation provides the tool to undertake such an experiment. Physicists from the University of California at Irvine, the University of Michigan, and the Brookhaven National Laboratory constructed a huge "swimming pool" containing 8,000 tons of pure water at a Morton Thiokol salt mine in Ohio. If any single proton in one of the water molecules were to decay, the resulting fragments traveling through the water would produce a pulse of Cherenkov light to be detected by one or more of the 2,048 individual Cherenkov detectors surrounding the pool.

Another large, water-filled Cherenkov detector, the Kamiokande II, operated by Japanese physicists at a site 300 kilometers west of Tokyo (originally designed to search for proton decays) has been upgraded to allow detection of neutrinos from space. This detector has provided confirmation of the unexpectedly low neutrino flux from the sun, which has puzzled astronomers since it was reported by Raymond Davis, Jr., in 1967 using another type of neutrino detector. The Kamiokande II also detected the neutrino burst from the 1987 supernova, confirming models of the duration and intensity of neutrino emission in supernovas.

Cherenkov detectors are also employed by radiochemists to identify and count decaying nuclei. Because Cherenkov radiation occurs only if the charged particle is traveling faster than the speed of light in the detection material, Cherenkov detectors can be used to count rare decays in which a high energy, or fast-moving, particle is emitted in a background of many more low-energy events below the detection threshold. Cherenkov detectors have been used to determine the amount and type of radioactive material present in plant and animal tissue, environmental materials, nuclear reactor effluents, and biomedical fluids. Astronomers have used Cherenkov detectors to understand the properties of the cosmic rays. In 1956, Frank McDonald of the University of Iowa combined Cherenkov detectors with scintillation counters to obtain the charge and energy of individual cosmic rays. Early balloon-borne experiments using this combination of detectors were able to determine the relative proportions of each element in the cosmic rays. Cosmic ray analysis advanced further when similar paired detectors measuring 6 square meters flew in the third High Energy Astronomical Observatory satellite launched by the National Aeronautics and Space Administration (NASA) in 1979. The blue glow of Cherenkov radiation emitted from the water pools surrounding many nuclear reactors is also a familiar sight to reactor workers and members of the public who have been permitted to tour nuclear reactor sites.

Bibliography

Close, Frank, Michael Marten, and Christine Sutton. *The Particle Explosion*. New York: Oxford University Press, 1987. This well-illustrated book makes extensive use of color photographs in explaining the world of subatomic particles to general audiences. It describes how Cherenkov detectors were used in Segrè's discovery of the antiproton, the search for proton decay, neutrino experiments, and efforts to reveal other elusive subatomic particles.

Collins, George B., and Victor G. Reiling. "Cherenkov Radiation." *Physical Review* 54 (October 1, 1938): 499-503. This article reviews the discovery of Cherenkov Radiation, describes the theory of its emission, and reports the authors' results in determining the color spectrum of the emitted light. Although a technical article, it should be understandable with a high school-level physical science course.

Jelley, John V. *Cherenkov Radiation and Its Applications.* Elmsford, N.Y.: Pergamon Press, 1958. This book is the definitive scientific description on Cherenkov radiation. Although intended for specialists, the first chapter, which presents an extensive historical account of Cherenkov's contribution and the observations of this phenomenon which predate his work, is appropriate for general audiences. The extensive citations and reference list will assist readers interested in locating original papers on the topic.

Jordan, W. H. "Radiation from a Reactor." *Scientific American*, October, 1951, 54-55. Provides a nonmathematical description of how Cherenkov light is emitted and describes the early experiments in the United States to follow up on Cherenkov's discovery. The blue glow of Cherenkov radiation surrounding an operating nuclear reactor is shown on the cover.

Koshiba, Masa-Toshi. "Observational Neutrino Astrophysics." *Physics Today* 40 (December, 1987): 38-42. This well-illustrated, nontechnical article describes the construction, operation, and results from the Japanese Kamiokande II proton decay and neutrino detector. How Cherenkov radiation from these particles is produced and detected is described, and the results for solar neutrino observations and the 1987 supernova are discussed.

Ross, H. H., and G. T. Rasmussen. "Modern Techniques and Applications in Cherenkov Counting." In *Liquid Scintillation Counting: Recent Developments*, edited by Philip E. Stantey and Bruce A. Scoggins. New York: Academic Press, 1974. Although written for specialists, this chapter provides a clear description of many of the applications of Cherenkov detectors to problems in chemistry, biology, and environmental science. The authors explain how the unique characteristic of Cherenkov detectors make them the instrument of choice for particular scientific experiments.

George J. Flynn

Cross-References

Einstein States His Theory of Special Relativity: $E = mc^2$ (1905), p. 297; Hess Discovers Cosmic Rays Through High-Altitude Ionizations (1912), p. 532; Fermi Proposes the Neutrino Theory of Beta Decay (1933), p. 992; Fluorescent Lighting Is Introduced (1936), p. 1080; Davis Constructs a Solar Neutrino Detector (1967), p. 1830.

ZWICKY AND BAADE PROPOSE
THEIR THEORY OF NEUTRON STARS

Category of event: Astronomy
Time: 1934
Locale: Mount Wilson Observatory, California

Zwicky and Baade proposed that a neutron star formed during the explosion of a supernova

Principal personages:
WALTER BAADE (1893-1960), a German-American astronomer
FRITZ ZWICKY (1898-1974), a Swiss astronomer
LEV DAVIDOVICH LANDAU (1908-1968), a Soviet physicist
RUDOLF MINKOWSKI (1895-1976), a German-American astronomer

Summary of Event

Aristotle thought that the stars, the sun, and the planets were located on crystal spheres that moved around the stationary Earth. He considered the sphere of the stars to be perfect and unchanging, but the earth corrupt and imperfect. The heavens did appear pure and immutable for tens of thousands of years. There were lapses in that purity such as motion of the planets among the stars, but the ancients explained those transgressions as a result of the nearness of the planets to the tainted Earth. On rare occasions, a new star would appear, shining so brightly that it was visible during the day, and finally growing dim over several months. These were called *novas* from the Latin word for new, because they seemed to be new stars. Research, centuries later, would reveal how wrong that name is.

These novas were rare and random in their appearance. In the past two millennia, there were only seven bright novas that remained visible in the northern sky for at least six months. In A.D. 185 in the constellation Centaurus, the Chinese recorded a "guest star" that lasted for twenty months, and another in A.D. 393 in Scorpius lasted for eight months.

The nova of 1006 in Lupus was visible for several years and was recorded by the Chinese, Japanese, Europeans, and Arabs. The nova in Taurus in 1054 lasted twenty-two months and was noted by the Chinese and Japanese. There is evidence from several petroglyphs in the American Southwest that the Indians living there observed the event. A mystery surrounds the European records; few if any recordings are known, although there was ample opportunity to do so. The Chinese and Japanese recorded the 1181 nova in Cassiopeia, but again the Europeans did not. The last two sightings are important because the one in 1572 in Cassiopeia was observed by the last great pretelescopic astronomer, Tycho Brahe. It was Brahe who gave novas their name. Because of his study of the nova of 1572, known as "Brahe's star," and his subsequent book entitled *De Nova Stella*, Brahe's reputation was made. King Frederick II of Denmark became his patron and subsidized the building of an astronomical observatory on the island of Hveen. Brahe built the finest, most accurate instruments and collected astronomical data for several decades.

Johannes Kepler, who was Brahe's assistant in later years, studied the 1604 Ophiuchus nova, "Kepler's star." After Brahe's death in 1601, Kepler analyzed the astronomer's data for an explanation of the motion of the planets. The appearance of the nova drove Kepler to greater efforts that resulted in three laws of planetary motion.

Over the centuries, advances in telescopes and other astronomical instruments led to the collection of more data about novas. The analysis suggested that novas were not a simple class of stars. Some novas were bright and rare, while others were much fainter and more common. Fritz Zwicky and Walter Baade recognized in 1934 that two distinct phenomena were occurring and redesignated the brighter novas as supernovas.

Astronomers now know that novas occur predominantly in binary star systems, with a frequency of ten to fifteen times a year in our galaxy. One of the system's stars is in the red giant phase, but the other star has collapsed to the white dwarf stage. In the life cycle of stars, they are "born" from collapsing clouds of gas and dust. During this collapse, one or more stars form. When the star's interior pressure and temperature is high enough, four hydrogen atoms fuse into helium with a small amount of mass converted to energy. The energy radiates into space as light and other forms of electromagnetic radiation.

The star's mass will determine the length of its life cycle. Low-mass stars such as the Sun fuse the hydrogen slowly and have lifetimes of tens of billions of years. The most massive stars have lifetimes measured in tens of millions of years because they convert hydrogen to helium very rapidly. As the star "dies," it can have one of several possible deaths. The low-mass star depletes its hydrogen supply, grows in size to become a red giant, and then collapses to a white dwarf phase. It shines by its stored heat and not hydrogen fusion, and will cool eventually to a black dwarf stage. A star that was the size of the Sun will shrink to the size of Earth.

A binary system, where both stars are near the end of their life cycles, is the common source of nova explosions. Material from the red giant star is pulled onto the white dwarf's surface. When enough of it accumulates, it will fuse to helium and produce the brightening that can be seen as a nova. Thus, the contradiction in the name nova: It is not a new star, but rather the death throes of a white dwarf in a binary system.

A supernova, on the other hand, is the very rapid explosion of a more massive star near the end of its life cycle. This is evident because in Taurus, in the location of the 1054 nova, lies a gaseous mass known as the Crab nebula. Calculations of the velocity of the cloud's gas show that it started its outward journey in 1054. As the massive star converts its hydrogen to helium, it reaches a point where the hydrogen is exhausted. It collapses, but its internal heat and pressure increase to the point where helium is converted to carbon. This process of conversion to elements with higher atomic numbers and followed by a collapse continues until the star's core is the element iron. Elements with atomic numbers greater than iron will fuse only if energy is added. At this point, gravity continues the collapse, and the outer layers hit the core and bounce. The star explodes, sending a large percent of its mass into space. The remainder of the supernova collapses to become a neutron star or a black hole, depending on the remnant's mass.

The neutron was discovered in 1932, and several years later, Zwicky and Baade, and independently Lev Davidovich Landau, postulated that a supernova led to the formation of a neutron star. The pressure of the star's collapse after the explosion overcomes the atoms' electrical forces and fuses protons and electrons into neutrons. This explanation was not verified experimentally until Jocelyn Bell discovered the first pulsar in 1967.

At first, astronomers thought that the pulsed radio signal was from an extraterrestrial intelligence. Further research revealed more pulsars and a natural explanation of their origin. The explanation was that a rapidly rotating neutron star with a very strong magnetic field was generating the signal pulse. When the supernova remnant collapses, its angular momentum is conserved. In the same way that a rotating ice skater pulling in her or his arms spins faster, the collapsing star also rotates faster. Its original magnetic field also contracts and grows in strength. Interactions of the rotating magnetic field and electrons produce the radio signal that pulses because the magnetic field points toward Earth twice every rotation.

Zwicky, Baade, and Rudolf Minkowski made further observations of the light coming from various supernovas in the 1930's, and these observations led to the discovery that there are two types of supernovas. With the discovery of Supernova Shelton in the Magellanic Cloud, there is the possibility of a third type of supernova. Celestial events such as asteroid impacts have shaped the history of Earth. An understanding of supernovas gives astronomers an understanding of the early history of stars and planets.

Impact of Event

For millennia, humankind has wondered how the planets originated. The discovery of supernovas and what they signify clarifies the problem. The evidence suggests that the universe began roughly 15 billion years ago with the big bang. At that time, all energy of the universe was confined within a small sphere that exploded—the big bang. The fireball cooled and energy was transformed into elemental particles: electrons, protons, and neutrons. With further cooling, the hydrogen and helium formed, but little, if any, of the higher atomic number elements were formed. As the universe cooled and expanded, the clouds of hydrogen and helium collapsed to form stars, and these stars formed into galaxies.

As these stars aged, the more massive exploded as supernovas. The high-energy levels of the blast fused some of the star's elements into elements above iron on the periodic table. With the star's collapse and explosion, all the elements of the periodic table spewed into the surrounding space, enriching the interstellar medium. After enough stars had gone supernova, planets could form along with the next generation of stars that formed from the enriched gas and dust clouds. Before this time, planets could not exist. Life as it is known now could not exist because there was no carbon, nitrogen, and other essential elements from which to construct it.

Another implication of supernovas is the role they play in the formation of solar systems. The stars and their attendant planets form from a collapsing cloud of gas and dust. This leads to the question of how that process starts. Calculations suggest that gravity plays a role. Gravity is an attractive force that causes masses to move toward one another, as in a dropped hammer falling to the ground. Gravity does produce the cloud's collapse, but it is an inefficient process. Gravity alone would take too long to produce a solar system. The process requires something else to speed it up.

Supernovas provide the initial push to start the collapse. Interstellar space is not empty. It contains gas and dust molecules that are spread sometimes thinly in some areas of space and denser in others. As the supernova explodes, a shock wave rushes outward, sweeping the gas and dust before it. This increases the density of the gas and helps to initiate the cloud's collapse. If viewed from Earth, the areas hit by the shock wave would have an arc-shaped appearance. Astronomers have observed these in several areas of our galaxy. Sometimes, the explosion leads to a chain reaction of star formation. As a star forms, it goes through a stage where it pushes large quantities of gas outward. This, in turn, pushes the interstellar gas and dust, and increases its density. This also causes more collapse and star formation, which produces more shock waves and more collapse, and so on.

Astronomers have detected areas in the galaxy where stars appear to be forming, such as the Orion nebula and the Pleiades. Astronomers estimate that these stars are only hundreds of thousands of years old. Astronomers are trying to determine if planets will form around those stars and if life will develop on some of them. Astronomers know it happened at least once before.

Bibliography

Bethe, Hans, and Gerry Brown. "How a Supernova Explodes." *Scientific American* 252 (May, 1985): 60-68. Bethe was the first person to show how stars convert mass into energy. Discusses the mechanics of the massive star's implosion and resulting explosion. Also explores the star's preexplosion history. Rich with figures and diagrams; for the informed reader.

Charles, Philip, and J. Leonard Culhane. "X-Rays from Supernova Remnants." *Scientific American* 233 (December, 1975): 36-46. Points out that when a supernova occurs, huge amounts of energy in the form of electromagnetic radiation are sent into space. X rays produced by the explosion are analyzed for information about the explosion.

Herbst, William, and George Assousa. "Supernovas and Star Formation." *Scientific American* 241 (August, 1979): 138-145. Shows how theory and observations support the idea that supernovas trigger the formation of other stars. Also discusses the formation of the spiral structure of some galaxies.

Kirshner, Robert. "Supernovas in Other Galaxies." *Scientific American* 235 (December, 1976): 89-101. Points out that, because supernovas are rare phenomena in Earth's galaxy, scientists must look to other galaxies such as the Andromeda galaxy to find examples to study. This reveals a difference in supernovas that leads to the classifications of Type I and Type II supernova explosions.

Mitton, Simon. *The Crab Nebula*. New York: Charles Scribner's Sons, 1978. An in-depth study of the 1054 supernova in the constellation Taurus. Covers the historical records of the Asian and American Indian observers, the telescopic observations of the Crab nebula, the formation of a neutron star, and how pulsars pulse.

Schramm, David, and Robert Clayton. "Did a Supernova Trigger the Formation of the Solar System?" *Scientific American* 239 (October, 1978): 124-139. Explores the implications of small amounts of decay product from short-lived radioactive isotopes found in primitive meteorites. Concludes that the original isotopes were formed in a nearby supernova explosion that triggered the formation of the solar system.

Seward, Frederick, Paul Gorenstein, and Wallace Tucker. "Young Supernova Remnants." *Scientific American* 253 (August, 1985): 88-96. Reports on the X-ray data obtained from the Einstein X-Ray Observatory and its relationship to supernova remnants. Shows that the X-ray spectrums for Type I and Type II supernovas are different.

Stephenson, F. Richard, and David Clark. "Historical Supernovas." *Scientific American* 234 (June, 1976): 100-107. Reports on seven supernovas of the last two millennia and the search for their remnants. Also discusses the recorded observations by various cultures.

Wheeler, J. Craig, and Robert Harkness. "Helium-Rich Supernova." *Scientific American* 259 (November, 1988): 50-58. Reveals that there is a Type Ib subcategory supernova similar to a nova explosion because it occurs in a binary star system. A massive companion star expands and drives matter into the other star. This rips that star's outer layer away, which exposes the core that subsequently collapses and explodes.

Stephen J. Shulik

Cross-References

Hartmann Discovers the First Evidence of Interstellar Matter (1904), p. 213; Russell Announces His Theory of Stellar Evolution (1913), p. 585; Eddington Formulates the Mass-Luminosity Law for Stars (1924), p. 785; Chandrasekhar Calculates the Upper Limit of a White Dwarf Star's Mass (1931), p. 948; Oppenheimer Calculates the Nature of Black Holes (1939), p. 1150; Bell Discovers Pulsars, the Key to Neutron Stars (1967), p. 1862.

CARLSON INVENTS XEROGRAPHY

Category of event: Applied science
Time: 1934-1938
Locale: Astoria, New York

Carlson was the first to develop techniques of electrophotography, which made modern copying machines possible

Principal personages:
CHESTER F. CARLSON (1906-1968), an American physicist and patent attorney who developed the first electrostatic copying process
JOHN H. DESSAUER (1905-   ), a chemist and director of research and engineering at Xerox Corporation who directed the production of the first Xerox copier
OTTO KORNEI (1903-   ), a German engineer who assisted Carlson
R. M. SCHAFFERT (1905-   ), a physicist at Battelle Memorial Institute in Columbus, Ohio, who directed much of the early developmental research leading to the first practical electrostatic copier
JOSEPH C. WILSON (1909-1971), the president of Xerox Corporation during the years of its most explosive growth

Summary of Event

On October 22, 1938, Chester F. Carlson, assisted by Otto Kornei, succeeded in making the first copy by an electrostatic process. The text of this first, dim copy was simply "10-22-38 Astoria," commemorating the date and the location of the event in Astoria, New York. Little did the two men know that their invention would lead to a multibillion dollar industry.

Carlson came to New York from California, where he had earned a bachelor's degree in physics in 1930 at California Institute of Technology in Pasadena. In order to save money on textbooks, Carlson often found himself laboriously copying long-hand from a book. Perhaps it was this task, combined with his background in physics, that inspired his curiosity about copying methods. Soon he began to experiment. Lacking a real laboratory, he worked at first in the kitchen of his apartment, but later moved his workshop to the room in Astoria where the memorable event took place.

In 1937, Carlson had taken out a patent on the process of electrostatic copying, but had not constructed a copying machine to take advantage of the process. Carlson hired Kornei, a German engineer, as an assistant.

The process that Carlson and Kornei developed and brought to fruition in 1938 used a novel application of static electricity as a means of trapping an image. There are chemical elements such as sulfur and selenium that display an interesting electrical characteristic called photoconductivity. The ability of these substances to hold electrostatic charges is much less under illumination than in the dark. Since an image for copying is merely a two-dimensional pattern of light and dark areas, Carlson believed that such an image could be captured as a pattern of electrostatic charges, greater in dark areas of the image but less in the light areas. The actual copy could then be made by cleverly translating this electrostatic pattern back into black and white. Thus, the first copy was made using a zinc plate coated with sulfur to capture the image and using powder which clung by static attraction to the charged parts of the plate (dark parts of the image). Copying was completed by pressing the plate and its adhering powder to waxed paper and applying heat. The powder image became embedded in the wax as an image that became permanent when the wax cooled.

The electrostatic copying process had several advantages over conventional photography. The copying element (coated plate) could be used repeatedly, and no expensive silver was consumed in the process. Also, development of the image was simpler, requiring no baths of liquid chemicals and darkrooms.

Carlson was convinced that his method had commercial potential that could be realized with proper financing and development. With Kornei's help, Carlson constructed a prototype copier housed in a wooden box. Carlson then began to seek funding for further development of his invention. After six years of repeated failure, Carlson met Russell Dayton of Battelle Memorial Institute. Carlson won a promise from Dayton of an invitation to demonstrate the process at Battelle. In the spring of 1944, the demonstration took place at the Institute in Columbus, Ohio. Among those attending was R. M. Schaffert, head of the Graphic Arts Division at Battelle, who implemented a research program at Battelle. Over the next few years, a group of workers, including William E. Bixby, C. David Oughton, John F. Rheinfrank, and Lewis E. Walkup, improved Carlson's process and took out several patents. A key finding was that the element selenium is superior to sulfur for electrostatic copying. Continued efforts were made to attract financial backing for the Battelle research, but the only support came from the U.S. Army Signal Corps and from a small company in Rochester, New York, called Haloid Company. Haloid was in business mainly to supply giant Eastman Kodak with certain photographic products and was in need of new products, particularly in the recessionary economy following World War II. An agreement was signed between Haloid and Battelle in 1946, in which Haloid agreed to provide twenty-five thousand dollars per year for research. With this support, Battelle began to aim at the production of a practical copier that could be sold commercially.

By October 22, 1948, the tenth anniversary of Carlson's first copy, work had progressed far enough that a demonstration could be made at a meeting of the Optical Society of America in Detroit, Michigan. This meeting marks the debut of "xerography" (from Greek words meaning "dry writing"), which was coined as a euphemism for the more technical-sounding term "electrophotography." In 1950, the first "Model-A" copier emerged. It was successful mainly for the preparation of Multilith masters, but not particularly successful as a document copier. In spite of the modest success of the model A, personnel at Haloid and Battelle were now convinced that a high-quality document copier was possible, and they set out to make one. Haloid invested heavily, and staked its future on this copier. Although many on Wall Street were skeptical, the new copier (known as the Model 914) was finally introduced in 1960. The Model 914 (so-called because it used 9 × 14 inch paper) weighed 272 kilograms and operated automatically and rapidly enough to produce copies at the rate of four hundred per hour. Although the copier used the principles discovered by Carlson, many of the technical details were different. Electrostatic charging of the platen (selenium-coated plate) was now accomplished by a corona discharge. In this method, a shielded high-voltage wire was drawn across the platen. Users of the copier saw a brilliant light from this discharge, and sensitive noses could smell traces of ozone formed from the interaction of the discharge with the surrounding air. In spite of its size and occasional tendency to overheat, the Model 914 became very popular; demand increased beyond the most optimistic predictions. At this time, Haloid changed its name to Xerox Corporation, and set about putting up factories to produce the new copier which *Fortune* magazine called the most successful commercial product ever introduced. By 1962, ten thousand Model 914 copiers were in use.

Customers who ordered the Model 914 found themselves confronted with a novel strategy. The copier could be leased for a small monthly fee, plus a charge for each copy made. If there were any malfunctions, Xerox would either have it repaired or replace the copier. This arrangement helped to ensure customer acceptance of the new technology; as the popularity of copying increased, those pennies per copy began to add up to important profits for Xerox. By 1965, Americans were making 20 billion copies per year.

The invention of xerography will always be attributed to Carlson, and rightly so. His creativity brought the various physical principles together, with the technology needed to produce the first electrostatic copier. Credit for the modern automatic copier must go to the team effort of many scientists, engineers, and businessmen who had the courage to keep on working on what most thought was a lost cause.

Impact of Event

Xerography had a great impact on the people and institutions most directly associated with the discovery. From 1959 to 1969, Xerox Corporation grew from eighteen hundred employees to fifty-five thousand. Those fortunate enough to have bought Xerox stock in the 1940's or early 1950's saw each share transformed into 180 by stock splits, as well as a rise in per share price to more than hundred dollars. Carlson's portion of stock was worth more than $100 million, and many Xerox employees became millionaires.

Some of the wealth from xerography was given philanthropically by Carlson, or by Xerox Corporation to universities, hospitals, and other recipients. Carlson was very generous, as exemplified by his donation of a laboratory at California Institute of Technology, and other donations totaling about $150 million. Xerox Corporation became one of the most generous of corporate donors, regularly diverting 1 percent of its profits to educational institutions and 0.5 percent to charitable causes.

The rapid penetration of copying machines into office practice brought advantages and disadvantages, as technological advances always do. The most obvious advantage was a breakthrough in rapid, clear communication uninhibited by tedious mechanical details. The demand for this was so great that total copies made rose to an estimated annual rate of 70 billion in 1975 and to more than ten times that figure by 1985. Copying was expensive in terms of time used, paper consumption, and the need to circulate and file (or discard) all the copies. In 1990, a survey conducted for Minolta Corporation showed that 118 hours a year was spent at the copier. The Federal government, which maintains more than fifty thousand copiers, must increase its file storage by about 14,000 cubic meters yearly.

Beyond the sheer volume of copying, the nature of the material copied can be problematical. The U.S. Secret Service reported that advanced color copiers can make good copies of currency and stock certificates, leading to the possibility of fraud. More widespread is the problem of copying of copyrighted material, which is regarded as a threat to authors and publishers, but is almost irresistible to consumers, particularly to scholars and scientists.

Unauthorized copying may be a problem in a variety of ways. In the Soviet Union, until about the late 1980's, access to copiers was strictly regulated. The government feared copying of secret documents and of clandestine literature detrimental to the regime. In other countries, unauthorized copying may consist of employee use of a corporate copier for personal material. Frequently copiers are operated by a key or magnetically coated plastic card which can be kept secure. It is also now possible to prepare documents on special paper which prevents a copy from being made in an ordinary copier.

From its modest beginnings, xerography has now grown to an industry that does more than $30 billion of business per year and involves about twenty different manufacturers worldwide. High-speed copiers can produce two copies per second, and copiers have been made small enough to fit in a briefcase. Use of hard copies for interoffice communication may decline as computer networks are increasingly used for electronic mail, but xerography is certain to be an important office process for many years to come.

Bibliography

Dessauer, John H. *My Years with Xerox: The Billions Nobody Wanted*. Garden City, N.Y.: Doubleday, 1971. Dessauer, an organic chemist, was employed by the Haloid Corporation and its successor, Xerox, from 1935 until his retirement in 1970. He recounts the inside story of the development of practical copying machines, and the people who made it possible.

Dessauer, John H., and Harold E. Clark, eds. *Xerography and Related Processes*. London: Focal Press, 1965. One chapter of this book consists of Carlson's account of the history of electrostatic recording. There is a picture of the first experimental copy dated October 22, 1938, and drawings from some of Carlson's earliest patents.

Jacobson, Gary. "Carlson's Timeless Lessons on Innovation." *Management Review* 78 (February, 1989): 13-16. A brief review of the history of Xerography on its fiftieth anniversary by one of the authors of *Xerox: American Samurai*. Jacobson draws on Carlson's notebooks for insights into his creativity.

Jacobson, Gary, and John Hillkirk. *Xerox: American Samurai*. New York: Macmillan, 1986. Has been praised as an inspirational story of American competitiveness versus the Japanese and criticized for adulation of Xerox. There are historical details about Carlson, Joseph C. Wilson, and the early days of Xerox. Contains a glossary of copier-related terms and some statistics on the industry. There is no bibliography, but there are references to magazine and newspaper articles throughout the text.

Lehmbeck, Donald R. "Electrophotographic Processes and Systems." In *Neblett's Handbook of Photography and Reprography*, edited by John M. Sturge. 7th ed. New York: Van Nostrand Reinhold, 1977. Largely technical in coverage, this material devotes some attention to color copying as well as black-and-white copying.

Schaffert, R. M. *Electrophotography*. Rev. ed. New York: Focal Press, 1975. Trained in chemical physics, Schaffert devotes a chapter to a thorough discussion of the xerox process, with charts, graphs, and references to the technical literature, including patents. There are photographs and descriptions of commercially available copiers and facsimile equipment.

John R. Phillips

Cross-References

Hewitt Invents the Mercury Vapor Lamp (1901), p. 108; Louis and Auguste Lumière Develop Color Photography (1907), p. 375; Land Invents a Camera/Film System That Develops Instant Pictures (1948), p. 1331.

BEEBE AND BARTON SET A DIVING RECORD IN A BATHYSPHERE

Category of event: Earth science
Time: August 11-15, 1934
Locale: Atlantic Ocean, 8 kilometers southeast of Bermuda

Beebe and Barton pioneered the exploration of the ocean depths, contributed to the knowledge of deep sea life, and provided a model for the further development of deep-diving vehicles

Principal personages:
WILLIAM BEEBE (1877-1962), a naturalist and a curator of ornithology who organized and made the dives
OTIS BARTON (1899-   ), the engineer who designed the bathysphere and joined Beebe on most of the dives
JOHN TEE-VAN (1897-1967), a general associate with the Zoological Society who was Beebe's chief assistant
GLORIA HOLLISTER ANABLE (1903?-1988), a research associate with the Zoological Society who communicated with the bathysphere
JOCELYN CRANE GRIFFIN (1909-   ), a technical associate with the Zoological Society who assisted Beebe

Summary of Event

The first half of the twentieth century was an age of exploration. On land, both the North and South Poles were conquered, and the most remote portions of Africa, Asia, and South America were revealed to explorers, paleontologists, and archaeologists. In the air, humans traveled in airplanes and dirigibles and assaulted the heights of the atmosphere in balloons. Until the 1930's, however, the vast depths of the oceans remained largely unexplored.

People did know something of the oceans' depths. Soundings and nettings of the ocean bottom had been made many times by a number of expeditions since the 1870's. Diving helmets had allowed humans to descend more than 91 meters below the surface, and the submarine allowed them to reach a depth of nearly 120 meters. There was no firsthand knowledge, however, of what it was like in the deepest reaches of inner space.

The person who gave the world the first account of life at the great depths was William Beebe. When he announced in 1926 that he was attempting to build a craft to explore the ocean, he was already a well-known naturalist. Although his only degrees had been honorary doctorates, he was graduated as a special student in the Department of Zoology of Columbia University in 1898. He began his life-long association with the New York Zoological Society in 1899. His first specialty had been in ornithology, and he made his name in that field through a four-volume monograph on pheasants, which he studied in the field for many years. He recounted the events of these and many other trips in a number of popular books and articles.

It was during a trip to the Galápagos Islands that Beebe turned his attention to oceanography. He became the first scientist to use a diving helmet in fieldwork, swimming in the shallow waters. He continued this shallow water work at the new station he established in 1928, with the permission of English authorities, on the tiny island of Nonesuch in the Bermudas. Beebe realized, however, that he had reached the limits of the current technology and that to study the animal life of the ocean depths would require a new approach.

While he was considering various cylindrical designs for a new deep-sea exploratory craft, Beebe was introduced to Otis Barton. Barton, a young New Englander who had been trained as an engineer at Harvard University, had turned to the problems of ocean diving while doing postgraduate work at Columbia University. Although he had begun designing a spherical diving device as early as 1926, the reports of Beebe's forthcoming attempts temporarily dissuaded Barton from pursuing its development. By December, 1928, however, Barton had heard nothing further of Beebe's work, so he brought his blueprints to Beebe. Beebe immediately saw that Barton's design was what he was looking for, and the two went ahead with its construction.

The bathysphere, as Beebe named the device, weighed 5,000 pounds, with a diameter of 1.45 meters and steel walls 3.8 centimeters thick. The door, weighing 400 pounds, would be fastened over a manhole with ten bolts. Four windows, made of fused quartz at the suggestion of Edwin Elway Free, the New York physicist and lecturer, were ordered from the General Electric Company at a cost of five hundred dollars each. A 250-watt water spotlight, loaned by the Westinghouse Company, provided the exterior illumination; and a telephone, loaned from the Bell Telephone Laboratory, provided the means for communicating with the surface. The breathing apparatus consisted of two oxygen tanks that allowed two liters of oxygen per minute to escape into the sphere. During the dive, the carbon dioxide and moisture were removed, respectively, by a tray containing soda lime and calcium chloride. A winch, using steel cable, would lower the bathysphere.

On June 3, 1930, Beebe and Barton took the completed bathysphere out for a test dive. They lowered the unmanned craft to a depth of 610 meters. When the craft was raised, the communications line was tangled around the cable. An unperceived twisting had occurred in transferring the cable from its original spool onto the winch, and this twisting undid itself under water. Three days later, a second unmanned test dive was made. This time, all went well, and only about a quart of water seeped into the sphere, when it returned from a depth of 457 meters.

At 1:00 P.M., the first manned dive commenced. Beebe and Barton descended to a depth of 244 meters. A small leak had started through the door at 91 meters, but it was no worse than during the test dive. A short circuit in one of the switches showered them with sparks momentarily, but the descent was largely a success. Beebe and Barton had descended farther than had any human before.

Two more days of diving yielded more minor inconveniences and a final dive record of 435 meters below sea level. On these dives, Beebe and the other members of his staff (ichthyologist John Tee-Van and zoologist Gloria Hollister Anable) saw many species of fish and other marine life that had been seen only after being caught in nets. These first dives proved that an undersea exploratory craft had potential value, at least for deep water.

Beebe's group, now joined by a new associate, Jocelyn Crane Griffin, set out once again with the bathysphere in the fall of 1932. Two unmanned test dives initially yielded only a bathysphere full of cold sea water; a new window had been improperly installed. After fixing it, the group prepared for another round of manned dives. The most dramatic of the dives came on September 22. The National Broadcasting Company (NBC) had arranged to do a live broadcast on a Sunday afternoon. The first attempts had to be postponed because of weather and other technical problems, but on that afternoon, even though the seas would normally have been too rough, Beebe and Barton made a descent. The last several hundred meters of the descent were carried live, and a large audience heard Beebe's conversation with Anable. Several new species of fish were tentatively identified. A new depth record was set at 671 meters; Beebe decided to come up at that point because of the buffeting the bathysphere was taking as the mother ship was tossed by waves. After the 1932 dives, the bathysphere went on display at the Century of Progress Exhibition in Chicago.

In late 1933, Gilbert Henry Grosvenor, president of the National Geographic Society, offered to sponsor another series of dives. Although a new record was not a stipulation, Beebe was determined to give him one. Beebe still considered the primary purpose of the dives to be scientific. He had thought to include cosmic ray analysis experiments on the dives, but Robert Andrews Millikan, the Nobel Prize-winning physicist, responded that the bathysphere would not be submerged long enough for any useful data to be obtained. Similarly, spectrographic data could not be gathered because the smallest spectroscope could not fit through the door of the bathysphere.

The bathysphere was completely refitted before the new dives. Again, many companies donated the equipment Beebe needed. Notable was a more modern breathing apparatus donated by the Air Reduction Company. The outer sphere was altered also.

An unmanned test dive to 920 meters was made on August 7, 1934, once again off Nonesuch Island. Minor adjustments were made, and on the morning of August 11, the first dive commenced, attaining a depth of 765 meters and recording a number of new scientific observations. Several days later, on August 15, the weather was again right for the dive.

This dive also paid rich dividends in the number of species of deep-sea life observed. Finally, with only a few turns of cable left on the winch spool, a record depth of 923 meters—more than half a kilometer below the ocean's surface—was attained. The ascent was marred by the breaking of a guy rope used to spool the incoming cable, but this was scarcely noticed by Beebe and Barton.

Later dives included the other members of the group. Anable descended to a depth of 368 meters, a record for a woman. Griffin reached a depth of 351 meters. Tee-Van descended to 457 meters on August 27. After these dives, Beebe turned his focus to shallow-water dives in the Pacific Ocean.

Impact of Event

The work of Beebe and Barton with the bathysphere marked both an end and a beginning. It marked an end in the sense that although it showed that undersea exploration was a scientifically profitable enterprise, it also pointed out that the way in which Beebe pursued it was a dead end. He had originally sought to build a new exploration craft precisely because he saw the limitations of what was then the best method of exploration: the rigid diving suit or diving helmet. Although the bathysphere solved the immediate problems of diver mobility and depth limitations, however, it did not cut the "umbilical cord"—the bathysphere was still dependent upon a surface vessel. Further, there were inherent problems with the basic design. The bathysphere had no fail-safe contingency should the sphere become separated from the cable. The danger of such a catastrophic failure was always a possibility. Technologically, the bathysphere was near its design limits: The deeper one went, the more steel cable that was needed; the more cable needed, the heavier the weight of the cable-bathysphere, thus calling for larger and larger winches and mother ships, also raising the cost. The inability to maneuver horizontally also limited its scientific effectiveness.

Barton continued to work on the bathysphere design for some years. It was not until 1948, however, that his new design, the benthoscope, was finally constructed. It was similar in basic design to the bathysphere, though the walls were increased to withstand greater pressures. Other improvements were made, but the essential strengths and weaknesses of the original bathysphere remained. On August 16, 1949, Barton, diving alone, broke the record he and Beebe had set fifteen years earlier, reaching a depth of 1,372 meters off the Santa Cruz Islands in Southern California.

The bathysphere effectively marked the end of the tethered exploration of the deep, but it pointed the way to other possibilities. The first advancement in this area came in 1943, when Jacques Yves Cousteau and Émile Gagnan developed the Aqualung underwater breathing apparatus, allowing unfettered and largely unencumbered exploration down to about 61 meters. This was by no means deep diving, but it was clearly a step along the lines that Beebe had envisioned for underwater research.

A further step came in the development of the bathyscaphe by Auguste Piccard, the renowned Swiss physicist who, in the 1930's, conquered the stratosphere in high-altitude balloons. The bathyscaphe itself was a balloon but operated in reverse. A spherical steel passenger cabin was attached beneath a large float filled with gasoline for buoyancy. Several tons of iron pellets held by electromagnets acted as ballast. The bathyscaphe would sink slowly to the bottom of the ocean, and when its passengers wished to return, the ballast was dumped. The craft would now slowly (or more rapidly) rise to the surface. Although it was constructed before the bentho-scope in 1948, early tests were partial failures. In 1953, however, both the French navy's FNRS-3 under Georges Houot and Pierre-Henri Willm and the *Trieste* under Piccard and his son Jacques set new records. On August 14, Houot and Willm dove to 2,099 meters without touching bottom off Provençal. The Piccards touched bottom off Capri on September 30, some 3,000 meters.

Finally, spheres of any kind were surpassed by improved submarines designed for deep diving exploration. A craft that existed when Beebe began became the design that would ultimately conquer the ocean depths. Yet, it cannot be denied that all of these further attempts owed something to the courageous and scientific spirit of Beebe and Barton.

Bibliography

Barton, Otis. *The World Beneath the Sea*. New York: Thomas Y. Crowell, 1953. Barton tells the story of his life from shortly before his first meeting with Beebe up to the period after his record-setting dive. The account is heavy with anecdotes and opinions and should be used only to supplement Beebe's account (cited below). Photographs.

Beebe, William. *Half Mile Down*. New York: Harcourt, Brace, 1934. Beebe's definitive popular account of the dives, some of which had been published earlier in *National Geographic* and other popular magazines. Includes technical appendices by Barton, Tee-Van, Anable, and Griffin, as well as photographs, illustrations, and an index.

Guberlet, Muriel L. *Explorers of the Sea: Famous Oceanographic Expeditions*. New York: Ronald Press, 1964. Popular, episodic account of a number of ocean explorers, loosely defined. A bit too enthusiastic, but a good story. Bibliography and an index.

Piccard, Jacques, and Robert S. Dietz. *Seven Miles Down: The Story of the Bathy-scaphe* Trieste. New York: G. P. Putnam's Sons, 1961. Piccard, pilot on all dives of the *Trieste* and son of its inventor, and Dietz, the first American to make a dive in the bathyscaphe, tell the story of the dives made from 1948 to 1960. Useful for comparisons between the crafts and their descents. Photographs and an index.

Soule, Gardner. *The Greatest Depths: Probing the Seas to Twenty-thousand Feet and Below*. Philadelphia: Macrae Smith, 1970. A popular account written by a reporter that covers all aspects of deep-sea study. Quotes freely from many other works, and includes a few interesting comments from Beebe's second wife. Photographs, bibliography, and an index.

Welker, Robert Henry. *Natural Man: The Life of William Beebe*. Bloomington: Indiana University Press, 1975. An unconventional biography of Beebe that delves into critical analysis. Indispensable for understanding Beebe. Scholarly, but very readable. Photographs, notes, and an index.

George R. Ehrhardt

Cross-References

The First German U-Boat Submarine Is Launched (1906), p. 350; Haldane Develops Stage Decompression for Deep-Sea Divers (1907), p. 365; Piccard Travels to the Stratosphere by Balloon (1931), p. 963; Cousteau and Gagnan Develop the Aqualung (1943), p. 1219; The Sealab 2 Expedition Concludes (1965), p. 1792; The *Glomar Challenger* Obtains Thousands of Ocean Floor Samples (1968), p. 1876; Deep-Sea Hydrothermal Vents and New Life-Forms Are Discovered (1977), p. 2058.

GIBBON DEVELOPS THE HEART-LUNG MACHINE

Category of event: Medicine
Time: Fall, 1934
Locale: Boston, Massachusetts

Gibbon developed and tested, in animals and then humans, the first artificial device to oxygenate and circulate blood during surgery, thus beginning the era of open-heart surgery

> *Principal personages:*
> JOHN H. GIBBON, JR. (1903-1974), a cardiovascular surgeon who developed the heart-lung machine from its initial stages to its successful use in open-heart surgery
> MARY HOPKINSON GIBBON, a research technician who contributed to the early development of the heart-lung machine
> THOMAS J. WATSON, the Chairman of the Board of International Business Machines who provided the services of IBM's experimental physics laboratory, model machine shop, and engineers
> T. L. STOKES and J. B. FLICK, the researchers in Gibbon's laboratory who dramatically improved the oxygenation process
> BERNARD J. MILLER, a cardiovascular surgeon and research associate who participated in the testing and design modifications
> CECELIA BAVOLEK, the first human to undergo successfully open-heart surgery using the heart-lung machine

Summary of Event

In the first half of the twentieth century, cardiovascular medicine had many triumphs. Effective anesthesia, antiseptic conditions, and antibiotics made surgery of all kinds safer; blood typing, anticlotting agents, and blood preservatives made blood transfusion practical; cardiac catheterization (feeding a tube into the heart), electrocardiography (ECG), and fluoroscopy (visualizing living tissues with an X-ray machine) made the nonsurgical diagnosis of cardiovascular problems possible. These advances were put to use solving problems of disease, injury, and birth defects in blood vessels and around the heart.

As of 1950, however, there was no safe way to treat damage or defects within the heart. To make such a correction, this vital organ's function must be interrupted. The problem was how to keep the body's tissues alive while working on the heart. While some surgeons practiced so-called blind surgery where they inserted a finger into the heart through a small incision without observing what they attempted to correct, others attempted to reduce the body's need for circulation by slowly chilling the patient until the heart stopped. Still other surgeons used "cross-circulation," where the patient's circulation was connected to a donor's circulation. All these approaches carried profound risks of hemorrhage, tissue damage, and death.

Not until the successful development of the pump-oxygenator, or heart-lung machine, did heart surgery as it is known today become truly possible. The heart-lung machine uses mechanical devices to oxygenate and circulate the blood during heart surgery. It was developed over a period of more than twenty years through the persistence of John H. Gibbon, Jr., who, on May 6, 1953, first used it successfully in a human being. Ironically, Gibbon's first interest in such a machine arose from his concern for a patient with an obstruction of lung circulation rather than a heart defect. In February of 1931, Gibbon witnessed the death of a young woman whose lung circulation was blocked by a blood clot. Because her blood could not pass through her lungs, she slowly lost consciousness from lack of oxygen. As he monitored her pulse and breathing, Gibbon thought about ways that might circumvent the obstructed lungs and straining heart and provide the oxygen required. Because surgery to remove such a blood clot in the pulmonary artery was often fatal, her surgeons operated only as a last resort. Though the surgery took only 6.5 minutes, the young woman never regained consciousness. This experience prompted Gibbon to pursue what few people then considered a practical line of research. At the time, experimental devices for pumping blood during transfusion and for oxygenating blood during isolated perfused organ experiments were already under investigation. Gibbon sought to create a device capable of doing both: circulating blood around the heart and oxygenating it. Once practical for use in human surgery, it would permit the treatment of not only pulmonary obstruction but also abnormalities of the heart.

Gibbon began the project in earnest in 1934, when he returned to the laboratory of Edward D. Churchill at Massachusetts General Hospital for his second surgical research fellowship. He was assisted by Mary Hopkinson Gibbon. Together, they developed a surgical preparation in experimental cats to remove blood from a vein, supply it with oxygen, and return it to an artery using tubes inserted into the blood vessels. Their objectives were to assemble a device that would keep the blood moving, spread it over a very thin layer to pick up oxygen efficiently and remove carbon dioxide, and avoid both clotting and damaging blood cells. Their initial attempts included using a vertical revolving cylinder for gas exchange. This applied centrifugal force to spread the blood over a very thin layer in an oxygen-filled chamber. A piston-type pump was used for blood circulation. Ultimately, they modified this arrangement to use a gentler roller pump, which had no valve surfaces. This reduced the damage to blood cells and the surfaces available for clot formation. They reported in 1937 that heart and lung function could be artificially maintained for fifty minutes and the animal's normal heart function restored for a period of several hours. After their return to the University of Pennsylvania School of Medicine in 1935, they repeated their experiments under sterile conditions and reported in 1939 that prolonged survival after heart-lung bypass was possible in experimental animals.

World War II interrupted the progress of this work; it was resumed by John Gibbon at Jefferson Medical College in 1944. Shortly thereafter, he attracted the interest of Thomas J. Watson, Chairman of the Board of IBM, who provided the services of IBM's experimental physics laboratory and model machine shop as well as the assistance of engineers Al Malmrose, Don Rex, Leo Farr, and John Enstrom. IBM constructed and modified two experimental machines over the next seven years, and these engineers contributed significantly to the evolution of a machine that would be practical in humans.

The most critical problem presented by the ambition to take over heart-lung function in humans was the efficiency of gas exchange required to oxygenate such a large flow of blood. This problem was addressed by T. L. Stokes and J. B. Flick who, while working in Gibbon's laboratory, observed that turbulence in the blood greatly enhanced gas exchange in the oxygenator. They demonstrated and reported in 1950 that lining the oxygenation cylinder with a wire screen could produce turbulence and the desired oxygenation effect without creating a foam from broken blood cells.

Bernard J. Miller joined Gibbon's group in January of 1950 and contributed to the final stages in developing the second IBM machine, which was completed in 1951. After testing a series of materials to improve the oxygenation surface, they settled on multiple stainless-steel wire mesh screens suspended in parallel within an oxygen-filled plastic chamber. The screens were coated with a protein solution to permit a complete film to spread over them. The electronic circuit developed to control blood flow through the system was improved, and a filter was incorporated into the circuit to prevent air bubbles or incipient blood clots from reentering the body. Safety systems to maintain power and prevent combustible gases (then used as anesthesia) from entering the system were incorporated into the device, and blood pressure, flow, and hydrogen ion concentration were continuously monitored in the circuit. By 1952, the survival rate for animals maintained by this device was 90 percent.

Gibbon's first attempt to use the pump-oxygenator in a human was in a fifteen-month-old baby. This attempt failed, not because of a malfunction or a surgical mistake but because of misdiagnosis. The child died following surgery because the real problem was not corrected by the surgery. On May 6, 1953, the heart-lung machine was first used successfully on Cecelia Bavolek. In the six months before surgery, she was hospitalized three times for symptoms of heart failure when she could not engage in normal activity.

With her circulation connected to the heart-lung machine for forty-five minutes, the surgical team headed by Gibbon was able to observe directly and close an opening between her atria and establish normal heart function. Two months later, an examination of the defect revealed that it was fully closed and Bavolek resumed a normal life. Though Gibbon reflected some years later that he may have opened a Pandora's box, the age of open-heart surgery had begun.

Impact of Event

John Gibbon devoted most of his career to developing the pump-oxygenator, or heart-lung machine. His success depended on a network of critical discoveries made by many others before him and joined with concurrent discoveries to lead to future developments of which only some could be anticipated by cardiovascular scientists of the time.

Heart-lung bypass alone could not make open-heart surgery a truly practical technique. When it was possible to keep tissues alive by diverting blood around the heart and oxygenating it, other questions already under investigation became even more critical: how to stop and restart the heart, how to evaluate and prevent or correct erratic heart beats, how to prolong the survival of bloodless organs, how to measure oxygen and carbon dioxide levels in the blood, and how to safely prolong anesthesia during complicated surgery. Thus, following the first successful use of the heart-lung machine, surgeons and engineers continued to refine the methods of open-heart surgery. Many scientists, including those working with Owen Wangenstein at the University of Minnesota and John Webster Kirklin at the Mayo Clinic, employed and improved the technique so consistently in the late 1950's that by 1960 it was a standard operative procedure.

The immediate gains were forms of surgery to correct many kinds of congenital defects (birth defects) within the heart. A hole in the wall between two of the heart's chambers such as an atrial septal defect or a ventricular septal defect could be exposed now to plain view and sewn closed because blood was diverted around the heart. Valvular stenosis, a stiffening or narrowing of the heart valves, could be relieved with far less risk of permanent damage to the valve because surgeons now could judge the appropriate type and size of correction necessary. Transposed great arteries (that is, misdirected major arteries) could be severed now and rejoined to their appropriate connections with the aid of heart-lung bypass.

Furthermore, the heart-lung apparatus set the stage for the advent of "replacement parts" solutions for many types of cardiovascular problems. Cardiac valve replacement was first successfully accomplished by Albert Starr and M. L. Edwards in 1960 by placing an artificial ball valve between the left atrium and ventricle. In 1967, R. G. Favaloro performed the first coronary bypass surgery, grafting sections of a leg vein into the heart's circulation to divert blood around clogged coronary arteries. Likewise, the first successful heart transplant (Christiaan Barnard, 1967) and the controversial Jarvik-7 artificial heart (William DeVries, 1982) required the ability to stop the heart and keep the body's tissues alive during time-consuming and delicate surgical procedures. While cardiovascular science awaits the developments that will permit the prevention or true cure of the conditions that compromise cardiac functions, these corrective surgical measures, which make use of the heart-lung apparatus, continue to contribute to prolonging life.

Bibliography

Comroe, Julius H., Jr. "The Heart and Lungs." In *Advances in American Medicine: Essays at the Bicentennial*, edited by John Z. Bowers and Elizabeth F. Purcell. Vol. 2. New York: Joshua Macy, Jr. Foundation, 1976. An excellently written history of American contributions to the knowledge of cardiovascular and pulmonary function. Comroe makes the distinction between the corrective successes of modern surgery and its failure to prevent many modern maladies. Furthermore, he puts the significance of Gibbon's success into context by examining the many scientific discoveries upon which it built (including the recognition of contributions from two important but often uncredited female scientists: Maude Abbott and Helen Taussig) and the many important developments to which it led.

_____. *The Retrospectroscope: Insights into Medical Discovery.* Menlo Park, Calif.: Von Gehr Press, 1977. Comroe uses a historical perspective to make an insightful and readable examination of the conditions in which important medical discoveries have been made. This work is invaluable to anyone interested in studying the process of science. Included are several references to John and Mary Gibbon, who worked at the University of Pennsylvania when Comroe was an instructor there in pharmacology.

Davis, Goode P., Jr., Edwards Park, and the Editors of U.S. News Books. *The Heart: The Living Pump.* Washington D. C.: U.S. News Books, 1981. A beautifully illustrated and photographed volume for the general public. Historical, experimental, and clinical aspects of the heart's function are presented simply and accurately. Treatment and prevention of cardiovascular disease are given ample consideration, as are experimental and clinical techniques. Gibbon's work is put in perspective with other surgical research of the time. Glossary. Excellent for high school or college students.

Gibbon, John H., Jr. "The Development of the Heart-Lung Apparatus." *The Review of Surgery* 22 (1970): 231-244. John Gibbon's very readable personal account of his experiences through a career devoted to the development of the heart-lung machine with a consideration of the problems to be solved in the project and its impact on his life. Includes photographs of the original device and experimental surgery in progress.

Miller, Bernard J. "The Development of Heart Lung Machines." *Surgery, Gynecology, and Obstetrics* 154 (1982): 403-414. Miller's account of the evolution of heart-lung apparatus from before Gibbon's era through stages following the first successful use of the apparatus. It is technically complete, especially with respect to modifications made during the stages of development from 1950 to 1954 when Miller was a research associate at Jefferson Medical College.

Moore, Francis D. "Surgery." In *Advances in American Medicine: Essays at the Bicentennial*, edited by John Z. Bowers and Elizabeth F. Purcell. Vol. 2. New York: Joshua Macy, Jr. Foundation, 1976. An accessible review of the history of American surgery from colonial times to the present. Moore asserts that two features unique to American surgery after World War II contributed to developments such as Gibbon's: government support and the availability of animals as experimental models. Includes a photograph of John and Mary Gibbon inspecting the heart-lung machine.

Laura Gray Malloy

Cross-References

Einthoven Develops the Forerunner of the Electrocardiogram (1900's), p. 41; Landsteiner Discovers Human Blood Groups (1900), p. 56; Carrel Develops a Technique for Rejoining Severed Blood Vessels (1902), p. 134; Crile Performs the First Direct Blood Transfusion (1905), p. 275; McLean Discovers the Natural Anticoagulant Heparin (1915), p. 610; Drinker and Shaw Develop an Iron Lung Mechanical Respirator (1929), p. 895; Blalock Performs the First "Blue Baby" Operation (1944), p. 1250; Favaloro Develops the Coronary Artery Bypass Operation (1967), p. 1835; Barnard Performs the First Human Heart Transplant (1967), p. 1866; Gruentzig Uses Percutaneous Transluminal Angioplasty, via a Balloon Catheter, to Unclog Diseased Arteries (1977), p. 2088; DeVries Implants the First Jarvik-7 Artificial Heart (1982), p. 2195.

YUKAWA PROPOSES THE EXISTENCE OF MESONS

Category of event: Physics
Time: November, 1934-February, 1935
Locale: Osaka, Japan

Yukawa first postulated the existence of mesons, which later became known as pi-mesons or pions, as fundamental carriers of the nuclear force field

Principal personages:
HIDEKI YUKAWA (1907-1981), a Japanese physicist and winner of the 1949 Nobel Prize in Physics
ERWIN SCHRÖDINGER (1887-1961), an Austrian physicist and philosopher who was the winner of the 1935 Nobel Prize in Physics
WERNER HEISENBERG (1901-1976), a German physicist who was a winner of the 1932 Nobel Prize in Physics

Summary of Event

The existence of positively charged nuclear states was experimentally confirmed in the physics of 1910 to 1920. These nuclei contained several positive charges that should compel them to fly apart by the electromagnetic coulomb repulsion. Why the nucleus stayed together at all was of foremost concern to theoretical physicists.

In 1932, three new particles—the neutron, positron, and deuteron (a heavy nuclear isotope of hydrogen)—were discovered, adding confusion to some fledgling nuclear models that were emerging. In the same year, nuclei were broken apart by the growing family of particle accelerators. Prior to 1932, only the proton, electron, and the massless photon were admissible into the realm of elementary particle physics. Most working physicists were trying to model nuclear structure with some combination of protons and electrons and the discovery of neutrons, which caused considerable confusion.

At the age of twenty-two, Hideki Yukawa set two dominant research themes as goals: to investigate the quantum mechanics of the atomic nucleus and to develop relativistic quantum mechanics. Quantum mechanics had been developed by Werner Heisenberg, Max Born, and Erwin Schrödinger in the 1920's, and the wave descriptions that the Schrödinger picture suggested were appealing to Yukawa.

By 1932, Yukawa had arrived at the notion that the nuclear force was a primary force and not derivable from electromagnetism or gravity. This was a break with most thinking in theoretical physics, which was attempting to explain nuclear structure as some combination of positive charges (protons) and negative charges (electrons). Unfortunately, there were a considerable number of problems associated with Yukawa's theory. First, the electrons and protons each have spin angular momentum of $\frac{1}{2}$, as does the neutron. If one takes as an example the deuteron, the simplest compound nucleus in nature, one finds that it has a charge of $+1$ and a spin of 1. If it were composed of two protons and one electron, it would have a charge of $+1$, but its spin would be either $1/2$ or $3/2$ because spins, like charges, are arithmetically additive.

In October, 1934, Yukawa became convinced that a meson was responsible for nuclear forces. Mesons originally were defined as being midsized or middleweights, as compared with lightweight leptons ("light ones") or heavyweight baryons ("massive ones"). Yukawa realized that the small range of nuclear forces required a force carrier of a particular mass. Nuclear forces, as was known at the time, had a range of the order of only 0.02 trillionth of a centimeter, or 2×10^{-15} meters. Yukawa saw that there was an inverse relationship between mass and distance or range. A small-mass particle such as the electron acted over sizable distances hundreds of times greater than the nucleus. Protons and neutrons, being very massive, acted over distances of the order of $1/10$ the nuclear dimensions.

In November, 1934, Yukawa presented his initial paper on the existence of such mesons to the Osaka branch of the Physico-Mathematical Society of Japan. This paper, which later earned for him the Nobel Prize in Physics, postulated the existence of what were to become pi-mesons, or pions. He concluded that their masses should be about two hundred times that of the electron, or about $1/10$ that of the proton or neutron. In fact, when pions were discovered experimentally after World War II, their masses were found to be about 270 times that of the electron, or $1/7$ that of the proton. The uncharged pion, called the pi-naught, has a mass 264 times that of the electron, while the charged pions—pi-plus and pi-minus—each has a mass of 139.57 MeV/c^2. Mass units of MeV/c^2 are considered most convenient since the electron is the lightest particle at 0.511 MeV/c^2 and the highly popular proton/neutron are less than 1,000 MeV/c^2. Yukawa wrote the paper in English, and it was published in the February, 1935, *Proceedings of the Physico-Mathematical Society of Japan*.

Yukawa viewed the nuclear force as a quantum effect whereby a sizable quantum of energy was exchanged between the proton and the neutron in the nucleus. His original paper called for only two such quantums—the pi-plus and the pi-minus—but experimentally it was found that a third uncharged species—the pi-naught—also occurred. Each of these pions, or nuclear quantums, has 0 spin angular momentum and thus contributes nothing to nuclear spin states. This 0 spin feature makes them "bosons," obeying Bose-Einstein statistics, which in turn allows two or more to exist in the same quantum states within a specific nucleus.

In his paper, Yukawa concluded that he had fulfilled his first research objective in bringing quantum theory into nuclear physics to explain nuclear structure. That he had done so in such a spectacular way earned for him the Nobel Prize in Physics and elevated Japanese physics to the highest regard in the worldwide scientific community. He was able to enter the scientific elite by predicting the existence of a clearly detectable family of experimental particles whose mass, spin, and charge he was able to arrive at from theoretical considerations. Seldom if ever has such a clear, incisive, and elegant prediction been verified in physics. Pions proved to be universal carriers of the strong forces at low energies and largely responsible for holding nuclei together.

In 1937, two American physicists, Seth Neddermeyer and Carl David Anderson, discovered what they thought was Yukawa's meson family in cosmic rays. Ten years later, it was generally agreed that their particle, now named the muon, or mu-meson, was not the carrier of the strong nuclear interaction, even though it had almost exactly the mass and charge states predicted by Yukawa.

In 1948, Cecil Frank Powell and his coworkers at Bristol, England, found the pi-plus and pi-minus meson tracks in photographic emulsions left for several months on mountain tops. Only the year before, in 1947, the American physicist J. Robert Oppenheimer suggested in a cogent theoretical argument that the uncharged pion, not predicted by Yukawa, might exist also. It was found experimentally in 1950 at both Berkeley and Stanford in California.

Yukawa was awarded the Nobel Prize in Physics in 1949 for the meson theory of nuclear forces one year after his predicted particles were discovered experimentally. He could safely claim that he had completed his first great thematic quest in theoretical physics.

Impact of Event

Yukawa's paper did not catch the attention of the physics community until the discovery of the muons two years later. Yukawa wrote a letter to *Nature*, a prestigious science journal in England, stating that this discovery might be the particles that he had predicted. The editors rejected his paper and claim, but he published a note in a Japanese journal that established precedence for his claim. The discovery of muons at several places throughout the world in the next few years motivated physicists to look for explanations of what they might be, and Yukawa's mesons seemed close enough to focus the attention of many theorists.

His paper clearly delineated nuclear forces from the electromagnetic and gravitational forces of nature and gave it a theoretical foundation as being a different set of physical effects. Now, physics can be broken into four types of forces: nuclear strong (Yukawa's), electromagnetic, weak, and gravity.

Now, physics admits hundreds of mesons, of which Yukawa's pions were the first predicted types. The branch of physics that Yukawa envisaged has broken into particle physics and nuclear physics, and pions are still the lightest mass hadrons (particles that enter the strong nuclear interaction). Their relatively small mass makes them interact over the greatest range, and they are responsible for all relatively low-energy nuclear interactions.

As one moves to higher energies, pions are helped by the likes of rho-mesons. Most modern physicists suggest that the pions are not the fundamental cause of the nuclear interactions but are composed of smaller units called quarks, which are held together by gluons. In 1964, the American physicist Murray Gell-Mann proposed a theory of the strong nuclear interactions based on smaller subunits called quarks. This led eventually to quantum chromodynamics and the standard model of particles and nuclei, which ultimately had thirty-six quarks and eight gluons being responsible for nuclear forces. The gluons more or less take the role that Yukawa envisioned for his mesons, but they have spins of 1, which makes them more compatible with a set of modern field theories called gauge field theories. The pions, having spins of 0 and being massive, are unable to muster enough freedom to explain all the effects that have been noted in particles and high-energy nuclei.

Experimentally newer and higher-energy particle accelerators have caused the number of mesons to rise almost exponentially every decade since Yukawa proposed them. As of the 1990's, more than two hundred mesons are firmly established, and more have given experimental hints of existing. Most experimental physicists expect that many more mesons will be discovered in the future as newer and more energetic particle accelerators are built. Many of the newer mesons are very heavy, much heavier than protons and neutrons; therefore, the word meson has lost its middleweight meaning and now designates any integral spin particle that undergoes the strong nuclear interaction, as defined by Yakawa in 1935. Modern elementary physics owes its existence to Yukawa's efforts in predicting pions.

Bibliography

Brown, Laurie M. "Hideki Yukawa and the Meson Theory." *Physics Today* 39 (December, 1986): 55-62. This brief article describes how Yukawa's ideas contrasted with and were received by physicists of the time.

Fuchs, Walter R. *Physics for the Modern Mind*. Translated by M. Wilson and M. Wheaton. New York: Macmillan, 1967. Chapter 7 is devoted to elementary particles but gives a series of models of how Yukawa's meson exchange works between protons and neutrons in nuclei by considering pions as balls in a ballgame. Excellent descriptions and graphics for precollege-age students.

Nobelstiftelsen. *Physics*. Vol. 3. New York: Elsevier, 1964. Contains Yukawa's brief Nobel acceptance speech and a good motivation essay on his work by the editors. The Yukawa article is followed by one on Powell, the experimental discoverer of the pions; it sheds considerable perspective on Yukawa's insights.

Stuewer, Roger E., ed. *Nuclear Physics in Retrospect*. Minneapolis: University of Minnesota Press, 1979. A good reference for physics students and those interested in majoring in physics in college. Pages 160 to 171 give a good view of Yukawa's contribution as seen by a fellow nuclear theorist.

Yukawa, Hideki. *Tabibito (The Traveler)*. Translated by L. Brown and R. Yoshida. Singapore: World Scientific, 1982. This book is a personal testament of Yukawa from his early childhood until he published his mesonic theory of nuclear forces in 1935. Includes an excellent description of how working Japanese academic scientists lived and worked before World War II.

John P. Kenny

Cross-References

Rutherford Discovers the Proton (1914), p. 590; Chadwick Discovers the Neutron (1932), p. 973; Cockcroft and Walton Split the Atom with a Particle Accelerator (1932), p. 978; Anderson Discovers the Positron (1932), p. 983; Quarks Are Postulated by Gell-Mann and Zweig (1964), p. 1767; Gell-Mann Formulates the Theory of Quantum Chromodynamics (QCD) (1972), p. 1966.

CHAPMAN DETERMINES THE LUNAR
ATMOSPHERIC TIDE AT MODERATE LATITUDES

Category of event: Earth science
Time: 1935
Locale: Imperial College, London, England

Chapman determined the lunar air tide, which is the effect of the moon's gravitation on the earth's atmosphere

Principal personages:
JULIUS BARTELS (1899-1964), a German geophysicist who collaborated with Chapman on a two-volume set on geomagnetism
SYDNEY CHAPMAN (1888-1970), an English mathematician and geophysicist who investigated why the earth's magnetic field varies with periods equal to the lunar day and its submultiples
PIERRE-SIMON LAPLACE (1749-1827), a French astronomer and mathematician who was the first to describe the dynamical theory of atmospheric tide
JAMES CLERK MAXWELL (1831-1879), a Scottish physicist who developed the kinetic theory of gases in 1867

Summary of Event

Sydney Chapman, an applied mathematician and geophysicist, after professorships in Manchester, London, and Oxford, was named in 1951 as the Advisory Scientific Director and Professor of Geophysics at the University of Alaska, and in 1955, the Senior Research Fellow at the National Center for Atmospheric Research in Boulder, Colorado. Chapman was a prolific producer and contributor to a greater understanding of the atmosphere. His work in the determination of the lunar air tide was among the more than three hundred scientific papers he either authored or co-authored in such areas as the earth's magnetism; theory of nonuniform gases; solar plasma, geomagnetism, and aurora; and composition of the ionosphere. He also modified, during the period 1912 to 1917, the accurate kinetic theory of gases proposed by James Clerk Maxwell in 1867, thereby discovering gaseous thermal diffusion and confirming it experimentally. Another accomplishment was his demonstration of the power of thermal diffusion in highly ionized gases such as those in a solar corona.

Atmospheric tide, or atmospheric oscillation, is an atmospheric motion of the scale of the earth in which vertical accelerations are neglected. Atmospheric tides are produced by both the sun and the moon. They may be thermal, which is a variation in atmospheric pressure caused by the diurnal differential heating of the atmosphere by the sun; or gravitational, caused by the attraction of the sun or moon. The semidiurnal lunar atmospheric tide is gravitational. On the other hand, atmospheric tides produced by solar twenty-four, twelve-, eight-, and six-hour pressure fluctuations act on the earth's atmosphere by means of its gravitational field and also by emitting electromagnetic radiation and particles toward it. The amplitude of the lunar atmospheric tide is so small that it is detected only by careful statistical analysis of a long record, such as was done by Chapman in 1918 and again in 1935.

Lunar tides are the rise and fall of the oceanic surface twice in each lunar day as a result of the rotation of the earth in a nonuniform external gravitational field. The atmosphere is subject to the same tide-producing gravitational forces as the oceans; this periodic change in atmospheric pressure is called the "equilibrium atmospheric" tide. At the equator, the calculated equilibrium tide pressure variation at ground level is 0.022 millimeter of mercury. Lunar twelve-hour pressure fluctuations have been observed on the ground and are believed to be of purely gravitational origin; however, it is customary to refer to those periodic pressure fluctuations observed on the ground as atmospheric tides. In 1842, at an observatory on Saint Helena Island, the lunar semidiurnal pressure oscillation was determined to have a mean of about 0.055 millimeter, thus exceeding the calculated equilibrium tide of 0.022 millimeter by a factor of 2.5. The dynamical theory of atmospheric tides goes back to 1778, when Marquis Pierre-Simon Laplace first published his conclusions on the theory. According to Laplace, the barometric amplitudes in equatorial regions, as a result of the gravitational action of the sun and moon, should be about 0.0109 millimeter and 0.025 millimeter, respectively, and decrease rapidly with the increase of latitude.

Chapman, in 1918, was the first to determine the lunar atmospheric tide from barometric readings at a moderate latitude at the Greenwich Observatory in England. His conclusions were based on a long series of meteorological records such as the barometer, wind, and temperature, that had been collected by the Greenwich Observatory during the period from 1854 to 1917. He also analyzed the magnetic data to determine the lunisolar daily variations of the magnetic field. Lunisolar is the mutual relationship, or combined attraction, of the moon and sun. Solar and lunisolar daily magnetic variations are caused by electric currents in the ionosphere, which are induced motions produced thermally and tidally. This relationship between the ionosphere and air tides led to Chapman's later formulation of an idealized ionized layer.

Chapman, in these and later calculations, used the mathematical theory of statistics, which was emerging as a major scientific tool. Statistics is a branch of mathematics dealing with the collection, analysis, interpretation, and presentation of masses of numerical data. He saw how statistics could be used to improve the quality of inferences in important sections of his study of atmospheric lunar tides. The rigorous statistical procedures allowed him to make clear determination and to elucidate features of tides in the earth's atmosphere that are caused by the moon's gravitational attraction. Of specific importance were significant figures, which are the figures of a number that begins with the first figure to the left that is not a zero and ends with the last figure on the right that is not a zero, or is considered to be exact. Mathematical numbers are known to any accuracy required and carry any number of significant figures. The mean of more than ten and less than one thousand numbers may contain one or more significant figures. Using this basis gave Chapman an advantage in finding the lunar tide from barometric readings in high latitudes. He followed this achievement by determinations at more than fifty stations of the amplitude in millimeters during phases of the lunar semidiurnal mean atmospheric tide for the four equinoctial months; he presented his conclusions in 1935. Chapman found that the fundamental period of the free oscillation of the atmosphere as a whole is about twelve mean solar hours. Mean amplitudes and phases of the lunar semidiurnal atmospheric tide for the four equinoctial months had a mean of approximately 0.03 millimeter at 30 degrees south latitude, 0.038 millimeter at 20 degrees, 0.045 millimeter at 10 degrees, and 0.060 millimeter at the equator. At 10 degrees north, the barometric pressure was about 0.052 millimeter; it was 0.028 millimeter at 20 degrees, 0.022 millimeter at 30 degrees, 0.018 millimeter at 40 degrees, and 0.013 millimeter at 50 degrees.

This work aroused Chapman's interest in geomagnetism and its connection with solar phenomena and led to his theoretical researches in these fields. He is best known for his research in geomagnetism and his pioneer work on the photochemistry of the upper atmosphere and on nocturnal emission of light by atoms of oxygen and sodium. In 1940, he coauthored, with Julius Bartels, a two-volume work on geomagnetism. This complete work was an excellent contribution to the understanding of the external field of a uniformly magnetized sphere, the magnetic field at the earth's surface, electric currents in and beyond the ionosphere, local and world indices of geomagnetic disturbance, sunspots and magnetism, and the twenty-seven-day recurrence in geomagnetic disturbance. As part of his study of the lunar tide, he investigated why the earth's magnetic field varies with periods equal to the lunar day (27.3 days) and its submultiples. He showed that this was the result of a tidal movement in the earth's atmosphere caused by the Moon.

Impact of Event

Contributions by Chapman had a great impact in extending knowledge of the lunar tide in the earth's atmosphere. His analysis of many years of barometer, wind, and temperature recordings, along with his magnetic data, was facilitated by expert use of statistical analysis, which at the time of his study was a new mathematical theory. The use of physical observations and an innovative mathematical theory were truly scientific pioneering. The impact of the magnetic data that he collected and analyzed resulted in his determination of the lunisolar daily variations of the magnetic field. As a consequence of his work in the atmosphere and magnetic field, Chapman developed a deep interest in geomagnetism and its connection with solar phenomena. These interests led to several major publications, which were: *The Earth's Magnetism* (1936; 2d ed. 1951), *The Mathematical Theory of Non-uniform Gases*, with T. G. Cowling (1939; 3d ed. 1970), *Geomagnetism*, with Julius Bartels (1940), *IGY: Year of Discovery* (1959), *Solar Plasma, Geomagnetism, and Aurora* (1964), *Atmospheric Tides: Thermal and Gravitational*, with Richard S. Lindzen (1970), and *Solar-Terrestrial Physics*, with Syun-Ichi Akasofu (1972).

Chapman's research and studies of the atmospheres of the earth and sun produced a photochemical theory of atmospheric ozone and inferred that the oxygen in the upper atmosphere, above 100 kilometers height, would be largely dissociated. This conclusion was confirmed later by rocket-borne mass spectrometers. Another of his inferences was that airglow, or the self-luminescence of the atmosphere at night, is energized mainly by the oxygen dissociation energy stored in the atmosphere during the sunlight hours. His work in this area led later to his presidency (1953 to 1959) of the central organizing committee for the International Geophysical Year, in which he led the planning of the auroral program. Because solar and lunisolar magnetic variations are caused by electric currents in the ionosphere, it was logical that his research efforts would be directed in this area, and thus lead to his formulation of an ideally ionized layer—the Chapman ionized layer—which was used much later by radio physicists in studies of radio propagation and other research.

His work in thermal diffusion, or heat transfer between two parts of a solid, liquid, or gas, which are at different temperatures, in the absence of convection was important for separating isotopes for atomic fission. Chapman made major contributions to the history of science, and his creative genius was recognized by his peers by the many awards he received.

Bibliography

Chapman, Sydney. *IGY: Year of Discovery; the Story of the International Geophysical Year.* Ann Arbor: University of Michigan Press, 1959. This book is an exception in that scientific achievement is rarely written by a major participant. A popular account of the events that took place during the International Geophysical Year of 1957 to 1958; represents four lectures Chapman gave at the University of Michigan in October, 1958. A good reference for the general public, as well as high school and college students.

Clancy, Edward P. *The Tides: Pulse of the Earth.* Garden City, N.Y.: Doubleday, 1968. Primarily about ocean tides, but refutes Chapman's resonance theory of solar semidiurnal oscillation in the chapter on tides in the atmosphere. Suggests that the diurnal oscillation is the extraordinary phenomenon. Well written, and a good general reference.

Fleagle, Robert C., and Joost A. Businger. *An Introduction to Atmospheric Physics.* New York: Academic Press, 1963. A college-level text that presents a good understanding of the relationship of matter as expressed in the principles of physics. Some of the areas covered include gravitational effect, properties of atmospheric gases, properties and behavior of cloud particles, and solar and terrestrial radiation. Numerous mathematical formulas and graphs, and a good bibliography.

Hanle, Paul A., and Von Del Chamberlain, eds. *Space Science Comes of Age: Perspectives in the History of the Space Sciences.* Washington, D.C.: Smithsonian Institution Press, 1981. A compilation of essays from a symposium held at the National Air and Space Museum. A good reference for the general public on the early contributions to the field. Contains little mathematics or physics.

Wylie, Francis E. *Tides and the Pull of the Moon*. Brattleboro, Vt.: Stephen Greene Press, 1979. An easy-to-read book written for the general public. Covers the lore and legends of tides and the moon in history, astrology, and astronomy. Explains how gravitational attraction of the moon and sun causes tides. A few black-and-white photographs and reference notes after each chapter help explain the text.

Earl G. Hoover

Cross-References

Teisserenc de Bort Discovers the Stratosphere and the Troposphere (1898), p. 26; Kennelly and Heaviside Propose the Existence of the Ionosphere (1902), p. 174; Fabry Quantifies Ozone in the Upper Atmosphere (1913), p. 579; The First Rocket with More Than One Stage Is Created (1949), p. 1342.

WATSON-WATT AND ASSOCIATES
DEVELOP THE FIRST RADAR

Category of event: Applied science
Time: 1935
Locale: Radio Research Station, Slough, England

Radar was a major factor in the allied victory of World War II and now pervades civilian life, including scientific research

> *Principal personages:*
> SIR ROBERT WATSON-WATT (1892-1973), the father of radar who proposed the chain air-warning system
> ARNOLD F. WILKINS, the person who first calculated the intensity of a radio wave

Summary of Event

Sir Robert Watson-Watt, a scientist with twenty years of experience in government research, led the development of the first radar. In 1915, during World War I, he joined the Meteorological Office. He began work on the detection and location of thunderstorms at the Royal Aircraft Establishment in Farnborough and remained there throughout the war.

Thunderstorms were known to be a prolific source of atmospherics, and Watson-Watt began the design of an elementary radio direction-finder that gave the general position of such storms. Research continued after the war and reached a high point in 1922 when sealed off cathode-ray tubes first became available. With assistance from J. F. Herd, a fellow Scot who had joined him at Farnborough, he constructed an instantaneous direction-finder using the new cathode-ray tubes that gave the direction of thunderstorm activity. It was admittedly of low sensitivity, but it worked and was the first of its kind.

He did much of this work at a new site at Ditton Park, near Slough, where the National Physical Laboratory had a field station devoted to radio research. In 1927, the two endeavors were combined as the Radio Research Station; it came under the general supervision of the National Physical Laboratory, with Watson-Watt as the first superintendent. This became a center with unrivaled expertise in direction finding using the cathode-ray tube and in studying the ionosphere using radio waves.

Radar introduced some new and revolutionary concepts into warfare, and in doing so gave birth to entirely new branches of technology; it was inevitable that these would continue after the war and have a widespread impact on many aspects of civilian life.

In the application of radar to marine navigation, the long-range navigation system developed during the war was taken up at once by the merchant fleets that used military-style radar equipment without modification. In addition, PPI type radar systems, which could detect buoys and other ships and obstructions in closed waters, particularly under conditions of low visibility, proved particularly useful to peacetime marine navigation. In the same way, radar was adopted to assist in the navigation of civil aircraft. The various types of track guidance system developed after the war were aimed at guiding aircraft in the critical last hundred kilometers or so of their run into an airport. Subsequent improvements in the system meant that an aircraft could place itself on an approach or landing path with great accuracy.

The ability of radar to measure distance to an extraordinary degree of accuracy resulted in the development of another instrument; this instrument provided pilots with a direct measurement of the distance from the airport from which they departed and the distance to the terminal airport. This instrument was used first in Australia, then spread to the Northern Hemisphere. It has been updated since, miniaturized, and transistorized. Along with these aids, ground-based radars were developed for the control of aircraft along the air routes or in the airport control area.

Conventional ground survey methods had reached a high degree of sophistication well before the war. These methods involved a system of triangulation, whereby a series of triangles were built up from a single measured baseline. The angles of each triangle were measured to a high degree of precision, but only occasional checks of distance were possible when the terrain allowed it. In a remote or inhospitable country, such checks simply could not be carried out and the accuracy suffered accordingly. With the advent of the wartime-developed OBOE blind bombing system, maps were changed, after which an aircraft could be placed with an accuracy of 18 or 27 meters over particular targets. Radar provided an entirely new dimension in that the triangulation could be established by the accurate measurement of distance alone. It was not even necessary to traverse the intervening ground; an aircraft could fly over the terrain, position itself from two radar beacons on the ground, and record simultaneously its position by vertical photography.

Meteorological services around the world, using ground-based radar, can give warning of approaching rainstorms. Airborne radars have proved to be a great help to aircraft by allowing them to recognize and avoid potentially hazardous storm areas. This type of radar is used also to assist research into cloud and rain physics. Radar-equipped research aircraft observe the radar echoes inside a cloud as rain develops and then fly through measuring the water content, and so on.

The development of electronic computers can be traced back, not so much to radar itself, but to the enormous advances in circuit design, which were an integral part of radar research during the war. During that time, some elements of electronic computing had been built into gunnery predictors and bombsights; later it was realized that a whole range of computing operations could be performed electronically. By the end of the war, many pulse-forming networks, pulse-counting circuits, and memory circuits existed in the form needed for an electronic computer. Today, a broad spectrum of calculating machines exists, ranging from giant instruments dedicated to scientific research to intermediate machines for industrial and business functions, to the minicomputers found in many homes. This is a case in which wartime radar has paid back its debt to pure science many times over.

The discipline of radio astronomy began with observations by Karl Jansky in 1933 at the Bell Laboratory at Holmdell, New Jersey. It was concluded that the radio signals were coming from out of space and were called "cosmic noise." Radar engineers called it Jansky noise in trying to characterize the echo from radar targets. In particular, there was an unusual amount of radar noise when the antennas were pointed at the Sun, which increased at the time of sun-spot activity. All this information lay dormant until after World War II. Many of these investigators turned their attention to interpreting the cosmic noise. The pioneers were Sir Bernard Lovell at Manchester, England; Sir Martin Ryle at Cambridge, England; and Joseph Pawsey of the Commonwealth of Science Industrial Research Organization, in Australia. The intensity of radio waves were calculated by Arnold F. Wilkins.

As more powerful tools became available toward the end of World War II, curiosity caused experimenters to try getting echoes from the moon. This was accomplished successfully in the late 1940's and led to experiments on other objects in the solar system: the planets, satellites, comets, and asteroids.

Impact of Event

Among the civilian activities adopting the use of radar technology were marine navigation, aids to civil aviation, aids to surveying, meteorology, electronic computers, and radio and radar astronomy. In marine navigation, it is unusual to find even a cabin cruiser or the humblest fishing vessel without its radar antenna. These needs created a worldwide market for these devices.

In civil aviation, the long-range system was used by long-range aircraft on the main ocean crossings. This was supplemented by airborne radar, which provided navigational assistance by identifying the terrain ahead of the aircraft at night or under conditions of low visibility. It is useful especially in regions where there are distinctive land-water boundaries, as in the southwest Pacific. An added bonus is the ability to identify heavy rain and storm areas that the aircraft should avoid. The radars provide the position of all aircraft within the jurisdiction of an airport. They are extremely valuable in the regions of high-traffic density around capital cities. There is no doubt that, even in clear weather, present-day landing rates could never have been achieved without the widespread use of such systems.

The radar aids to surveying were of inestimable value in remote parts of countries like Australia and Africa, which might contain minerals and other resources. Radar in meteorology has become an accepted part of any television weather report. In the case of very damaging storms, such as hurricanes or extreme hailstorms, the U.S. Weather Bureau maintains several Lockheed aircraft to fly directly through the eye of hurricanes of the Florida and California coasts. They carry advanced radars and sophisticated instrumentation and have saved many lives by pinpointing precisely where and when such storms are likely to hit inhabited regions.

The speed with which electronic computer development took place is remarkable, and the secrets of operating the machines are not confined to adults with special training; young children seem to be completely at ease with them. One wonders what the impact on society will be when today's computer prodigies reach adulthood.

Today, radio technology has become a tool of radio astronomers in trying to understand the universe. For example, the cosmic background radiation studies have been a building block for the big bang theory of the origin of the universe. Large radio telescopes exist in almost every country on Earth for studies of the sun, the planets, stars, galaxies, and quasars to the very edge of the universe.

Today, astronomers use powerful radars in making regular observations of all the objects of the solar system all the way to the detection of Titan, a satellite of Saturn. Also, observations made from radar on spacecraft can characterize the surfaces of cloud-covered objects such as Venus and Titan.

Bibliography

Bowen, E. G. *Radar Days*. Bristol, England: Adam Hilger, 1987. Bowen describes how airborne radar helped to defeat Hitler and the bombers of the Luftwaffe. The early accounts of English radar usually were written from the viewpoint of someone in the higher echelons of government or as seen by the management. Written from the point of view from those who performed laboratory studies, followed by flight trials in which the lone experimenter tried to simulate the problems likely to be met in upcoming battles. The book does not pretend to be a complete history of radar.

Clark, Ronald W. *Tizard*. Cambridge, Mass.: MIT Press, 1965. In 1940, the Tizard Mission was sent to the United States to disclose English secret technical advances, including radar, in return for U.S. help on technical and production matters. No comprehensive account of the Tizard mission has ever been written, but this book makes reference to the mission.

Guerlac, Henry. *Radar in World War II*. Los Angeles: Tomash, 1987. Concerns the use of radar during World War II. For the interested reader.

Rowe, Albert P. *One Story of Radar*. Cambridge, England: Cambridge University Press, 1948. The period at St. Athan will be remembered for the start of mass production of airborne radar and for fitting these sets to aircraft at an unprecedented rate. As that work drew to a close, another move was contemplated. The decision of where to relocate was decided by events at Dundee, where things had reached crisis point. The fiction that Dundee was a good place for radar research could no longer be maintained and another move had to be made.

Sullivan, W. T., ed. *The Early Years of Radio Astronomy*. New York: Cambridge University Press, 1984. Discusses the history of radio astronomy. For a wide audience.

N. A. Renzetti

Cross-References

The German *Meteor* Expedition Discovers the Midatlantic Ridge (1925), p. 805; Jansky's Experiments Lead to the Founding of Radio Astronomy (1930), p. 934; Reber Builds the First Intentional Radio Telescope (1937), p. 1113; Reber Makes the First Radio Maps of the Universe (1942), p. 1193; Franklin and Burke Discover Radio Emissions from Jupiter (1955), p. 1492; Ryle Constructs the First Radio Interferometer (1955), p. 1496; A Radio Astronomy Team Sends and Receives Radar Signals to the Sun (1959), p. 1598.

TURING INVENTS THE UNIVERSAL TURING MACHINE

Category of event: Mathematics
Time: 1935-1936
Locale: Cambridge, England

Turing invented a precise concept of an abstract computing machine, providing a basis for both the theory of computation and the development of digital computers

Principal personages:

ALAN MATHISON TURING (1912-1954), an English mathematician, logician, and cryptanalyst, and Fellow of the Royal Society who was one of the founders of computer science

ALONZO CHURCH (1903-   ), an American logician and philosopher who developed a concept of effective computability equivalent to Turing computability

DAVID HILBERT (1862-1943), the German mathematician who posed the decision problem that Turing's paper solved

KURT GÖDEL (1906-1978), the German logician who discovered the incompleteness of arithmetic and who coinvented the concept of recursive functions

JOHN VON NEUMANN (1903-1957), a Hungarian-American mathematician and physicist who helped design early digital computers

Summary of Event

In 1931, Kurt Gödel proved that arithmetic (and mathematics) is either inconsistent or incomplete, meaning that any consistent axiom system for arithmetic must fail to include some true arithmetical statements. This result answered the first two of the three questions that David Hilbert had posed three years earlier: Is mathematics complete? Is it consistent? Is it decidable? The last question asks if there is a definite procedure (algorithm) that is guaranteed to produce a correct answer as to whether an arbitrary mathematical sentence is true. After Gödel's proof, there was much speculation that mathematics must be undecidable. In the late spring of 1935, shortly after having been made a Fellow of King's College, Cambridge, Alan Mathison Turing set out to prove it. To do so, Turing needed a precise concept of "definite procedure," which led him to invent what are now called Turing machines.

A Turing machine is an abstract machine rather than a physical machine: It is used to define or describe algorithms precisely—not to execute them. Any Turing machine has three components: a control unit, which takes any of a finite number of states; a two-way infinite tape, which is divided into squares capable of holding any one of a finite number of symbols; and a read-write head, which writes a symbol, moves left or right over the tape, and reads the new square. The behavior of such a machine on the next step is fully determined by its current state and the symbol being read. Specific Turing machines are described with tables of quintuples, such as <Q0, A, B, R, Q1>, which means: If the machine is in state Q0 and reading the symbol A, then write the symbol B (replacing the symbol A), move right on square on the tape, and go into state Q1. It can be stipulated that a Turing machine will halt when it enters a state for which no quintuple exists.

As a simple example, here is a machine which determines the parity of a string of zeroes and ones, when the read-write head starts at the right-most digit (that is, the machine will report "1" if the string has an odd number of ones, otherwise, it reports "0"):

$$<Q0, 0, 0, L, Q0>$$
$$<Q0, 1, 1, L, Q1>$$
$$<Q1, 0, 0, L, Q1>$$
$$<Q1, 1, 1, L, Q0>$$
$$<Q0, b, 0, L, Q2>$$
$$<Q1, b, 1, L, Q2>$$

In this machine, state Q0 signifies that the string has even parity so far, and Q1 signifies odd parity. The first tuple scans a zero in the even-parity state; the read-write head moves left, and the machine stays in even parity. The next tuple scans a one and so changes the state from even to odd parity. The next two tuples are similar but describe the machine's behavior when in the odd-parity state. The final two states recognize the end of the string ("b" stands for the blank symbol), write the answer (at the head of the input string), and stop (by entering the undefined state Q2).

One of the remarkable things about Turing machines is that they are universal; that is, they are capable of performing the computations done by any other Turing machine. This is achieved by encoding that other machine's table of quintuples in a numerical string (called the Gödel number of the machine); then, this number can be written on the universal machine's input tape. The universal machine simulates the target machine by examining and interpreting the appropriate quintuple on the tape. This encoding of the target machine is analogous to software programs on modern digital computers.

With this basis, Hilbert's third question can be answered by proving that mathematics is undecidable. For any Turing machine, the question can be asked whether, when given a certain input, the machine will halt. One also can ask the broader question whether or not there is a Turing machine named halter, which, when given the Gödel number for a target machine and that machine's input, can decide in finitely many steps whether the target machine would stop with that input. (This is called the halting problem.) If one assumes that halter exists, one can ask the self-referential question: What happens if halter encounters the Gödel number for itself? Turing proved that in such a case, halter will halt if and only if it does not halt; in other words, whichever way one turns, there is a contradiction, so halter cannot exist. (See A. K. Dewdney's chapter "The Halting Problem" in *The Turing Omnibus* for a more complete description of the proof.) Turing also demonstrated that there are mathematical statements for which any decision procedure would presuppose the existence of halter. Thus, he established the existence of undecidable mathematical statements.

Turing presented these results in his paper "On Computable Numbers, with an Application to the Entscheidungsproblem" in 1936. Shortly before, however, Alonzo Church had published his proof of the undecidability of mathematics using a different formalism called the lambda calculus. Since the two methods of proof were substantially different, Turing's paper was accepted for publication. First, however, Turing was obliged to show in an appendix that Turing computability and Church's definition of effective calculability were equivalent. Both papers argued for the Church-Turing thesis (sometimes called Church's thesis), which asserts that their equivalent concepts of computability precisely capture the intuitive concept of an effective procedure or definite algorithm. Since this intuitive concept cannot itself be exactly specified, the thesis is unprovable. Nevertheless, it is a remarkable fact that every adequate substitute for "effective procedure" has been proved to be equivalent, including the contemporaneous formulations by Emil Post and by Stephen Kleene (the latter using general recursive functions). Furthermore, every coherent extension of the concept of Turing machines has been shown to possess exactly the same computational power as Turing machines themselves, as long as they adhere to the same standard of definiteness, for example, not allowing randomized state changes. (Note that "power" here refers to the range of functions that can be computed and not to the informal notion of the speed of computation.) For example, adding multiple tapes or multiple read-write heads per tape in no way increases the set of functions that a Turing machine can compute, although some computations will become faster. Von Neumann machines—everyday office computers and personal computers—are likewise no more powerful than Turing machines (for that reason they sometimes are mistakenly called Turing machines).

There are, of course, machines that are not as powerful as Turing machines, such as finite automata. The convergence of all sufficiently general kinds of machine on the class identified by Church and Turing seems explainable only by assuming the truth of the Church-Turing thesis.

Impact of Event

The invention of the Turing machine provided a precise concept of computation, helping to pave the way for the introduction of practical computing machinery. While the Turing machine as such would make an impractical computing device (since storing everything on tape would be impossibly slow), it anticipated much of the function required for practical computers. During and immediately after World War II, various engineering efforts produced the first working electronic digital computers. Especially noteworthy are the Electronic Numerical Integrator and Calculator (ENIAC), developed from 1943 to 1946 at the University of Pennsylvania, and the Automatic Computing Engine (ACE) computer at England's National Physical Laboratory, designed by Turing in 1945. The ENIAC led to a more general computer design by John von Neumann, which has had a pervasive effect in the computer industry; most computers are classified now as von Neumann machines.

Beyond providing a model for practical computation, the concept of Turing computability has supported the development of much of the theory of computer science. In addition to its bearing on the nature of unsolvable problems, Turing computability has been instrumental in studying the degrees of solvability of problems—more accurately, the computational complexity of problems, a major research area in theoretical computer science. Computational complexity is measured by the amount of time (number of steps) required by an optimal Turing machine to solve a problem. The complexity of a problem is expressed as a function of its size; thus, the size of the problem to search sequentially a list of N items to find a specific item is merely N; the time it takes, on average, is directly proportional to $N/2$. Two classes of complexity are of special interest: polynomial time problems and exponential time problems. Polynomial time problems require a polynomial function of the problem size to complete—such as, $N/2$, N, N squared, and so on. Exponential time problems require 2 to the Nth power, or 2 to the N-squared power, and so on, to complete. Exponential problems always grow faster than polynomial problems in the computation time required, and so are often called intractable. An important set of problems, called NP problems, are defined in terms of a special class of Turing machine. It is an unproved, but widely believed, thesis that many NP problems are necessarily exponential.

Since Gödel, Turing, and others collectively proved that mathematics cannot be completely mechanized, it might be thought that Turing should have been pessimistic about the prospects for artificial intelligence—that is, the attempt to mechanize intelligence. In fact, however, Turing believed that whatever limits apply to machines in this regard apply to humans equally well—that neither human nor machine can have access to all mathematical truths or to an infallible decision procedure. Turing, in his 1950 paper "Computing Machinery and Intelligence," created the well-known Turing Test for intelligence, providing the main backdrop for philosophical inquiries in artificial intelligence since that time. In recognition of Turing's achievements, the Association for Computing Machinery has named their most prestigious annual research award the ACM Turing Award.

Bibliography

Davis, Martin, ed. *The Undecidable.* New York: Raven, 1965. A collection of many of the seminal articles in the development of computation theory and logic. Includes original papers alluded to above by Church, Gödel, Kleene, and Post. These papers are accessible to those already acquainted with formal logic. Reprints the original paper by Turing, "On Computable Numbers, with an Application to the Entscheidungsproblem." *Proceedings of the London Mathematical Society* 42 (January, 1937): 230-265.

Dewdney, A. K. *The Turing Omnibus.* Rockville, Md.: Computer Science Press, 1989. A collection of short and engaging tutorials on sixty-one different topics in computer science. This readable tribute to Turing was written by the "Mathematical Recreations" columnist for *Scientific American*.

Garey, Michael R., and David S. Johnson. *Computers and Intractability: A Guide to the Theory of NP-Completeness*. San Francisco: W. H. Freeman, 1979. A standard, introductory college text on computational complexity. Provides a very accessible survey for those with some college-level mathematics or logic. Contains an exhaustive list of NP-complete problems known as of 1979.

Hodges, Andrew. *Alan Turing: The Enigma*. New York: Simon & Schuster, 1983. A thorough, enjoyable biography of Turing. Includes a lengthy, fascinating account of Turing's successful cracking of Nazi Germany's encryption devices. Also provides background material to Turing's foundational work on artificial intelligence in the late 1940's.

Hofstadter, Douglas R. *Gödel, Escher, Bach: An Eternal Golden Braid*. New York: Basic Books, 1979. The concepts of self-reference, recursion, and infinite regress are woven into an absorbing tapestry. Explicates Gödel's incompleteness theorem, drawing analogies with M. C. Escher's reflexive drawings and the musical edifices of Bach. Nontechnical, but lengthy.

Minksky, Marvin. *Computation: Finite and Infinite Machines*. Englewood Cliffs, N.J.: Prentice-Hall, 1967. An especially clear introduction to automata and computation theory, used as a freshman college textbook. Presupposes no college-level mathematics, but it does introduce and use formal notation. Minsky is a leading figure in artificial intelligence.

Turing, Alan. "Computing Machinery and Intelligence." *Mind* 59 (October, 1950): 433-460. An exploration of the concepts of human and machine intelligence. Introduces the famous Turing Test for intelligence. Reprinted frequently; for example, in Alan Ross Anderson, ed. *Minds and Machines*. Englewood Cliffs, N.J.: Prentice-Hall, 1964.

Kevin B. Korb

Cross-References

Gödel Proves Incompleteness-Inconsistency for Formal Systems, Including Arithmetic (1929), p. 900; A Secret English Team Develops Colossus (1940's), p. 1155; Eckert and Mauchly Develop the ENIAC (1943), p. 1213; Shockley, Bardeen, and Brattain Discover the Transistor (1947), p. 1304; The First Electronic Stored-Program Computer (BINAC) Is Completed (1949), p. 1347; UNIVAC I Becomes the First Commercial Electronic Computer and the First to Use Magnetic Tape (1951), p. 1396.

RICHTER DEVELOPS A SCALE
FOR MEASURING EARTHQUAKE STRENGTH

Category of event: Earth science
Time: January, 1935
Locale: Pasadena, California

Richter devised a scale for measuring the strength of earthquakes based on their seismograph recordings

Principal personages:
> CHARLES RICHTER (1900-1985), an American seismologist who developed the first practical scale for measuring the strength of earthquakes
> BENO GUTENBERG (1889-1960), a German-American seismologist who first determined the radius of Earth's core
> KIYOO WADATI (1902-   ), a pioneering Japanese seismologist who independently discovered many important concepts in seismology
> HIROO KANAMORI (1936-   ), a Japanese seismologist who had been active in applying the concepts of plate tectonics to seismology
> GIUSEPPE MERCALLI (1850-1914), an Italian physicist, volcanologist, and meteorologist who devised the most widely used earthquake intensity scale
> MICHELE STEFANO DE ROSSI (1834-1898), an Italian geologist and archaeologist who devised the first earthquake intensity scale
> FRANÇOIS-ALPHONSE FOREL (1841-1912), a Swiss geologist and geographer who jointly devised an earthquake intensity scale with de Rossi

Summary of Event

Earthquakes range in strength from barely detectable tremors to catastrophes that devastate large regions and take hundreds of thousands of lives. The human impact of earthquakes is not an accurate measure of their power; minor earthquakes in heavily populated regions may cause great destruction, whereas powerful earthquakes in remote areas may go unnoticed. To study earthquakes, it is essential to have an accurate means of measuring their power.

The first attempts to measure the power of earthquakes was the development of intensity scales, which relied on damage effects and reports by witnesses to measure the force of vibration. The first such scale was devised by Michele Stefano de Rossi and François-Alphonse Forel in 1883. It ranked earthquakes on a scale of 1 to 10. The de Rossi-Forel scale proved to have two serious limitations: Its level 10 encompassed a great range of effects, and its description of effects on human-made and natural objects was so specifically European that it was difficult to apply the scale elsewhere. To remedy these problems, Giuseppe Mercalli published a revised intensity scale in 1902. The Mercalli scale, as it came to be called, added two levels to the high end of the de Rossi-Forel scale, making its highest level 12. It also was re-written to make it more globally applicable. With later modifications by Charles F. Richter, the Mercalli scale is still in use.

Intensity measurements, even though they are somewhat subjective, are very useful in mapping the extent of earthquake effects. Nevertheless, intensity measurements are still not ideal measuring techniques. Intensity varies from place to place, is strongly influenced by local geologic factors, and different observers frequently report different intensities. There is a need for an objective method of describing the strength of earthquakes with a single measurement.

An objective technique for determining the power of earthquakes was devised in the early 1930's by Richter at the California Institute of Technology in Pasadena, California. The eventual usefulness of the scale that came to be called the Richter scale was completely unforeseen at first. In 1931, the California Institute of Technology was preparing to issue a catalog of all earthquakes detected by its seismographs in the preceding three years. Several hundred earthquakes were listed, most of which had not been felt by humans, but only detected by instruments. Richter was concerned about the possible misinterpretations of the listing. With no indication of the strength of the earthquakes, the public might overestimate the risk of earthquakes in areas where seismographs were numerous, and underestimate the risk in areas where seismographs were few. To remedy the lack of a measuring method, Richter devised the scale that now bears his name. He defined the magnitude of an earthquake as the logarithm of the height of its seismograph trace in microns (thousandths of a millimeter), as recorded on a standard instrument. Thus, an earthquake that produced a trace one millimeter (1,000 microns) high would be magnitude 3, one that produced a trace a centimeter high (10,000 microns) would be magnitude 4, and so on. These measurements were defined for a standard seismograph magnifying ground motion twenty-eight hundred times and located 100 kilometers from the earthquake. The magnification of the instrument means that the actual ground motion caused by a magnitude 3 earthquake 100 kilometers away is not 1 millimeter but only 1/2,800 millimeter, or only about three thousand times the diameter of an atom. By comparing records for earthquakes recorded on different devices at different distances. Richter was able to create conversion tables for measuring magnitudes for any instrument at any distance. The scale was also set up so that any event likely to be felt by humans would have a positive magnitude, because scales with zero and negative numbers tend to be confusing.

Richter had hoped to create a rough means of separating small, medium, and large earthquakes, but he found that the scale was capable of making much finer distinctions. Most magnitude estimates made with a variety of instruments at various distances from earthquakes agreed to within a few tenths of a magnitude. Richter formally published a description of his scale in January, 1935, in the *Bulletin of the Seismological Society of America*. Other systems of estimating magnitude had been attempted, notably that of Kiyoo Wadati, published in 1931, but Richter's system proved to be the most workable scale yet devised and rapidly became the standard.

Over the next few years, the scale was refined. One critical refinement was in the way seismic recordings were converted into magnitude. Earthquakes produce many types of waves but it was not known which type should be the standard for magnitude. So-called surface waves travel along the surface of the earth. It is these waves that produce most of the damage in large earthquakes; therefore, it seems logical to let these waves be the standard. On the other hand, earthquakes deep within the earth produce few surface waves. Magnitudes based on surface waves would be too small for these earthquakes. Deep earthquakes produce mostly waves which travel through the solid body of the earth, or so-called body waves. Actually, two scales are needed: one based on surface waves and one on body waves. Richter and his colleague Beno Gutenberg developed scales for the two different types of waves, which are still in use. Magnitudes estimated from surface waves are symbolized by a capital M, those based on body waves are denoted by lowercase m.

From a knowledge of Earth movements associated with seismic waves, Richter and Gutenberg succeeded in relating the energy output of an earthquake with its magnitude. Each increase of one Richter magnitude corresponds to about a thirty-fold increase in energy. A magnitude 6 earthquake releases about as much energy as a one-megaton nuclear explosion; a magnitude 0 earthquake releases about as much energy as a small car dropped off a two-story building.

An additional refinement to the Richter scale was developed in the 1970's. Extremely large earthquakes release their energy over time spans as long as several minutes and over a fault break of hundreds of kilometers. The highest seismograph trace for the earthquake, however, measures the energy received at only one instant. It is also possible to estimate energy released from the length of the fault rupture and the amount of fault displacement and by this measure, conventional magnitudes for the largest earthquakes are too small. A magnitude corrected for the long duration and great spatial extent of the largest earthquakes is called a seismic-moment magnitude. A seismic-moment magnitude scale was devised by Hiroo Kanamori during the 1970's. On this scale, unlike the conventional Richter scale, some of the greatest earthquakes exceed magnitude 9.

Impact of Event

The Richter scale is a good example of an accidental scientific discovery. Richter's original intent had been to develop a scale for very rough measurements, but the scale proved to be useful on a completely unforeseen scale. Richter scrupulously avoided using the term "Richter scale" in his writings, and went to some length to give credit to other researchers who also had similar ideas. The Richter scale has now become firmly established in popular and professional usage.

The Richter scale had been in use among scientists for about fifteen years before it began to be widely quoted by the press in the 1950's. Just as scientists had, the press found it useful to have a single number to define the strength of earthquakes. Initially, there was much confusion over the difference between magnitude and intensity. Also, the logarithmic nature of the scale, clear enough to scientists, was widely misunderstood. It was not until about 1970 that the press generally stopped describing the Richter scale as running from one to ten.

The scientific utility of the Richter scale stems from its logarithmic nature. Wave phenomena occur over a great range of intensities and are best described by logarithmic scales; other examples include the speed and shutter settings on cameras (each step doubles or halves the original amount of light) and the decibel scale for sound. Virtually all the important physical quantities associated with waves are proportional to the amplitude of the wave raised to some power; such relationships are very simple to express in logarithmic terms. Because the magnitude of an earthquake is defined as the logarithm of its ground motion, many of the physical dimensions of earthquakes, such as their energy release, are directly and simply related to magnitude. Also, it is simple to develop equations to relate ground motion, magnitude, and distance from an earthquake.

The Richter scale has made it possible to compare the energy output of earthquakes in a quantitative way and to derive new understandings of earthquake phenomena. For example, most of the energy released by earthquakes is released by the few most powerful ones. Also, earthquakes are more powerful in some geologic settings than in others. The greatest earthquakes (up to magnitude 8.9) are associated with faults on or bordering the continents, whereas earthquakes along the mid-ocean ridges rarely exceed magnitude 6.5. Deep earthquakes are rarely as strong as magnitude 7. These differences provide important insights into the forces at work in the earth.

Bibliography

Bolt, Bruce A. *Earthquakes: A Primer.* San Francisco: W. H. Freeman, 1978. A generally nontechnical account of earthquakes, their effects, and methods of studying them. Includes a good description of magnitude and intensity.

Boore, David M. "Motion of the Ground in Earthquakes." *Scientific American* 237 (December, 1977): 68-87. A description of the types of waves generated by earthquakes and the instrumental techniques used in measuring them. Includes a description of the seismic-moment magnitude scale.

Gutenberg, Beno, and Charles F. Richter. *Seismicity of the Earth.* 2d ed. New York: Hafner, 1965. A pioneering study of earthquake locations and magnitudes around the world. Contains extensive tables of large earthquakes.

Press, Frank. "Earthquake Prediction." *Scientific American* 232 (May, 1975): 14-20. A summary of research efforts and seismic clues used in an attempt to predict earthquakes. Although short-term prediction of earthquakes has turned out to be much more difficult since the mid-1970's, Press gives a useful summary of the kind of information that seismic studies can provide.

Richter, Charles F. *Elementary Seismology.* San Francisco: W. H. Freeman, 1958. A college-level textbook on seismology. Although dated in many ways, it is valuable for Richter's personal description of the origin of the Richter scale.

United States Geological Survey. *Earthquakes and Volcanoes* 21 (January/February,

1989). A special issue devoted to the measurement of earthquakes and an excellent short survey of seismology. Includes maps of seismic activity, locations of seismographs, how seismographs work, and an explanation of magnitude and intensity.

Wesson, Robert L. "Predicting the Next Great Earthquake in California." *Scientific American* 252 (February, 1985): 35-43. A summary of modern field and theoretical techniques used in estimating earthquake risk and predicting earthquake magnitudes. Of particular interest is the fact that the location and approximate magnitude of the 1989 Loma Prieta earthquake were accurately predicted in this article.

Steven I. Dutch

Cross-References

Wiechert Invents the Inverted Pendulum Seismograph (1900), p. 51; Oldham and Mohorovičić Determine the Structure of the Earth's Interior (1906), p. 340; Wegener Proposes the Theory of Continental Drift (1912), p. 522; Hess Concludes the Debate on Continental Drift (1960), p. 1650.

CAROTHERS PATENTS NYLON

Category of event: Applied science
Time: February, 1935-October, 1938
Locale: Wilmington, Delaware

Carothers developed the theory of condensation polymers, applying his insights to the synthesis of new high molecular weight substances, including nylon

Principal personages:
WALLACE HUME CAROTHERS (1896-1937), an American organic chemist who did the research in polymer chemistry that led to the development of nylon
CHARLES M. A. STINE (1882-1954), an American chemist and director of chemical research at Du Pont who inaugurated the company's fundamental research program
ELMER KEISER BOLTON (1886-1968), an American industrial chemist who directed the development of nylon into a commercial textile fiber

Summary of Event

In the twentieth century, American corporations created industrial research laboratories. Their directors became the organizers of inventions, and their scientists served as the sources of creativity. Du Pont's research program, through its most famous invention—nylon—became the model for scientifically based industrial research in the chemical industry.

Nylon was not the first commercially important polymeric material. From the late nineteenth century, several cellulose derivatives appeared, such as celluloid and rayon. The word "plastic" entered the vocabulary in the 1890's for this class of materials. The first important purely synthetic polymer was Bakelite. Discovered in 1907 by Leo Baekeland, it was a phenol-formaldehyde moldable plastic and a major commercial success. Its success encouraged American industry to search for more special purpose plastics.

During World War I, Du Pont tried to diversify, concerned that after the war it would not be able to expand with only explosives as a product. It hired organic chemists and built a research laboratory. It hoped to master organic chemical reactions and produce synthetic dyestuffs. By 1921, Du Pont had put $20 million into the venture but lacked both the theoretical understanding and know-how to succeed in organic synthesis. Instead, it bought what it needed to diversify from outside, becoming a producer of rayon, cellophane, and other products.

In this context of dependency on outside inventions, Charles M. A. Stine, Du Pont's director of chemical research, proposed that Du Pont should move into fundamental research by hiring first-rate academic scientists and giving them freedom to work on important problems in organic chemistry. He convinced company executives that a program to explore the fundamental science underlying Du Pont's technology would ultimately result in discoveries of value to the company. In 1927, Du Pont gave him a new laboratory for research. Stine had given a new role to the industrial research laboratory; it was not to be affiliated with manufacturing departments but was to generate new knowledge. Stine visited universities in search of brilliant, but not yet established young scientists. He hired Wallace Hume Carothers. Stine suggested that Carothers do fundamental research in polymer chemistry. Before the 1920's, polymers were a mystery to chemists. Polymeric materials were the result of ingenious laboratory practice, and this practice ran far ahead of theory and understanding. German chemists debated whether polymers were mysterious aggregates of smaller units held together by some unknown special force or genuine molecules held together by ordinary chemical bonds. Hermann Staudinger asserted that they were large molecules with endlessly repeating units. Carothers shared this molecular view, and he devised a scheme to prove it by synthesizing very large molecules by simple reactions in such a way as to leave no doubt about their structure. Carothers clarified the nature of polymers, distinguished between addition and condensation types, and laid the basis for much of modern polymer science in terms of its methods, vocabulary, and understanding. His syntheses of polymers revealed that they were ordinary molecules but giant in size.

In April, 1930, Carothers' group produced two major innovations: neoprene synthetic rubber and the first laboratory-synthesized fiber. Neither was the goal of Du Pont's research. Neoprene was an incidental discovery during a project to study short polymers of acetylene. An unexpected substance appeared which polymerized spontaneously. Carothers studied its chemistry and developed the process into the first successful synthetic rubber made in the United States. The other discovery was an unexpected outcome of the group's project to synthesize polyesters by the reaction of acids and alcohols, each with two functional groups in their molecules so that the newly formed ester could continue to react indefinitely to form a high molecular weight substance. There was a molecular weight limit of about 5,000 to the size of the polyesters. Carothers realized that the reaction also produced water, and this substance was decomposing polyesters back into acid and alcohol. Carothers and his associate Julian Hill devised an apparatus to remove water as it formed. The result was a polyester with a molecular weight of more than 12,000, far higher than any previous polymer. Hill, while removing a sample from the apparatus, found that he could draw it out into filaments which on cooling could be stretched to form very strong fibers. This procedure, called "cold-drawing," oriented the molecules from a random arrangement into a long, linear one of great strength. The polyester fiber, however, was unsuitable for textiles because of its low melting point.

In June, 1930, Du Pont promoted Stine; his replacement as research director was Elmer Keiser Bolton. Both were organic chemists, but Bolton was a far more traditional industrial chemist. He had opposed Stine's 1927 fundamental research program; now he headed it. Bolton wanted to control fundamental research more closely, relating it to projects that would pay off and not allowing the research group freedom to pursue purely theoretical questions. Despite their differences, Carothers and Bolton shared an interest in fiber research. Carothers began to work on the synthesis of polyamides from acids and amines, reasoning that since simple amides had higher melting points than simple esters, the same would hold for their polymers. The polyamide research, however, was unsuccessful and by the end of 1933, all fiber work had ceased. In 1934, Bolton pressured Carothers to resume polyamide research. Carothers began trying different approaches to synthesis. On May 24, 1934, his assistant Donald Coffman drew a strong fiber from a new polyamide. This was the first nylon fiber, although not the one commercialized by Du Pont. The nylon fiber was high melting and tough, and it seemed a practical synthetic fiber might be feasible.

By the summer of 1934, the fiber project was the heart of the research group's activity. It prepared polyamides from many combinations of acids and amines. The one that had the best fiber properties was nylon 5-10, the numbers referring to the number of carbon atoms in the amine and acid chains. Yet, the nylon 6-6 prepared on February 28, 1935, became Du Pont's nylon. Nylon 5-10 had some advantages, but Bolton realized that its components would be unsuitable for commercial production, whereas those of nylon 6-6 could be obtained from chemicals in coal. Bolton pursued nylon's practical development, a process that required nearly four years. In April, 1937, Du Pont filed a patent for synthetic fibers, which included a statement by Carothers that there was no previous work on polyamides; this was a major breakthrough. After Carothers' death on April 29, 1937, the patent was issued posthumously and assigned to Du Pont.

Carothers was responsible for the discovery of the laboratory process for nylon, but Bolton was responsible for the commercial process. Du Pont wisely decided not to pursue the full range of possibilities of the fiber, but only the silk hosiery market. It knew that about $70 million was spent on silk hosiery each year. By focusing on this use of nylon, it would be easier to overcome the considerable obstacles involved in commercializing the fiber. The practical development was as exceptional as was the laboratory discovery. It took the skill and ingenuity of Du Pont's chemists and engineers several years to bring nylon into the marketplace. The first test of a yarn knitted into stockings came in February, 1937. It was not satisfactory, and it took until the end of 1937 to obtain high quality nylons. Du Pont made the first public announcement of nylon on October 27, 1938.

Impact of Event

The day after Du Pont's announcement in 1938, *The New York Times* ran articles on nylon, entitling one "New Hosiery Strong as Steel" to emphasize its strength. Another article focused on its indestructibility, stressing that it was made from simple substances in coal, air, and water. A well-orchestrated publicity campaign kept the public aware of nylon until in May, 1940, the first nationwide sales took place. During this eighteen-month interim, sample stockings became available and rave notices appeared. Du Pont called its exhibit at the New York World's Fair "The Wonder World of Chemistry," celebrating its acetate, cellophane, and neoprene products and, above all, nylon. Visitors saw a machine that rolled out sheer nylons. Newspapers reported that four million pairs of hosiery were sold, exhausting the supply in one day. Before year's end, 60 million pairs had been sold. Nylon heralded a future of synthetic polymers. They would become standard in clothing, building materials, and furnishings.

The entry of the United States into World War II, however, caused the diversion of all nylon into military uses. During the war, Du Pont tripled its production, and nylon served as a replacement for the silk of parachutes, as mosquito screens in tropical hospitals, as rope for towing gliders and mooring ships, and as surgical sutures and filters for blood plasma. As a moldable plastic, there were nylon gears, valves, bearings, and propellers for outboard motors. On the home front, nylon became a black-market item in great demand.

After the war, it took more than two years to retool manufacturing to make nylons. When the hosiery reappeared, the demand outstripped the supply, leading to riots in stores. Nylon became the biggest money-maker in the history of Du Pont. Its striking success led the company to create new uses for it and to create new "nylons" by fundamental research to ensure its future growth. By the mid-1950's, Du Pont produced new textile fibers, notably orlon, a polyacrylic, and dacron, a polyester. Coupled with nylon's spectacular growth, Du Pont had effected a revolution in manufacturing that propelled its earnings.

Nylon was a generic term for polyamides and several of them became commercially important in addition to nylon 6-6. These nylons found widespread use as both a fiber and as a moldable plastic. Since it resisted abrasion and crushing, was nonabsorbent, stronger than steel on a weight-for-weight basis, and almost nonflammable, it embraced an astonishing range of uses: laces, screens, surgical sutures, paint, toothbrushes, violin strings, coatings for electrical wires, lingerie, evening gowns, leotards, athletic equipment and clothing, outdoor furniture, shower curtains, handbags, sails, luggage, fish nets, carpets, slip covers, subway and bus seats, and in space as the safety nets on the space shuttle.

The invention of nylon stimulated notable advances in the chemistry and technology of polymers. Some historians of technology have even dubbed the postwar period as the "age of plastics," the age of synthetic products based on the chemistry of giant molecules made by ingenious chemists and engineers. The ever-increasing use of synthetics has also been regarded as a measure of a country's prosperity. The very success of nylon and other synthetics, however, has come at a cost. Several environmental problems have surfaced, such as those created by the nondegradable feature of some plastics, and there is the problem of the increasing utilization of valuable, vanishing natural resources, such as petroleum, which contains the essential chemicals needed to make polymers.

Bibliography

Adams, Roger. "Wallace Hume Carothers." *Biographical Memoirs of the National Academy of Sciences* 20 (1939): 291-309. This is the official biography of the National Academy of Sciences and written by Carothers' doctorate professor. It includes a bibliography of his articles and a listing of his patents.

Brun, Roger. "Of Miracles and Molecules." *American History Illustrated* 23 (December, 1988): 24-29, 48. This is an outstanding and well-written article on the social impact of nylon from its introduction as hosiery to its many uses over five decades and how nylon became associated with both glamor and toughness.

Hounshell, David A., and John Kenly Smith, Jr. "The Nylon Drama." *American Heritage of Invention and Technology* 4 (Fall, 1988): 40-55. Two American historians explore how Du Pont took Carothers' discoveries on synthetic fibers and translated them into a commercial textile fiber. This is the best account available on the difficult technological development that made nylon possible.

Marvel, Carl S. "The Development of Polymer Chemistry in America: The Early Days." *Journal of Chemical Education* 58 (July, 1981): 535-539. A good description by a leading American organic chemist of the contribution of Carothers and his contemporaries to the theory and practice of polymerization.

Smith, John K., and David A. Hounshell. "Wallace H. Carothers and Fundamental Research at Du Pont." *Science* 229 (August 2, 1985): 436-442. The authors contribute an excellent article on Carothers and his work at Du Pont. They provide a coherent narrative as well as insight into his brilliance as a theoretical chemist who could also lead a research group into unchartered territory and make important laboratory discoveries.

Albert B. Costa

Cross-References

Kipping Discovers Silicones (1901), p. 123; Brandenberger Invents Cellophane (1904), p. 238; Baekeland Invents Bakelite (1905), p. 280.

MONIZ DEVELOPS PREFRONTAL LOBOTOMY

Category of event: Medicine
Time: November-December, 1935
Locale: Lisbon, Portugal

Moniz pioneered the surgical treatment of psychiatric disorders, giving impetus to the widespread practice of lobotomy

Principal personages:
ANTÓNIO EGAS MONIZ (1874-1955), a Portuguese neurologist, political figure, and man of letters who was a cowinner of the 1949 Nobel Prize in Physiology or Medicine
PEDRO ALMEIDA LIMA (1903-   ), a neurosurgeon who performed the first prefrontal lobotomy under Moniz' direction
WALTER JACKSON FREEMAN (1895-1972), an American neuropathologist and neuropsychiatrist who became the foremost promoter and practitioner of lobotomy

Summary of Event

In the early twentieth century, there was no consensus in the medical community concerning the treatment of mental illness. In part, this lack of consensus reflected the opposition between two broad approaches to human development. On the one hand were those who stressed the biological determinants of behavior; on the other hand were those who stressed the role of environment and experience in shaping the psyche. (This division was mimed by the professional rivalry between neurologists and psychiatrists.) More fundamentally, however, this lack of consensus simply reflected a lack of knowledge.

As the number of patients admitted to hospitals for psychiatric treatment steadily increased (by 1938, according to an article in *The New England Journal of Medicine*, there was "one bed for mental disease for each bed for all other diseases in America"), the demand for effective treatment increased proportionately. The issues at stake were not only humanitarian—many psychiatric patients, especially those in state institutions, were condemned to live in utter misery with no hope for relief—but also financial, for the burden of maintaining such patients for years and even decades was enormous. This was the climate that encouraged the development and acceptance, in the 1930's, of such radical therapies as shock treatment (using drugs or electric shock to induce coma or convulsions) and lobotomy.

António Egas Moniz, the pioneer of lobotomy, was an extremely ambitious and multitalented man, with many interests outside his career in neurology. Prior to the development of lobotomy, he was best known for his work in cerebral angiography, which permits the visualization of the blood vessels in the brain after the injection of a radiopaque substance. He had hoped to receive a Nobel Prize for this work, which was done in the late 1920's, and he was very disappointed when it became apparent that such recognition was not forthcoming.

In August, 1935, Moniz traveled to London for the Second International Congress of Neurology. There, he attended a symposium on the frontal lobes of the brain, including a presentation by the Yale University researchers John Fulton and Carlyle Jacobsen on the effects of removing much of the frontal lobes of two chimpanzees. Moniz himself later asserted that this presentation was not decisive in the development of lobotomy, which, he said, he had been considering for some time. Contemporary observers, however, noted that Moniz seemed to be deeply impressed by the fact that the surgery had a calming effect on one of the chimpanzees, theretofore subject to fits of temper and other disturbances.

As Elliot Valenstein has shown, Moniz' interpretation of the Fulton-Jacobsen study was selective and deeply flawed, yet this misreading entered medical folklore and was even perpetuated by the Nobel Prize Committee in their citation for Moniz in 1949. Moniz ignored the fact that, while one of the subjects was indeed less agitated after the surgery, the other chimpanzee was affected in the opposite way, becoming much more temperamental and uncooperative after the surgery. This latter result did not accord with the presuppositions that Moniz brought to the London congress. He believed that many psychiatric disorders were caused by "abnormal adhesion" between nerve cells, as a result of which neural impulses "keep following the same path . . . constantly giving rise to the same morbid ideas, which are reproduced over and over again." This hypothesis of "fixed ideas" was sheer speculation, but the lack of evidence did not deter Moniz. He interpreted the Fulton-Jacobsen study as a confirmation of his belief that, if the nerve fibers in which the pernicious "fixed ideas" were conducted could be destroyed, the patient might experience significant improvement. Thus, in November, 1935, only three months after the London congress, Moniz made his first attempts at psychosurgery.

Long crippled by gout, Moniz himself did not perform the operations; rather, he directed his younger colleague, the neurosurgeon Pedro Almeida Lima. Initially, Moniz used injections of alcohol to destroy nerve fibers in the frontal lobes. The first operation took place on November 12, 1935. The patient was a sixty-three-year-old woman with a long history of mental illness. Two holes were drilled in the top of her skull and injections were made on both sides of the brain in the prefrontal area. In the following weeks, Moniz and Lima repeated this procedure with six more patients, steadily increasing the amount of alcohol injected. With his eighth psychosurgical patient, however, Moniz adopted a new method, cutting (or, at first, crushing) the nerve fibers. This surgery, performed on December 27, 1935, may be called the first lobotomy.

Moniz himself did not employ the term "lobotomy," which was first used in 1936 by his American disciple Walter Jackson Freeman and which became the standard designation for the operation in the United States. The term that Moniz coined for the operation was "leucotomy," from the Greek word for white (because the nerve fibers are white matter, as opposed to gray matter, which contains nerve-cell bodies); accordingly, the surgical instrument he employed was called the leucotome. This instrument, the design of which was refined and modified by Moniz and others, contained a retractable wire loop. After the leucotome had been inserted into the brain, this wire loop was extended and the instrument was rotated. In the first leucotomy, one such rotation (or "core," as Moniz termed it) was made on each side of the brain; in subsequent operations, as many as six cores were made on each side of the brain.

In 1936, Moniz published a monograph in which he reported on the outcome of psychosurgery for the first twenty patients he treated (including those treated with the alcohol-injection method). These patients suffered from a variety of disorders, ranging from disabling anxiety and depression to chronic schizophrenia. Moniz reported that of the twenty patients, seven had been cured as a result of the surgery and seven had improved; six were said to be unchanged. Despite the fact that Moniz' claims could not bear scrutiny (he overestimated improvement, underestimated postoperative difficulties, and failed to conduct adequate follow-up, basing most of his analysis on observations made within days of the operation), his monograph was widely hailed as persuasive evidence for the potential benefits of psychosurgery.

Impact of Event

Moniz' radical and well-publicized use of brain surgery to treat psychiatric disorders was both immediate and long-lasting. Within three months of the publication of Moniz' 1936 monograph, prefrontal lobotomies had been performed as far afield as Italy, Romania, Cuba, and Brazil, as well as in the United States, where the acceptance of lobotomy owed much to the advocacy of Freeman.

Freeman, a superb lecturer and a man of seemingly inexhaustible energy, was head of the neurology department at George Washington University when, in 1936, he read Moniz' monograph. Soon thereafter, assisted by a colleague, James Winston Watts, Freeman performed his first lobotomy; by the end of the year, he and Watts had performed twenty lobotomies. In 1942, Freeman and Watts published *Psychosurgery: Intelligence, Emotion, and Social Behavior Following Prefrontal Lobotomy for Mental Disorders*. The book was extremely influential, not only in the United States but also abroad. In the immediate postwar years, there was a dramatic increase in the number of lobotomies performed worldwide; in the United States, lobotomies increased from approximately five hundred a year in 1946 to five thousand in 1949. The Nobel Prize in Physiology or Medicine given to Moniz in 1949 for the development of the prefrontal lobotomy (he shared the award with Walter Rudolf Hess, a Swiss researcher recognized for his discovery of the function of the middle brain) further enhanced the credibility of psychosurgery.

Within only a few years, however, by the mid-1950's, the number of lobotomies performed annually began to decline steeply. There were two reasons for this sudden turnabout. The first was the development of tranquilizing drugs such as Thorazine, the widespread use of which was sufficient by itself to restrict lobotomy to exceptional cases. At the same time, serious concerns about the validity of lobotomy were being expressed in the medical community.

Some physicians had been opposed to lobotomy from the beginning, but as more long-term studies of lobotomized patients became available, it became evident that proponents of lobotomy, like Moniz before them, had not been objective in assessing the consequences of such surgery. While the operation as performed by Freeman and his colleagues became something quite different from the early attempts by Moniz, lobotomy always involved radical injury to the frontal lobes. Lobotomized patients frequently lost the ability to plan ahead, the ability to think abstractly, and other vital abilities. In many cases, particularly in the treatment of patients suffering from schizophrenia, lobotomy was not only excessively costly in psychic terms but also generally ineffective.

In the 1960's and 1970's, there was a growing awareness of ties between the government and science and a new appreciation of the threat of various kinds of mind control. As a result, further limitations were placed on the use of psychosurgery, including some legislative restrictions. Psychosurgery is still practiced in the United States on a small scale, with greater precision than ever before, thanks to technological advances and a much deeper knowledge of the brain's circuitry. Despite such advances, resistance to psychosurgery remains high, both in the medical profession and with the general public.

Bibliography

Freeman, Walter, and James W. Watts. *Psychosurgery: Intelligence, Emotion, and Social Behavior Following Prefrontal Lobotomy for Mental Disorders.* 2d ed. Springfield, Ill.: Charles C Thomas, 1950. Originally published in 1942, this landmark volume—part textbook, part popularizing manifesto, part how-to manual—had a worldwide influence in promoting lobotomy. While the book is dedicated to Moniz, Freeman and Watts eschewed his flights of speculation and sought to provide a solid rationale for psychosurgery. The volume is heavily illustrated, with copious references. The substantially expanded second edition reported the results of 619 lobotomies, compared to 80 reported in the first edition.

Fulton, John F. *Frontal Lobotomy and Affective Behavior: A Neuropsychological Analysis.* New York: W. W. Norton, 1951. Fulton (1899-1960), a leading figure in the American medical establishment of his time, received grants for several major studies of lobotomy. This short book, dedicated to Moniz and Lima, discusses lobotomies of animals as well as of human subjects; Fulton's overall assessment of the achievements of and prospects for lobotomy is very positive. Illustrated, with a bibliography.

Sackler, Arthur M., et al., eds. *The Great Physiodynamic Therapies in Psychiatry: An Historical Reappraisal.* New York: Hoeber-Harper Books, 1956. This compilation of articles selected from *The Journal of Clinical and Experimental Psychopathology* and the *Quarterly Review of Psychiatry and Neurology* includes Moniz' article "How I Succeeded in Performing Prefrontal Leukotomy." The volume also includes a brief biographical sketch of Moniz.

Shutts, David. *Lobotomy: Resort to the Knife.* New York: Van Nostrand Reinhold, 1982. Shutts provides a highly readable popularized survey of the history of lobotomy. While he recounts Moniz' development of lobotomy, Shutts devotes the bulk of his narrative to the life and work of Walter Freeman. Shutts is an engaging writer, but he is unreliable in detail; his book should be used only in conjunction with Valenstein's (cited below). Illustrated, with a bibliography.

Valenstein, Elliot S. *Great and Desperate Cures: The Rise and Decline of Psychosurgery and Other Radical Treatments for Mental Illness.* New York: Basic Books, 1986. The best available treatment of its subject, Valenstein's book presents lobotomy in its historical context, not as a bizarre aberration but rather as a representative if unusually dramatic case of "uncritical enthusiasm running rampant and causing great harm to desperate patients." Includes illustrations and extensive notes.

John Wilson

Cross-References

Cerletti and Bini Develop Electroconvulsive Therapy for Treating Schizophrenia (1937), p. 1086; Wilkins Discovers Reserpine, the First Tranquilizer (1950's), p. 1353; Sperry Discovers That Each Side of the Brain Can Function Independently (1960's), p. 1635; Hounsfield Introduces a CAT Scanner That Can See Clearly into the Body (1972), p. 1961; Janowsky Publishes a Cholinergic-Adrenergic Hypothesis of Mania and Depression (1972), p. 1976.

LEHMANN DISCOVERS THE EARTH'S INNER CORE

Category of event: Earth science
Time: 1936
Locale: Copenhagen, Denmark

Lehmann's research hypothesized an inner and outer core, which led to investigations by others to confirm that it was a viable theorem

Principal personages:

INGE LEHMANN (1888-?), the Danish seismologist who discovered that
Earth has an inner and outer core
JOHN MILNE (1850-1913), an English engineer who perfected a clockwork-
powered seismograph in 1893
RICHARD DIXON OLDHAM (1858-1936), a geologist who established that
P and S waves traveled through the interior of the earth
BENO GUTENBERG (1889-1960), a German seismologist who discovered
the boundary between the mantle and the outer core
ANDRIJA MOHOROVIČIĆ (1857-1936), a Croatian seismologist who found
the first evidence for a sharp boundary separating the crustal rocks
from the mantle

Summary of Event

Prior to the development of the seismograph, an instrument that records earth vibrations or earthquakes, very little was known about the composition of the shells underlying the surface of the earth. In the late 1800's, instrumentation and observations opened the seismological age. During this period, a basic knowledge evolved about vibrations generated by a seismic source. It was found that the vibrations travel outward through the earth. These vibrations, or waves, are transmitted through the earth with finite velocity. There are two major types of elastic waves established by the geologist Richard Dixon Oldham. The first variety is called a P wave because it causes the first, or primary disturbances, deforming the material by alternate lengthening and shortening in the direction of propagation of the wave. P waves also are termed "compressional waves" because the volume is alternately compressed and expanded. A second variety of elastic wave is an S wave, so called because it produces the secondary disturbance. The S wave is a transverse body wave that travels through the interior of an elastic medium. They do not change the volume of the medium, but do change the shape; for this reason, they are termed distortional, or shear waves, also. Both P and S waves pass through the interior of the earth; they therefore are termed "body waves."

When an earthquake occurs, its waves travel through the body of the earth and are recorded by a seismograph at earthquake observatories. These seismic waves carry to the surface information about that through which they have passed. In 1883, the English engineer John Milne surmised that every large earthquake at any point of the globe could be recorded if there were an instrument designed for that purpose; however, it was not until 1893 that he perfected the first clockwork-powered seismograph.

In later years, when extremely sensitive seismographs had been developed, it was found that some weak P waves actually were penetrating a shadow zone, an area opposite the projected core of the earth. The shadow zone, discovered in the research of Andrija Mohorovičić, was left unexplained in earlier research done by pioneers in the use of seismographs to map the interior. Inge Lehmann postulated the existence of an inner core that could reflect the rays back into the shadow zone.

At the Copenhagen Seismological Observatory, Lehmann had for a number of years been clearly observing waves through the core from Pacific earthquakes. Among these were shocks at Murchison and Hawke's Bay in New Zealand in 1928 and 1931, respectively. It was evident from these records that a P-type wave was arriving at stations that should have been within the shadow zone. This can be explained only if there is an inner core, about 1,250 kilometers in radius and of greater density than the outer core. Lehmann believed that core waves could be classified into three separate P wave types (P′). The standard explanation for the first two of these waves types was that the rays were defracted at the boundary between the mantle and core and focused toward the antipodes, places diametrically opposite to each other on the globe. She explained that the third type waves were reflections from another sharp discontinuity within the core itself. This family of waves are the core refractions. Beyond about 103 degrees, the direct P wave cannot be recorded because of the shadow effect of the core. Beyond this distance, the first wave to appear on long-period instruments is often PP, which does not penetrate so deeply, and so is able to avoid the obstacle. Short-period instruments show a refracted wave arising from complexities within the core, but it is not quite as prominent as P when it makes its reappearance at 142 degrees. Because it is deflected from its path and disappears altogether for nearly 40 degrees, it is called PKP, K standing for *Kern*, the German word for core.

In 1936, after ten years experience with interpretation of seismograms, records made by a seismograph, and a well-established scientific method, Lehmann was prepared for discovering the inner core. A first step was to calculate a direct problem. She assumed an earth model that was particularly simple. It had constant velocities in the mantle (10 kilometers per second) and core (8 kilometers per second). These were reasonable average values for both regions. She then introduced a small central core, which again had a constant velocity. These simplifications enabled her to take the seismic rays to be straight lines, therefore, travel times could be calculated by elementary trigonometry. She then showed by successive adjustments that a reasonable velocity and radius of the inner core could be found that predicted a travel-time curve close to the observations of the travel times of the third type of P waves (P′). In effect, she proved an existence theorem: A plausible three-shell earth structure could be defined that explained the features of the observed waves.

Lehmann's discovery of the inner core was very complicated; however, it convinced Beno Gutenberg in the United States and Harold Jeffreys in England that her hypothesis was a viable one. Within two years, they had independently carried out more detailed calculations involving many observed travel times of P′ waves and calculated by an inverse method both the radius of the inner core and the P-velocity distribution in it.

The discovery of the last major discontinuity within the globe was a mixture of direct and inverse procedures. Lehmann was careful to state in her paper entitled "P′," published in the *Bureau Central Seismologique International, Series A, Travaux Scientifique* (1936) that she had not proved the existence of an inner core.

Impact of Event

Lehmann's discovery of the inner core had both immediate and long-lasting effects. She showed that the whole pattern of observed PKP waves for 105 to 180 degrees could be explained if the core consisted of two shells, an outer one around an inner core. Gutenberg and Charles Richter, at the California Institute of Technology, and Jeffreys, working independently, concluded that the actual observations of travel times of core waves available to them agreed with a double-core hypothesis.

After the discovery of the inner core, the measured travel times could be transformed, using inverse theory, into plausible P velocities in the mantle and the outer and inner cores. Gutenberg and Jeffreys independently computed in late 1938 and 1939 the average velocity based on thousands of observed travel times of P and S waves. Their agreement was extremely close; in fact, their calculations were so well developed, that they have not been seriously altered after fifty years of scrutiny by other seismologists. Gutenberg and Jeffreys, however, disagreed over the nature of the boundary to the inner core. Gutenberg held that the interface was many tens of kilometers deep, but Jeffreys argued that a sharp boundary occurred.

In the 1960's, research by Bruce A. Bolt and Mary O'Neill at the University of California at Berkeley confirmed that, if the inner core surface was sharp, then a scrutiny of seismograms in the predicted time window at distances of 105 to 110 degrees should disclose unidentified earthquake onsets. Nuclear test explosions in Nevada and earthquakes were observed in 1970 at the Large-Aperture Seismic Array (LASA) in Billings, Montana, by Carl Romney, Edward Flinn, and E. R. Engdahl. Their studies concluded that the inner core has a sharp surface, and its radius is within a few kilometers of 1,216 kilometers.

The seismological evidence for a sharp inner core boundary raises the question of possible liquid-solid or solid-solid phase transitions in either a homogeneous material or in a multicomponent chemical system. If the transition from the inner to the outer core is a transition from the solid to the liquid form of a single material, then the boundary must be at the melting point, and a constraint is put on the thermal regime of the earth's interior. J. A. Jacobs, in *Nature* (1953), used this fact to explain how the mantle and inner core could be solid, while the outer core is liquid.

As a result of the development of sensitive seismographs, an expansion in the number of seismographic stations around the earth, and large capacity computers, a greater understanding of the earth is possible. The core has a role in many geophysical studies, and how it is affected during great earthquakes is being probed actively. If the physical properties inside the earth were better known, the frequencies and amplitude pattern for the resonant vibrations could be calculated, thereby improving earthquake prediction and thus preventing the loss of life.

Bibliography

Bolt, Bruce A. *Inside the Earth: Evidence from Earthquakes.* New York: W. H. Freeman, 1982. An easy-to-read, copiously illustrated introductory textbook covering the evolution of knowledge of the middle earth, types and measurements of earthquake waves, main shells of the earth, structural vibrations densities, elastic properties, and temperatures. Included is a guide to further reading.

Clark, Sydney P., Jr. *Structure of the Earth.* Englewood Cliffs, N.J.: Prentice-Hall, 1971. A brief and very readable introduction to the structure of the earth. Areas covered include geologic structures, the earth's magnetic field, plate tectonics, seismology and the earth's constitution from seismic evidence, and heat flow and the temperature in the earth. Includes many illustrations and references as well as suggestions for further reading.

Jacobs, J. A. *The Earth's Core.* New York: Academic Press, 1975. For graduate students and research workers in geophysics. Focuses on seismology and geomagnetism; contains many graphs and mathematical computations. Areas covered include the general properties of the earth, the origin of the core, thermal regime of the earth's core, its magnetic field and constitution, and cores of other planets. Each chapter has many references; includes both an author and subject index.

Ozima, Minoru. *The Earth: Its Birth and Growth.* Translated by Judy Wakabayashi. Cambridge, England: Cambridge University Press, 1981. An introductory course in geochemistry is essential for an understanding of the subject matter. Outlines the problems now being solved through isotope geochemistry. Of particular interest is the chapter on the formation of the layered structure of the earth, which discusses the existence of the earth's field. Moderately illustrated; does not contain a reference list.

Strahler, Arthur N., and Alan H. Strahler. *Environmental Geoscience: Interaction Between Natural Systems and Man.* New York: John Wiley & Sons, 1973. An introductory college textbook that weaves the basic principles of geoscience with environmental and resource problems. Of particular interest is the discussion of the magnetosphere and the core as the source for the generation of the earth's magnetism. Abundantly illustrated; includes a reference source for additional items on the magnetosphere.

Tarbuck, Edward J., and Frederick K. Lutgens. *The Earth: An Introduction to Physical Geology.* Columbus, Ohio: Charles E. Merrill, 1984. An introductory level text with a very good overview on the earth's interior. Well written and illustrated with color graphics. A good reference source for further information.

Earl G. Hoover

Cross-References

Wiechert Invents the Inverted Pendulum Seismograph (1900), p. 51; Oldham and Mohorovičić Determine the Structure of the Earth's Interior (1906), p. 340; Gutenberg Discovers the Earth's Mantle-Outer Core Boundary (1913), p. 552; Richter Develops a Scale for Measuring Earthquake Strength (1935), p. 1050.

MÜLLER INVENTS THE FIELD EMISSION MICROSCOPE

Category of event: Physics
Time: 1936
Locale: Berlin, Germany

Müller invented the field emission microscope, the first instrument to depict the crystal structure of metals and the forerunner of his more powerful field ion microscope

Principal personages:

ERWIN WILHELM MÜLLER (1911-1977), a physicist, engineer, research professor, and the recipient of many awards

EUGEN GOLDSTEIN (1850-1930), a German experimental physicist who was among the first to demonstrate the field emission effect and who coined the term "cathode ray"

RALPH HOWARD FOWLER (1889-1944), an English physicist whose theoretical studies led to the explanation of field electron emission by the science of quantum mechanics

ROBERT GOMER (1924-   ), an American chemist and physicist who became the first scientist to use the field emission microscope in the quantitative study of metal surfaces

Summary of Event

Erwin Wilhelm Müller began to study the physical process which would constitute the basis of the field emission microscope while he was a research physicist in Berlin from 1935 to 1937. Field emission is the emission of electrons, the negatively charged subatomic constituents of all matter, from a metal electrode under the influence of a strong electrical field into a vacuum. The strong field induces the electrons to travel in the direction of the field. In 1876, Eugen Goldstein had demonstrated this effect experimentally. Goldstein projected the image of a small coin onto the fluorescent wall of a vacuum tube by using the coin as the electron donating electrode, or cathode, of an electrical circuit, and the fluorescent wall of the tube as the electron receiving electrode, or anode. The resulting electrical field around the metal coin induced electrons to traverse the vacuum tube and strike the fluorescent wall. When the moving electrons struck the fluorescent coating of the tube wall, a blurred, glowing image of the coin appeared.

Müller's research involved electron emission from point sources, not flat sources such as coins. One particular source consisted of a sharply edged tungsten needle. At first, Müller was simply interested in the paths taken by the field emitted electrons. Since Müller was familiar with the work of Goldstein and others, he set out to construct a similar apparatus, replacing the flat coin with his convex metal needles in order to stimulate the electron flow.

Müller's vacuum tubes were more like light bulbs than tubes, with the hemisphere opposite the needlelike cathode coated with a fluorescent material. In 1936, when Müller applied an electric field of approximately 40 million volts per centimeter to this apparatus, he did not view an image of the needle point analogous to that of Goldstein's coin face. Instead, his images were single, unstable blotches of light and dark which were at first nearly impossible to interpret. He soon recognized that the images of the convex needles produced by the instrument were highly magnified, whereas Goldstein's images offered no magnification at all; they were mere representations. The apparatus was a crude version of the field emission microscope.

In order to overcome the poor image quality, Müller worked to improve the quality of the needle tip by the chemical and electrolytic preparation of fine, heat-treated metal wires. Such procedures allowed Müller to manufacture needles with tips that were no larger than 0.00002 centimeter in diameter. At this size, many of the needles were composed of one nearly perfect crystal of the metal. With such improvements, Müller was able to publish emitted electron images of the surface crystallographic structure of tungsten in the German journal *Zeitschrift für Physik* in 1937. The magnification of these images was so great that it offered the first glimpse of the metallic crystal structure at the level of the atoms making up the crystal lattice. These were the first applications of the new invention, dubbed the field emission, or field electron, microscope. Soon thereafter, Müller obtained similar micrographs of the crystal structures of molybdenum, platinum, nickel, and copper.

Müller realized the importance such an instrument would have on the study of metallic surfaces. Such an instrument could be used to study the adsorption, or the physics of adherence, of contaminating materials onto the very structure of the metal. He also recognized that the instrument would be useless without a firm understanding of the physical process upon which it depended—the field emission of electrons. The power of the field emission microscope would depend upon the limits that the physical process of field emission imposed upon it, for any scientific instrument is limited by the physical system upon which it depends in order to operate.

Two of the most important parameters in assessing the power of any microscope are magnification and resolution. While the former is a measure of the size of the smallest objects which the microscope can make visible, the latter measures the size of the objects which it can distinguish, and is thus a measure of accuracy. For example, a microscope that has a magnification of one hundred times will make objects appear one hundred times larger than they are in reality. A microscope with a resolution of 2 millimeters can distinguish objects that are separated by a distance of 2 millimeters. Objects which are separated by less than 2 millimeters will not be seen as distinct objects. The electron emission process influences both these parameters and would ultimately preclude the instrument from depicting the images of individual metal atoms within the crystal lattice.

Müller studied the effect of needle shape on the performance of the microscope throughout much of 1937. He discovered that the magnification of a field emission microscope depends upon the ratio of the fluorescent screen radius to the metal emitter radius. This underscores the importance of having a needle-shaped electron emitter. The more precise the tip of a needle is, the smaller its radius will be. The smaller this measure becomes, the larger the ratio of the screen radius to emitter radius becomes, and hence, the higher the magnification becomes. The reason that Goldstein's apparatus produced an unmagnified image of the coin was that the radius of the screen was approximately equal to that of the coin; thus, their ratio was approximately equal to one, yielding no magnifying power at all. This should not be interpreted as meaning that the needle emitter should be fashioned into the sharpest point possible with a radius approaching zero. Indeed, when Müller showed the instrument to the German physicist Max von Laue in 1937, von Laue maintained that the emitter should have the sharpest point that the particular metal, (and its associated crystal structure) would allow. Yet, based upon his knowledge of metallic crystal behavior, he reasoned that a smooth, hemispherical tip, albeit a very small one, would be the most efficient electron emitter. This was indeed the case.

When the needles had been properly shaped, Müller was able to realize magnifications of up to one million times. This magnification allowed Müller to view what he called "maps" of the atomic crystal structure of metals. While the magnification may have been great, however, the resolution of the instrument was severely limited by the physics of emitted electrons, which caused the images Müller obtained to be continually blurred.

Müller was well aware of the contemporary developments in quantum mechanics, especially those of Ralph Howard Fowler, which applied these theories to field electron emission. Quantum mechanics is the set of physical theories that describes phenomena at the subatomic level, which stated that entities such as electrons behave both as particles and as waves. Since the electrons have particle-like properties, they would have a particular velocity like any other moving particle. Since they also behaved like waves, they would have a particular wave length like sound waves or light waves. The electron velocity was extremely high and uncontrollably random, which caused the blurred micrographic images. In addition, the electrons had an unsatisfactorily high wave length. When Müller combined these two factors, he was able to determine that, theoretically, the resolution of the field emission microscope would never reach below 20 angstroms. This may seem quite small. In fact, a resolution of 20 angstroms is equal to a resolution of 0.000000002 meter. Yet, Müller noted that the atoms in an atomic crystal lattice are separated by only four to five angstroms. Thus, the field emission microscope could never depict single atoms, for it was a physical impossibility for it to distinguish one atom from another.

Impact of Event

Even with its inherent limitations, the field emission microscope had an enormous impact on two fronts: the field of surface science and Müller's development of the field ion microscope in the early to mid-1950's.

Robert Gomer, an American chemist and physicist, was among the first scientists to put Müller's invention to use in actual scientific investigation. Most other microscopes and magnifying instruments consist of an independent system of lenses which process the image of the specimen under investigation by focusing the reflection of some wavelength of radiation (visible light, X rays, and the like). The field emission microscope does not require such an apparatus, however. The specimen under study—the needle—is an integral part of the instrument, for it is also the electron emitting cathode. Whatever happens physically or chemically to the specimen will affect directly the resulting image. Gomer was attracted to the device because of this simplicity, and it was this simplicity that permitted the types of experiments he conducted.

Since size requirements dictated that the needle often consists of only one individual crystal of the metal, Müller realized that the properties of individual crystals could be examined. The most important of these properties was the adsorption of materials onto the needle surface. The instrument offered such a precise map of the crystal structure that a layer as thin as one one hundredth of an atom would affect the emission quality and hence the resulting image. Gomer used the field emission microscope to study the adsorption and desorption of materials such as barium.

Since the field of surface science was in its infancy at the time of Müller's invention, the field emission microscope provided the impetus which allowed this discipline to expand and flourish through the 1940's and 1950's. By the late 1950's, Gomer used the instrument to investigate and study the rate of migration of gases which diffused into the lattice itself. In order to achieve this, Gomer immersed a field emission microscope in a bath of liquid helium, creating an extremely high vacuum within the bulb. This allowed him to introduce gases such as hydrogen and oxygen into the bulb and view their movement through the crystal by viewing the subsequent changes in the emitter image. The studies of diffusion and adsorption allowed Gomer and others to view the gross molecular structure of any material which could be either embedded within or adsorbed onto the emitter surface. Medium-sized molecules of materials such as phthalocyanine have also been observed.

Despite these advances, Müller's studies of the limitations of the microscope eventually led to the development of the more powerful field ion microscope between 1951 and 1956. Rather than imaging the needle tip with emitted electrons, Müller used emitted positive ions. The ions had smaller velocities and shorter wavelengths than the much lighter electrons, and hence the inherent resolution problems of the field emission microscope were overcome at last. By 1956, Müller and his colleagues at the Pennsylvania State University's Field Emission Laboratory reported the first images of individual atoms in metal lattices.

Bibliography

Müller, Erwin W. "The Field Ion Microscope." *American Scientist* 49 (March, 1961): 88-98. While this article is largely devoted to Müller's work on the field ion microscope, it presents some introductory material to the physical limitations of the field emission microscope, which eventually led to the field ion microscope's development.

_____. "Field Ion Microscopy." *Science* 149 (August, 1965): 591-600. This article on the later and more powerful field ion microscope discusses Müller's realization of the resolving problems of the field ion microscope. It also discusses the ramifications of the fact that the imaging medium and sample are one and the same in both the field emission and field ion microscopes.

_____. "The Imaging Process in Field Ion Microscopy from the FEM to the Atom Probe." In *Chemistry and Physics of Solid Surfaces*, edited by Ralf Vanselow and S. Y. Tong. Cleveland: CRC Press, 1977. The most technically concise and accessible account of the development of the field emission microscope. Like most of Müller's work, it is presented in the context of the later field ion microscope. Müller traces the history of the field emission microscope and includes illustrations and micrographs from his original German publications, including micrographs of the tungsten crystal and barium adsorbed onto tungsten.

Müller, Erwin W., and Tien Tzou Tsong. "Fundamentals of Field Ion Microscopy." In *Field Ion Microscopy: Principles and Applications*. New York: Elsevier, 1969. Müller's most comprehensive account of the application of his inventions in the field of surface science. Its stress is mostly upon the later field ion microscope, but the introductory chapter gives a concise account of the historical events leading to the development of both instruments. The bibliography at the end of this chapter is especially useful to those interested in the original German papers on the field emission microscope.

Oudar, Jacques. "Recent Methods in the Study of Adsorption." In *Physics and Chemistry of Surfaces*. Glasgow: Blackie and Son, 1975. Devoted exclusively to the study of adsorption, the author details the use of both the field emission and the field ion microscopes in surface studies. It is adequately illustrated, although sparse in technical context. This text is devoted primarily to the theories of surface science and their subsequent testing, not the technology used in the laboratory.

William J. McKinney

Cross-References

Zsigmondy Invents the Ultramicroscope (1902), 159; Thomson Wins the Nobel Prize for the Discovery of the Electron (1906), p. 356; Bohr Writes a Trilogy on Atomic and Molecular Structure (1912), p. 507; Rutherford Presents His Theory of the Atom (1912), p. 527; Ruska Creates the First Electron Microscope (1931), p. 958; Müller Develops the Field Ion Microscope (1952), p. 1434.

THE COMPLETION OF BOULDER DAM CREATES LAKE MEAD, THE WORLD'S LARGEST RESERVOIR

Category of event: Applied science
Time: March 1, 1936
Locale: Black Canyon, Colorado River

Completion of the Boulder/Hoover Dam on March 1, 1936, meant that Lake Mead, the world's largest reservoir, became available for irrigation, for hydroelectric generation, and for storing excess water

Principal personages:

FRANK CROWE (1882-1946), a civil engineer who was superintendent of construction for the Boulder Dam

ARTHUR POWELL DAVIS (1861-1933), a hydrographer and engineer who directed the Reclamation Service in initial stages of development of the Boulder Dam

WALKER YOUNG (1884-1982), the engineer who represented the Bureau of Reclamation on the scene as construction engineer and led the preliminary tests of sites in Boulder and Black Canyons

ELWOOD MEAD (1874-1936), the commissioner of the Bureau of Reclamation who supported the project; Lake Mead is named after him

HERBERT HOOVER (1874-1964), the thirty-first President of the United States, for whom Boulder Dam was renamed on September 17, 1930

Summary of Event

The story of the Boulder/Hoover Dam begins with the efforts of Congressman Phil Swing and Senator Hiram Johnson of California to bring water to California's Imperial Valley. The opposition of Arthur Powell Davis, director of the Reclamation Service, advocate for a comprehensive Colorado River plan, and reclamation expert, forced Swing and Johnson to broaden their proposal. The result was the Boulder Canyon Project Act, which was first introduced in 1923. The bill was signed finally by President Calvin Coolidge on December 21, 1928, having overcome filibusters by Arizona's senators, court challenges, the opposition of the *Los Angeles Times*, and the mistrust of Eastern legislators.

On November 24, 1922, the Colorado River Compact was signed by six of the seven basin states. The residents of Arizona were convinced that the compact and proposals associated with it were part of a grand scheme to divert Arizona water to California. Nevertheless, the distribution pattern established for the Colorado's water by the compact made a high dam possible.

The Swing-Johnson Bill, as it came to be known, passed with the provision that appropriations would come only after sufficient revenue to meet amortization payments was guaranteed by the sale of the electricity generated. After the difficult task of computing a competitive rate was accomplished, contracts for more than $327 million were signed in the late spring of 1930. On July 3, 1930, Congress appropriated $10,666,000 for the first phase of the Boulder Canyon Project.

Determining where the high dam would be built had to occur before authorization. The Reclamation Service had begun the tests in April, 1920, and testing in Boulder Canyon began in January, 1921, with a team led by Walker Young. It was an enormous challenge to perform the tests in the hostile physical environment. (Young would be rewarded with the post of projects construction engineer.) Young's crew tested five sites in Boulder Canyon. The rock had to be examined for depth, texture, strength, and durability in the walls and the riverbed, in spite of flood-swollen waters and treacherous rock formations. By December, 1921, Young had narrowed the Boulder Canyon sites to one far-from-ideal spot and moved the team 48 kilometers to Black Canyon. Site "D" proved to be superior, and on February 1, 1924, the Reclamation Service recommended that the dam be built on that site.

Governor Fred Balzar of Nevada chose September 17, 1930, as the date on which to celebrate the project's beginning. By that time, 37 kilometers of track to the dam site had been laid by the Union Pacific Railroad and the specifications made known. Secretary of the Interior Ray Lyman Wilbur named the dam after Herbert Hoover, initiating a controversy that did not end until April 30, 1947. Wilbur surprised everyone with the announcement at the celebration, and his choice promptly became mired in partisan politics. (After Hoover was defeated, the new Secretary of the Interior Harold Ickes returned the name to Boulder Dam on May 8, 1933.)

Once the specifications were set, a bid deadline of March 4, 1931, was established. Each bid had to include a $2 million bid bond, and the winner was required to post a $5 million performance bond. The requirements were daunting in depression America, but a consortium of six companies was formed. These Western companies were accustomed to "rough-and-tumble" engineering and knew how to work in the hostile environment. They brought with them the most famous engineer of dams in the West, Frank Crowe; they beat the next lowest bid of $5 million and raised the capital for the two bonds. The final profit for the consortium amounted to between $10.4 million and $18 million. Crowe, an engineer of extraordinary qualifications, who inspired awe from construction contemporaries, had directed construction on three high dams and was the choice for superintendent of construction. Crowe and Young were old acquaintances who collaborated well in an atmosphere of mutual respect. Young was the "great delayer" to Crowe, but the already frenetic pace would have been unbearable without Young's cautious style. Young directed 150 inspectors to ensure that quality standards were maintained. Notwithstanding Young's careful approach, Crowe never deviated from his intention of combining profits with a quality product.

Crowe's challenge was great. He had to manage a large work force through three abortive strikes and unending seven-day work weeks, oversee on-site relations with the government, and handle the fractious individuals of the consortium that made up the six companies, while showing both innovation and resolve. Innovation was present in the development of a motor driven drilling rig, without which the four diversion tunnels could not have been built during the winter of 1932 to 1933, when the water was low. (Failure to meet the October 1, 1933, deadline for tunnel completion would have meant three thousand dollars a day in fines.)

Innovation was needed to devise the system for obtaining concrete from the mixing plant to the pouring site without hardening on the way. Speed with care was the criterion, and Crowe applied techniques he had used elsewhere. The staff carried 16 tons of concrete in each steel bucket over 25-ton cableways, all controlled by operators perched over the canyon rim. The lining of the diversion tunnels took 365,760 cubic meters of concrete, and 3.1 million cubic meters of concrete went into the 1.5-meter blocks of concrete, poured first into one column and then another. The concrete could not be poured in one continuous pour because its intense temperatures would produce stress fractures if the concrete dried too precipitously in the setting process. Each individual block was laced with a 2.5-centimeter pipe through which first river water, then ice-cold water, was pumped. Monitoring the process kept contraction even and prevented excessive stress. Once the block was cool, grout was pumped into the pipes, solidifying the block.

Crow's resolve was demonstrated in the unrelenting pace he demanded of everyone in his control. He turned the dam over to the government on March 1, 1936, two years, one month, and twenty-eight days ahead of schedule, in spite of intense heat, high waters, interference from various external sources, and labor troubles. Boulder Dam at completion stood higher than any of the high dams at 221.4 meters. It was 201 meters thick at bedrock, tapering to only 13.7 meters at the top. The curving crest extended 390.8 meters long and served as a highway. The final plan allowed for a maximum compressive stress of approximately 40 tons per square meter. The lake, 338 square kilometers in area and the largest reservoir in the world, was named after Elwood Mead, Commissioner of the Bureau of Reclamation. He had been a strong advocate for the dam during the entire period of construction.

Completion of the Boulder Dam during the world's most severe depression and so far ahead of schedule demonstrated the success of the capitalist system. The capitalist entrepreneurs behind the consortium proved that the system still worked, in spite of the internal and external doubts often expressed in the 1930's.

Impact of Event

The Boulder/Hoover Dam produced the results that its most strident and insistent advocates had claimed for it during the political debates of 1923 to 1928. To a visionary such as Davis, the dam promised to be the catalyst for a transformation of the West into an economically dynamic area. It is easy to see the specific effects that the dam had upon Arizona, California, and Nevada, but after the success of the Boulder Dam, great multipurpose water projects that could be duplicated throughout the West with comparable results became relatively commonplace.

The Imperial Valley owes its place as the greatest agricultural region in the world to the final phase of the Boulder Canyon Project, completed in October of 1940.

The drinking water brought to the Los Angeles Metropolitan Water District via the 386-kilometer Colorado River Aqueduct made possible the rapid growth of that area after the spring of 1941. By the end of 1939, the powerhouse at the dam had become the world's largest hydroelectric facility. Its power made the industrial development around Los Angeles possible. It is argued that, without the Boulder Dam, World War II would have lasted much longer. With changes and improvements, the power-house now produces more than 2 million kilowatts.

The water supplied from Lake Mead helped sustain the Las Vegas boom. The construction and tourist money (750,000 tourists from 1934 to 1935) helped to transform the city from a sleepy desert town to the core of a dynamic metropolitan area.

The test of the capacity of the dam to control rampant flood waters came on June 6, 1983, when 27,432 cubic meters of water per second rushed toward Lake Mead. On July 24, 1983, the crest saw 15,240 cubic meters per second diverted through the diversion tunnels. The spill lasted until September 6. The dam had prevented enormous destruction downstream as it was designed to do.

During the Depression years, the building of the Boulder Dam symbolized the resiliency of the American spirit and the permanence of the American dream. More tangibly, from 1931 to 1936, it provided work for thousands of desperate men.

Boulder/Hoover Dam and Lake Mead are prominent symbols of the vigorous and unrelenting transformation of the environment undertaken by Americans. They are, thus, prime examples of the ends—progress and economic development—justify the means philosophy that has dominated the thinking of many Americans. The drive for readily available water and inexpensive energy has tamed rivers like the Colorado and threatens to turn reservoirs such as Lake Mead into new salt lakes. The apparent success of the Boulder/Hoover Dam makes it that much easier to engineer other transformations of the environment in the name of progress.

Nevertheless, Boulder/Hoover Dam remains one of the engineering marvels of the twentieth century, visited annually by 750,000 people who gape and marvel at the sight and humankind's ability to perform feats that challenge human comprehension.

Bibliography

Berkman, Richard L., and W. Kip Viscusi. *Damming the West*. New York: Gross-man, 1973. An excellent volume about the process of damming Western rivers that makes it possible to place the Boulder Dam into a comprehensive picture. This broad perspective underscores the catalytic role of Boulder Dam.

Kleinsorge, Paul. *The Boulder Canyon Project: Historical and Economic Aspects*. Stanford, Calif.: Stanford University Press, 1940. Provides excellent coverage of the legislative battle over the Boulder Canyon Project Act, or Swing-Johnson Bill. Kleinsorge understands how the legislative process works and accurately describes the underside of that process.

McBride, Dennis. *In the Beginning: A History of Boulder City, Nevada*. Boulder City: Boulder City Chamber of Commerce, 1981. Discusses the people involved in the project, although in a somewhat romanticized manner. Gives a feeling that through all the trials and tribulations, a sense of community was established. For a wide audience.

Stevens, Joseph E. *Hoover Dam: An American Adventure.* Norman: University of Oklahoma Press, 1988. A superb account of the people who built the dam. Especially strong account of the technical aspects of the construction, but little attention to the environmental impact.

Watkins, T. H., et al. *The Grand Colorado: The Story of a River and Its Canyons.* Palo Alto, Calif.: American West, 1969. The Colorado River is one of the great and majestic rivers in the United States. This volume captures the spirit of that river as it passes through some of the most hostile, yet beautiful, naturescapes in this world. A majestic river deserves a majestic dam.

William F. Steirer, Jr.

Cross-References

Construction Begins on the Panama Canal (1904), p. 249; Construction Begins on the Empire State Building (1930), p. 906; The Verrazano Bridge Opens (1964), p. 1782.

FLUORESCENT LIGHTING IS INTRODUCED

Category of event: Applied science
Time: November 23, 1936
Locale: Washington, D.C.

Decorative lighting for the one hundredth anniversary celebration of the Patent Office was provided by fluorescent lamps, setting the stage for the widespread use of this efficient form of lighting

Principal personages:

VINCENZO CASCARIOLO (1571-1624), an Italian alchemist and shoemaker who found a fluorescent substance that glowed in the dark after exposure to sunlight, opening the art of fluorescent materials

FRANCIS HAUKSBEE (died c. 1713), a self-educated English scientist who produced the first human-made glow discharge in 1706

HEINRICH GEISSLER (1814-1879), a German glassblower who fabricated the first gaseous conduction tube

SIR GEORGE GABRIEL STOKES (1819-1903), an English physicist and mathematician who announced the scientific law that the wavelength of the light exciting fluorescence must be less than that of the emitted light

PETER COOPER HEWITT (1861-1921), an American electrical engineer who marketed the first low-pressure mercury vapor discharge lamps in 1901

Summary of Event

On the night of November 23, 1936, more than one thousand industrialists, patent attorneys, and scientists assembled in the main ballroom of the Mayflower Hotel in Washington, D.C., to celebrate the one hundredth anniversary of the Patent Office. A transport liner over the city radioed the names chosen by the Patent Office of America's "Twelve Greatest Inventors" and, as the distinguished group strained to listen to the radio voice for those names, "the room was flooded for a moment by the most brilliant light yet used to illuminate a space that size." Thus, *The New York Times* summarized the commercial introduction of the fluorescent lamp on the day following the event. The twelve inventors present were: Thomas Alva Edison, Robert Fulton, Charles Goodyear, Charles Hall, Elias Howe, Cyrus Hall McCormick, Ottmar Morganthaler, Samuel F. B. Morse, George Westinghouse, Wilbur Wright, and Eli Whitney. There was, however, no name to bear the honor for inventing fluorescent lighting. The honor for inventing fluorescent lighting is shared by many who participated in a very long series of discoveries.

The fluorescent lamp operates as a low-pressure, electric discharge inside a phosphor-coated glass tube, which contains a droplet of mercury and a rare gas, commonly argon. At room temperature, the droplet gives off a very weak vapor of mercury atoms. Because mercury ionizes more easily than the rare gas atoms, the mercury atoms control the discharge despite the much larger number of rare gas atoms. The inside of the glass tube is coated with fine particles of the phospher, a material which fluoresces when bathed in the strong ultraviolet radiation from the mercury atoms in the discharge. The light from a fluorescent lamp is composed mainly of the broad-spectrum, whitish light from the phosphor with a small, but significant, contribution from narrow-spectrum mercury emissions in the violet, blue, green, and yellow. In contrast to incandescent lamps, the fluorescent lamps give off light with little heat.

The high light efficiency of the fluorescent lamp is caused by a finely tailored match between the phosphor coating within the lamp and the mercury discharge. Commercial production of the fluorescent lamp followed only after a long sequence of events which instructed scientists on the colorful properties of fluorescent materials and of electrical discharges.

The setting for the introduction of the fluorescent lamp began at the beginning of the 1600's, when Vincenzo Cascariolo, an Italian shoemaker and alchemist, discovered a substance that continued its glow after exposure to strong sunlight. After exposure to the sun, the material gave off a bluish glow in the dark. The fluorescent substance was apparently barium sulfide and was so unusual for that time and so valuable that its formulation was kept secret for a long time. Gradually, however, scholars became aware of the preparation secrets of the substance and studied it and other luminescent materials.

Sir Isaac Newton, who favored the particle theory of light, studied fluorescence and incorrectly attributed the delayed emission of light to the time spent undergoing internal reflections within the grains of the substance. Sir George Gabriel Stokes, who favored the wave theory of light, studied the phenomenon as well. In 1852, he termed the afterglow "fluorescence" and announced a law that summarized the findings on fluorescent substances: The exciting light always has a shorter wavelength than the fluorescing light. For example, short wave violet light can produce longer wave green fluorescence, but green light does not produce violet fluorescence.

It is now known that shorter wavelengths correspond to higher light frequencies and energies, with frequency energies increasing from red, yellow, and green, through to violet, and ultraviolet. Thus, shorter wavelengths of light correspond to higher packets of energy. Stokes' law requires that the exciting light must be more energetic than the emitted fluorescence. Although light does have particle-like properties, the delayed emission is not caused by internal reflections but is caused by a real delay in emission during which the energy is held within individual atoms, or groups of atoms, inside the fluorescent material.

While these advances were being made on fluorescent substances, other workers were taking the steps needed to bring about practical discharge that could produce energetic light. In 1706, Francis Hauksbee fabricated an electrostatic generator. He then used a vacuum pump produced by Otto von Guericke to evacuate a vessel to a low pressure and tested his electrostatic generator. Therefore, Hauksbee obtained the first human-made electrical glow discharge by capturing lightning in a jar. Later, investigators worked on this novel form of trapped lightning. In 1854, Heinrich Geissler, a glassblower and apparatus maker, opened his shop in Bonn to make scientific instruments; in 1855, he produced a vacuum pump that used liquid mercury as an evacuation fluid. That same year, Geissler made the first gaseous conduction lamps while working in collaboration with the German scientist Julius Plücker. Plücker referred to these lamps as "Geissler tubes." Geissler was able to create red light with neon filling a lamp and light of nearly all colors by choice of gas within the lamps. Thus, both the neon sign business and the science of spectroscopy were born.

Geissler tubes were studied extensively by a variety of workers. At the beginning of the twentieth century, the practical American engineer Peter Cooper Hewitt put these studies to use by marketing the first low pressure mercury vapor lamps. The lamps were quite successful, although requiring high voltage for operation, appearing an eerie blue-green, and shining dimly by comparison with their eventual successor, the fluorescent lamp. At about the same time, systematic studies of phosphors had finally begun.

By the 1920's, a number of investigators discovered that the low pressure mercury vapor discharge marketed by Hewitt was an extremely efficient method for producing ultraviolet light, if the mercury and rare gas pressures were properly adjusted. With a phosphor to convert the ultraviolet back to visible, the Hewitt lamp made an excellent light source.

Scientists learned that the mercury vapor was proper if the coolest portion on the discharge wall was kept between 40 and 45 degrees Celsius, quite cool for a lamp. Under these conditions, the scientist found that 60 percent of the electrical energy entering the discharge appeared as ultraviolet energy radiating from the mercury atoms in the discharge.

Several commercial European laboratories began development of a practical fluorescent lamp in the early 1930's. Around 1934, United States laboratories undertook earnest efforts toward production. A range of durable and efficient phosphors were devised. Sturdy, but inexpensive, electrodes were designed for operation with special metal-oxide coatings which, when heated in the lamp, readily boiled off electrons to supply current to the discharge and so reduced the operating voltage from the high value found in the Hewitt lamp. At the same time, engineers developed transformer circuitry needed to start the lamp at somewhat elevated voltage, while operating it at the lower voltage available on the electrical lines. Finally, the light coming from the developing fluorescent lamps had to be measured and compared with other light sources. Electrical power is measured in watts, the number found on, for example, a 100-watt light bulb. Light power is measured in lumens. Invisible powers, such as ultraviolet or infrared light, contain no lumens. Thus, the number of lumens per watt of actual power must depend on color within the spectrum of visible light. Per watt, violet and red give fewer lumens than green and yellow, which lie near the middle of the spectrum and where the eye is most sensitive. The measurements demonstrated that the fluorescent lamp was quite efficient, at least twice that of an incandescent lamp of similar light output, depending on the phosphor blend chosen for the fluorescent lamp.

Early in 1936, the Patent Office announced plans for its centennial celebration, and new discoveries were invited for presentation. Fluorescent lighting was chosen to be among the new inventions displayed. On November 23, 1936, fluorescent lighting was introduced and an extraordinary editorial in *The New York Times* on November 24 carried these words: " . . . [W]e must look for the revolutionary inventions to come—engines driven by atomic energy, rocket ships that voyage in interplanetary space, lamps that glow without heat. . . ."

Impact of Event

The revolution of light that glowed without heat took place almost immediately. By 1938, production of fluorescent lamps was well under way. By April, 1938, four sizes of fluorescent lamps in various colors were offered to the public and more than 200,000 lamps were sold. When the United States entered World War II, the demand for efficient factory lighting soared. In 1941, more than 21 million fluorescent lamps were sold.

During 1939 and 1940, two great expositions—the New York World's Fair and the San Francisco International Exposition—helped popularize fluorescent lighting. Thousands of tubular fluorescent lamps formed a great spiral in the "motor display salon," the car showroom, of the General Motor exhibit at the New York World's Fair. Fluorescent lamps lit the Polish Restaurant and hung in vertical clusters on the flag poles along the Avenue of the Flags at the Fair, while 2-meter long, upright fluorescent tubes illuminated buildings at the San Francisco International Exhibition.

Technical advances improved the fluorescent lamp, especially in the area of light efficiency, commonly rated in lumens per watt. Depending on its exact shade, a perfectly efficient white source may yield 200-300 lumens per watt, while common, present-day 100 watt incandescent lamp with a normal lifetime of 750 hours of use has a light efficiency of slightly more than 17 lumens per watt. Even in 1938, the common 40-watt fluorescent lamp had an efficiency of about 45 lumens per watt. This efficiency increased to more than 57 lumens per watt by 1948 and to nearly 80 lumens per watt by the mid-1980's. All of this was accompanied by large increases in the useful life of the fluorescent lamp from about 2,000 hours in 1942 to nearly 20,000 hours in the mid-1980's.

The fluorescent lamp did have a number of drawbacks, which limited complete acceptance, and some of these persist today. One limitation is the need for a transformer ballast to operate the lamp; this has prevented any widespread use of fluorescent lamps in homes in the United States. It is much simpler to insert an incandescent lamp into a light socket than to replace a fluorescent lamp in a bulky light fixture. Another disadvantage of fluorescent lamps is their relatively poor color rendition, compared with sunlight or incandescent lamps. In comparison with the color of high pressure mercury vapor lamps and sodium vapor lamps, used for lighting highways and large areas, the color rendition of fluorescent lamps is excellent. The color of fluorescent lamps, however, is not highly uniform across the spectrum, because of the strong blue and green lines of mercury. Also, it is deficient in the red compared to the sun and, especially, to the incandescent lamp. Red colors are especially flattering to the skin tones of most people, and this severely limits the use of fluorescent lighting in the home and in mood settings outside the home.

Despite the limitations of the fluorescent lamp, the introduction of fluorescent lighting in 1936 presented a completely new form of lighting to the public with enormous advantages of high efficiency, long life, and relatively low cost. A new industry was born. It took the automobile industry fifteen years after the first cars were produced to reach $100 million in sales and the radio industry needed only five years to reach that level of sales. Yet, within three years after production of the first commercial lamps, the fluorescent lamp industry had reached that goal. Today, two-thirds of the world's lighting is supplied by fluorescent lighting.

Bibliography

Baud, John K., and Charles L. Amick. "Lighting." In *Encyclopaedia Britannica*. Vol. 14. Chicago: Encyclopedia Britannica, 1970. This is an excellent review of the history and development of modern lighting. The article tells how fluorescent lamps evolved and how they operate and places them in the overall context of lighting sources and applications.

Bova, Ben. *The Beauty of Light*. New York: John Wiley & Sons, 1988. The book gives an excellent, readable account of light, how it is seen, how it is used, and how it affects people. The book is authoritative but in simple language and with no equations. Chapter 14 discusses light sources and has some unkind, but true, words about the deficiencies of fluorescent lighting.

Elenbaas, W. *Fluorescent Lamps*. New York: Macmillan, 1959. Contains technical details about the fluorescent lamp. Elenbaas is an authority in the field and has gathered a set of articles by other experts, and himself, on all relevant areas of fluorescent lamps. Although technical in nature, the articles contain little mathematics and the few equations are simple.

Feldman, Eddy S. *The Art of Street Lighting*. Los Angeles: Dawson's Book Store, 1972. This delightful little book is "an attempt to record, before it is altogether too late, a fascinating aspect of our Los Angeles heritage"—its street lighting. With excerpts from the press and the politicians of Los Angeles, the book presents fifty-three pictures of a surviving artistry from the past light standards—street poles, still standing in 1972 but in imminent danger of extinction by replacement.

White, Harvey E. *Modern College Physics*. New York: Van Nostrand Reinhold, 1966. An introductory physics text. Light and optics are discussed in chapters 37 through 46, and chapter 45 briefly discusses light sources. All the chapters are short and there are many appealing figures, sketches, and photographs. White gives short, readable accounts of many topics. The physics are clear and simple.

Peter J. Walsh

Cross-References

Hewitt Invents the Mercury Vapor Lamp (1901), p. 108; Lamb and Retherford Discover the Lambshift (1947), p. 1293.

CERLETTI AND BINI DEVELOP ELECTROCONVULSIVE THERAPY FOR TREATING SCHIZOPHRENIA

Category of event: Medicine
Time: 1937
Locale: Münsingen, Switzerland

Cerletti and Bini were the first to introduce the idea of inducing convulsions for therapeutic purposes by using electric currents, as opposed to using convulsive drugs

Principal personages:
UGO CERLETTI (1877-1963), a professor of Neuropathology and Psychiatry at Rome University who conducted experiments on inducing seizures by means of electrical currents
LUCINO BINI (1908-   ), a brilliant clinician and Cerletti's assistant in the experiments on electroconvulsive therapy
LAZLO VON MEDUNA (1896-1964), a Hungarian psychiatrist credited with developing modern convulsive therapy

Summary of Event

The history of somatic treatment procedures in psychiatry (specifically, the use of electric currents for therapeutic purposes) has never followed a linear course of development. It is recorded that in A.D. 46 Scribonius Largus used the discharge of a torpedo fish to cure headaches and gout; the Romans used electric eels for similar purposes. In the sixteenth century, the Ethiopians applied electric catfish to mentally ill patients for the purpose of expelling "demons" from the human body. The point that all these diverse organic methods of treating mental illness have in common is that they are based on the belief that psychiatric conditions, particularly psychoses, can be influenced therapeutically by nonpsychological methods.

The invention of electroconvulsive therapy (ECT) by Ugo Cerletti and Lucino Bini in 1937 was entirely unrelated to earlier investigations on treating mental illness through the use of electric currents. The use of electroconvulsive therapy as a treatment for mental illness, rather, must be credited to the Hungarian psychiatrist Lazlo von Meduna, who first recognized the therapeutic effect of generalized seizures when he induced convulsions with pharmacologic agents.

Much of Meduna's research was in the neuropathology of schizophrenia, in a school that maintained that schizophrenia was an incurable, endogenous (originating internally), hereditary disease in which cerebral neurons were preferentially attacked. Other mental syndromes, particularly epilepsy, were considered exogenous (originating externally) in origin, and hence curable. Meduna's attempt to induce seizures in schizophrenics resulted from his hypothesis that there is a biological antagonism between the process that produces epileptic attacks and the process that produces schizophrenia. The effect of the epileptic convulsion is that it changes the chemical constituents in the organism in a way suitable for the cure of schizophrenia.

Consequently, in January of 1934, Meduna treated his first patient with intramuscular camphor in oil, causing the patient to have a seizure fifteen to twenty minutes after the injection. Meduna obtained the first remissions in schizophrenics with camphor in oil. He soon realized, however, that this technique was inconvenient because the patients convulsed only after considerable time, sometimes had more than one seizure, or did not convulse at all. He therefore replaced the camphor injections with intravenous pentylenetetrazol (Metrazol). The pharmacologic convulsive treatment with Metrazol, and some other convulsive drugs, was immediately recognized as a valuable treatment for schizophrenia and, as reported several years later, also for depression.

In 1936, Cerletti, in the Rome Clinic, adopted the Sakel method (named after its inventor, Manfred Sakel) of treating schizophrenia by means of insulin coma (insulin shock treatment). The following year, Cerletti and Bini replaced the pharmacological induction of seizures with an electric current. It was a logical sequence to Meduna's discovery. In 1870, electricity was used in animal experiments on epilepsy and it was found that electricity was the simplest way to induce seizures. Cerletti's involvement in such research was not treatment-directed but had the purpose of investigating problems of epilepsy. It was reasonable, then, that when Cerletti heard about Meduna's treatment, he wondered why electricity had not been used.

Cerletti expressed the enthusiastic opinion that "shock treatments" with insulin coma and Metrazol had changed psychiatry from a morbid science into a therapeutically active field, and he immediately developed an extensive research program to investigate electroconvulsive therapy. In his previous research on experimental epilepsy, Cerletti had induced seizures by applying the electrodes to the mouth and anus of dogs. His considerable hesitation about attempting this procedure in humans resulted from the fact that half of the dogs treated in this manner had died. It was Bini, however, who realized that death was caused by the current traveling through the heart. Consequently, when the investigators changed the location of the electrodes to the two temples of the dogs, the heart was no longer within the electric circuit, and no further animals were killed.

It was Bini who had first reported on Cerletti's studies at the First International Congress on New Treatments of Schizophrenia, in Münsingen, Switzerland, in 1937, after he heard that an electrical current was being used in a Rome slaughterhouse. Bini and Cerletti, however, delayed the clinical application of the treatment and visited the slaughterhouse, where they found that the animals were not killed by means of the electric current but were stunned only with electrodes applied to the head. The animals convulsed, and the actual killing was done before they regained consciousness. After spending two years performing experimental neuropathological studies to rule out brain damage, and finding that neither the dogs nor other animals succumbed to the electrically induced convulsions, the researchers considered it safe to proceed with the first application of electroconvulsive therapy to human beings.

The first patient was treated in April, 1938, with a very primitive machine constructed by Bini. Cerletti's understandable fear of allowing Bini to proceed with the treatment explains why, at first, a minimal amount of 80 volts for one-tenth of a second was applied. While the application of this voltage led to a short period of unconsciousness, no seizure resulted. A second stimulus of 90 volts for one-tenth of a second led to a somewhat longer "petit mal" (small seizure). After a minute, the patient awakened and began to sing a popular song. When the doctors discussed the prudence of a third stimulus, the patient unemotionally uttered something about dying, but did not object to a third, stronger application, which led to a generalized seizure. The patient, a completely incoherent schizophrenic, who had not been able to give his physicians any information about himself, received a total of nine treatments. During the two-year period of follow-up treatments, he was leading a normal life and maintained a job as a skilled worker.

After clinical application of electroconvulsive therapy had begun, Cerletti organized a detailed research program, giving assignments to the different members of his staff. The findings of this program were published (in Italian) in a monograph by Cerletti and Bini in 1942. In it they answered many important questions concerning the procedure, but the monograph remained unknown in American psychiatric literature. Later, Cerletti gave two English accounts of his work, in 1950 and 1956. These accounts, however, were partly distorted by Cerletti's belief that the injection of brain substance of electroshocked animals into psychiatric patients would eliminate the need for convulsions. He assumed that repeated seizures in animals produced a substance in the brain, which he called "acroagonine." Cerletti found that injections of such brain substances also increased the resistance of animals to certain infections. On psychotics, some improvement in affect (emotion) and anxiety was seen, but overall the results of this indirect method to reproduce the therapeutic effect of electroconvulsive therapy remained unsatisfactory.

Cerletti continued his research attempts to improve the electroconvulsive treatment techniques and to understand exactly how the treatment worked. He determined that the cerebral seizure was essential to the clinical results, while neither the currents used to elicit a seizure nor the motor aspects of the convulsion were significant. Anticipating some of the later interest in the hormonal effects of seizures, in 1956 Cerletti suggested that part of the vegetative syndrome induced by electroshock was localized in the diencephalic section of the cerebrospinal axis. Unfortunately, Cerletti never determined electroconvulsive therapy's exact mode of action.

Impact of Event

The discovery of electroconvulsive therapy had an immediate impact on the psychiatric community. In the late 1930's and early 1940's, the new therapy demonstrated by Cerletti and Bini largely replaced pharmacologic convulsive treatment. Moreover, following initial reports of the value of convulsive therapy in the treatment of affective disorders as well as schizophrenia, electroconvulsive therapy became the most widely used organic therapy in psychiatry during the years immediately preceding and following World War II. Interest in the convulsive therapies increased with the demands of war. Many physicians were trained in clinical psychiatry by the military, and the convulsive therapies were a significant part of their education as well as their military clinical experience. When patients failed to respond to one therapy, insulin coma and seizure therapy were combined. Some physicians increased the number and frequency of seizure inductions and found positive results—particularly in schizophrenia—to be related to number and frequency of seizures.

Electroconvulsive therapy, however, soon began to have a negative impact on some members of the psychiatric community. As the side effects of shock therapy as well as prefrontal lobotomy (another organic treatment discovered at about the same time as shock therapy and largely used to treat the same disorders) came to be more and more recognized, many maintained that the cure did more harm than the disease. By 1946, accusations of random and/or indiscriminate use of these techniques on patients (to deal with anything from homosexuality to psoriasis) questioned the effectiveness of these organic methods. At that time, the American Group for the Advancement of Psychiatry issued a statement declaring that widespread and dangerous abuses in the use of electroconvulsive therapy justified a campaign of professional education in the limitations of the technique and the institution of certain measures of control. In 1978, a Task Force of the American Psychiatric Association published a report of their findings on electroconvulsive therapy's current effectiveness.

By the 1950's, psychotropic drugs had all but replaced electroconvulsive therapy in the treatment of schizophrenia. The efficacy of tricyclic antidepressant drugs, the monamine oxidase inhibitors, stimulants, and lithium in depressive and manic disorders further reduced the interest in and use of electroconvulsive therapy. Consequently, many electroconvulsive therapy facilities were closed, and it was only in the mid-1960's, as the limitations of the antidepressant drug therapies were recognized, that interest in electroconvulsive therapy was rekindled.

Once again, however, a gradual decline in the use of the convulsive therapies occurred, although some scientists continued their studies in reduced numbers. Much research was devoted to understanding the seizure process and improving its safety. The usefulness of intensive treatments in severely ill schizophrenics was reexamined, with those receiving intensive treatments exhibiting better follow-up results in residual symptoms, work records, and rehospitalization rates than those treated with pharmacotherapy alone.

Whereas insulin coma has been virtually abandoned, electroconvulsive therapies continue to be used. Nevertheless, growing concern that electroconvulsive therapy may cause irreparable damage to the brain and that its use may contravene or deny patients' rights to decide knowingly what is done to them, led to judicial and legislative challenges to its use, as exemplified by the virtual ban on its use in California in 1974. Similar concerns voiced in England, Scandinavia, and Holland resulted in additional evaluations.

Ultimately, with improved equipment and techniques of treatment, clarification of the indications, and better education, the incidence of adverse reaction is declining.

Moreover, some researchers still believe that the legacy of this once experimental psychiatric treatment may eventually lead to a better understanding of brain function and behavior.

Bibliography

Abrams, Richard, and Walter B. Essman, eds. *Electroconvulsive Therapy.* New York: SP Medical and Scientific Books, 1982. This 280-page book is a standard reference work on the subject. It covers the biological foundations and clinical applications of the procedure, reflecting state-of-the-art technology. Included is an informative chapter of the history of convulsive therapy from ancient times to the present. The work of Cerletti and Bini is highlighted. Also contains a bibliography.

Breggin, Peter R. *Electroshock: Its Brain-Disabling Effects.* New York: Springer, 1979. This informative work describing the adverse effects of electroconvulsive therapy (including brain damage) is written in a style accessible to the layperson as well as the clinician. It performs a useful function of educating the reader about the uses and potential abuses of this form of therapy.

Cerletti, Ugo. "Old and New Information About Electroshock." *American Journal of Psychiatry* 107 (1950): 87-94. In this article by one of the coinventors of electroshock therapy, the author gives first a history of the origin of this practice, next offers a firsthand account of the invention, and finally discusses the first ten years of its application.

Fink, Max. *Convulsive Therapy: Theory and Practice.* New York: Raven Press, 1979. This work describes the use and efficacy of pharmacologic as well as electroconvulsive therapies in the treatment of psychiatric disorders. Aside from containing an extensive and comprehensive bibliography, the book also includes a brief but valuable history of electroconvulsive therapy.

Kalinowsky, Lothar, and Paul H. Hoch. *Shock Treatments, Psychosurgery, and Other Somatic Treatments in Psychiatry.* 2d ed. New York: Grune & Stratton, 1952. In this lengthy but rather dated work devoted to the organic treatment of psychiatric disorders, the authors include a useful chapter on the historical development of treatment procedures. Much information on Cerletti and Bini's discovery is provided.

Genevieve Slomski

Cross-References

Berger Develops the Electroencephalogram (EEG) (1929), p. 890; Moniz Develops Prefrontal Lobotomy (1935), p. 1060; Sperry Discovers That Each Side of the Brain Can Function Independently (1960's), p. 1635; Janowsky Publishes a Cholinergic-Adrenergic Hypothesis of Mania and Depression (1972), p. 1976.

THEILER INTRODUCES A VACCINE
AGAINST YELLOW FEVER

Category of event: Medicine
Time: 1937
Locale: New York

Theiler introduced the 17D vaccine for yellow fever, which was one of the deadliest epidemics during the nineteenth and the twentieth centuries

Principal personages:
MAX THEILER (1899-1972), a South African microbiologist and specialist in tropical medicine who was a researcher at the Rockefeller Institute and a Nobel Prize laureate in Physiology or Medicine in 1951
WILBUR AUGUSTUS SAWYER (1879-1951), an American physician who was the first director of the yellow fever laboratory at the Rockefeller Institute and recruited Theiler to work at the laboratory
HUGH SMITH (1902-   ), an American physician who was Theiler's assistant at the yellow fever laboratory

Summary of Event

In the early years of the twentieth century, yellow fever, which had been supposed to be endemic to the jungles of South and Central America, was spreading around the world wherever the mosquito *Aëdes aegypti* could carry the virus. Mosquito larvae traveled well in casks of water aboard trading vessels and spread the disease to North America and Europe. Yellow fever caused by a virus, transmitted by mosquitoes, infects humans and monkeys. The virus is transmitted in two distinct ways; urban yellow fever is transmitted among humans by the mosquito *Aëdes aegypti*, while jungle yellow fever is transmitted from monkeys to humans by a number of different mosquitoes living in the tropical forest canopy. After the bite of the infecting mosquito, there is an incubation period of several days. The onset of symptoms is abrupt, with headache, nausea, and vomiting. Because the virus destroys liver cells, yellowing of the skin and eyes is common. Approximately 10 percent to 15 percent of patients die after exhibiting terrifying signs and symptoms. Death occurs usually from liver necrosis and liver shutdown. Those that survive recover completely and are immunized. At the beginning of the twentieth century, there was no cure for yellow fever. The best that medical authorities could do was to quarantine the afflicted. Those quarantines usually waved the warning yellow flag, which gave the disease its colloquial name—yellow jack.

After the *Aëdes aegypti* mosquito was clearly identified as the carrier of the disease in 1900, efforts were made to combat the disease by eradicating the mosquito. Most famous in these efforts were Walter Reed and the Cuban physician Carlos J. Finlay. This strategy was successful in Panama and Cuba and made possible the construction of the Panama Canal. Still, the yellow fever virus continued to be endemic to the tropics, and the opening of the Panama Canal increased the danger of its spreading onboard the ships using this new route.

Max Theiler, who was born and grew up in South Africa, traveled to London in 1919 to enter medical school. When his premedical education in South Africa was not recognized by the University of London, he enrolled in the four-year teaching program of St. Thomas Hospital. After being confronted with the frustrating inability of the medical field of that time to cure a wide array of serious illnesses, he decided to enter the field of laboratory medicine. He completed a four-month course at the London School of Hygiene and Tropical Medicine, where he was invited to come to the United States and work with Andrew Watson Sellards in the department of tropical medicine at Harvard University. Under the direction of Sellards, Theiler started working on the identification of the yellow fever organism. The first problem he faced was finding a suitable laboratory animal that could be infected with yellow fever. Until that time, the only animal successfully infected with yellow fever was the rhesus monkey, which was expensive and difficult to maintain under laboratory conditions. Theiler succeeded in infecting laboratory mice with the disease by injecting the virus directly into their brains.

Laboratory work for investigators and assistants coming in contact with the yellow fever virus was extremely dangerous. At least six of the scientists at the yellow fever laboratory at the Rockefeller Institute died of the disease and many other workers were infected. In 1929, Theiler was infected with yellow fever; fortunately, the attack was so mild that he recovered quickly and resumed his work.

Theiler drew enough virus from a monkey that had died of yellow fever to infect one mouse, then pass it on to another and a third; all of them died of encephalitis. The virus from the third mouse was then used to infect a monkey. Although the animal showed signs of yellow fever, it recovered completely. When Theiler passed the virus through more mice and then into the abdomen of another monkey, it showed no symptoms of the disease. The results of these experiments were published by Theiler in the journal *Science* and drew sharp criticism from Sellards, who still pursued the theory of a bacterial origin of yellow fever. This article caught the attention of Wilbur Augustus Sawyer, director of the Yellow Fever Laboratory at the Rockefeller Foundation International Health Division in New York. Sawyer, who was working on a yellow fever vaccine, offered Theiler a job at the Rockefeller Foundation, which Theiler accepted. Theiler's mouse-adapted, "attenuated" virus was given to the laboratory workers, along with human immune serum, to protect them against the yellow fever virus. This type of vaccination, however, carried the risk of transferring other diseases, such as hepatitis, in the human serum.

In 1930, Theiler worked with Eugen Haagen, a German bacteriologist, at the Rockefeller Foundation. Together, they succeeded in culturing yellow fever virus in chick embryo cells, which made possible an unlimited supply for experimentation. The strategy of the Rockefeller laboratory was a cautious, slow, and steady effort to culture a strain of the virus so mild it could do no damage to a human but strong enough to confer a long-lasting immunity. They started with a new strain of yellow fever harvested from a twenty-eight-year-old West African named Asibi, later known as the Asibi strain. It was a highly virulent strain that proved fatal to 95 percent of monkeys that were infected with it in four to seven days. Culturing the Asibi virus proved to be a problem. It would not grow in the first sixteen different cultures tried. The seventeenth culture made of minced mouse embryos was successful. This culture was subcultured every five days to avoid contamination. From time to time, Theiler or his assistant would test the culture on a monkey and note the speed with which it was killed.

The actual turning point in the laborious process passed unnoticed in 1935. It was not until April, 1936, that Hugh Smith, Theiler's assistant, called to his attention an odd development as noted in the laboratory records of strain 17D. In its 176th culture, 17D failed to kill the test mice. Some were paralyzed, but even those recovered nicely. Two monkeys who received a dose of 17D in their brains survived a mild attack of encephalitis, and those who took the infection in the abdomen showed no ill effects whatever. Oddly, subsequent subcultures of the strain went on killing monkeys and mice at the usual rate. When Theiler and Smith retraced the cultures, they found that the change from lethal to benign had occurred somewhere between the 89th and 114th cultures of 17D. The only explanation possible was that a mutation had occurred unnoticed.

The batch of strain 17D was tried over and over again on monkeys, with no harmful symptoms and resulting in immunizing the animals effectively. Then, it was tried on the laboratory staff, including Theiler and his wife Lillian. The batch performed in humans had the same immunizing effect. Neither Theiler nor anyone else could explain how the mutation of the virus had resulted. Attempts to duplicate the experiment, using the same Asibi virus, have failed. Still, this was the first safe vaccine for yellow fever. In June, 1937, Theiler reported this crucial finding in the *Journal of Experimental Medicine*.

Impact of Event

Following the discovery of the vaccine, Theiler's laboratory became a production plant for 17D virus. It was cultured in chicken eggs. Before World War II, some 1.3 million vaccination doses were sent to Brazil and other South American countries. After the United States entered the war, 8 million servicemen were given the vaccine before they were shipped to tropical war zones. In all, approximately 50 million people were vaccinated in the war years.

Scientific interest in yellow fever declined sharply following the discovery of the vaccine and was not renewed until the early 1980's. As a result, little progress was made in understanding the physiology and pathology of the disease. The focus of scientific interest in the 1980's was on diagnosis, care, and management of patients. Still, no specific treatment for yellow fever was found and treatment efforts focused primarily on fever reduction.

Although the vaccine, combined with effective mosquito control, eradicated the disease from urban centers, yellow fever is still endemic in the area between 10 degrees north latitude and 40 degrees south latitude in the Americas. Urban transmission has not occurred since 1942. About one hundred cases of jungle yellow fever occur annually in Bolivia, Brazil, Colombia, and Peru. Periodically, the disease reaches other countries in South and Central America. In Africa, the endemic zone lies between 16 degrees north latitude and 10 degrees south latitude. Several severe epidemics occurred in East Africa since the discovery of the vaccine. About forty thousand people were infected in Sudan in 1940, fifteen hundred of whom died. The most severe outbreak of yellow fever ever known occurred from 1960 to 1962 in Ethiopia; 100,000 people were infected and 30,000 died. Severe outbreaks of yellow fever continued in the 1980's in Ghana, Burkina Faso, and Nigeria; thousands died in these epidemics.

It has been known since 1930 that the yellow fever virus is identical in the Americas and in Africa. Nevertheless, modern techniques have shown clear differences at the molecular level. Development of new laboratory techniques also enables serological diagnosis of yellow fever in a few hours in the field.

The 17D yellow fever vaccine prepared by Max Theiler in 1937 continues to be the only vaccine in use by the World Health Organization more than fifty years after its discovery. The way in which the vaccine was prepared changed very little during those years. There is a continuous effort by the World Health Organization to immunize preventively people living in endemic zones.

Bibliography

Bendinger, Elmer. "Max Theiler: Yellow Jack and the Jackpot." *Hospital Practice*, June 15, 1988, 211-244. An excellent article on the life story of Max Theiler. Opens with Theiler's childhood in South Africa, where he began his fascination with biology, and continues through his brilliant scientific career.

Bres, P. L. J. "A Century of Progress in Combating Yellow Fever." *Bulletin of the World Health Organization* 64 (December, 1986): 775-786. Most of this article surveys the epidemiological situation of yellow fever in the fifty years that followed the discovery of the vaccine. Discusses the major scientific advancements in the study of the virus and the disease. Contains a short description of the history of the yellow fever epidemics and the research on yellow fever.

Hill, Ralph Nading. *The Doctors Who Conquered Yellow Fever.* New York: Random House, 1957. Depicts the story of the fight against yellow fever through the life story of Walter Reed. It also includes a brief description of the developments in the fight against the disease following Reed's death up to the discovery of the 17D vaccine by Theiler.

Strode, George K., ed. *Yellow Fever.* New York: McGraw-Hill, 1951. The most authoritative book on yellow fever. Chapters were written by the foremost experts in the field, including a chapter by Max Theiler on the virus. Covers topics such as the history of the fight against yellow fever, the vaccine against the disease, the cost of this fight, and related topics.

Williams, Greer. *Virus Hunters.* New York: Alfred A. Knopf, 1959. Discusses the development of a vaccine against yellow fever. Chapter 15 "Theiler: Yellow Fever's Second Exit" describes Theiler's work. Annotated bibliography.

Gershon B. Grunfeld

Cross-References

Reed Establishes That Yellow Fever Is Transmitted by Mosquitoes (1900), p. 73; Gorgas Develops Effective Methods for Controlling Mosquitoes (1904), p. 223; Calmette and Guérin Develop the Tuberculosis Vaccine BCG (1921), p. 705; Zinsser Develops an Immunization Against Typhus (1930), p. 921; Salk Develops a Polio Vaccine (1952), p. 1444; Sabin Develops an Oral Polio Vaccine (1957), p. 1522; A Vaccine Is Developed for German Measles (1960), p. 1655; A Genetically Engineered Vaccine for Hepatitis B Is Approved for Use (1986), p. 2326.

WEIDENREICH RECONSTRUCTS THE FACE OF PEKING MAN

Category of event: Anthropology
Time: Fall, 1937-Winter, 1938
Locale: Peking and Chou-K'ou-tien, China

Weidenreich reconstructed the face of the oldest known hominid, clarifying the path of human evolution and providing the first glimpse of Peking man

Principal personages:
> FRANZ WEIDENREICH (1873-1948), a German anatomist, physical anthropologist, paleoanthropologist, and Director of the Cenozoic Research Laboratory in Peking (now Beijing) from 1934 to 1941
> DAVIDSON BLACK (1884-1934), a Canadian physician, anatomist, and paleoanthropologist who was the first to identify Peking man
> PIERRE TEILHARD DE CHARDIN (1881-1955), a French Jesuit, philosopher, archaeologist, and paleontologist who excavated the Peking man site of Chou-K'ou-tien (now Zhoukoudian)
> WENG CHUNG PEI (1904-   ), a Chinese archaeologist who worked with Black and Weidenreich and who found the first Peking man skull in 1929
> JOHAN GUNNAR ANDERSSON (1874-1960), a Swedish geologist and paleoanthropologist who discovered the site at Zhoukoudian

Summary of Event

As early as 1900, Western scientists knew that China was an ideal place to look for fossil humans. Western visitors had discovered isolated humanlike teeth in Chinese drugstores, where they were called "dragon's teeth" and sold as medicine. In 1918, the Swedish geologist Johan Gunnar Andersson discovered a major deposit of Pleistocene fossils in a cave outside the village of Zhoukoudian, located near Beijing. These fossils appeared to be about 500,000 years old. Looking for fossil mammals and hoping for fossil humans, Andersson began excavating the site in 1921. Shortly thereafter, Davidson Black, a professor of anatomy at the Peking Medical Union, persuaded the Rockefeller Foundation to establish the Cenozoic Research Laboratory in Beijing. It became the center for excavations at Zhoukoudian and for the analysis of material found at that site.

Based on isolated teeth, Black formally identified Peking man in 1927, calling him *Sinanthropus pekinensis*. In 1929, the Chinese archaeologist Weng Chung Pei discovered the first nearly complete skull cap of a *Sinanthropus pekinensis*, providing the first real evidence that early man existed in China. This discovery seemed to confirm Black's belief that humanity's ancestor was to be found in the Far East. Furthermore, stone tools, burned animal bones, and animal bones with clear-cut marks were found in association with the skull cap, giving definite evidence of culture. When Black died of a heart attack in 1934, he was succeeded by Franz Weidenreich, who had been firmly established in Germany as an anatomist and physical anthropologist. Already renowned for his work in hematology and osteology, in 1928 he had written the definitive account of a Neanderthal-like skull found at Weimar-Ehringsdorf, Germany. In Beijing, he cooperated with the archaeologists who were actively involved in excavations such as Pei and Pierre Teilhard de Chardin. Weidenreich supervised the extraction of the bones from their rocky matrices, directed the scientific drawing of the fossils, and wrote reports of findings.

Although many human fossils had been found at Zhoukoudian by 1937, nearly all were damaged skull caps. The skull below the level of the ears was frequently destroyed, as were most facial bones. Bones from the lower skeleton were rare, but those that had been found were broken in a way that implied extraction of marrow. It has generally been assumed that Peking man had been the agent of this destruction and that he had been removing and eating brains and bone marrow. With the advent of the study of taphonomy—the natural conditions affecting preservation of human activities—it has been recognized that fossils as old as Peking man are frequently crushed and that the thinnest part of the bone in Peking man's skull was below the ears. Consequently, it is possible that the damage to these bones may have been caused by natural agencies. Nevertheless, it was impossible for modern scholars to reconstruct his face. They knew that he had a massive ridge of bone above his eyes, little or no forehead, his skull was long and low, and his brain was somewhat more than twice the size of a modern chimpanzee, but the scarcity of facial bones meant that they did not know what he looked like.

This knowledge was pieced together after the end of Fall, 1937. This was to be the last season at Zhoukoudian before the Japanese invasion put an end to fieldwork. Three fairly well-preserved skulls, all adults, were found in the same location. None of these individuals had complete faces. Nevertheless, enough of the three faces had survived that it was possible to reconstruct the appearance of Peking man.

Actually, it was a Peking woman who was reconstructed. One of the skulls, a female's, included a large fragment of the upper jaw. This was the important piece needed to fill in the picture of the *Sinanthropus* face. Only the nasal bones, a portion of the front of the upper jaw, the cheekbones, and part of the area around the eyes needed to be adapted from other individuals. The lower jaw was adapted from the lower jaw of a female found in 1936. Weidenreich was satisfied that his reconstruction was correct, since the entire reconstruction was based on real bones and had no imaginary details. According to Weidenreich's reconstruction, the face of Peking woman was heavy and large. Her eye sockets were larger than those of modern humans, and her eyes were set wide apart. Her nose was low and wide, but within the range of variation in modern humans. Her face was wide and jutted forward slightly. She had the usual *Sinanthropus* chin and forehead and the usual heavy brow ridge over her eyes and nose. Her head was small in comparison to modern humans but is larger than any ape's. Her skull was widest above the ears and then sloped upward and inward, and she had a slight ridge running from front to rear along the top of her head. She had a bony ridge at the back of her head, set slightly above a very thick neck. Despite these characteristics, she undeniably represents an ancestress of modern human beings.

Weidenreich left China in 1941, barely escaping incarceration in a Japanese prison camp. He had attempted to send the Peking man fossils out of China with the help of the United States Army. The bones of forty individuals—men, women, and children—from an important stage of human evolution were packed in footlockers and sent to the coast with American soldiers to be delivered to the S. S. *President Harrison* at the port of Zhingwangdao. Unfortunately, they disappeared after they left Beijing. It is not known whether they were stolen, lost, or destroyed by Japanese soldiers. Weidenreich and others attempted to locate the fossils after World War II, but to no avail. Although there were a number of mysterious stories about their whereabouts, the Peking fossils were never found. The disaster of this loss has been partly compensated for by the excellent casts, photographs, and drawings made by laboratory technicians in China. That is all that is left of the major finds from Zhoukoudian. In recent years, archaeologists in China have continued the search for Peking man. No further fossils of Peking man have been found at Zhoukoudian, but they have been found elsewhere in China. It is regrettable that the bones so carefully studied by Weidenreich and others are no longer available for further research. New and sophisticated methods of analysis could have been used to extract further secrets from them, and it is unlikely that such a large population of early man will ever be found again.

Impact of Event

At the time that Weidenreich made his reconstruction, Peking man, together with his cousin, Java man, was the earliest accepted ancestor of modern people. Neanderthals and related types from Europe and the Middle East were far too recent and far too similar to modern man to qualify as early ancestors. Although the Australopithecines had been discovered in South Africa as early as 1924, they were not accepted as being on the human line of evolution until the 1950's. At the time of the great discoveries of Peking man, an acrimonious debate was percolating over whether the Australopithecines were large apes or early hominids. The discoveries from Zhoukoudian excited the world, because Peking man and his Javanese cousins stood alone as man's undisputed ancestors. In a certain sense, they still stand alone. In later years, Peking man, Java man, and other related types later found in Africa and Europe have been reclassified as *Homo erectus*, thought to have lived between 1 million years ago and about 150,000 years ago. They are the first members of the genus *Homo* and the immediate forerunners of our species, *Homo sapiens*. They were the first to use fire, first to have habitations, first to use stone tools with a definite style, and first to inhabit the temperate regions of Europe and Asia; they are indisputably human. Furthermore, the fossils found at Zhoukoudian remain unique in the annals of human prehistory. Although *Homo erectus* has been found elsewhere, his remains usually consist of fragmentary and isolated finds that often have been removed by natural processes from where they died. Nowhere else have so many individuals been found that are more or less contemporaneous and who died on the spot, surrounded by their tools, their hearths, and their garbage. As a result, the fossils from Zhoukoudian can tell us what the range of variation was for this species; their relatively *in situ* position tells much about how they lived and what they ate. They are fundamental in defining the species *Homo erectus*, and they are unique pieces in the puzzle of human evolution.

Bibliography

Brace, C. Loring. *The Stages of Human Evolution: Human and Cultural Origins*. 2d ed. Englewood Cliffs, N.J.: Prentice-Hall, 1988. A well-written general account of human evolution that also contains a short history of evolutionary thought, together with descriptions of the discovery of important human fossils and the controversies that frequently ensued. Illustrated, with a bibliography and an index.

Howells, W. W. "*Homo erectus* in Human Descent: Ideas and Problems." In Homo erectus: *Papers in Honor of Davidson Black*, edited by Becky A. Sigmon and Jerome S. Cybulski. Toronto: University of Toronto Press, 1981. A clear and succinct summary of current scientific thought regarding Peking man's position in human evolution. Somewhat technical, but indispensable for an understanding of the current status of *Homo erectus*. Illustrations, a map of fossil hominid sites, and an excellent bibliography.

Koenigswald, Gustav Heinrich Ralph von. *Meeting Prehistoric Man*. Translated by Michael Bullock. New York: Harper & Brothers, 1956. Koenigswald, who worked in Java and later at the American Museum of Natural History, was a close associate of Weidenreich. Although now outdated scientifically, Koenigswald's enjoyable discussion of "dragon's bones" and of the exhilaration of the early finds in Java and China remains of interest. Illustrations.

Shapiro, Harry L. *Peking Man: The Discovery, Disappearance, and Mystery of a Priceless Scientific Treasure*. New York: Simon & Schuster, 1974. Shapiro, associated with the American Museum of Natural History for more than fifty years, knew Weidenreich well. His book combines good scholarship with exciting narrative. Illustrated, with charts of geological time and of Peking man's place on the evolutionary tree.

Weidenreich, Franz. "The Face of Peking Woman: Latest Developments Regarding our Celebrated Ape-Like Relative." *Natural History* 41 (May, 1938): 358-360. A description of the reconstructed face written for the general public, this article introduced Peking woman to the world. The satisfaction that Weidenreich felt regarding his reconstruction is depicted in this short article. Excellent illustrations, with bibliography.

Lucy Jayne Botscharow

Cross-References

Boule Reconstructs the First Neanderthal Skeleton (1908), p. 428; Zdansky Discovers Peking Man (1923), p. 761; Dart Discovers the First Recognized Australopithecine Fossil (1924), p. 780; Leakey Finds a 1.75-Million-Year-Old Fossil Hominid (1959), p. 1603; Simons Identifies a 30-Million-Year-Old Primate Skull (1966), p. 1814; Anthropologists Discover "Lucy," an Early Hominid Skeleton (1974), p. 2037; Sibley and Ahlquist Discover a Close Human and Chimpanzee Genetic Relationship (1984), p. 2267; Hominid Fossils Are Gathered in the Same Place for Concentrated Study (1984), p. 2279; Scientists Date a *Homo sapiens* Fossil at Ninety-two Thousand Years (1987), p. 2341.

SEGRÈ IDENTIFIES THE FIRST ARTIFICIAL ELEMENT, TECHNETIUM

Category of event: Physics
Time: January-September, 1937
Locale: Palermo, Italy

Segrè positively identified and characterized the first human-made chemical element, technetium, atomic number 43

Principal personages:

EMILIO GINO SEGRÈ (1905-1989), a physicist who identified three chemical elements and was the cowinner of the 1959 Nobel Prize in Physics for the discovery of the antiproton

ENRICO FERMI (1901-1954), a physicist who prepared radioisotopes of elements by neutron bombardment and received the 1938 Nobel Prize in Physics for preparing new radioactive elements

ERNEST ORLANDO LAWRENCE (1901-1958), a physicist who invented the cyclotron for the study of artificial radioactivity and was awarded the 1939 Nobel Prize in Physics

ROBERT LISLE WATTERS (1925-   ), a health physicist who studied the role of various radionuclides in health and the environment

Summary of Event

The periodic table of chemical elements is an ordered array of the elements positioned to reflect the similarities and trends among the different discrete substances that compose matter. When originated in the mid-1800's, controversy arose regarding placement of the limited number of chemical elements known at that time. The Russian chemist Dmitry Ivanovich Mendeleev is credited with the foresight to leave voids within the framework of his representation of the periodic table predicting that as yet undiscovered elements would fill these voids. In the years following his predictions, the majority of these missing elements were discovered and properly placed within the framework of the modern periodic table, with some notable exceptions. Even after a more thorough understanding of atomic structure, as developed in the early 1900's, and with the work of Henry G. J. Moseley, who utilized X-ray spectral data to ascertain the atomic numbers of the elements available to him—thus providing experimental support to the periodic array previously based solely upon similarities of chemical and physical properties and trends—voids remained. The periodic table is arranged in order of increasing atomic number, that is, the number of protons within the nucleus of each atom of an element.

There were no reports of discovery in the scientific literature on the isolation and identification of elements with atomic numbers 43, 61, and 85. The search for these elements among the rocks and minerals of the world was intense. Searching was not altogether random. The element 43 in particular, because of its reserved location in the framework of the periodic table, would have properties similar to those of manganese. Mendeleev had tentatively named the element ekamanganese and predicted some of its chemical and physical properties. Scientists concentrated their search upon ores and minerals known to contain those elements whose chemical behavior would be close to that of the missing element. Several claims were made for the discovery of element atomic number 43 (later to be named technetium). The earliest of these was in 1887. All claims, however, were subsequently proved false until 1925, when Walter Noddack, Ida Tacke, and Otto Berg, based upon unobserved X-ray spectral lines, reported a new element identified as atomic number 43. Each chemical element emits, under proper experimental treatment, X rays uniquely characteristic of that element. The emissions of known elements had been studied thoroughly and their wavelengths and relative intensities tabulated. Given, for example, an unknown substance, one could generate the X-ray spectrum of the sample, match it to the tabulated values, and identify its composition. Recognition of a previously unreported X-ray spectrum warranted the claim that a new element had been discovered. Following their initial claim of discovery, in which they named their element masurium, they attempted to isolate a pure sample of the element from the mineral columbite, the source material of their newly defined X-ray spectrum. Because they were unable to do this and without a pure sample to support their claim, their discovery was rejected.

During the period when the search for the natural occurrence of atomic number 43 was taking place, another seemingly unrelated series of scientific investigations was under way. Natural radioactivity had been observed first at the beginning of the twentieth century. Certain naturally occurring substances sent out emissions spontaneously; that is, they were radioactive. Notable among these was uranium. The study of radioactivity, the identification of radioactive emissions (now recognized as coming from the nucleus of the emitting atom), and potential implications of this phenomenon for humanity were beginning to be recognized. Among the early pioneers in the study of radioactivity and the structure of that atom was Enrico Fermi, an Italian physicist. Fermi received the Nobel Prize in Physics in 1938 for his work on the production of artificially produced radioactive elements. Upon bombardment of a stable chemical element with nuclear particles, frequently new and often unstable isotopes are formed. Artificial radioisotopes are of enormous interest not only for the information they provide regarding the structure of matter but also for their practical applications in industry, medicine, and other areas.

Emilio Gino Segrè was the first of many graduate students to receive his Ph.D. degree in physics under the guidance of Dr. Fermi. He later received the 1959 Nobel Prize in Physics with coworker Owen Chamberlain for their discovery of the subatomic particle, the antiproton. Segrè collaborated with Fermi on several studies pertaining to the interactions of particles with matter. These studies provided him with considerable insight into various nuclear processes. While serving as director of the physics laboratory at the University of Palermo, Italy, he received a sample of irradiated molybdenum sent to him by Ernest Orlando Lawrence. Lawrence had developed the cyclotron, a huge device weighing hundreds of tons and costing millions of dollars. The cyclotron is capable of propelling nuclear particles to great energies. When these high-energy particles strike a target, they interact with the target material, producing artificial radioactive isotopes. Study of these isotopes and their decay contributed greatly to the understanding of matter and to the applications of radioisotopes for both peacetime and military use. The Lawrence Radiation Laboratory at the University of California at Berkeley was and remains today a leading center for the study of nuclear processes.

In December, 1939, Lawrence sent Segrè the molybdenum metal sample that had been bombarded by deuterium nuclei for several months in the cyclotron. Segrè and his research group undertook to study the effects of this bombardment and to isolate and identify the artificial radioisotopes produced. Separation of radioisotopes by chemical means—the only means available in 1937—was not an easy task. The transmuted products are many and are themselves undergoing radioactive decay forming further substances. Often, the quantity of each transmuted element is negligibly small, too small to be weighed by ordinary means. The presence of these products is generally ascertained indirectly by measuring their characteristic radio or X-ray emissions. Because these emissions are frequently very similar, prior chemical separations are mandatory if one is to say with certainty that a particular radionuclide is present. The slightest contamination of one component by another as complete chemical separation is seldom if ever achieved; it clouds the observed emissions.

It had been predicted from theoretical considerations that technetium could be one of the radioactive products formed from bombardment of molybdenum with deuterons. Segrè and his group were prepared to observe among the several predicted products (including isotopes of zirconium, niobium, and molybdenum) previously unreported emissions that might be attributed to technetium. Following lengthy chemical separations involving fusion, precipitation, filtration, and volatilization, an emission activity was observed that could not be assigned to any known element. This activity was attributed to atomic number 43 and results were first reported in September, 1937 (C. Perrier and E. Segrè, *Journal of Chemical Physics*, 1937). A series of papers by Segrè and his associates followed this initial notice and further characterized technetium by identifying several of its isotopes and studying its chemical and radiochemical properties. In 1947, Segrè reported formation of technetium from uranium fission rather than bombardment of molybdenum. The first significant quantity of the element, gram amounts, was prepared by others in 1952 from uranium fission products. Because of the availability of fissionable uranium from nuclear reactors, it is this source from which technetium is now prepared in commercially available quantities. The radiochemical data of Segrè's group could not be disputed, and the name technetium (symbol Tc) was given atomic number 43.

Scientists ask whether or not technetium occurs naturally. The half-life of the longest technetium isotope, Tc-97 is 2.6×10^6 years. Half-life refers to the time interval for one-half of any newly formed radioactive substance to decompose by emission of radioactive particles or rays. In the second half-life interval, half of the remaining amount decomposes. It is estimated that radioisotopes with half-lives of less than 1.5×10^8 years would be virtually undetectable considering the time interval between the present and when the earth was formed. Because of natural radioactive fission of uranium from interaction with cosmic radiation, however, it is suggested that some, albeit a small amount of, Tc can be found naturally. Pieter H. M. Van Assche (*Nuclear Physics*, 1988) estimates this amount to be on the order of 10^{-13} gram per gram of uranium ore and that this amount was sufficient to produce the X-ray emissions reported by Noddack, Tacke, and Berg in 1925.

Impact of Event

With the identification of technetium and later astatine by Segrè and coworkers, the missing gaps in the periodic table of the elements were filled. Although some questioned whether human-made elements should be recognized as true chemical forms, their complaints were quickly dispelled; credit for the discovery of technetium was given to Segrè and his research group. As with other radionuclides—both natural and artificial—studies of their properties have enhanced the understanding of matter and its composition and decomposition. Technetium, through its spectral emissions, has been identified on distant stars. Because of the known half-lives of the various technetium isotopes, these data provide evidence regarding the time origin and composition of these stars.

Elemental technetium alone and in various alloys exhibits the property of superconductivity; that is, it passes an electric current with negligible resistance. As with all superconducting materials, this property is exhibited only at temperatures approaching absolute zero, yet as developments in this field advance, technetium may find a role in the manufacture of superconducting magnets.

The greatest use of technetium is in the field of medicine as a radiochemical tracer. "A wide variety of tissues can be visualized with ^{99m}Tc radiopharmaceuticals, including the kidneys, bones, lungs, heart, liver, brain, and thyroid. Although other radionuclides are used in nuclear medicine, of the millions of diagnostic imaging procedures conducted each year, over 80% involve the use of ^{99m}Tc." (Thomas C. Pinkerton, Carla P. Desilets, Daniel J. Hoch, Martin V. Mikelsons, and George M. Wilson, *Journal of Chemical Education*, 1985). The metastable technetium isotope ^{99m}Tc emits a 0.143 million electronvolt gamma radiation with a half-life of 6.0 hours transforming itself into the more stable ^{99}Tc isotope. Combining ^{99m}Tc into compounds uniquely essential for various body organs and functions allows one (by monitoring the emitted gamma radiation) to determine the extent and duration necessary for incorporating these compounds into various bodily functions. If in monitoring this incorporation, one finds deviation from the expected normal body utilization of these materials, an abnormality is indicated and appropriate medical treatment can be started. Because of its short half-life, the ^{99m}Tc-containing compound rapidly loses its radioactivity, causing little if any long-term damage to the patient.

Technetium, with its numerous chemical oxidation states, forms a variety of chemical compounds, in particular those incorporating organic molecules similar to or identical to those found in body organs. Technetium is taken up easily in these organs and suited for a specific organ whose normal function is suspect. Studies on other animal species and on various plant functions also incorporate technetium containing radionuclides.

As with all substances, there is potential danger both to humankind and to the environment if technetium-containing compounds are carelessly used. Considerable information is available regarding the hazards of technetium and its proper and careful handling.

Bibliography

Barr, Robert Q. "Technetium." In *Van Nostrand's Scientific Encyclopedia*, edited by Douglas M. Considine. 6th ed. Vol. 2. New York: Van Nostrand Reinhold, 1984. A brief summary of technetium tracing its history, isolation, chemistry, and applications to industry and medicine.

Boyd, G. E. "Technetium and Promethium." *Journal of Chemical Education* 36 (January, 1959): 3-14. A detailed account tracing the discovery, chemistry, and uses of these two radioactive elements.

Deutsch, Edward, Karen Libon, and Silvia Jurisson. "Technetium Chemistry and Technetium Radiopharmaceuticals." In *Progress in Inorganic Chemistry*, edited by Stephen J. Lippard. Vol. 30. New York: John Wiley & Sons, 1983. This review of technetium includes its chemical reactions, electrochemistry, and chromatographic separation techniques, and briefly discusses radiopharmaceuticals.

Holden, Norman E. "The Delayed Discovery of Nuclear Fission." *Chemistry International* 12 (September/October, 1990): 177-185. A very personal account of the activities of those associated with the events leading to the discovery of nuclear fission.

Kotegov, K. V., O. N. Pavlov, and V. P. Shvedov. "Technetium." In *Advances in Inorganic Chemistry and Radiochemistry*, edited by H. J. Eeleméus and A. G. Sharpe. Vol. 11. New York: Academic Press, 1968. This overview of technetium traces its history, nuclear and chemical properties, separation procedures, and uses.

Paneth, F. A. "The Making of the Missing Chemical Elements." *Nature* 159 (January, 1947): 8-10. A discussion on the search for atomic numbers 43, 61, 85, and 93. The article urges the discoverers of artificial elements to name their discoveries.

Pinkerton, Thomas C., et al. "Bioinorganic Activity of Technetium Radiopharmaceuticals." *Journal of Chemical Education* 62 (November, 1985): 965-973. A detailed discussion of technetium imaging for studying functions in the thyroid, brain, kidney, liver, bone, and heart.

Gordon A. Parker

Cross-References

Lawrence Develops the Cyclotron (1931), p. 953; Chadwick Discovers the Neutron (1932), p. 973; Cockcroft and Walton Split the Atom with a Particle Accelerator (1932), p. 978; Frédéric Joliot and Irène Joliot-Curie Develop the First Artificial Radioactive Element (1933), p. 987; Seaborg and McMillan Make Element 94, Plutonium (1941), p. 1181; The Tevatron Particle Accelerator Begins Operation at Fermilab (1985), p. 2301; The Superconducting Supercollider is Under Construction in Texas (1988), p. 2372.

KREBS DESCRIBES THE CITRIC ACID CYCLE

Categories of event: Biology and chemistry
Time: March, 1937
Locale: University of Sheffield, England

Krebs postulated the operation of a series of chemical oxidation and reduction reactions that convert the food humans eat to energy in a form useful to the cells of the human body

Principal personages:

SIR HANS ADOLF KREBS (1900-1981), a biochemist who played a major role in the development of the new science of biochemistry and was awarded the 1953 Nobel Prize in Physiology or Medicine

WILLIAM ARTHUR JOHNSON (1913-   ), a student of Krebs with whom he published the original formulation of the citric, or tricarboxylic, acid cycle

HANS LEO KORNBERG (1928-   ), a research associate of Krebs with whom he discovered an important modification of the citric acid cycle

ALBERT SZENT-GYÖRGYI (1893-1986), a biochemist whose studies of the oxidation of organic acids provided Krebs with vital data for his own discoveries; winner of the 1937 Nobel Prize in Physiology or Medicine

FRANZ KNOOP (1875-1946), an early contributor to the biochemical study of carbon compounds

CARL MARTIUS, an organic chemist who, together with Knoop, provided Krebs with a vital link in the oxidative process

Summary of Event

The foods humans eat consist largely of carbohydrates, fats, and proteins; each of these classes represents a source of energy and molecules required for growth and repair of tissue. Maintaining or restoring health demands a detailed understanding of the conversion of these foods into energy and chemical building blocks. The central problem in the early 1930's was that of describing exactly how this conversion is conducted in the cell.

When Sir Hans Adolf Krebs first became interested in these questions, it had been established that the carbohydrates, or sugars and starches, are converted to carbon dioxide, a gas. As these names imply, the chemical structures involve the carbon atom. It had been known for many years that this single element is the main constitutent of all living matter. It is not obvious from the names that many complex molecules, or unique collections of six to thousands of carbon atoms, are converted to a specific substance of a single carbon atom. This idea is important because it suggests that such a process might take place in a series of steps rather than all at once. In fact, it was well known that energy is transformed more efficiently in such a series.

Little was known at that time about the nature of these steps as applied to the carbohydrates, although some progress had been made with the fats and proteins. Krebs had heard of a proposal that combined two acetate fragments, each containing two carbon atoms, to form a four-carbon structure called succinate. Both of these structures are acids that had been shown to involve carbon atoms that had reacted with the element oxygen. These facts and ideas were entirely consistent with respiration, which involves breathing in oxygen and breathing out carbon dioxide. More important, they suggested a research lead that turned out to be vital: the study of acid oxidation.

Krebs appreciated that the most promising approach to the problem of describing the chemistry that takes place in the cell was the study of the rates, or velocity, at which possible intermediate molecules are oxidized. He made an important contribution in the development of a sensitive method of following the changes of pressure in oxygen as the acid was being transformed. In this way, he found that a number of acids are oxidized rapidly enough to play a role in the overall conversion sequence.

His most important discovery concerned the common food substance citric acid, which had long been known to be connected directly with the healthy operation of the body. Not only does citrate—the form of an acid in cells—undergo oxidation rapidly but also it speeds up, or catalyzes, respiratory chemistry. This effect of a compound causing a greater increase in the rate of a reaction had been demonstrated previously in 1935 for several acids by Albert Szent-Györgyi. Unlike those acids, citrate possesses three acidic carbon atoms. Furthermore, in 1937, Carl Martius and Franz Knoop showed exactly how citrate is converted into succinate. Now, Krebs had all the information he needed to propose a pathway describing the conversion of a carbohydrate into carbon dioxide.

The key feature of Krebs's hypothesis is that the process is cyclic in design. It is apparent that each step, or individual change of one molecule into another, must be connected to the next. Biochemists refer to such an arrangement as a pathway. In asserting that the pathway is cyclic, Krebs linked the last chemical reaction to the first as well. The scheme involves some material being constantly fed into the pathway and reacting, or undergoing a chemical change, with one of the products of the last reaction of the sequence.

To be specific, acetate, already proposed by other scientists, enters from the food supply. Reaction takes place with a four-carbon acid, oxaloacetate, which Krebs suggests is a product of the final chemical conversion in his cycle. The product, by a well-known chemical reaction, is citrate.

There is an unexpected characteristic of many pathways that leads to the breakdown of substances: They may require first the synthesis of a more complicated structure, in this case, citrate. Such apparently wasteful indirect steps can be explained by considerations such as efficiency and control of the complex process.

Krebs's proposal for what he called the tricarboxylic, or citric, acid cycle has come to be known as the Krebs cycle. Citrate contains as part of its structure a carbon atom linked sequentially to an oxygen atom and a hydrogen atom. Such an arrangement is characteristic of the common substance alcohol and may be easily lost, or eliminated, along with another hydrogen atom as a molecule of water; this process is known as dehydration. The product formed, aconitate, can undergo the reverse process of hydration and produce another alcohol, called isocitrate. This sequence is a clear example of apparently unproductive chemistry. While the chief concern is oxidation, none has taken place in three chemical reactions. These mysteries can be explained by the fact that citrate is very difficult to oxidize, while isocitrate undergoes such chemical change easily.

The next step in the Krebs cycle involves oxidation, but in a surprising way. The element oxygen is not directly involved. Such chemistry had been known long before Krebs's work, and required chemists to look at oxidation in more general terms. The most satisfactory view is that oxidation demands that a substance lose electrons from its structure. Such a definition includes, but is much broader than, reaction with oxygen.

The very nature of this extended view brings about a fundamental chemical concern of direct interest in terms of the Krebs cycle. When chemists say a substance must lose electrons, they must not be taken too literally. The electrons are transferred actually to some other chemical; that is, they are gained also in a process called reduction. First, it is necessary to look at another basic understanding of the biochemist. In essentially every chemical reaction that makes up the myriad chemical processes called metabolism, a highly specific and efficient catalyst, called an enzyme, is found. For many of these enzymatic reactions to occur, a second component, or coenzyme, is also required. In the Krebs cycle, there are specific coenzymes that are reduced by accepting the electrons lost, as, for example, when isocitrate is oxidized. As isocitrate is oxidized, it becomes a very unstable substance known as a beta-ketoacid. In spontaneously losing a molecule of carbon dioxide, it provides a route to one of the known final products of respiration. This event does not prove that Krebs is right, but it demonstrates that his proposal is in accord with experimental observations.

The subsequent steps in the Krebs cycle are similar in that they involve oxidations and loss of carbon dioxide, coupled with the reduction of coenzymes. The final production of oxaloacetate is the result of an oxidation of malate whose structure involves an alcohol similar to isocitrate. Thus, the cycle is prepared to begin again with the arrival of another acetate group.

Many men and women worked untold years to provide evidence that Krebs's brilliant hypothesis is a valid approximation of the truth.

Impact of Event

At the beginning of the nineteenth century, chemists were fascinated by the extraordinary changes that matter undergoes in living organisms. It is from this interest that the designation "organic" was used for the ubiquitous carbon compounds of nature. It was generally believed, however, that these reactions could not be studied outside of living beings.

In the century between the 1830's and the 1930's, this "vital force theory" was so completely abandoned that a new science, biochemistry, was born. Krebs, as one of the principal founders of such studies, provided a vital link between biology and chemistry. In the early years of the twentieth century, a great interest was developing in the exact and quantitative study of chemical reactions. Krebs contributed to both of these modern movements by his leadership in using and developing precise instruments and techniques for the examination of metabolic reactions.

The proposal of the citric acid cycle was met with characteristic scientific skepticism, because it was a breathtaking leap into uncharted territory. It was about a decade before the conversion of pyruvate to citrate was demonstrated experimentally. There were severe criticisms directed toward the hypothesis, especially because so much of its experimental justification remained to be found.

In time, most working biochemists came to accept the cycle as a hypothesis, and a huge amount of extremely important experimental work was conducted. Much of the refinement was done by Krebs and his students, but in a review characteristic of his generosity, he gives full credit to many other workers who contributed significantly to the development of his basic scheme, such as William Arthur Johnson and Hans Leo Kornberg.

Of central importance is the fact that Krebs's original proposal, although greatly enhanced and extended, has stood the test of many studies. For example, while the proposal was originally conceived to explain the oxidation of carbohydrates, it was shown later that all major foodstuffs are readily accommodated by its chemistry. Furthermore, the functioning of the cycle in plant, as well as animal, tissue soon became apparent. About two-thirds of all the oxidation that takes place in plants and animals using carbohydrate, fat, or protein takes place through the Krebs cycle.

One modern textbook of biochemistry calls the discovery of the Krebs cycle the greatest imaginative and experimental accomplishment of that science. The breadth of application of the cycle is so great that it lies at the very heart of life, a concept that is not understood completely. Its greatest feature is demonstrated in its delicate control of chemical rates of conversion and balanced supply of vital molecular building blocks for the growth and repair of tissue.

In 1970, a volume of essays was dedicated to Krebs on the occasion of his seventieth birthday. In a dedication, his research director asked, "What had he [Krebs] achieved since 1925?" The answer: "He had discovered the essential chemical reactions of energy-transformations in life. . . ."

Bibliography

Bartley, W., H. L. Kornberg, and J. R. Quayle, eds. *Essays in Cell Metabolism: Hans Krebs Dedicatory Volume*. New York: Wiley-Interscience, 1970. While the essays are highly technical, they are usually introduced and often interspersed with vivid and unique personal recollections of Krebs's former students and colleagues. Essential for the full appreciation of Krebs as a scientist and as a person.

Bodner, George M. "Metabolism, Part II: The Tricarboxylic Acid (TCA), Citric Acid, or Krebs Cycle." *Journal of Chemical Education* 63 (August, 1986): 673-677. Good description of the chemical reactions involved, along with clear examples of the importance of the Krebs cycle to other biochemical processes. Especially strong discussion of the experimental evidence and historical perspective.

Igelsrud, Donald E. "How Living Things Obtain Energy: A Simpler Explanation." *The American Biology Teacher* 51 (February, 1989): 89-93. A well-written presentation for the biology teacher and the nonspecialist. The classroom suggestions are an aid to the reader's understanding.

Kornberg, H. L. "H. A. Krebs: A Pathway in Metabolism." In *The Metabolic Roles of Citrate*, edited by T. W. Goodwin. New York: Academic Press, 1968. A fascinating biographical sketch by one of Krebs's students and close collaborators. Full of highly personal observations and rare insight.

Krebs, H. A. "The History of the Tricarboxylic Acid Cycle." *Perspectives in Biology and Medicine* 14 (Autumn, 1979): 154-170. Krebs not only describes the origin of his ideas and their development but also offers details concerning their success. A revealing analysis of how one scientist finds a solution when others, just as brilliant, overlook it.

Krebs, H. A., and H. L. Kornberg. *Energy Transformations in Living Matter: A Survey*. Berlin: Springer-Verlag, 1947. Krebs and Kornberg give a careful review of the citric acid cycle as a means of changing energy from foods to forms directly useful for the organisms. Much of the detail is very technical, but large introductory sections throughout the text can be read with a reasonable degree of understanding by the interested person.

Krebs, H. A., and M. B. V. Roberts. *The Citric Acid Cycle: An Historical Analysis*. New Rochelle, N.Y.: Audio Learning, 1973. Contains eleven slides, one cassette, and one manual. A discussion between Krebs and an English scientist. The slides illustrate the chemical reactions. Accompanied by a printed text containing the slides, additional material, questions for discussion, and supplementary readings. Invaluable description of the history and goals of biochemistry.

McMurray, W. C. *Essentials of Human Metabolism*. New York: Harper & Row, 1977. Especially good in placing the Krebs cycle in the overall metabolic picture. Treats the regulation of the cycle and the role of the mitochondria in some detail. An excellent glossary of important terms and a list of common acronyms.

Quayle, J. R. "Obituary: Sir Hans Krebs, 1900-1981." *Journal of General Microbiology* 128 (1982): 2215-2220. Far more than the usual obituary, written by a colleague and admirer. Full of inside detail of Krebs as a person, scientist, and coworker. Provides important information about the development of the entire field of biochemistry.

Steiner, Robert F., and Seymour Pomerantz. *The Chemistry of Living Systems*. New York: D. Van Nostrand, 1981. A well-written, detailed review of the chemistry of the Krebs cycle and its relationship to oxidative phosphorylation. Includes an array of thought-provoking questions and a list of suggested readings at various levels.

K. Thomas Finley
Patricia J. Siegel

Cross-References

Hopkins Discovers Tryptophan, an Essential Amino Acid (1900), p. 46; Grijns Proposes That Beriberi Is Caused by a Nutritional Deficiency (1901), p. 103; Hopkins Suggests That Food Contains Vitamins Essential to Life (1906), p. 330; McCollum Names Vitamin D and Pioneers Its Use Against Rickets (1922), p. 725; Steenbock Discovers That Sunlight Increases Vitamin D in Food (1924), p. 771; Szent-Györgyi Discovers Vitamin C (1928), p. 857; Lipmann Discovers Acetyl Coenzyme A (1951), p. 1390.

REBER BUILDS THE FIRST
INTENTIONAL RADIO TELESCOPE

Category of event: Astronomy
Time: June-September, 1937
Locale: Wheaton, Illinois

Reber built the first reflecting radio telescope for the systematic study of radio emission from space, marking the beginning of intentional radio astronomy

Principal personages:
GROTE REBER (1911-   ), an American radio engineer and amateur astronomer who built the first reflecting radio telescope and made the first radio maps of the universe
KARL JANSKY (1905-1950), an American radio engineer who first made and identified the accidental discovery of radio emissions from space
SIR BERNARD LOVELL (1913-   ), an English radio astronomer who built the first of the giant radio telescopes following Reber's work
HEINRICH HERTZ (1857-1894), a German physicist who is best known for his discovery of radio waves in 1887
GUGLIELMO MARCONI (1874-1937), an Italian electrical engineer and co-winner of the 1909 Nobel Prize in Physics for demonstrating radio transmission across the Atlantic Ocean

Summary of Event

Intentional radio astronomy began in 1937 when Grote Reber built the first reflecting radio telescope at his home in Wheaton, Illinois, only fifty years after the discovery of radio waves by Heinrich Hertz in 1887 at Karlsruhe, Germany, and five years after the first report of radio waves from space. Hertz had produced radio waves with a spark generator at about 50 million oscillations per second (50 megahertz) and measured a wavelength of about 6 meters, indicating a wave velocity equal to the speed of light (300 million meters per second). His work demonstrated that radio waves and light waves are both electromagnetic waves differing only in frequency and wavelength. Radio waves are the longest waves in the electromagnetic spectrum, which also includes infrared, visible light, ultraviolet, and X rays at increasingly higher frequencies and shorter wavelengths.

The early study of radio was directed toward the development of wireless communications, leading to transatlantic transmission and reception of radio signals in 1901 by Guglielmo Marconi. In 1932, Karl Jansky reported his accidental discovery of radio waves from space. At the Bell Telephone Laboratories in New Jersey, he built a rotating dipole-array wire antenna sensitive to 15-meter radio waves to study the static noise that interferes with radio communications. In addition to the usual atmospheric static, he detected a weak, steady hiss that appeared four minutes earlier each day. Since this corresponds to the twenty-three-hour fifty-six minute apparent daily motion of the stars, he concluded that he was receiving cosmic radio noise from outside the solar system.

Jansky's work was published in a series of scientific papers starting in 1932. His results made the front page of *The New York Times*, and a national radio network broadcast ten seconds of radio hiss from space. Despite this publicity, no scientist followed up Janksy's discovery until Grote Reber, a twenty-five-year-old radio engineer and amateur astronomer, decided to build a large parabolic dish for radio reception in his side yard at his home in Wheaton, Illinois, 40 kilometers west of Chicago. It was the first intentional radio telescope and the only one in operation until after World War II.

Reber was an avid radio amateur who built his first transceiver at age fifteen and began to communicate with other amateurs around the world. He received an electrical engineering degree in 1933 from what is now the Illinois Institute of Technology, and began working for the Stewart-Warner Company in Chicago. After reading Jansky's papers, he recognized the importance of his discovery. He also realized that greater progress could be made with equipment specially designed to measure cosmic static at radio frequencies. He began to plan the construction of a large reflecting dish with associated receiving equipment that could measure the detailed distribution of radiation intensities throughout the sky at different wavelengths.

Although he had no outside support, Reber decided to build as large a reflector as he could in order to obtain maximum resolution (separation of sources) at radio frequencies. His reflector design also had the capability of tuning to different wavelengths by changing the antenna feed at the focus of the parabolic dish. He decided on a 6.1-meter focal length and a dish diameter of 9.4 meters, based on the length of the longest two-by-fours available locally. Working with only a minimum of help from June to September, 1937, he completed his radio telescope at a cost of thirteen hundred dollars of his own money. This instrument remained in his yard for ten years; it was a source of amazement and wild rumors among local residents and visitors.

To minimize expense, Reber used a meridian-transit mounting that could be pointed up and down in a north-south plane (declination), while scanning east and west (right ascension) was provided by the earth's rotation. The differential gear from a Ford Model-T truck was used to change the elevation angle of the dish. The reflecting dish consisted of seventy-two radial wooden rafters cut to parabolic shape with a tolerance of about 0.5 centimeter, with forty-five pieces of galvanized sheet metal screwed over the rafters to form the reflecting surface. The entire structure weighed nearly two tons.

Using custom-made vacuum tubes from the University of Chicago and other radio components from his employer, Reber began with a receiver designed for the shortest possible operating wavelength of 9 centimeters. This would give the best angular resolution and would be more sensitive to thermal radiation than at the longer wavelength detected by Jansky. Unfortunately, scanning at 9 centimeters gave no response, so he began to doubt that thermal radiation was the source of Jansky's observations. By the summer of 1938, Reber had upgraded his receiver to detect 33-centimeter waves at a greater sensitivity, but still failed to find any radiation of celestial origin. A still longer wavelength could be conveniently detected with a cylindrical cavity made from a 2-by-4 meter sheet of aluminum, setting the operating wavelength at 1.87 meters. A dipole antenna in the cavity resonator at the dish's focus gave positive results by the spring of 1939, after two years of persevering work.

Reber did most of his observing from midnight to dawn to avoid interference from automobile ignitions. By April, the plane of the Milky Way crossed the meridian late at night, and it became apparent that our galaxy emitted 1.87-meter radio waves. The intensity of the cosmic radiation was determined by reading a microammeter at one-minute intervals while monitoring the audio signal to detect and remove periods of local interference. His initial results were published in February, 1940, in the *Proceedings of the Institute of Radio Engineers*, where he noted that his estimated intensity was far below that reported by Jansky at the 15-meter wavelength. This led Reber to the conclusion that the source of the cosmic radiation could be explained by interactions between electrons and positive ions (charged atoms) in an ionized gas rather than from thermal emission. Over the next five years, he obtained the first radio maps of the galaxy at two different wavelengths and identified a number of important radio sources in different parts of the galaxy.

As virtually the only active radio astronomer in the world, Reber operated his telescope in Wheaton for ten years before it was finally moved to a United States Bureau of Standards field station in 1947. The telescope was again relocated in 1960 to the National Radio Astronomy Observatory at Green Bank, West Virginia, where it remains on public view and is occasionally used for demonstration purposes. In 1954, Reber moved to Tasmania, Australia, where he constructed a huge wire-antenna array telescope to measure radiation at a wavelength of 150 meters in the Southern Hemisphere.

Impact of Event

The success of Reber's pioneering radio telescope led to the rapid development of radio astronomy after World War II and the construction of increasingly larger and more sophisticated radio telescopes. Early work in radio astronomy was done by adapting radar scanning dishes retired from wartime service. Their electronic receivers were much more sensitive than the relatively simple devices used by Jansky and Reber. In fact, radio emission from the sun was first observed accidentally by James S. Hey, when anti-aircraft radars, operating between 4 and 8 meter wavelengths in England, experienced severe noise jamming on February 27 and 28 of 1942. Analysis of this phenomenon showed that the signals came from the sun during unusual sunspot activity, but publication was withheld until after the war. Reber also detected solar radio emissions in 1943.

One of the first applications of radar to radio astronomy began in 1946 at Jodrell Bank, an experimental botanical site of Manchester University. Here, a group led by

Sir Bernard Lovell used radar astronomy to study daytime meteor activity in great detail, even though it was invisible to ordinary sight. In 1947, they constructed a fixed, upward-looking parabolic reflector, 66 meters in diameter, with a reflecting surface consisting of wire mesh spread over a frame on the ground. This instrument was limited to vertical reception, with scanning mainly from the earth's rotation. Lovell soon began to plan a giant fully steerable reflector that could explore radio phenomena throughout the universe. Construction of the 76-meter radio telescope at Jodrell Bank Experimental Station took six years, with the turret rack of a battleship to move the huge dish. It was designed to operate at 21 centimeters after it was discovered that interstellar atomic hydrogen radiates at that wavelength. The telescope was completed in 1957, in time to track the first man-made satellite, Sputnik 1. This instrument gave productive results in many investigations, including emissions from the sun, the galaxy, and several discrete radio sources.

In the United States, the National Radio Astronomy Observatory began operation at Green Bank, West Virginia, with a 26-meter dish in 1959, followed by a 91-meter transit telescope in 1962 and a 43-meter steerable telescope in 1965. For more than twenty-five years, the 91-meter telescope with its wire-mesh reflecting dish was the largest movable telescope in the United States until it collapsed from metal fatigue in 1989. The largest fully steerable radio telescope is the 100-meter dish completed in 1970 at Effelsburg near Bonn, West Germany. The largest single radio telescope is the 305-meter fixed bowl built in 1963 of wire mesh in a natural valley near Arecibo, Puerto Rico. Larger telescopes provide sharper images, but the best resolution can be achieved by connecting two or more radio telescopes together electrically in an array to give a resolving power equivalent to a single dish with a diameter equal to the size of the array. The Very Large Array (VLA) in the high desert near Socorro, New Mexico, began operation in 1980 with twenty-seven dishes, each 26 meters in diameter, forming a Y-shaped array 27 kilometers long, with a resolution comparable to that of the best optical telescopes.

Bibliography

Abell, George O., David Morrison, and Sidney C. Wolff. *Exploration of the Universe*. 5th ed. Philadelphia: Saunders College Publishing, 1987. A standard college textbook on astronomy with a good chapter on radio telescopes, including some discussion of Reber's work. Many of the most important radio telescopes are described with a good variety of photographs. Several chapters discuss the results of radio astronomy.

Hey, J. S. *The Evolution of Radio Astronomy*. New York: Science History Publications, 1973. A good history of radio astronomy by one of the pioneers in its development. The first chapter describes the work of Jansky and Reber, followed by chapters on the rise of radio astronomy after World War II. The 76-meter telescope at Jodrell Bank and other early radio telescopes are discussed with illustrations and references.

Spradley, Joseph L. "The First True Radio Telescope." *Sky and Telescope* 76 (July,

1988): 28-30. An introductory article in a popular astronomy magazine on Reber's background and work. Design, construction, and operation of the first intentional radio telescope is described, including photographs of the telescope and the original model used in its design.

Sullivan, W. T. III, ed. *The Early Years of Radio Astronomy*. Cambridge, England: Cambridge University Press, 1984. A series of articles by the pioneers of radio astronomy on its early development. Grote Reber's 1958 article from *Proceedings of the Institute of Radio Engineers* is entitled "Early Radio Astronomy at Wheaton, Illinois" and includes about a dozen early photographs not in the original article. An article by Lovell is entitled "The Origins and Early History of Jodrell Bank."

Verschuur, Gerrit L. *The Invisible University Revealed*. New York: Springer-Verlag, 1987. This book, subtitled "The Story of Radio Astronomy," provides a good description of the results of radio astronomy with more than one hundred photographs and radio contour maps. Concluding chapters give a history from Jansky and Reber to the present and a summary of the most important radio telescopes.

Joseph L. Spradley

Cross-References

Marconi Receives the First Transatlantic Telegraphic Radio Transmission (1901), p. 128; The Principles of Shortwave Radio Communication Are Discovered (1919), p. 669; Jansky's Experiments Lead to the Founding of Radio Astronomy (1930), p. 934; Watson-Watt and Associates Develop the First Radar (1935), p. 1040; Reber Makes the First Radio Maps of the Universe (1942), p. 1193; Ryle's Radio Telescope Locates the First Known Radio Galaxy (1946), p. 1271; Franklin and Burke Discover Radio Emissions from Jupiter (1955), p. 1492; Ryle Constructs the First Radio Interferometer (1955), p. 1496; The Jodrell Bank Radio Telescope Is Completed (1957), p. 1539; A Radio Astronomy Team Sends and Receives Radar Signals to the Sun (1958), p. 1598; Bell Discovers Pulsars, the Key to Neutron Stars (1967), p. 1862.

CALLENDAR CONNECTS INDUSTRY WITH INCREASED ATMOSPHERIC CARBON DIOXIDE

Category of event: Earth science
Time: 1938
Locale: England

Callendar noted the increasing level of carbon dioxide in the earth's atmosphere and traces it to human activity

Principal personages:
SVANTE AUGUST ARRHENIUS (1858-1927), a Swedish physicist and chemist who studied the industrial revolution and concluded that coal increased the level of carbon dioxide in the earth's atmosphere
BERT R. BOLIN (1925-   ), a Swedish meteorologist who made worldwide carbon dioxide measurements on the air-intake systems of commercial aircraft flying the polar route
G. S. CALLENDAR, an English physicist who speculated that increasing carbon dioxide levels were the probable cause for a warming of North America and Europe
CHARLES D. KEELING (1928-   ), an American marine geochemist whose specialties include geochemistry of carbon and oxygen, atmospheric chemistry, and the influence of atmospheric carbon dioxide on the carbon cycle and on world climate
SYUKURO MANABE (1931-   ), a Japanese-born meteorologist who specializes in the study of climate variation

Summary of Event

Carbon dioxide is a colorless, tasteless, transparent gas that is present in very small quantities, about 0.03 percent by volume, in the air that humans breathe in, and in larger quantities in the air that is breathed out, because it is a waste product of the process by which life is maintained. It also has the interesting property that, while it allows the electromagnetic energy of the sun's rays to pass through it unhindered to the surface of the earth, when the warm surface of the ground or ocean radiates heat upward at infrared frequencies, this heat is absorbed by carbon dioxide. This process by which heat is trapped near the surface of the earth is called the "greenhouse effect." It operates for other gases in the air; but unlike other gases, the proportion of carbon dioxide in the air is increasing steadily as a result of human activity. There is no doubt that the burning of fossil fuels—coal, oil, and natural gas—releases carbon dioxide into the atmosphere.

A few decades after the beginning of the Industrial Age, scientists began to question the effect of increased burning of carbon-based fossil fuels on the atmosphere. Carbon-based fuels are the chief energy source for the earth's population, and, as a result, the human impact on the global carbon cycle is far-reaching. Fossil fuels are hydrocarbon molecules whose chemical energy is released when they are burned, the principal emission from this combustion being carbon dioxide gas. The effect of carbon dioxide gas is that it heats the lower atmosphere as carbon dioxide concentrations increase. Svante August Arrhenius, a Swedish physicist and chemist, was one of the first to write about increased carbon dioxide levels in the atmosphere. In the mid-1880's, he announced his survey of the first few decades of the Industrial Revolution and concluded that humans were burning coal at an unprecedented rate. Arrhenius knew that carbon dioxide trapped infrared radiation that would otherwise have reflected back out to space. He used measurements of infrared radiation from the full moon in his first calculations of the possible effects of anthropogenic (of human origin) carbon dioxide. His conclusions were that the average global temperature would rise as much as 9 degrees if the amount of carbon dioxide in the air doubled from its preindustrial level.

Arrhenius' work did not gain acceptance until G. S. Callendar, an English physicist, speculated in 1938 that increasing carbon dioxide levels were the probable cause for a warming of North America and Northern Europe that meteorologists had begun to observe in the 1880's. Carbon dioxide is transparent to incoming ultraviolet but opaque to the resulting reradiation in the infrared. Because carbon dioxide also absorbs incoming infrared radiation, it is an integral part of the mechanism of global heat balance. Without compensating charges, increased levels of carbon dioxide will result in higher temperatures. The increase in the effective emissivity of infrared radiation from the earth, with resulting atmospheric heating, is responsible for the so-called greenhouse effect. Callendar was the first to assemble a large body of measurements from several scientific sources and predict significant temperature change from anthropogenic carbon dioxide.

Direct measurements of the temperature effects of carbon dioxide are difficult because the underlying natural fluctuations in temperature do not provide a stable baseline against which to reference anthropogenic disturbances. Callendar, working from this disadvantage, collected data from several scientists. They were odd, rather unsystematic, and somewhat unreliable data; however, they agree with later, more precise observations.

Several factors worked against widespread acceptance of Callendar's study, one of which was that a warming seemed to be replaced by a temperature decline around 1940. Another was that most scientists in the 1930's were too busy with the exploitation of petroleum for new products and believed that the problem of excess carbon dioxide would be absorbed in the oceans, not the atmosphere. Callendar remained convinced by his 1938 study and noted in 1958, that since 1942, the carbon dioxide content had continued to rise at a rate of about 0.2 percent per year. Concern about atmospheric pollution as a direct result of humans virtually exploded in the late 1960's, when many of the industrial nations began to promulgate laws and write regulations covering atmospheric pollution by manufacturers. The early work done by investigators such as Callendar was remarkably correct considering the fact that the work was done during a time when there were no computers to allow for the development of models to add innumerable variables and analyze them.

There are uncertainties about what has caused the increased levels of carbon dioxide in the atmosphere; for example, the rate of absorption of excess carbon dioxide by the ecosystem and oceans, the rate of production of carbon dioxide by destruction of forests, the cooling effect of increasing aerosols—both anthropogenic and from revived volcanic activity—and feedback effects of water vapor and clouds. Nevertheless, it is abundantly clear that there is a connection, as Callendar noted in 1938, between human activity and air pollution. The energy crisis in the mid-1970's and the increasing sophistication of numerical atmospheric circulation models have led to greatly increased interest and investigation of the carbon dioxide greenhouse effect. In 1975, V. Ramanathan pointed out that the greenhouse effect is enhanced by the continued release into the atmosphere of chlorofluorocarbons, even though their combined concentration is less than a part per billion by volume.

Many physicists look to the computer models and view the steadily rising concentration of atmospheric carbon dioxide as a prelude to climatological catastrophe; at the other extreme, there is a group of scientists that concentrates on more empirical data. Syukuro Manabe utilizes mathematical models of climate change. Empirical data relies on experience or observation alone, often without regard for system and theory. The empiricists believe that any change in the climate caused by the rising levels of carbon dioxide will be indistinguishable from those natural climatic fluctuations. They foresee that higher concentrations of carbon dioxide will tend to stimulate photosynthesis and so increase the productivity of crops and the efficiency with which they use water. The empirical approach depends on finding some natural event that temporarily disturbs the heat balance of the atmosphere; an example is the great dust storms of the 1930's in the southwestern United States. By monitoring the temperature changes and flow of radiative heat during such natural events, it is possible to measure the response of the real world to the perturbation.

Impact of Event

In the several decades after Callendar first noted that humans were causing increased levels of carbon dioxide in the atmosphere, it has been found that the much more abundant constituent carbon monoxide is also increasing as a result of automobile exhausts and other combustion processes. Although carbon monoxide does not make a direct impact in enhancing the greenhouse effect, it does play an indirect role by serving as a sink for the hydroxyl radical, which acts as a catalyst in modulating the increase of nitrous oxide from combustion processes. Also contributing to carbon monoxide is the use of chemical fertilizers and the increase of methane from biogenic and industrial production.

From 1957 to 1975, the amount of carbon dioxide in the air has increased from 312 to 326 parts per million, almost 5 percent. This trend has been measured by American scientists under Charles D. Keeling since 1957, and by Swedish meteorologists led by Bert R. Bolin since 1963, in areas far away from any localized source of carbon dioxide so that the background and thus the worldwide trends in carbon dioxide might be observed. The Americans collected data on Mauna Loa, Hawaii, and at the South Pole, while the Swedes made their measurements on the air-intake systems of commercial aircraft flying the polar route.

In addition to research in the atmosphere, considerable research is being done in glacial areas of the world. Two teams of European and United States researchers in 1990 drilled through more than two miles of ice searching for trapped air bubbles and entombed crystals that will reveal what the weather was like during the past 200,000 years. On the summit of Greenland, the highest point on the vast ice mound that almost completely covers the world's largest island, scientists are seeking an answer to the most pressing question in climatology; namely, will rising levels of carbon dioxide and methane heat the earth and melt the polar ice caps. Evidence from ice cores drilled by Soviet researchers in Antarctica show that rising levels of carbon dioxide in the atmosphere have resulted in warmer temperatures several times during the 200,000 years of recent Earth history.

Bibliography

Breuer, Georg. *Air in Danger: Ecological Perspectives of the Atmosphere.* New York: Cambridge University Press, 1980. A very good account of the atmosphere; should be of interest for the lower college-level and advanced senior high school student. One chapter covers carbon dioxide increase and features a good discussion of the risk associated with higher levels of carbon dioxide in the atmosphere. Well written. Few illustrations, but a good reference source for additional reading.

Goudie, Andrew. *The Human Impact: Man's Role in Environmental Change.* Cambridge, Mass.: MIT Press, 1982. An excellent general reference on the human impact in altering the earth's environment. Of special interest for the senior high school student, lower-level college student, and interested public is the chapter on the impact of humans on climate and the atmosphere. Of particular interest is the carbon dioxide problem and other gases. Copiously illustrated.

Kellog, William W., and Robert Schare. *Climate Change and Society: Consequences of Increasing Atmospheric Carbon Dioxide.* Boulder, Colo.: Westview Press, 1981. A condensed report of a workshop at Aspen Institute's West Berlin, Germany, Conference Center from May 18 to 22, 1980. The conference addressed the political, economic, social, and ethical implications of a global environment regarding the carbon dioxide problem. Easy to read; an ideal reference for the upper-level college student. Each chapter has a long list of additional readings.

McKibben, Bill. *The End of Nature.* New York: Random House, 1989. Written in the narrative and contains no illustrations or mathematical formulas. Should appeal to the upper-level high school student and general public who have an interest in environmental issues. Addresses the scientific evidence about the greenhouse effect, the depletion of the ozone layer, and an array of other ecological ills.

Morgan, Joseph M., Michael D. Morgan, and James H. Weirsman. *Introduction to Environmental Science.* San Francisco: W. H. Freeman, 1980. A college-level text;

well written, illustrated, and contains numerous references after each chapter. Of particular interest are the chapters on air pollution and air quality management. The former chapter highlights the human impact on environmental problems with specific examples, and the latter outlines the steps being taken to mitigate future pollution.

Schneider, Stephen H. *Global Warming: Are We Entering the Greenhouse Century?* San Francisco: Sierra Club Books, 1989. Should appeal to the senior high school student, lower-college level student, and the general public. Examines the causes of world climate change that may raise world temperatures by −12 degrees Celsius in less than one hundred years. Provides an authoritative, entertaining look at the science, personalities, and politics behind the problem of global warming. Explains in clear, nontechnical language what is scientifically well known, what is speculative, and where major uncertainties lie.

Schneider, Stephen H., and Lynne Morton. *The Primordial Bond: Exploring Connections Between Man and Nature Through the Humanities and Science.* New York: Plenum Press, 1981. For readers who have a general interest in climate and how humans are changing it. Written by a climatologist who speaks out strongly on how man is drastically disturbing the delicate balance of the world climate system. Of particular interest is the chapter on global cycles of life. A few illustrations; each chapter contains additional references. Nontechnical.

Wilson, Richard, Steven D. Colombe, John D. Spengler, and David Gordon Wilson. *Health Effects of Fossil Fuel Burning: Assessment and Mitigation.* Cambridge, Mass.: Ballinger, 1980. A technical reference, but a good information source for the lower-level college student and interested general public. Glossary and extensive bibliography; numerous tables that help clarify the text. Of particular interest are the chapters on health effects of air pollutants from coal combustion and extrapolation of effects at lower exposures.

Earl G. Hoover

Cross-References

Steinmetz Warns of Pollution in *The Future of Electricity* (1908), p. 401; Ford Produces Automobiles on a Moving Assembly Line (1913), p. 542; Burton Introduces Thermal Cracking for Refining Petroleum (1913), p. 573; Fabry Quantifies Ozone in the Upper Atmosphere (1913), p. 579; Müller Discovers That DDT Is a Potent Insecticide (1939), p. 1146; Manabe and Wetherald Warn of the Greenhouse Effect and Global Warming (1967), p. 1840; The United States Government Bans DDT Use to Protect the Environment (1972), p. 1982; Rowland and Molina Theorize That Ozone Depletion Is Caused by Freon (1973), p. 2009; The British Antarctic Survey Confirms the First Known Hole in the Ozone Layer (1985), p. 2285; The Chernobyl Nuclear Reactor Explodes (1986), p. 2321.

HOFMANN SYNTHESIZES THE POTENT PSYCHEDELIC DRUG LSD-25

Category of event: Chemistry
Time: 1938
Locale: Basel, Switzerland

While pursuing ergot alkaloid medicinal chemistry research, Hofmann synthesized LSD-25 in 1938, but did not discover its potent psychogenic properties until 1943

Principal personages:
ALBERT HOFMANN (1906-   ), a Swiss research chemist at Sandoz Laboratories who synthesized or isolated many important ergot alkaloids including Hydergine, LSD-25, and psilocybin
ARTHUR STOLL (1887-?), an internationally known chemist who was the director of pharmaceutics research at Sandoz and Hofmann's mentor
WERNER STOLL (1915-?), a Swiss psychiatrist who performed the first human clinical studies with LSD at the University of Zurich in 1947

Summary of Event

For thousands of years, people have searched to find tranquillity, spiritual enlightenment, and guidance in understanding and defining their role in the natural world. Both primitive and modern religions frequently advocate the use of aids such as meditation, fasting, or the ritual use of psychoactive plants to alter one's perception of the world and to achieve a harmonious state of being. Mescaline, a natural substance occurring in peyote cactus, and psilocybin, found in various species of mushrooms, have been used in religious rituals in Mexico since the Aztec era, and are only two examples of the dozens of psychoactive plants distributed throughout the world. Such plants contain substances that have a profound ability to influence consciousness—the innermost essence of being.

Mystical experiences are difficult to express and are often beyond words. Thus, a number of words have been fashioned to define and describe the psychic effects of such natural substances. Because these compounds often induce visual hallucinations (colors, patterns, objects, flights of imagination), perceived by the taker as either drug-induced fantasy or less often as reality, the term hallucinogen is commonly employed. Such compounds also have been termed psychotomimetic drugs because people suffering from psychoses are often plagued by hallucinations and altered states of reality.

The term "psychedelic" (mind-expanding), coined by Canadian psychologist Humphry Osmond, was widely used in the 1960's. Since then, the hallucinogenic drug lysergic acid diethylamide (LSD) stands alone as having achieved a notoriety matched only by its potency. On a per weight basis, LSD is ten thousand times more active than mescaline.

As told firsthand by the "father" of LSD, Albert Hofmann, in his 1980 book *LSD, My Problem Child*, the discovery of LSD began not as a quest for a drug with fantastic properties but as a disappointment to the chemist working in a research laboratory that was investigating derivatives of natural products for use as medicines. After completing his dissertation research at the University of Zurich, in which he determined the chemical constituents of chitin (the structural material of wings, shells, and claws of insects and crustaceans) in only three months, Hofmann joined the pharmaceutical research group at Sandoz Limited in Basel, Switzerland in 1929. Hired by Arthur Stoll, director of the laboratory, Hofmann spent several years working with ergot alkaloids. These natural compounds are produced by a parasitic fungus of rye and were an area of interest to Stoll. In 1918, Stoll had isolated the pure active principle of ergot, ergotamine, and this natural product was used widely as a treatment for migraine and as a hemostatic remedy in obstetrics to stop uterine bleeding after childbirth. In the early 1930's, several research groups, including Sandoz, published simultaneous reports that the principal active ingredient of ergotamine was a simple alkaloid, subsequently named ergobasine by Stoll. By chemical degradation, it was determined that ergobasine was composed of two chemical constituents: lysergic acid and the amino alcohol, propanolamine. With this knowledge and further research into the chemistry of these compounds, Hofmann began to synthesize many artificial ergot alkaloids, all derivatives of lysergic acid.

In 1938, Hofmann produced his twenty-fifth substance in a series of lysergic acid derivatives, lysergic acid diethylamide, abbreviated LSD-25 (for the German spelling of the compound, *Lysergsaure-diathylamid*). This synthesis had been planned to produce a compound with properties similar to the drug Coramine, a circulatory and respiratory stimulant. Animal tests with LSD-25, however, aroused no special interest at Sandoz. Further testing was discontinued and LSD was forgotten.

Over the next five years, Hofmann developed several commercially successful drugs including Hydergine, an effective geriatric remedy that was Sandoz's most successful pharmaceutical product. Despite his obvious successes, Hofmann decided to produce LSD-25 once again to provide samples to the pharmacology department for further testing, an unusual undertaking as the compound had been rejected already for further testing. On April 16, 1943, when Hofmann was performing the final purification step of the synthesis of LSD-25, he was affected by dizziness and a remarkable restlessness. He stopped working and went home where, as later reported to Stoll, he "sank into a not unpleasant intoxicatedlike condition, characterized by an . . . uninterrupted stream of fantastic pictures, extraordinary shapes with intense, kaleidoscopic play of colors."

Hofmann attributed this remarkable experience to working with LSD-25, but he was skeptical. He was a chemist who had worked with very toxic compounds for years and had meticulously neat work habits. He wondered if a drop of the chemical had touched his fingertips. If so, LSD-25 was a very potent psychogenic compound. With full knowledge by Stoll and his assistants, Hofmann carefully planned a self-experiment with LSD-25. As recorded in his laboratory notebook, Hofmann took merely 0.25 milligram of the drug dissolved in water at 4:20 P.M. on April 19, 1943. At 5:00 P.M., he recorded that he felt dizzy, anxious, and had visual distortions and an urge to laugh. That was his last entry in the notebook. Hofmann became overwhelmed by the hallucinogenic experience and asked his assistant to escort him home by bicycle.

Hofmann later describes the next two hours as a nightmare. He was convinced that he had poisoned himself and that he was going to die. Yet, both his assistant and the doctor who was summoned to attend him observed nothing out of the ordinary other than extremely dilated pupils. His respiration and heartbeat were normal and the assistant said they had bicycled to his home at a good speed. With the constant assurances of his companions, by 8:00 P.M. Hofmann was no longer panic-stricken, although this LSD experience was much stronger than his previous experience a few days earlier. One hallucinogenic feature of the drug that astounded Hofmann was synesthesia, the overflow from one sensory modality to another in which colors are "heard" and sounds may be "seen." The effects subsided gradually and he was able to sleep.

The next morning, feeling refreshed and without a hangover, Hofmann went to work and reported on the previous day's experiences to Stoll and Ernst Rothlin, director of the pharmacology laboratory. Both expressed disbelief over the fraction of a milligram dose of LSD; a psychoactive compound of such potency seemed unbelievable. Several days later, Rothlin and two colleagues repeated Hofmann's LSD experiment but took only one-third the dose that Hofmann had ingested. The LSD effect was remarkable and all doubts about Hofmann's statements were eliminated.

It was determined later that for his first self-experiment, Hofmann ingested five to eight times the optimal dose of LSD necessary to achieve the psychedelic state. LSD is such a potent substance that experimental doses in humans are calculated in micrograms (1 microgram equals one-millionth of a gram) per kilogram body weight.

Laboratory animal studies proved to be of little value in examining the psychic effects of LSD because lower animals do not respond to the drug except at extremely high doses. Animal studies have demonstrated that LSD has an extremely low toxicity potential in comparison to its effective dose in humans. There are no recorded deaths attributed to the direct action (overdose) of LSD, although deaths have been recorded as accidents or as suicides accomplished under the influence of LSD. The danger of the drug lies not in its toxicity, but rather in the unpredictability of its psychic effects.

Impact of Event

In 1947, Werner Stoll, a Zurich psychiatrist and the son of Arthur Stoll, was the first to publish reports of his self-experiments with LSD and results of experimental studies involving both healthy normal volunteers and psychiatric patients. In 1953, Sandoz applied to the United States Food and Drug Administration to study LSD as an investigational new drug and supplied the drug to authorized investigators.

In the 1950's, hundreds of scientific papers were written that examined the use of LSD as a model for psychosis, as a psychotherapeutic aid to help patients see themselves and their problems from a detached perspective, in the treatment of alcoholism, and as therapy for terminal cancer patients to help them deal with their own mortality.

A darker side of investigations with LSD evolved as well. The United States Army and Central Intelligence Agency both conducted experiments with LSD as a chemical warfare agent and as a sort of "truth serum" for interrogating spies or prisoners-of-war. Many of the subjects were dosed secretly with LSD. As later revealed, the army sponsored LSD experimental research on more than fourteen hundred people between 1956 and 1967 that often blatantly violated ethical codes of conduct established for human experiments.

In the mid-1950's, Aldous Huxley, a philosopher and writer, published two books (*The Doors of Perception*, 1954; *Heaven and Hell*, 1956) that described his experiences with the peyote cactus hallucinogen, mescaline. Huxley's concept of "chemical keys" as an alternative to meditation to alter one's perception attracted the attention of two Harvard University professors, Timothy Leary and Richard Alpert. These researchers began studies with graduate students using the mushroom hallucinogen, psilocybin, but later used LSD as the drug of choice. Although the original work was conducted under proper scientific controls and with a physician present, by 1963, the studies apparently had become little more than off-campus LSD parties, with no semblance of a scientific method. Leary and Alpert were dismissed from the university. Alpert moved to the West Coast where he abandoned the drug. Leary continued to advocate the use of LSD and in 1966 founded a religious movement, the *L*eague of *S*piritual *D*iscovery, whose motto was "turn on, tune in, and drop out."

The LSD movement expanded rapidly to students, writers, and artists more interested in the possibilities of self-exploration of the psychedelic experience than in scientific experimentation. By 1967, the "Psychedelic Age" had arrived and evolved into a distinct subculture with its own language, music, and art forms. LSD became "acid" and users were "acid heads." An LSD experience was a "trip." Words like "bummer," "freak-out," and "bad trip" were used to describe panic or psychotic reactions to LSD. Bright fluorescent "day-glo" colors appeared in the palettes of psychedelic artists. Many popular music groups of the day had veiled references to drugs in the lyrics; music by the English group The Beatles ("Lucy in the Sky with Diamonds") and that of San Francisco-based bands including Jefferson Airplane, Jimi Hendrix, and The Grateful Dead became known as "acid rock."

The use of LSD declined sharply because of widely publicized concern over "bad trips," prolonged psychotic reactions, and personality changes in some people who took LSD. Other publicized adverse effects of LSD (chromosome damage and birth defects), although never validated, contributed to its decline. By 1970, LSD was included in the same regulatory category as the narcotic heroin; drugs that had no proven, effective use in medicine or scientific investigations.

Bibliography

Bowman, William C., and Michael J. Rand. "Psychotropic Drugs," and "Social Pharmacology: Drug Use for Nonmedical Purposes." In *Textbook of Pharmacology*. 2d ed. Oxford, England: Blackwell Scientific Publications, 1980. A brief treatment of the history and pharmacology of major hallucinogens. Describes the spread of LSD from controlled clinical experiments to street use of the drug. Discusses adverse psychiatric reactions and social consequences of LSD use, but dismisses some of the dangers attributed to LSD.

Hoffer, A., and Humphry Osmond. *The Hallucinogens*. New York: Academic Press, 1967. By no means outdated and should be consulted by any serious student of the hallucinogens. More than four hundred references support the extensive literature review that covers the history, pharmacology, and psychiatric uses of LSD, how the drug works, and the psychedelic state of mind induced by LSD.

Hofmann, Albert. *LSD, My Problem Child*. Translated by Jonathan Ott. New York: McGraw-Hill, 1980. An excellent firsthand account of the history of LSD. Hofmann describes his career as a chemist at Sandoz and conveys the excitement and joys of a scientist immersed in his work. Details his collaboration with Albert Stoll on ergot alkaloids, his self-experiments with LSD, and his later work with other hallucinogens. The last third of the book is devoted to his encounters with people such as Huxley and Leary.

Jaffe, Jerome H. "Drug Addiction and Drug Abuse." In *Goodman and Gilman's The Pharmacological Basis of Therapeutics*, edited by A. S. Gilman, L. S. Goodman, T. W. Rall, and F. Murad. 7th ed. New York: Macmillan, 1985. Good explanation and description of the altered states of consciousness and the hallucinations induced by LSD. Standard pharmacology text discussions about the pharmacology and toxicity of LSD.

Julian, Robert M. *A Primer of Drug Action*. 5th ed. New York: W. H. Freeman, 1988. A chapter on psychedelic drugs features a number of lengthy quotes from Hofmann's original writings to describe the LSD experience. Julian stresses that fears of long-term damage to society caused by widespread use of LSD appear to be unfounded, and that most once-heavy users of the drug say they ceased to take it simply because they tired of it and had no further need to experience its effects.

Ray, Oakley, and Charles Ksir. *Drugs, Society, and Human Behavior*. 5th ed. St. Louis: Times Mirror/Mosby, 1990. Recommended for nonscientists. Thorough treatment of hallucinogens with an interesting discourse on the history, use, and politics of LSD during the 1960's.

Stevens, Jay. *Storming Heaven: LSD and the American Dream*. New York: Perennial Library, 1987. Written twenty years after "the summer of love," Stevens' book looks back at the 1960's psychedelic movement as part comedy, part tragedy. Gives sketches of many of the advocates of LSD including Leary, Allen Ginsberg, and Ken Kesey. Describes the CIA's experiments with LSD and discusses the impact of the era in present American life.

Wolfe, Tom. *The Electric Kool-Aid Acid Test*. New York: Farrar, Straus, & Giroux,

1968; Bantam ed., 1981. A historical novel based on three years of the novelist Ken Kesey's life as the leader of the "Merry Pranksters" in the San Francisco bay area at the height of the LSD phenomenon.

Brian L. Roberts

Cross-References

Cerletti and Bini Develop Electroconvulsive Therapy for Treating Schizophrenia (1937), p. 1086; Jacobsen Introduces a Drug for the Treatment of Alcoholism (1948), p. 1314; Wilkins Discovers Reserpine, the First Tranquilizer (1950's), p. 1353; Janowsky Publishes a Cholinergic-Adrenergic Hypothesis of Mania and Depression (1972), p. 1976.

KAPITSA EXPLAINS SUPERFLUIDITY

Category of event: Physics
Time: 1938
Locale: Institute for Physical Problems, Moscow

Kapitsa discovered ideas relating to superfluidity in liquid helium and techniques that remain basic to modern low-temperature physics

Principal personages:
PYOTR LEONIDOVICH KAPITSA (1894-1984), a Soviet physicist who was internationally known for his contribution to advances in diverse branches of physics and winner of the 1978 Nobel Prize in Physics
LEV DAVIDOVICH LANDAU (1908-1968), a Soviet physicist who developed the theory of liquid helium and was awarded the 1962 Nobel Prize in Physics
ERNEST RUTHERFORD (1871-1937), the winner of the 1908 Nobel Prize in Chemistry who pioneered atomic research
ISAAK YAKOVLEVICH POMERANCHUK (1913-); ILYA MIKHAILOVICH LIFSHITZ (1917-); and NIKOLAI NIKOLAEVICH BOGOLIUBOV (1909-), a few of the eminent Soviet physicists who further explored superfluidity

Summary of Event

A thorough and systematic study of the properties of materials whose temperature is close to absolute zero was made possible when in 1908, Heike Kamerlingh Onnes (1853-1926) of the University of Leiden succeeded in liquefaction of helium. Among many unexpected properties, it was found that electrical resistance of many metals approached a constant as the temperature was lowered, and in some cases, it vanished entirely at some characteristically low temperature, found to depend on the magnetic field. Kamerlingh Onnes, thus, had discovered superconductivity in liquefying helium, and for his many achievements in the area of low-temperature physics, he was awarded the Nobel Prize in Physics in 1913.

As the properties of various metals near liquid helium temperature (4.20 Kelvins) were being investigated, by 1920 it became evident that liquid helium exhibits strange and unusual properties around 2.20 Kelvins, thus making it a subject of intense study. In 1924, Kamerlingh Onnes and coworkers found that liquid helium density has a maximum at around 2.30 Kelvins and a graph of density versus temperature shows a cusp rather than a smooth curve as in the analogous case of water. After several attempts, Willem Hendrik Keesom (1876-1956) of Leiden succeeded in solidifying liquid helium under several atmospheric pressures and showed that the melting curve (pressure versus temperature) bends at the lower end so as to appear almost parallel to the temperature axis. This led Kamerlingh Onnes to surmise that under atmospheric pressure, helium may remain a liquid down to absolute zero temperature. By 1927, Keesom and coworkers observed an increase in the dielectric constant of liquid helium, as well as peculiar variations in the specific heat at around 2.20 Kelvins. It was suggested that a phase change in liquid helium occurs at 2.19 Kelvins, such that normal "liquid helium I" prevails at higher temperature, while stable "liquid helium II" exists at lower temperature. A curve of specific heat of liquid helium as a function of temperature resembles the Greek letter lambda, and the critical temperature at which phase transition occurs is known as the "lambda point."

In addition to these accumulated perplexing properties of liquid helium, in 1935, Keesom and his daughter A. P. Keesom discovered that helium II exhibits a seemingly infinite thermal conductivity. At the University of Cambridge, John Frank Allen and his collaborators, in addition to confirming Keesom's result, showed that the thermal conductivity of helium II differed from the ordinary because of its dependence on the temperature gradient. In 1938, Allen and his coworkers were to find two of the three important properties of helium II.

Pyotr Leonidovich Kapitsa arrived at the Cavendish Laboratory in 1921. After initially working under the supervision of Ernest Rutherford, he received his Ph.D. in 1923 and remained at Cambridge until 1934. By early 1930, he was honored by The Royal Society of Science and installed as a Royal Society Professor and the director of the newly constructed Mond Laboratory. During this time, Kapitsa had achieved "liquefaction of helium by an adiabatic method without precooling with liquid hydrogen," a common procedure since Kamerlingh Onne's work. Kapitsa, who returned to the Soviet Union in 1934 for a visit, was not permitted to leave (until 1965) and was named director of a new Institute of Physical Problems in 1935.

The apparent lack of "explanation to the abnormal thermal conductivity of helium II" evident from Keesom's experimental results, confirmed by Allen and collaborators, provided the setting for Kapitsa's work. In a 1938 article that appeared in *Nature*, he suggested that the thermal conductivity of helium II, below the lambda point, occurs via the convection currents rather than the normal conduction process. He pointed out that such convection current can be maintained only if the viscosity of helium II is exceedingly low. The experimental data pointed to the fact that viscosity of helium II was at least eight times less than that slightly above the lambda point (2.20 Kelvins). Kapitsa showed experimentally that the viscosity of "helium II was at least ten thousand times less than that of gaseous hydrogen at low temperature," supposedly the least viscous of fluids. Based on these supporting arguments, Kapitsa proposed that helium II "below the lambda point assumes a special kind of state," which he called "superfluid." He was able to demonstrate the low viscosity (the internal resistance to flow) by allowing helium to flow through a narrow slit of 5 $\times$ 10^{-7} meters formed by two polished glass disks. He found that helium II passed through the slit rapidly below the lambda point but scarcely flowed above it.

A few months later, Allen and his collaborators at Cambridge discovered that around 1.08 Kelvins, a small heat flow, which was passed electrically, produced a rise in the liquid helium level in a closed bulb at the heated end. It should have fallen because of increased vapor pressure, and this was found to be the case for larger heat flows. When the experiment was repeated with a modified apparatus such that the top of the bulb at the hot end of the capillary was open, thus sharing the vapor pressure with the helium bath, no difference in the result was noted. They also found "fountain effect," in which a hydrodynamic flow through a capillary resulted when liquid helium was heated by radiation. In 1938, John Gilbert Daunt and Kurt Mendelssohn of the University of Oxford reported yet another property of superfluid, the phenomenon of the "creeping film." They demonstrated that when an empty beaker was lowered into the liquid, it filled to the level of the helium bath, even though the rim of the beaker was above the liquid level. It was observed that the level of the liquid in the beaker dropped at the same rate at which the beaker filled when it was partly lifted above the bath.

In a 1941 paper, Kapitsa proved, in addition to his original hypothesis, that helium II flow was composed actually of two currents: one flowing along the wall of the capillary and the other through the center in the opposite direction. He showed further that heat transfer in helium II is produced by these oppositely directed convection currents of different heat content. Kapitsa also assumed that the heat content of the flow of thin films along the wall was different, resulting from the molecular force of the surface, as opposed to the flow along the center. Through a series of experiments, Kapitsa established that below the lambda point, helium II is a mixture of normal fluid and superfluid and that the concentration of the latter increases as the temperature is lowered. He showed that superfluid has zero entropy and as one approaches absolute zero, helium II is transformed entirely into superfluid, which flows without friction, unlike the normal fluid that experiences drag as it transports heat. He also confirmed Daunt's and Mendelssohn's result; namely, if the fluid is forced out through a fine capillary, its temperature falls as much as three- to four-tenths of a degree. Seeking to demonstrate that heat transport in helium II is the result of movement of fluid, Kapitsa fashioned a movable vane and suspended it at the mouth of a flask filled with fluid so that any flow would be observable by the deflection of the vane. He then filled the electrically heatable flask with liquid helium and immersed it in a helium bath. By placing the movable vane at the mouth of the flask and applying heat to it, he was able to observe the deflection of the vane, proving conclusively that the liquid flows. During World War II, research activities in the area of low-temperature physics were suspended in the West, while in the Soviet Union, Kapitsa and other prominent physicists such as Lev Davidovich Landau progressed at a rapid rate, the latter formulating an elaborate quantum theory of liquid helium during 1940 to 1941.

Impact of Event

Following Kapitsa's hypothesis of superfluidity, numerous unexpected and puzzling properties of liquid helium were discovered, but none could be explained theoretically. From 1940 to 1941, Landau, of Kapitsa's Institute, advanced an elaborate quantum theory of liquid helium. Independently, Laslo Tisza of the Collège de France advanced some of the qualitative aspects of the theory of helium II, such as zero entropy and "second sound." Landau's theory of superfluidity describes quantum mechanically all observed macroscopic properties of liquid helium below the lambda point at 2.19 Kelvins. The two fluids, each in a different state, are assumed to coexist as a mixture of separate quantum states capable of independent simultaneous motion, free of mutual drag, as if through each other. The new state—the superfluid state emerging through a phase change in the normal fluid—is nonviscous and has zero entropy. The transition from normal to superfluid increases with decreasing temperature and tends to complete at 0 Kelvins. The normal viscous fluid transports heat, and in a sense, it is heat itself, flowing against the background of superfluid at ground state or zero energy.

Kapitsa had shown in one of his experiments that while normal fluid escaping from a flask that was being electrically heated deflected the movable vane, the quantity of liquid helium remained unchanged. The explanation of this phenomenon is that superfluid countercurrent flowed back into the flask, keeping the quantity of fluid constant. Landau's theory assumes the superfluid flow to be "irrotational," and according to the theory of hydrodynamics by the well-known eighteenth-century Swiss mathematician, Leonhard Euler (1707-1783), the flow of such nonviscous fluid past a solid surface should not exert a force on the body. Thus, normal fluid current in one direction and the countercurrent in the opposite direction would keep the quantity of fluid in a container unchanged.

The theory of liquid helium predicts the so-called second sound. Based on the propagation of two different kinds of waves, one associated with the normal fluid and the other with the superfluid, both moving simultaneously in opposite directions with different velocities, Landau's theory should lead to a second sound, in addition to the ordinary sound. The initial effort to detect the "second sound" failed in 1940. It soon became evident, however, that while the ordinary sound waves are associated with cyclical compression and rarefaction of fluid which propagates through the fluid, the second sound waves oscillating in opposite directions would be too weak to detect. Such counteroscillations of normal and superfluid were realized as giving rise to oscillations of heat relative to cold superfluid background of ground state. Thermal waves can be expected to radiate and are susceptible to excitation (hence, detection) by appropriately tuned temperature oscillators. A. P. Peshkov successfully confirmed the occurrence of second sound in helium II. In recognition of his theory of liquid helium, Landau was awarded the 1962 Nobel Prize in Physics.

Eminent Soviet physicists, such as Ilya Lifshitz, Isaak Yakovlevich Pomeranchuk, Nikolai Nikolaevich Bogoliubov, and others, continued to explore superfluidity after Landau's death. The work done on liquid helium in the United States pointed to the fact that critical phase change in helium II is brought on by the formation of microscopic vortices, experimentally verified by William Frank Vinen of Mond Laboratory in Cambridge. It soon became obvious that since helium is composed of two stable isotopes—helium-4 and helium-3—it should exhibit different statistical characteristics. Helium-4 would obey Bose-Einstein statistics, whereas helium-3 atoms conform to Fermi-Dirac statistics, and therefore liquid helium composed of pure helium-3 isotope would show totally different characteristics. In 1949, Edward Roger Grilly, Edward Frederic Hammel, and Stephen George Sydoriak, of Los Alamos showed that helium-3 liquefies at 3.20 Kelvins. Experiments indicate that helium-3 does not become superfluid and that it is a new and even more interesting quantum fluid in comparison with helium-4.

The study of superfluid and low-temperature physics has progressed at a rapid rate since Kapitsa's hypothesis and experiments. Kapitsa is said to have believed firmly that the secrets of nature are revealed only at the limits of physical phenomena. After nearly half a century, he was awarded the 1978 Nobel Prize for his contribution to low-temperature and plasma physics.

Bibliography

Kapitsa, P. L. *The Collected Papers of P. L. Kapitza.* Edited by D. ter Haar. 4 vol. Oxford: Pergamon Press, 1926-1970. In these highly technical volumes, one can observe Kapitsa's contributions to physics. His papers appearing in Volume 2, pertaining to superfluidity, are simple to follow. A serious reader should not pass up the opportunity of studying these volumes. Ter Haar's work in bringing Kapitsa's scientific papers to the English-speaking world has opened up a new vista of Soviet science.

Kedrov, Fedor B. *Kapitza: Life and Discoveries.* Translated by Mark Fradkin. Moscow: Mir, 1984. Kedrov's account of Kapitsa's scientific career and his life in the Soviet Union under Joseph Stalin is that of a journalist. In addition to numerous factual details, this volume contains a complete list of Kapitsa's scientific and nontechnical writings and related works. This book should be viewed as a primer to Kapitsa's long and productive career.

Lifshitz, Eugene M. "Superfluidity." *Scientific American*, 198 (June, 1958): 20. A well-written account of Kapitsa's discovery of the phenomenon of superfluidity and the historical development of low-temperature physics. Written for the general reader by a well-known Soviet scientist.

Lubkin, Gloria B. *Nobel Prizes: To Kapitza for Low Temperature Studies. Physics Today* 31 (December, 1978): 17-19. This article captures the essence and importance of Kapitsa's work.

Perry, Albert. Introduction to *Peter Kapitza on Life and Science*, by Pyotr L. Kapitza. New York: Macmillan, 1968. In addition to a brief sketch of Kapitsa's life, this volume contains several of his essays. Kapitsa's work with Cavendish Laboratory is well explored by Perry in the three essays discussing reminiscences and recollections about Rutherford.

Spruch, Grace Marmor. "Pyotr Kapitza, Octogenarian Dissident." *Physics Today* 32 (September, 1979): 34-36. This brief account of Kapitsa's career appeared a year after he won the Nobel Prize for his discovery of superfluidity. A perceptive reader will be able to discern Kapitsa's development from a prisoner in a gilded cage to an effective dissident who treads a narrow path.

Trigg, George L. *Landmark Experiments in Twentieth-Century Physics.* New York: Crane, Russak, 1975. A highly readable and accurate technical account, with appropriate references to chronological developments of low-temperature physics from 1908, when Kamerlingh Onnes succeeded in liquefaction of helium, is offered in this volume. Extensive excerpts from Kapitsa's original papers that appeared in *Nature* enhance the contents.

Wilson, David. *Rutherford: Simple Genius.* Cambridge, Mass.: MIT Press, 1983. Rutherford played a crucial role in Kapitsa's life. An account of the special bond that existed between the teacher and his unique student appears in chapter 16 of this interesting book.

V. L. Madhyastha

Cross-References

Rutherford Presents His Theory of the Atom (1912), p. 527; Rutherford Discovers the Proton (1914), p. 590; Bednorz and Müller Discover a High-Temperature Superconductor (1986), p. 2311.

HAHN SPLITS AN ATOM OF URANIUM

Categories of event: Physics and chemistry
Time: December, 1938
Locale: Kaiser Wilhelm Institute for Chemistry, Berlin (Dahlem), Germany

Hahn led the group that established uranium fission

Principal personages:

OTTO HAHN (1879-1968), a German physical chemist, codiscoverer of element 91 protactinium, namesake for element 105 hahnium, and winner of the 1944 Nobel Prize in Chemistry for his discovery of nuclear fission

LISE MEITNER (1878-1968), an Austrian-Swedish physicist; codiscoverer of element 91 protactinium, and first female winner of the Fermi award (for her work on fission)

FRITZ STRASSMANN (1902-1980), a German chemist who received the Fermi award for work on nuclear fission

ENRICO FERMI (1901-1954), an Italian-American physicist who played a key role in the discovery of fission, in the development of nuclear reactors, and of the atomic bomb; received the 1938 Nobel Prize in Physics

IRÈNE JOLIOT-CURIE (1897-1956), a French physicist, codiscoverer of artificial radioactivity who received the 1935 Nobel Prize in Chemistry together with her husband

FRÉDÉRIC JOLIOT (1900-1958), a French physicist, codiscoverer of artificial radioactivity who received the 1935 Nobel Prize in Chemistry with his wife

PAVLE PETAR SAVIĆ (1909-   ), a Yugoslavian physical chemist who looked for transuranic elements with Irène Joliot-Curie

OTTO ROBERT FRISCH (1904-1979), an Austrian-English physicist who worked with his aunt, Lise Meitner, to explain nuclear fission

Summary of Event

When Adolph Hitler seized power in Germany on January 30, 1933, Otto Hahn did not think Hitler's regime would last. But Hitler was still in power ten years later, and Hahn refused to work on military research for Hitler. In this the world was fortunate, for military research in Hahn's field led to the atomic bomb.

Hahn was a superb experimentalist; specifically, he was a radiochemist. He headed the department of radioactivity of the chemical division of the Kaiser Wilhelm Research Institute in Berlin, and had done so since its inception in 1912. Together with a colleague, Lise Meitner, he discovered a new element which they named protactinium. He enjoyed a modest fame which gave him some protection against Hitler's followers.

Much of Hahn's work lay in discovering the chain of decay products of the naturally occurring radioactive elements. Uranium, for example, is a natural element which is radioactive; that is, it emits radiation. Upon so doing, it changes or decays into a "daughter" element, thorium. Thorium, in turn, decays to radium, which decays to radon, and so forth, with the ultimate end product being a stable form of lead. As one element decays into another, three types of radiation may be emitted. Ernest Rutherford, under whom Hahn once studied, named them for the first three letters of the Greek alphabet: alpha, beta, and gamma. Uranium, thorium, and radium all emit alpha particles when they decay. In 1909, Rutherford showed that alpha particles are actually helium nuclei, and in fact, this is where Earth's helium originates. The helium with which one fills balloons comes from gas wells drilled in the ground. It got there because natural radioactive elements in the dirt and rocks emitted alpha particles as they decayed. Helium itself is stable and is not radioactive. In trying to understand radioactive decay, some scientists pictured a uranium nucleus as composed of swarms of alpha particles. They imagined that alpha decay occurred when one of the alpha particles managed to break free and leave the swarm. In the uranium decay chain, there are eight steps in which alpha particles are emitted; there are six steps in which a beta particle is emitted. Beta particles are the familiar electrons, but in this case they are emitted by the nucleus. One normally thinks of the nucleus as a ball of neutrons and protons, but it is not clear where the electron comes from. For a very crude model, suppose that a neutron is a proton (positive charge) and an electron (negative charge) somehow crammed together. In beta decay, a neutron must change into a proton and an electron. Hence, when the beta particle (electron) is ejected from the nucleus, the nucleus is left with one more proton (positive charge) than it formerly had.

Going beyond natural radioactivity, artificial radioactivity was discovered in 1934 by Irène Joliot-Curie and Frédéric Joliot. They showed that alpha particles striking the nuclei of light elements, such as aluminum, could make those elements radioactive, however, alphas were ineffective at making heavy elements radioactive, because alpha particles are composed of two protons bound together with two neutrons; heavy elements are composed of a large number of protons (92 for uranium) and a larger number of neutrons. The large positive charge of the heavy elements repel the positive charge of the alpha particle and keep it from penetrating the nucleus.

When alpha particles were allowed to fall on the light element beryllium, a strange new particle was emitted. In 1932, James Chadwick showed that this new particle had zero charge, and consequently, it was named the neutron. The neutron made a wonderful nuclear bullet because it was not repelled by the positively charged nuclei as the alpha particle had been. It became popular to bombard various elements with neutrons and to look for interesting results. Enrico Fermi did exactly that. What usually occurred was that the target nucleus absorbed the incoming neutron, and then beta decayed into the element having one more proton. In a fateful experiment,

Fermi bombarded uranium with neutrons. He expected to make a new element beyond uranium, a "trans-uranic" element. He made trace amounts of the elements which would be called neptunium and plutonium.

Since Hahn and Meitner were experts on the chemistry of the heavy radioactive elements, they repeated Fermi's experiment to analyze the results more carefully. Fritz Strassmann, a young German analytical chemist, joined their group in 1935. By early 1938, they had found ten different radioactive elements where Fermi had found only a few. Supposing the main ones to be beta decay daughters, Hahn, Meitner, and Strassmann proposed four transuranic elements, but they did so with reservations. Although they had seen evidence of their new elements, they had not been able to isolate them cleanly.

Pavle Petar Savić, a chemist from Yugoslavia, was now working with Irène Joliot-Curie. They claimed to have found thorium after bombarding uranium with neutrons. Hahn's group thought it unlikely that one neutron could knock an alpha particle out of uranium and change it to thorium. They carefully checked for thorium, but could find none. Savić and Joliot-Curie then claimed to have found a radioactive element which they could not separate from lanthanum. In a similar vein, Hahn's group found a radioactive product which they supposed was a type of radium, but they could not chemically separate it from barium.

In the waning weeks of 1938, Hahn and Strassmann did a remarkable series of complex experiments. Their experiments were difficult because they had to work with small samples. Hahn's group had only a weak neutron source; consequently, some of the daughter nuclei were produced only by the thousands. (It can be compared with the million billion atoms to be found in a pencil dot.) With Hahn's expertise, they used techniques such as fractional crystallization wherein relatively pure crystals of various substances crystallize at different temperatures from a hot solution.

Hahn had pioneered the technique of tracing a substance by its radioactivity in which case one does not need weighable quantities of the target substance. Daughter atoms are often created "glowing hot," which makes them stand out. Such nuclei are said to be in an excited state. Even if they could be seen with the naked eye, these nuclei would not look hot because they don't give off normal heat as they cool or "de-excite." Instead, they emit packets of energy called gamma rays. Hahn and Strassmann had sensitive Geiger-Müller counters with which to detect these gamma rays. From the number of rays detected, they could estimate the number of atoms in their sample. In time, Hahn and Strassmann firmly established that the "radium" which they thought they had formed, and had been unable to separate from barium, was in fact radioactive barium. As impossible as it seemed to them, a single neutron caused the uranium nucleus to split into two roughly equal parts. Their scientific paper announcing that man had split the atom was published December 22, 1938.

Impact of Event

Hahn asked Meitner to develop a theory that would make sense of his results.

Meitner and her nephew Otto Frisch became absorbed in the problem for some time. It seemed impossible to them that the nucleus should be brittle and seemingly split into two parts as if a neutron struck it along a cleavage line. In fact, Frisch recalled that Niels Bohr had suggested that the nucleus was not brittle, but was more like a drop of liquid. Frisch visualized the nucleus as a liquid drop struck by a neutron, causing it to vibrate. Oscillations could build up which would break the original drop into two drops. Since these smaller drops would both be positively charged, they would repel each other with tremendous force. Borrowing a term used to describe the splitting of cells in biology, Frisch later named the process "fission." Because of the strength of the electrical repulsion, the fission fragments should fly apart with millions of times the energy involved in chemical reactions. It took Frisch only a few hours to set up an experiment in his laboratory and to detect the energetic fission fragments.

Another characteristic of fission was soon discovered: Each fission releases two or three neutrons. These neutrons can cause other fissions which cause still more fissions in what is called a chain reaction. If this reaction is controlled, one can build a nuclear reactor and use it for an energy source. If the reaction is allowed to proceed without control, a bomb can turn itself to incandescent vapor in less than one millionth of a second.

Thus, Hahn's work formed an essential link in the chain which led to both nuclear power and nuclear weapons. As the power of the nucleus became available, some predicted that nuclear power would be so cheap, it would be provided free as a government service. Others saw in nuclear weapons a way to end World War II and to make future wars unthinkable. It can be argued that the use of the atomic bomb on Japan ultimately saved many lives by making an invasion of mainland Japan unnecessary. There is no doubt that the terror of nuclear war has been of prime importance in keeping the superpowers from directly attacking each other during the years of the Cold War.

Hahn's own life can summarize the societal impact of his work. During World War I, Hahn worked with Fritz Haber to use poison gas as a weapon. When Hahn expressed reservations, Haber argued that gas could bring an early end to the war and thereby save lives. Later, Hahn was so upset when he saw the agony of Russian soldiers who had been gassed that he attempted to use his own respirator to aid them. During World War II, although Hahn avoided direct military work, he did not actively speak out against government policies. Yet, during the 1950's, Hahn became politically active and quite outspoken against the misuse of nuclear power and against large stockpiles of nuclear weapons.

Bibliography

Hahn, Otto. *New Atoms: Progress and Some Memories*. New York: Elsevier, 1950. A collection of popular level papers about the discovery of fission and related topics, it includes his Nobel lecture, as well as some personal reminiscences from the history of natural radioactivity.

_____. *Otto Hahn: A Scientific Autobiography.* Edited and translated by Willy Ley. New York: Charles Scribner's Sons, 1966. An easily read work, includes many helpful footnotes by translator Willy Ley. It also features historical photographs, translations of three of Hahn's key scientific papers on discovering fission, biographical notes on forty-two scientists, a synoptic calendar of Hahn's life, and a comprehensive bibliography of Hahn's publications.

Irving, David. *The German Atomic Bomb.* New York: Simon & Schuster, 1967. The gripping popular account of the efforts by Germany's scientists and government to develop the atomic bomb. It gives the author's views as to why they failed despite their early start over the allies' bomb programs. It tells in detail Hahn's story of discovering fission.

Rhodes, Richard. *The Making of the Atomic Bomb.* New York: Simon & Schuster, 1986. An exhaustive popular account of the making and use of the American atomic bomb. The story is told in considerable detail and is possibly the most comprehensive single volume on the subject. It includes the story of Hahn's discovery of fission and places it within the worldwide perspective of the many nations which then sought the atomic bomb. It also includes an extensive bibliography. Despite its length, the book is spellbinding.

Shea, William R., ed. *Otto Hahn and the Rise of Nuclear Physics.* Boston: D. Reidel, 1983. A collection of copiously referenced papers on Hahn's discoveries of nuclear fission, nuclear isomerism, radiothorium (thorium-228), and related matters. It includes a fine chapter on Hahn and social responsibility. It is accessible to the general reader, but a little more difficult than other books by Hahn.

Charles W. Rogers

Cross-References

Becquerel Wins the Nobel Prize for the Discovery of Natural Radioactivity (1903), p. 199; Einstein States His Theory of Special Relativity: $E = mc^2$ (1905), p. 297; Bohr Writes a Trilogy on Atomic and Molecular Structure (1912), p. 507; Rutherford Presents His Theory of the Atom (1912), p. 527; Chadwick Discovers the Neutron (1932), p. 973; Frédéric Joliot and Irène Joliot-Curie Develop the First Artificial Radioactive Element (1933), p. 987; Seaborg and McMillan Make Element 94, Plutonium (1941), p. 1181; Fermi Creates the First Controlled Nuclear Fission Chain Reaction (1942), p. 1198; The World's First Nuclear Reactor Is Activated (1943), p. 1230; The First Atomic Bomb Is Successfully Detonated (1945), p. 1265; Teller and Ulam Develop the First H-Bomb (1951), p. 1401; The United States Opens the First Commercial Nuclear Power Plant (1957), p. 1557.

THE BOURBAKI GROUP PUBLISHES
ÉLÉMENTS DE MATHÉMATIQUE

Category of event: Mathematics
Time: 1939
Locale: Paris, France

The *"Bourbaki circle"* of French mathematicians published the first of more than sixty monographs surveying and synthesizing the abstract structure of extant operational mathematics

Principal personages:
ANDRÉ WEIL (1906-   ), a French mathematician
JEAN DIEUDONNÉ (1906-   ), a French mathematician

Summary of Event

From the publications of Georg Cantor, Giuseppe Peano, through the logicist work of Bertrand Russell and Alfred North Whitehead's *Principia Mathematica* (1910-1913), to the formal axiomatics of David Hilbert's *Grundlagen der Geometrie* (1899; *The Foundations of Geometry*, 1902) and *Grundzüge der Theoretischen Logik* (1928; *Principles of Mathematical Logic*, 1950), mathematics has evolved through several distinct phases in regards to its degree of abstraction, self-consistency, and unity. Notwithstanding the apparent limits of formalization attendant on Kurt Gödel's incompleteness theorems in 1931, in many areas of applied mathematics there remained numerous active followers of Hilbert's axiomatics. Axiomatics, for Hilbert, remained the means to provide and explain the deductive structure of logical and mathematical conceptual systems, isolating the general principles that serve as axioms from which all other key consequences can be deduced. Hilbert maintained that there are no innate differences in the degree and kind of rigor, clarity, and internal consistency between one branch of mathematics and another, with axiomatics providing the language and method for unifying all mathematical specializations.

The modern ideas of Peano, Russell, Hilbert, and others have loosened many of the traditional connections of mathematics with specific ideas about "number" and "quantity," instead underscoring the general roles of abstract structures and axioms. As Hermann Weyl in *Philosophie der Mathematik und Naturwissenschaft* (1927; *Philosophy of Mathematics and Natural Science*, 1949) has discussed, key features of Hilbert's mathematical views that survived Gödel and intuitionist criticism include reliance on abstract deduction, an autonomous language and method continually concerned with solving outstanding practical problems and creation of new and more comprehensive and integrative concepts and methods.

In contrast to the practically inapplicable logicism of Frege and Russell, and Brouwer's intuitionism, Hilbert's outlook was at least in part that of a working applications-oriented mathematician. Throughout the 1930's, the pragmatic counterbalance to formalist foundation studies included widespread use of Hilbert space representations in statistical and quantum mechanics, the efforts of Kolmorgorov on probability theory, and eventually the diverse effects of the composite French mathematical group, Nicolas Bourbaki.

Notwithstanding a 1949 biographical note on "Professor Bourbaki" of the "Royal Poldavian Academy and Nancago University," the name Bourbaki designates a largely anonymous group of principally French mathematicians, first organized shortly before World War II. Although never acknowledged, André Deleachet in his text on mathematical analysis includes as key Bourbaki circle members noted mathematicians André Weil, Jean Dieudonné, Henri Cartan, Charles Chevalley, Jean Delsarte, and Samuel Erlenberg, most originally associated with the École Normal Supérieure in Paris. Some have suggested that the pseudonym "Bourbaki" refers to the Greco-French general Charles Bourbaki, defeated in the Franco-Prussian War by unconventional German tactics, and thus obliquely to many French mathematicians responding to a perceived "germanic" onslaught of strict Hilbertian formalists. The nature of the Bourbaki group's systematic approach to and interpretation of mathematics was first presented in the initial volumes of the *Éléments de mathématique*, in 1939, since continued in several annual installments under the aegis of the Séminaire Bourbaki. As recounted by noted mathematician Laurent Schwartz, each of the Bourbaki volumes is the result of periodic group meetings, whose resulting drafts involve lengthy criticism and revisions. Intended as high-level textbooks for "working mathematicians" at the post-graduate level and above, one of the *Éléments'* avowed purposes is to serve as a perplexed mathematician's guide to the structural unity of all mathematics, in the face of its apparent splintering into separate and uncommunicating specialisms.

Although in many respects incorporating the spirit and some of the technologies of Hilbert's formal axiomatics, as a prologue "Bourbaki" clearly distinguishes the latter's logical formalism from its own "structural axiomatics." In this structuralist approach, functions, operations, transformations, and substitutions are but different names for various types of fundamental relations. Bourbaki criticizes Hilbert's overemphasis on logico-deductive reason as the sole basis and unifying principle for mathematical relations, calling it the only external form and vehicle that the mathematician gives to his thought. What the Bourbakian method sets as its aim is exactly that which it believes Hilbert's logical formalism cannot by itself supply; namely, the profound creativity and intelligibility of mathematics.

Taking a "naive realist" approach assuming mathematical theories as "given" and ignoring metamathematical questions on the nature and existence of mathematical objects or the connections between language and intuition, "structural relations" or structures are simply posited as the most fundamental points of common access for conceptually unifying the diversity of mathematical theories. Although never defined to the full satisfaction of many readers, mathematical structures are characterized by Bourbaki as abstract common or generic concepts that can be applied to different sets of elements whose nature has been specified, common properties expressible in the same way in different mathematical theories, and the form of a possible system of related objects that ignores specific material features of the objects not relevant to their abstract interrelations. In contrast to premathematical givens or assumptions of Russell, Hilbert, or L. E. J. Brouwer, Bourbaki structures are described as practical and useful tools from which the global aspects of a mathematical problem or theory can be reconstructed from its local aspects.

As outlined in a number of ancillary journal publications in the *American Journal of Symbolic Logic* and the *American Mathematical Monthly*, the main Bourbakian structural principles propose a hierarchy and network of interrelations between mathematical subdisciplines and theories. Particular structures are thought of as inhering in specific sets, the fundamental mathematical entity of the Bourbaki system. As understood by Bourbaki, set theory is considered as the systematic study of a triadic hierarchy of structures, each structure characterized by a suitable set of axioms, and serving as a conceptual network or linkage between different theories of present-day mathematics. Bourbaki cites the most basic of the three levels as including three general families of mathematical structures from which all (sub) branches derive; namely, algebraic, ordinal, and topological structures.

The main structural features of the algebraic family are its forms of "reversibility" as best characterized by inversion and negation operators. Prototypical properties of ordinal or order structures are those networks, or lattices, defined via the predecessor/successor relation. The most abstract fundamental structure—the topological—is characterized by the basic concepts of neighborhood, continuity, and limit. Beyond the first structural level of parent structures are so-called multiple structures, involving combinations of two or more fundamental structures simultaneously. Bourbaki cites as examples of multistructures topological algebra (including topological entities and properties and algebraic composition rules) and algebraic topology (including algebraic entities and properties together with topological construction rules). Finally, the level of particular or special structures corresponds to the different theories and branches of contemporary mathematics, not seen as independent and separate areas, but as crossroads where several general- and multiple-structures intersect and meet. The legitimacy and plausibility of this structurally integrative approach in mathematics is for Bourbaki based on the closer, but largely unperceived, functional unity between different mathematical theories and departments arising from the internal evolution of mathematics since about 1860. In contrast to Hilbert's formal axiomatics, Bourbaki repeatedly states that the total number and interconnections between multiple- and particular-structures cannot be delimited or classified in advance. For Bourbaki, Hilbert's original program of complete axiomatization is possible only for certain "univalent" mathematical theories (such as relational logic and geometry), which are determined entirely by a finite system of explicit axioms. Although easier said than shown, Bourbaki repeatedly argues that it is necessary to identify and explicate parent and multistructures by working with the rich fields of particular structures in which higher-level abstractions are embedded.

Impact of Event

The subsequent impact and history of Bourbaki's initial publications has largely been continued contributions to structurally explicating other domains of pure and applied mathematics. As an example of three intersecting multistructures discussed in later volumes, the *Éléments* considers the theory of real numbers. If considered with regard to compositional rules such as addition and multiplication, the real numbers form an algebraic "group," which is a set or class of relations having a special characteristic property such as symmetry. If arranged according to their ordinal magnitudes, the real numbers encompass an ordered set. Finally, examining the theory of continuity and limits for real numbers in the most general fashion necessitates recourse to central connectivity and adjacency properties of a topological space. Thus, in principle there are many advantages of a structuralistic mathematics. Most notably, once a theorem is proven for a general abstract structure, it is applicable immediately for any specific realization of that structure. For example, developments in the theory of measure and integration can be structurally applicable to some aspects of probability theory, by virtue of the common parent set of structural axioms.

Bourbaki has subsequently endorsed the view that the most appropriate foundation for mathematics is a combination of axiomatic set theory and symbolic logic. In this view, mathematical entities (numbers, geometric figures, and the like) are never given in isolation, but only in and as part of parent and multistructures. Nevertheless, in contrast to Hilbert, Bourbaki replies that mathematicians cannot map out all structures by working mechanically with symbols, but require their own special "intuition" to inform but not eliminate symbolism, formalisms, and axiomatics. What counts is not formal limits in themselves but whether a domain of mathematics is enlarged permanently by a study of its structural axioms.

The efforts of the Bourbaki circle to generalize axiomatically those (multiple and particular) mathematical structures in overlapping theories has continued in the more than sixty volumes and numerous journal papers appearing since 1939. To date, the order of publication of the *Éléments* has reflected only multistructures corresponding to particular extant areas of algebra, topology, topological vector space, integration theory, group theory, and Lie algebras. Not all the originally proposed topics of the Bourbaki circle have as yet been examined. In many cases, the Bourbakian structuralist approach has made it considerably more simple to see the general structures than the many previous hypotheses in areas such as the theory of fields, groups, lattices, and numbers. It is also true that in some classical areas of mathematics, it has not proven so simple to perceive and formulate mathematical theories in terms of axiomatized structures.

As the process of structural axiomatization continues, Bourbaki employs sometimes colorful idiosyncratic modifications of ordinary language whenever formal accuracy can be preserved along with intuitive perspicacity. This among other aspects of the Bourbaki movement has motivated several other new approaches during the 1960's to reformulate elementary mathematics, in some cases contributing driving ideas behind the so-called new math in grade-school teaching. More particularly, the "structural" theory of mathematics by Bourbaki directly stimulated, and in some cases interacted with, the efforts of Jean Piaget and others to outline the structural genesis and psychological development of mathematical and logical abilities in children. Piaget and others have focused on the question of whether the mathematical architectures of the Bourbaki circle are simply arbitrary axioms or are in some manner actually innate and natural in respect of human cognition.

Some mathematicians and educators have reacted negatively to Bourbaki structuralism, fearing that its dream of all-inclusive axiomatics is too inflexible and too removed from specific content and examples. Many educators, in particular, emphasize that it is clearly possible to derive adequately and apply many aspects of classical mathematics without knowing their parent structures and their interconnections. Other more supportive developments in philosophy and critical theory, such as the diverse "structuralisms" of Claude Lévi-Strauss, Louis Althusser, Michel Foucault, Michel Serres, and others, bear a superficial resemblance to the jargon and rigor of the Bourbaki mathematics. Bourbaki structures should not be confused with Thomas Kuhn's *Structures of Scientific Revolutions* (1962) or with other American philosophers debating how knowledge of abstract structures "matches" real structures of the physical world.

With the retirement of its original founders, it remains to be seen whether the colossal task of the Bourbaki project will be continued and completed beyond the roughly 25 percent now extant. Nevertheless, even the initial efforts of Bourbaki's structuralist mathematics have provided a stimulating and efficient method and model for organizing scientific as well as mathematical hypotheses in areas such as mathematical physics, linguistics, and economics, where there is adequate prior development and strong basic relationships that lend themselves to systematization.

Bibliography

Beth, Evert Willem. *Formal Methods.* New York: Gordon & Breach, 1962. Discusses typical influences of Bourbaki structuralism.
Beth, Evert W., and Jean Piaget. *Mathematical Epistemology and Psychology.* Translated by W. Mays. New York: Gordon & Breach, 1966. The primary source for Piaget's structuralism.
Fang, J., ed. *Towards a Philosophy of Modern Mathematics.* Hauppauge, N.Y.: Paideia Press, 1970. The best source for Bourbaki papers.
Gerock, Robert. *Mathematical Physics.* Chicago: University of Chicago Press, 1985. Discusses other Bourbaki and Piaget influenced analyses.
Kneebone, G. T. *Mathematical Logic and the Foundations of Mathematics: An Introductory Survey.* New York: D. Van Nostrand, 1963. A good introduction to the set theory, logical, and axiomatic methods of Bourbaki.

Gerardo G. Tango

Cross-References

Hilbert Develops a Model for Euclidean Geometry in Arithmetic (1898), p. 31; Russell Discovers the "Great Paradox" Concerning the Set of All Sets (1902), p. 184; Brouwer Develops Intuitionist Foundations of Mathematics (1904), p. 228; Zermelo Undertakes the First Comprehensive Axiomatization of Set Theory (1904), p. 233; Russell and Whitehead's *Principia Mathematica* Develops the Logistic Movement in Mathematics (1910), p. 465; Gödel Proves Incompleteness-Inconsistency for Formal Systems, Including Arithmetic (1929), p. 900; Cohen Shows That Cantor's Continuum Hypothesis Is Independent of the Axioms of Set Theory (1963), p. 1751.

MÜLLER DISCOVERS THAT DDT
IS A POTENT INSECTICIDE

Category of event: Chemistry
Time: 1939
Locale: Switzerland

Müller discovered that a chlorinated organic compound called dichloro-diphenyl-trichloroethane (DDT) was an effective insecticide for controlling vectors of disease and causes of devegetation

Principal personages:
> PAUL HERMANN MÜLLER (1899-1965), a Swiss chemist who discovered the insecticidal property of DDT and was awarded the 1948 Nobel Prize in Physiology or Medicine
> OTHMAR ZIEDLER, a German chemist who originally synthesized DDT while researching substitution reactions of aromatic organic molecules

Summary of Event

It has been known for centuries that numerous species of insects are vectors of human diseases and causative agents of agricultural devegetation. The scientific community recognized this problem, and numerous researchers attempted to discover insecticides that were potent to insects, yet relatively innocuous to humans, animals, and vegetation. Prior to the discovery of DDT in 1939 by Paul Hermann Müller, inorganic, arsenic-based insecticides were most commonly developed because of their effectiveness in controlling insects. These insecticides, which were initially used during the latter half of the 1800's, however, were found to be very toxic to humans and other mammals. Other common insecticides utilized prior to the 1940's were the inorganic fluorinated compounds plus organic-based nicotine, pyrethrum, and derris compounds. These substances, however, had limited application and insufficient permanent effect because of their instability in the environment.

Müller, a Swiss chemist, worked on developing an alternative to the most widely used inorganic arsenic-based insecticides while employed by the Swiss firm J. R. Geigy during the mid-1930's. Thus, Müller did not concentrate on modifying the noncarbonaceous "inorganic" compounds consisting of the metal arsenic and other elements, which, when combined, produce arsenic salts, oxides, or hydrides depending on the elemental composition. Instead, he focused on carbon-containing "organic" compounds, which, when combined with the element chlorine, produce organochlorine compounds.

Müller's task was to synthesize an original compound or to discover an existing one that would not only be an effective and safe insecticide but also would be economic and without malodor. Müller had determined from a review of published scientific literature regarding patented insecticides that the most effective mode of inducing insecticidal activity was via direct contact of the compound with the insect. This meant that it was not necessary for the insects to consume the insecticides in order for a toxic effect (that is, death) to occur. He also concluded that for an insecticide to be effective, especially for agricultural use, it needed to be chemically stable and, accordingly, relatively resistant to decay or inactivation in the environment.

As a result of his conclusions drawn from the literature, Müller decided to study organochlorine compounds. Many compounds in this class were already known to be relatively chemically stable under ambient conditions. In addition, an organochlorine compound called chloroform was already known to exhibit insecticidal properties. Accordingly, Müller focused on studying organochlorine compounds that contained a chemical group similar to the chloroform molecule. He eventually discovered an organochlorine molecule that exhibited potent insecticidal activity.

In 1939, Müller and his research group at J. R. Geigy developed an insecticide product that they named Gesarol. Müller had discovered that the active ingredient in Gesarol was insecticidal when tested against beetles and moths. The active ingredient was DDT, for the organochlorine compound dichloro-diphenyl-trichloroethane, which was originally synthesized in the laboratory of Othmar Ziedler, a German chemist, in 1874. Ziedler's intention was not to develop an insecticide but to determine the substitution reactions involving chlorine atoms and aromatic organic compounds. The organochlorine compound DDT was discovered by Ziedler as one of many products of such reactions, but its insecticidal property was unknown to anyone until years later.

Although the insecticidal properties of DDT were discovered by Müller in 1939 and its use was deployed almost immediately by the Swiss government to control the devastating Colorado beetle, its approval by the United States government for use as an insecticide was not initiated to any degree until 1944. The American government, via several federal health agencies, conducted tests during 1942 and 1943 to determine the effectiveness of DDT. In addition, tests were conducted also to determine potential long-term (chronic) and immediate (acute) health effects to humans. Based on the results of the governmental tests, it was concluded that DDT was indeed effective for terminating insect pests, yet relatively innocuous to human health. The product Gesarol with its active ingredient, DDT, was suggested by the J. R. Geigy company for possible use to combat the insect vectors confronted by the American troops engaged in World War II and stationed in Europe, Africa, and the South Pacific, where they were exposed to typhus-carrying lice and mosquitoes that transmitted malaria. The idea was derived from historical documentation of the use of the insecticide pyrethrum during 1900 in Cuba and 1904 in Panama to destroy the species of mosquitoes that transmitted yellow fever (*Aëdes*) and malaria (*Anopheles*) to humans. Although pyrethrum did not exhibit permanent activities, its use and the resulting benefits to soldiers in Cuba and workers in Panama demonstrated an effective application of an insecticide in order to decrease the outbreak of human diseases resulting from insect vectors. As a consequence of this historical account, the effectiveness of DDT, and the perceived innocuous impact to humans, the insecticide was selected by the United States government in 1944 as the optimal insecticide for use to protect American troops from the insect vectors that transmitted typhus and malaria. Later, the insecticide was released for agricultural and general commercial purposes following the war.

Impact of Event

The impact of using DDT as an insecticide can be viewed both positively and negatively. From a positive perspective, the insecticide proved to be instrumental in controlling insect pests and, in turn, preventing outbreaks of disease and destruction of vegetation. In contrast, DDT was shown eventually to exhibit greater toxicity and potential for adverse environmental impact than originally reported.

It was documented that the use of DDT in Italy and Japan during World War II resulted in the cessation of outbreaks of typhus by the decimation of lice. The use of DDT in Naples during early 1944 to delouse clothing, the native people, and American and English troops marked the first reported time in which a typhus epidemic was able to be ended at will. Equally as important, delousing programs using DDT helped to prevent future outbreaks of typhus in epidemic proportions.

Outbreaks of malaria, which is transmitted by mosquitoes and was endemic in the South Pacific islands during the war, were also decreased as a result of using DDT. The chemical insecticide was discharged from airplanes and sprayed liberally over the islands to control the proliferation of mosquitoes, without reported cases of toxicity to humans. As a result of the reported effectiveness of DDT in decreasing outbreaks of typhus and malaria among military personnel and its use to end and prevent typhus epidemics during the World War II era, Müller was rewarded with the 1948 Nobel Prize in Physiology or Medicine.

Following the release of DDT for agricultural and commercial purposes, the insecticide was used extensively on farms and in residential areas. Although effective and appreciated for protecting crops and combating insect infestations, there was an upsurge of concern regarding the toxicity of DDT. Evidently, the initial toxicity testing conducted by the American government during the early 1940's and the lack of reported cases of illness among exposed troops during World War II were not accurate indicators of potential long-term or chronic health effects to humans.

Indiscriminate use of DDT during the postwar years resulted in reported contamination of food, water, and soil. In turn, the insecticide passed through the food chain, and DDT residues were detected in humans and other animals. It was discovered later that DDT has the propensity to absorb into and through biological tissue and accumulate in body fat. In addition, excessive exposure to DDT was determined to increase the risk of damaging the nervous system in humans and other mammals. These findings resulted in the eventual ban of DDT for use in the United States approximately thirty years following the discovery of its insecticidal property. It should be noted that although the insecticide is stable in the environment, tends to accumulate in fat tissue, and has the potential to induce adverse environmental impact, DDT did not cause any reported fatalities to humans. Indeed, in comparison to other alternatives at the time, DDT was relatively safe. Unfortunately, the misuse and overuse of DDT led to excessive environmental contamination and, subsequently, to an end of its legal use.

Bibliography

Asimov, Isaac. *Asimov's Biographical Encyclopedia of Science and Technology.* 2d rev. ed. Garden City, N.Y.: Doubleday, 1982. This reference provides biographical summaries of 1,195 great scientists, including Müller, and an overview of his discovery of the insecticidal property of DDT.

Dunlap, Thomas R. *DDT: Scientists, Citizens, and Public Policy.* Princeton, N.J.: Princeton University Press, 1981. Provides a historical perspective about DDT and detailed descriptions of its use and impact.

Jukes, Thomas H., et al. *Effects of DDT on Man and Other Mammals.* New York: Irvington, 1973. Contains detailed papers regarding the effectiveness and toxicity of DDT.

McGraw-Hill. Modern Scientists and Engineers. 3 vols. New York: McGraw-Hill, 1980. This reference provides detailed, yet concise biographical summaries of several outstanding scientists of the twentieth century and their major contributions.

Taton, René, ed. *Science in the Twentieth Century.* Translated by A. J. Pomerans. New York: Basic Books, 1966. Provides an overview of the historical sequences of events that influenced the development of the various scientific disciplines and applications.

Whorton, James. *Before "Silent Spring": Pesticides and Public Health in Pre-DDT America.* Princeton, N.J.: Princeton University Press, 1974. Focuses on the history and evolution of insecticides in response to a need to control insects, which affected agriculture and public health.

Michael S. Bisesi

Cross-References

Reed Establishes That Yellow Fever Is Transmitted by Mosquitoes (1900), p. 73; Gorgas Develops Effective Methods for Controlling Mosquitoes (1904), p. 223; Insecticide Use Intensifies When Arsenic Proves Effective Against the Boll Weevil (1917), p. 640; Zinsser Develops an Immunization Against Typhus (1930), p. 921; Theiler Introduces a Vaccine Against Yellow Fever (1937), p. 1091; Carson Publishes *Silent Spring* (1962), p. 1740; The United States Government Bans DDT Use to Protect the Environment (1972), p. 1982.

OPPENHEIMER CALCULATES THE
NATURE OF BLACK HOLES

Categories of event: Astronomy and physics
Time: February 15, 1939
Locale: Berkeley, California

Oppenheimer calculated that stellar matter could collapse under intense gravitational pressure to form what would later become known as a black hole

Principal personages:
> J. ROBERT OPPENHEIMER (1904-1967), an American physicist, director of the project to develop the first atomic weapon, and a leading innovator in American theoretical physics
> GEORGE MICHAEL VOLKOFF (1914-   ), a student of Oppenheimer who coauthored the paper published in 1939 that defined the nature of black holes
> KARL SCHWARZSCHILD (1873-1916), a German physicist who demonstrated that not even light could escape from the gravitational field of a very tightly confined, exceedingly large mass
> LEV DAVIDOVICH LANDAU (1908-1968), a Soviet physicist who postulated that matter in massive stars collapses into very tightly packed regions; winner of the 1962 Nobel Prize in Physics
> HARTLAND S. SNYDER (1913-   ), a student of Oppenheimer who described with him in mathematical terms how stars of great mass contract to gravitationally collapse

Summary of Event

Sir Isaac Newton first formulated the mathematical nature of gravity and its relationship to mass in 1692. Newton formulated that the more massive an object, the more gravity it possesses. Such a relationship is true for all objects with mass, including a child's marble, the earth, and massive stars. Shortly after Newton's brilliant philosophical and mathematical treatment of gravity, scientists began to consider the limits of mass and gravity. In 1796, Pierre-Simon Laplace used the eighteenth century notion that light was made of microscopic particles, or corpuscles, and reasoned that if there were a sufficiently massive body somewhere in the universe, these light corpuscles could not escape from its surface. Yet, Laplace's reasoning was nothing more than armchair musings on the limits of Newtonian gravity.

In 1915, German physicist Albert Einstein reconsidered Newton's description of gravity with profound effect in a treatment he called the "theory of relativity." Einstein's theory united such seemingly disparate ideas as light, energy, time, space, matter, and gravity into a single formulation, enabling all these concepts to be treated as unified elements of single conditions for the first time.

Later that year, German physicist Karl Schwarzschild considered the new philosophy of gravity, as proposed by Einstein. Schwarzschild began to ponder the relativistic mathematical implications of a point in space emanating an intense gravitational field and what an observer would see as that point in space was approached. He was contemplating Einstein's notion that light was affected, or bent, when traveling through a gravitational field, a concept substantiated in 1913 when the light of a star was apparently bent while traveling through the gravitational field of the sun.

Schwarzschild's mathematics were designed to establish the limits of relativity and the degree of the bending effect on light, not to define what would later become known as a "black hole." The significance of Schwarzschild's work was not only that he had uncovered some extremely interesting concepts based on relativity but also that some remarkable effects were mathematically allowed by relativity that seemed to violate even common sense.

Schwarzschild discovered that as one approaches his theoretical focal point of intense gravity (such as the earth's mass concentrated in a single point), space literally curves in on itself and relativity dictates that not even light can escape such a point. More significantly, Schwarzschild discovered that the intense gravitational field need not be confined to a single point in space. His calculations demonstrated that such effects could be observed if one compressed the earth to a sphere with a diameter of 1 centimeter. This relationship of mass to diameter has become known as the Schwarzschild radius.

In 1939, American physicist, J. Robert Oppenheimer and his student, George Michael Volkoff, were doing calculations on the nature of extremely massive star cores at the University of California, Berkeley. They were contemplating the theory of Soviet physicist Lev Davidovich Landau who, a decade before, had used Newton's theory of gravity in the first theoretical treatment to describe the center of very dense stars known as neutron stars. Landau believed that if a star were massive enough, the core would contract and be composed of densely packed neutrons; hence, the term neutron star.

The discussion of stellar densities continued, and it was suggested to Landau that if the density were great enough, the core of the star would continue to collapse even beyond the neutron state to a single point. Landau dismissed this suggestion as "ridiculous," insisting that his calculations demonstrated aptly that this could never happen.

Oppenheimer and Volkoff reasoned that there was nothing in the relativistic calculations that would prevent collapse beyond the neutron star state and added that Landau had used Newtonian concepts, which had been superseded by relativistic concepts. On February 15, 1939, they published their paper in the *Physical Review*. Oppenheimer and Volkoff continued to speculate even after their paper was published; they teamed up with another one of Oppenheimer's graduate students, mathematics prodigy Hartland S. Snyder, and formulated a more refined mathematical picture of such a hypothetical stellar collapse. In this treatment, published less than a year after the Oppenheimer-Volkoff paper, Oppenheimer and Snyder described in detail the effects of such a stellar collapse. They discussed the effects that would prevent such a collapse, including a rapid spin rate, stellar explosions, and internal pressure that would act to resist the collapse. Still, they speculated that a truly massive star could not help but collapse in on itself. Eventually, light would bend back into the star, as would any other form of radiation, until it no longer could escape. "The star thus tends to close itself off from any communication with a distant observer; only its gravitational field persists."

In these two papers, Oppenheimer and his students were the first to address the idea of a black hole as more than an academic exercise. They related not only the idea of such an object but also related it to stellar concepts and went on to define mathematically the limits of such an object. At no time during any of these discussions did the term "black hole" ever arise. Indeed, even Oppenheimer had no idea that such an object really existed, and if it did, how it might ever be detected (by his own definition, the object would tend to cut itself off from any outside communication). The first use of the term "black hole" was made by Princeton physicist John A. Wheeler in 1967.

In late 1963, a group of scientists convened in Dallas, Texas, for a meeting entitled "An International Symposium on Gravitational Collapse and Other Topics in Relativistic Astrophysics." At this meeting, the relationship of very strong, high-energy point sources emanating from space were to be discussed, and the strong suspicion was that these point sources of extraordinary energy could well be caused by the collapse of very massive stars to or beyond the Schwarzschild radius. The meeting was chaired by Oppenheimer. Also in attendance were Martin Schwarzschild, son of Karl, and Wheeler, who contributed his long-held convictions that black holes did, in fact, exist.

No black hole has ever been directly observed to offer definitive proof of their existence, but strong indirect evidence exists that they are actual inhabitants of our own galaxy.

Impact of Event

The Oppenheimer-Volkoff paper was an important early use of Einstein's relativity because it deliberately challenged Landau's use of classical Newtonian physics within the same predictive environment. It demonstrated clearly the superiority of relativistic physics compared to classical physics, which broke down so significantly as to become useless in predicting stellar conditions.

It was precisely for this purpose that Oppenheimer employed relativistic physics in his now famous discussion of the core of neutron stars. Oppenheimer, however, quickly realized that beyond the value of his paper to contrast Newtonian and classical physics, beyond its value to justify his view of neutron stars, there was born in it a wildly conjectural concept that there was a class of star so dense that it devoured itself and became, in essence, a hole in space and time, where space literally curved in on itself.

In his follow-up paper, Oppenheimer used the mathematical genius of Snyder to refine further the concept of a black hole to the point that it became a well-defined physical entity. It was Oppenheimer's refinement of the idea that took the concept of black holes from a physical abstraction to a physical entity.

The Oppenheimer-Snyder work defined the black hole in terms that are still used in the 1990's. When it was determined twenty years later that there was a class of bizarre stellar objects that emitted prodigious quantities of energy, Oppenheimer's studies surfaced and were applied to define further the strange environment and makeup of these objects.

Oppenheimer's work discussed the relativistic concepts of observing a black hole from nearby space and even within the direct physical influence of a black hole. Today, his work remains an important tool for explaining the extremes of relativistic physics.

An understanding of black holes is a vital piece of the vast puzzle of the universe. There may be a black hole lurking at the heart of nearly every galaxy, and black holes may hide a significant portion of the mass of the universe. Such answers are vital to predicting whether the universe will continue expanding indefinitely or will ultimately collapse upon itself.

Black holes are used widely in a variety of cosmological and astrophysical theories. They are blamed for everything from hot jets of matter seen ejected from the center of some galaxies to energetic X-ray pulses emitted from star groups. The science and theory of these enigmatic objects remain some of the most startling and interesting ideas in science in the late twentieth century.

Bibliography

Asimov, Isaac. *The Collapsing Universe*. New York: Walker, 1977. Asimov provides an easy-to-grasp look at the story of black holes as seen from the layperson's perspective. In his easy-to-read style, Asimov attacks the discussion from both the historical and scientific points of view.

Crease, Robert P., and Charles C. Mann. *The Second Creation*. New York: Macmillan, 1986. In this book, Crease and Mann follow the making of twentieth century physics from its nineteenth century roots to the most enigmatic mysteries of the late 1980's. Examines characters and personalities as well as the issues of physics. Although this work makes little mention of Oppenheimer's famous black hole paper of 1939, it offers a unique and fascinating glimpse into his character and personality.

Harwit, Martin. *Cosmic Discovery*. New York: Basic Books, 1981. This book offers a readable style and approach that details the development of the black hole concept and Oppenheimer's contribution. The book is written somewhat stiffly from the lay perspective, but it contains valuable information, photographs, and illustrations.

Shipman, Harry L. *Black Holes, Quasars, and the Universe*. New York: Houghton Mifflin, 1976. In this excellent book, black holes are covered extensively in a readable style and related to their cosmic cousins, the pulsars and quasars. The book relates how Oppenheimer's work with pulsars dovetailed into the black hole theory and how both are related to quasars. The book is thoroughly illustrated and is quite readable by those with a good background in the sciences.

Sullivan, Walter. *Black Holes: The Edge of Space, the End of Time*. Garden City, N.Y.: Doubleday, 1979. This excellent book is well illustrated and easy to read, offering a clear picture of the revolution in physics that led to the theoretical discovery of black holes by Oppenheimer and his colleagues. It details the pioneering efforts of Einstein and Schwarzschild and describes the historic 1963 Dallas conference, where the concept of black holes was first announced to the public.

Wheeler, John A. *A Journey into Gravity and Spacetime*. New York: W. H. Freeman, 1990. Wheeler, the Princeton physicist who coined the term "black hole," depicts gravity from its simplest forms to the black hole. The book is written for the armchair scientist, but is full of interesting stories and is lavishly illustrated in color so that anyone can enjoy it piecemeal or in its entirety.

Dennis Chamberland

Cross-References

Hartmann Discovers the First Evidence of Interstellar Matter (1904), p. 213; Einstein States His Theory of Special Relativity: $E = mc^2$ (1905), p. 297; Russell Announces His Theory of Stellar Evolution (1913), p. 585; Einstein Completes His Theory of General Relativity (1915), p. 625; Schwarzschild Develops a Solution to the Equations of General Relativity (1916), p. 630; Einstein's Theory of Gravitation Is Confirmed over Newton's Theory (1919), p. 684; Eddington Publishes *The Internal Constitution of the Stars* (1926), p. 815; Hubble Confirms the Expanding Universe (1929), p. 878; Bell Discovers Pulsars, the Key to Neutron Stars (1967), p. 1862; Wheeler Names the Phenomenon "Black Holes" (1968), p. 1881.

A SECRET ENGLISH TEAM DEVELOPS COLOSSUS

Category of event: Applied science
Time: The early 1940's
Locale: Bletchley Park, England

A secret team of specialists developed Colossus, the first all-electronic calculating device, in response to the need to decipher German military codes during World War II

Principal personages:
>THOMAS H. FLOWERS, the electronics expert who led the team that de-
>signed and built the Colossus and who was a major proponent for the
>use of vacuum tubes in computers
>MAX H. A. NEWMAN (1897-   ), a gifted mathematician and lecturer
>who was responsible for formulating the requirements for Colossus
>ALAN MATHISON TURING (1912-1954), a brilliant mathematician who
>contributed to the codebreaking computers that were the forerunners
>of Colossus
>C. E. WYNN-WILLIAMS, a member of the Telecommunications Research
>Establishment who worked on the electronic components of Colossus

Summary of Event

In 1939, during World War II, a team of scientists, mathematicians, and engineers met at Bletchley Park, outside London to discuss the development of machines that would break the secret code used in Nazi military communications. The Germans were using a machine called "Enigma" to communicate in code between headquarters and field units. The Enigma used a substitution code whereby a set of letters were substituted for the ones that normally made up the words. This in itself was not new; however, the Enigma enciphered (coded) only one letter and then shifted to a new position so that each letter of every word had a different key. The senders and receivers of the codes knew which rotor was being used for the substitution. The machine-made code used several rotors and so had vast substitution possibilities, which made the code extremely difficult to decode. The Enigma was portable, easy-to-use, and seemingly generated unbreakable codes. Polish scientists, however, had been able to examine a German Enigma and were able to break the codes from 1928 to 1938 by using electromechanical codebreaking machines called "bombas." In 1938, the Germans made the Enigma more complicated, and the Polish were no longer able to break the codes. In 1939, the Polish machines and codebreaking knowledge passed to the British.

Alan Mathison Turing was one of the mathematicians gathered at Bletchley Park to work on codebreaking machines. Turing was one of the first people to conceive of the universality of digital computers. He first mentioned the "Turing machine" in

1936 in an article published in "Proceedings," a publication of the London Mathematical Society. The Turing machine is a hypothetical device for solving any problem dependent on mathematical computation and is not restricted to only one task, hence, the universality feature. Turing's original and innovative contributions made him essential to the team working on codebreaking machines. Turing suggested an improvement to the Bletchley codebreaking machine, the "Bombe," which had been modeled on the Polish "bomba." This improvement increased the computing power of the machine. The Bombe was an electromechanical relay machine that was similar to the Enigma. The Bombe did not decode messages itself, but worked out the position of the Enigma rotors. Once the position of the Enigma rotors was known, the message could be decoded by specialists. The codebreaking machines replaced the tedious method of decoding by hand, which in addition to being slow, was ineffective in dealing with very complicated encryptions that were changed daily.

The Bombe was very useful until 1942, when the Germans started using a more sophisticated cipher machine known as the "Fish." The Fish used a binary code (a system of numbers in base two, in which the only numerals are 0 and 1). Max H. A. Newman, who was in charge of one subunit at Bletchley Park, believed that an automated device could be designed to break the codes produced by the Fish. Thomas H. Flowers, who was in charge of a switching group at the Post Office Research Station at Dollis Hill, had been approached to build a special purpose electromechanical device for Bletchley Park in 1941. The device was not useful, and Flowers was assigned to other problems. He worked closely with Turing, Newman, and C. E. Wynn-Williams of the Telecommunications Research Establishment (TRE) to develop a machine to break the Fish codes. The Dollis Hill team worked on the tape driving and reading problems, and Wynn-Williams' team at TRE worked on electronic counters and the necessary circuitry. Their efforts produced the Heath Robinson, which could read two thousand characters per second. The Heath Robinson used vacuum tubes, an uncommon component in the early 1940's. The vacuum tubes performed more reliably and rapidly than the relays that had been used for counters. Heath Robinson and the companion machines proved that high-speed electronic devices could successfully do cryptoanalytic work (solve decoding problems). Entirely automatic in operation once started, the Heath Robinson was put together at Bletchley Park in the spring of 1943. The Heath Robinson machine had a small total output because of problems with reliability and, when the machine overheated, it was known to seize up and catch fire. The team working on the problems finally solved them and was able to use the machine in codebreaking. The Heath Robinson was inadequate for the codebreaking needs shortly after it was put into use, so work began on a bigger, faster, and more powerful machine: the Colossus.

Flowers led the team that designed and built the Colossus in eleven months at Dollis Hill. The first Colossus (Mark I) was a bigger, faster version of the Heath Robinson and read about five thousand characters per second. Colossus had approximately 1,500 vacuum tubes, which was more than any tried elsewhere at the time. Although Turing and Wynn-Williams were not directly involved with the design of the Colossus, their previous work on the Heath Robinson was crucial, since the first Colossus was based on the Heath Robinson.

Colossus was operational at Bletchley Park in December, 1943, and Flowers made arrangements for the manufacture of the time-consuming components in case other machines were required. The request for additional machines came in March, 1944. The second Colossus, the Mark II, was extensively redesigned and was able to read twenty-five thousand characters per second because it was capable of parallel operations (it carried out several different operations at once, instead of one at a time) and, in addition, it had a short-term memory. The Mark II was in operation on June 1, 1944. Several more machines were made, each with further modifications, for a total of ten. The Colossus machines were special-purpose, program-controlled electronic digital computers, the only known electronic programmable computer in existence in 1944. The use of electronics allowed for a tremendous increase in the internal speed of the machine.

After World War II ended in 1945, the Bletchley team disbanded. The fates of the Colossus, Heath Robinson, and Bombe machines were not known for certain, since the British government considered the codebreaking work at Bletchley Park a state secret. Approximately ten thousand men and women who worked there were sworn to secrecy and worked under the "need to know" rule. (A person was told only the information needed to complete an assigned task.) The commitment to secrecy was so effective that no one outside the project knew about the codebreaking work at Bletchley Park for more than thirty years after World War II ended. The British government officially revealed some information on the work and the people involved in 1975, but the rest of the information is still considered a state secret.

Impact of Event

The full impact of the development of the Colossus is difficult to assess accurately because all the information about the project has not been revealed. The Colossus machines gave Britain the best codebreakers during World War II and provided information that was crucial for the Allied victory. The information decoded by Colossus, the actual messages, and their influence on military decisions still remains classified.

The later work of several of the people involved with the Bletchley Park projects was important in British computer development after the war. Newman's and Turing's postwar careers were closely involved with emerging computer advances. Newman went to Manchester University shortly after the war. He was interested in the impact of computers on mathematics and received a grant from the Royal Society in 1946 to establish a calculating machine laboratory at Manchester. He was also involved with postwar computer growth in Britain. Several other members of the Bletchley Park team joined Newman at Manchester, including Turing in 1948. Before going to Manchester University, however, Turing joined Britain's National Physical Laboratory (NPL). At NPL, Turing worked on an advanced computer known as the Pilot Automatic Computing Engine (Pilot ACE). While at NPL, Turing proposed the concept of a stored program, which was a controversial but extremely important idea in computing. A "stored" program is in residence inside the computer and then a particular program and data are fed through an input device simultaneously. (The Heath Robinson and Colossus machines were limited by utilizing separate input tapes, one for the program and one for the data to be analyzed.) Turing was among the first to explain the stored program concept in print. He was also among the first to imagine how subroutines could be included in a program. (A subroutine allows separate tasks within a large program to be done in distinct modules, a directed detour within a program. After the completion of the subroutine, the main program takes control again.) Turing also contributed to the computer output facilities, worked on the art of programming, and wrote the first Manchester programming manual.

Some of the people who were involved in the Colossus project and its predecessors contributed to Britain's postwar computer development. During World War II, the codebreaking work at Bletchley Park enabled Allied forces to make informed, decisive moves that eventually resulted in Allied victory. The full story of the Colossus and the people at Bletchley Park will not be known, however, until the British government declassifies the information.

Bibliography

Coombs, Allen. "The Making of Colossus." *Annals of the History of Computing* 5 (July, 1983): 253-259. Coombs provides an account of how the Colossus was built and put into operation. As one of the people who actually worked on the machine, Coombs offers an entertaining and well-informed report of the various problems and concerns involved with the operation of the Colossus.

Flowers, Thomas. "The Design of Colossus." *Annals of the History of Computing* 5 (July, 1983): 239-252. Flowers, who designed the Colossus, describes how the machine evolved from the earlier Heath Robinson machine. Flowers provides background information on the Heath Robinson and the modifications that had to be made in order to produce the first Colossus. The article is well written and a valuable firsthand account.

Good, Irving J. "Pioneering Work on Computers at Bletchley." In *A History of Computing in the Twentieth Century*, edited by N. Metropolis, J. Howlett, and Gian-Carlo Rota. New York: Academic Press, 1980. This chapter by one of the men who worked on Colossus provides interesting, firsthand observations about the development of the Heath Robinson and Colossus machines. The account is admittedly incomplete, since Good operated on the "need to know" basis and because some of the information was still classified.

Hodges, Andrew. *Alan Turing: The Enigma*. New York: Simon & Schuster, 1983. The Colossus is only one of several projects that Hodges covers in his focus on Alan Turing, his life, his profession, brilliance, and the times he lived in. This is definitely a book to read if one is interested in the history of computing, rather than only one project.

Randell, Brian. "The Colossus." In *A History of Computing in the Twentieth Century*, edited by N. Metropolis, J. Howlett, and Gian-Carlo Rota. New York: Academic Press, 1980. Randell offers one of the most complete accounts of the Colossus and the work done at Bletchley Park. He has gathered information from numerous sources, including official government releases, interviews with those directly involved with the project, and material already in the public domain. The result is a thoughtful, informative work. Illustrated, with extensive references.

Ritchie, David. *The Computer Pioneers: The Making of the Modern Computer.* New York: Simon & Schuster, 1986. Ritchie's book is a well-written, entertaining account of the people involved with early computer developments. He relies on information from other published sources for the chapters covering the Bletchley Park project, but presents the information in a refreshing manner. Ritchie provides a brief but helpful summary of the machines discussed in his book, as well as a glossary of terms, notes on sources, and recommendations for further reading.

Williams, Michael R. *A History of Computing Technology.* Englewood Cliffs, N.J.: Prentice-Hall, 1985. Williams' book is a good general survey of the history of computer developments. He begins with a brief history of numerical systems, starting with the Egyptians, and ends with the supercomputers of the 1970's. The focus of his work is on the American developments, although he does write briefly about the work at Bletchley Park.

Patricia Summers

Cross-References

Eckert and Mauchly Develop the ENIAC (1943), p. 1213; The First Electronic Stored-Program Computer (BINAC) Is Completed (1949), p. 1347; UNIVAC I Becomes the First Commercial Electronic Computer and the First to Use Magnetic Tape (1951), p. 1396; Bubble Memory Devices Are Created for Use in Computers (1969), p. 1886; The Floppy Disk Is Introduced for Storing Data Used by Computers (1970), p. 1923; Apple II Becomes the First Successful Preassembled Personal Computer (1977), p. 2073; The IBM Personal Computer, Using DOS, Is Introduced (1981), p. 2169; IBM Introduces a Personal Computer with a Standard Hard Disk Drive (1983), p. 2240; Optical Disks for the Storage of Computer Data Are Introduced (1984), p. 2262.

LIBBY INTRODUCES THE CARBON-14
METHOD OF DATING ANCIENT OBJECTS

Categories of event: Chemistry, archaeology, and physics
Time: The late 1940's
Locale: University of Chicago, Chicago, Illinois

Radioactive decay of carbon 14 has been used to measure the age of archaeological objects going back ten thousand years or more

Principal personages:
WILLARD FRANK LIBBY (1908-1980), the American chemist who discovered the carbon-14 dating method, for which he won the 1960 Nobel Prize in Chemistry
CHARLES WESLEY FERGUSON (1922-1986), a scientist who demonstrated that carbon 14 dates before 1500 B.C. needed to be corrected
SERGE ALEXANDER KORFF (1906-   ), a cosmic ray physicist who first measured neutrons in the upper atmosphere, which stimulated Libby's interest in searching for radioactive carbon in nature

Summary of Event

Carbon dioxide in the earth's atmosphere contains a mixture of three carbon isotopes: about 99 percent carbon 12, about 1 percent carbon 13, and approximately one atom in a trillion (one part in 10^{12}) of radioactive carbon 14. Plants absorb carbon dioxide from the atmosphere during photosynthesis and animals eat the plants, so all living plants and animals contain a small amount of radioactive carbon. When the plant or animal dies, its radioactivity slowly decreases. The half-life for carbon 14 is known to be about fifty-seven hundred years. The carbon-14 activity will drop to one-half after one half-life, one-fourth after two half-lives, one-eighth after three half-lives, and so on. After ten or twenty half-lives, the activity would be too low to be measurable. Coal and oil, which were formed from organic matter millions of years ago, have long since lost any carbon-14 activity. Wood samples from an Egyptian tomb or charcoal from a prehistoric fireplace a few thousand years ago, however, can be dated with good reliability from the left-over radioactivity.

Historically, radioactive carbon 14 was discovered in the laboratory before being observed in the atmosphere. The cyclotron particle accelerator had been invented by Ernest O. Lawrence in the early 1930's at the University of California, Berkeley. In 1934, it was used to bombard nitrogen gas in a cloud chamber, producing some tracks that were attributed to carbon 14. Nevertheless, the amount of carbon 14 was insufficient to measure its radioactivity.

In the early 1930's, Willard Frank Libby was a graduate student at Berkeley working on his Ph.D. in chemistry. For his thesis research, he built a Geiger counter, the first radiation detector of this type constructed in the United States, based on a design that had been published by Hans Geiger in Germany in 1928. Libby's thesis was an investigation of some rare earth elements that have very low levels of natural radioactivity.

In 1939, the cyclotron group at Berkeley set out on a systematic search to find out if there were any long-lived isotopes of the biologically important elements hydrogen, carbon, nitrogen, and oxygen. Bombardment of nitrogen by neutrons produced a small amount of carbon, which was converted chemically to calcium carbonate and then put inside one of Libby's Geiger counters as a coating on the wall. The activity caused by carbon 14 was immediately evident. The experimenters wanted to measure its half-life, but this is difficult to do for long-lived activities because they decrease so slowly. The half-life could be estimated only roughly at this time to be in the range from 1,000 to 100,000 years. World War II brought a halt to basic research as scientists were recruited for various military needs. Libby worked on the atomic bomb project, in particular on the separation of uranium isotopes. In 1945, he returned to academic life as a professor at the University of Chicago, where he would resume a search for radioactive carbon in nature.

During the 1930's, an investigation of cosmic rays in the upper atmosphere had been conducted by Serge Alexander Korff at New York University. He had developed a special type of Geiger counter filled with boron gas to detect neutrons. Using high-altitude balloons, Korff showed that neutrons were present there. He suggested that the neutrons probably would be absorbed by ordinary nitrogen in the atmosphere to form radioactive carbon 14, which would then enter the biosphere. In early 1947, Libby started the crucial experiment to test for radioactive carbon in nature. He decided to test samples of methane gas from two different sources. One group of samples came from the sewage disposal plant at Baltimore, Maryland, which is rich in fresh organic matter. The other sample of methane came from an oil refinery, which should contain only ancient carbon from fossils whose activity would have completely decayed. The experimental results confirmed the expectation: The methane from fresh sewage was radioactive but the methane from oil was not radioactive. Evidently, radioactive carbon is present in fresh organics but it decays away eventually.

After this initial success, more than two years of intense effort were needed to develop radiocarbon dating into a quantitative method for archaeology. The carbon radioactivity is so weak that elaborate precautions are necessary to shield against natural background radiation. For example, Libby reported that his unshielded radiation counter had a background of about five hundred counts per minute, mostly as a result of cosmic rays. Surrounding the detector with 20 centimeters of steel on all sides reduced the background to about one hundred counts per minute. Further reduction was achieved by surrounding the counter with a guard ring of eleven radiation detectors. If any external cosmic rays passed through the guard ring, they would momentarily inactivate the sample counter. The guard ring reduced the background to about six counts per minute. With a fresh carbon sample in place, the counter measured twelve counts per minute, or twice the background. Using counting times of forty-eight hours per sample or longer, it was possible now to measure statistically significant counts above background.

The first archaeological object analyzed by carbon dating, obtained from the Metropolitan Museum in New York, was a piece of cypress wood from the tomb of King Djoser of Egypt, whose age from historical evidence was about forty-six hundred years. A small sample of carbon obtained from this wood was deposited on the inside of Libby's counter, giving a count rate that was about 40 percent less than the activity of modern organic carbon. In order to convert this lesser activity to an age, the half-life of carbon 14 had to be measured in a separate experiment, which was done at Argonne National Laboratory. The resulting age of the wood calculated from its residual radioactivity was about thirty-eight hundred years. Considering that this was the first object to be analyzed, even such rough agreement with the historic age was considered to be encouraging.

In order to establish the validity of radiocarbon dating, Libby analyzed known samples of varying age. These include tree ring samples from A.D. 1072, A.D. 575, and one redwood from 979 B.C., as well as artifacts from Egyptian tombs going back to about 3000 B.C. In 1949, he published an article in the journal *Science* that contained a graph comparing historical age and measured radiocarbon age for eleven objects. The data showed good agreement within 10 percent, giving confidence in the general method. Archaeologists were starting to become interested in carbon dating to find out the age of objects for which no historic date was known.

The validity of radiocarbon dating depends on an important assumption; namely, that the abundance of carbon 14 in nature has been constant over many thousands of years. If carbon 14 was less abundant at some point in history, organic samples from that era would have started with less radioactivity. When analyzed today, their reduced activity would make them appear to be older than they really are. Samples of known age are needed going back many millennia to check how reliable their carbon dates are.

Written historical records, unfortunately, do not extend further back than about 3000 B.C. Nevertheless, prehistoric wood samples with reliable ages can be obtained from tree-ring counting, what is known as the science of "dendrochronology." Some bristlecone pines in California are the oldest known living trees, going back more than four thousand years. Charles Wesley Ferguson from the Tree-Ring Research Laboratory at the University of Arizona measured the age of bristlecone pine trees and found that carbon-14 dates before 1500 B.C. needed to be corrected. Remnants from nearby dead stumps can extend the time scale even further. The carbon-14 content of various tree rings with known ages can be measured in the usual way. The results show that radiocarbon dates are older than dendrochronological dates by as much as several hundred years for the oldest samples. Apparently, the carbon-14 content of the atmosphere has not been constant. It has been suggested that changes in the earth's magnetic field may have deflected cosmic rays so that fewer of them hit the upper atmosphere and thus created less carbon 14. In any case, tree-ring counting gives reliable dates that can be used to correct the radiocarbon measurements back to about 6000 B.C.

As instrumentation for carbon-14 counting has improved over the years, more laboratories have become interested in dating research. A special journal called *Radiocarbon* publishes lists of dates as well as technical articles on apparatus. International radiocarbon conferences have been held every two or three years since 1954. The total number of individual carbon-14 determinations has been estimated to be more than 100,000, coming from more than eighty different laboratories. New applications are being developed to the study of prehistoric climate and geology as well as archaeology and cultural history.

Impact of Event

The New York Times on May 30, 1947, gave a brief report that Libby had found radioactive carbon 14 in nature, presumably the result of cosmic rays. The *Times* went on to say, rather vaguely, that this may provide "a new yard-stick for measuring various earth periods." In March of 1949, in the journal *Science*, Libby published his first list of carbon dates for objects of known age, spanning the time period from A.D. 1000 to almost 3000 B.C. In 1952 came the first edition of Libby's book, *Radiocarbon Dating*, which stimulated other laboratories to start similar research programs. By 1960, Libby's contribution already had proved its value to scientists worldwide, leading to the award of the 1960 Nobel Prize in Chemistry.

Some interesting samples were dated by Libby's group. The Dead Sea Scrolls had been found in a cave by an Arab shepherd in 1947, but some Bible scholars at first questioned whether they were genuine. The linen wrapping from the Book of Isaiah was tested for carbon 14, giving a date of 100 B.C., which helped to establish its authenticity. Human hair from an Egyptian tomb was dated to be nearly five thousand years old. Well-preserved sandals from a cave in eastern Oregon were dated to be ninety-three hundred years old. A charcoal sample from a prehistoric site in western South Dakota was about seven thousand years old. Typical uncertainties in dating such objects are plus or minus 10 percent of the age, although recent measurements tend to be more precise.

The Shroud of Turin, located in Turin, Italy, has been a controversial object for many years. It is a linen cloth, more than 4 meters long, which shows the image of a man's body, both front and back. Some people think it may have been the burial shroud of Jesus Christ after his crucifixion. A team of scientists in 1978 were permitted to study the shroud, using infrared photography, analysis of possible blood stains, microscopic examination of the linen fibers, and other methods. The results were ambiguous. A carbon-14 test was not permitted at this time because it would have required cutting a piece about the size of a handkerchief from the shroud.

A new method to measure carbon 14 was developed in the early 1980's. It is called accelerator mass spectrometer, or AMS. It does not count the radioactivity of carbon like Libby did it. Instead, a mass spectrometer directly measures the ratio of carbon 14 to ordinary carbon. The main advantage of this method is that the sample size needed for analysis is about a thousand times smaller than before. The Archbishop of Turin permitted three laboratories with the appropriate AMS apparatus to test the shroud material. The results agreed that the material was from the fourteenth century, not from the time of Christ. The figure on the shroud may be a watercolor painting on linen.

Since Libby's pioneering experiments in the late 1940's, carbon 14 has established itself as a reliable dating technique for archaeologists and cultural historians. Further improvements are continuing to be developed to increase the precision, to use smaller sample size, and to extend the time scale back to fifty thousand years or older.

Bibliography

Deevey, Edward S. "Radiocarbon Dating." *Scientific American* 186 (February, 1952): 24-28. Written by the Director of the Geochronometric Laboratory at Yale University. A series of photographs show how a wood sample is prepared so that its weak radioactivity can be counted.

Hedges, Robert E., and John A. J. Gowlett. "Radiocarbon Dating by Accelerator Mass Spectrometry." *Scientific American* 254 (January, 1986): 100-107. Describes the authors' work to improve carbon dating by using a mass spectrometer to measure the carbon-14 content of samples instead of radioactive decay.

Libby, Willard F. *Radiocarbon Dating*. 2d ed. Chicago: University of Chicago Press, 1955. Written by the discoverer of the radiocarbon dating method; shows with numerical calculations how radioactive carbon is formed and distributed around the world. Describes in detail sample preparation and low-level counting procedures. Gives a tabulation of several hundred samples.

_____. "Radiocarbon Dating." In *The Frontiers of Knowledge*. Garden City, N.Y.: Doubleday, 1975. An excellent, short description of the carbon-dating technique, written for a nontechnical audience. Includes photographs of some interesting objects whose age was measured such as the linen wrapping from the Book of Isaiah Dead Sea Scroll.

Renfrew, Colin. "Carbon-14 and the Prehistory of Europe." *Scientific American* 225 (October, 1971): 63-72. Some prehistoric dates before 4000 B.C. obtained with carbon 14 were shown to be in error. A readable article showing how scientific results are subject to correction as more information is accumulated.

Taylor, Royal Erwin. *Radiocarbon Dating: An Archaeological Perspective*. New York: Academic Press, 1987. Written by an archaeologist who is knowledgeable about the physics and chemistry of carbon dating; gives a broad-ranging perspective over the past forty years of accomplishments in this field. A historical chapter on Libby provides many interesting biographical details.

Wilson, Ian. *The Mysterious Shroud*. Garden City, N.Y.: Doubleday, 1986. In the style of a detective story, compiles the best evidence both for and against the idea that the famous "Shroud of Turin" may have been the burial cloth of Jesus Christ after his crucifixion. Includes more than one hundred photographs and an extensive bibliography.

Hans G. Graetzer

Cross-References

Geiger and Rutherford Develop the Geiger Counter (1908), p. 412; Millikan Names Cosmic Rays and Investigates Their Absorption (1920), p. 694; Carter Discovers the Tomb of Tutankhamen (1922), p. 730; Lawrence Develops the Cyclotron (1931), p. 953; Archaeologists Unearth Ancient Scrolls (1947), p. 1298; An Ancient Sanctuary Is Discovered in El Juyo Cave, Spain (1979), p. 2110.

THE FIRST COLOR TELEVISION BROADCAST
TAKES PLACE

Category of event: Applied science
Time: 1940
Locale: New York City

The Radio Corporation of America (RCA) and the Columbia Broadcasting System (CBS) both demonstrated color television systems, although the RCA system was not adopted until 1953

Principal personages:
PETER CARL GOLDMARK (1906-1977), the head of the Columbia Broadcasting System's research and development laboratory who was credited not only with the creation of color television but also with the development of the 33⅓ revolutions-per-minute, long-playing phonograph record
WILLIAM S. PALEY (1901-1990), the businessman who took over CBS and aggressively pushed it to compete, first with radio, then with the television industry
DAVID SARNOFF (1891-1971), the founder of RCA who led the company to the top of the American broadcasting business

Summary of Event

Although there had been demonstrations of color television in Scotland in 1928 (by Englishman John L. Baird), 1940 serves as the benchmark for the invention of a medium that would come to dominate the television technology during the latter third of the twentieth century. Two events in 1940 denote that year as the beginning of color television. First, on February 12, 1940, RCA demonstrated its color television system privately, including to members of the Federal Communications Commission (FCC), an administrative body that had the authority to set standards for an electronic color system. The demonstration did not go well; indeed, David Sarnoff, the head of RCA, canceled a planned public demonstration and returned his engineers to the Princeton, New Jersey, headquarters of RCA's laboratories.

On September 1, 1940, CBS struck its blow for a competition to determine the color system that would become the standard for the United States. On that late summer day, CBS demonstrated a sequential color system to the public, based on the research of an engineer, Peter Carl Goldmark. CBS's color technology in 1940 was the superior of the two systems. Goldmark, by breaking down the television image into three primary colors through a set of spinning filters in front of black and white, caused the video to be viewed in color. This was additive color.

Although Goldmark had been at work as a research engineer at CBS since January, 1936, he did not attempt to develop a color television system until March, 1940, after witnessing the spectacle of the Technicolor motion picture *Gone with the Wind* (1939). Inspired, Goldmark began to tinker in his tiny CBS laboratory in the headquarters building in New York City.

If a decision had been made in 1940, the CBS color standard would have been accepted as the national standard. The FCC was, at that time, trying to establish a black-and-white standard. Color television seemed decades away. A 1941 decision by the FCC to adopt standards only for black-and-white television left the issue of color unresolved. This standards recommendation was based on the advice of the National Television Standards Committee representing electronics manufacturers and leading research scientists.

That decision did not mean the two leading broadcasting companies in the United States accepted it. Control of a potentially lucrative market as well as personal rivalry threw William S. Paley, head of CBS, and Sarnoff into a race for the control of color television. Both companies would pay dearly in terms of money and hours of time, and it would take until the 1960's before the United States would turn into a nation of color television watchers.

RCA's leadership in the development of the accepted black-and-white television system gave the National Broadcasting Company (NBC) a head start over CBS. Once black and white became the standard in the late 1940's, however, CBS saw the creation of a workable color system as a potential weapon to counter the advantage long held by NBC.

CBS took a far different tactic from that of RCA. Goldmark alone did the work for the CBS Laboratories. In contrast, RCA relied on a corporate laboratory of highly skilled but nameless scientists. Sarnoff ran RCA laboratories as a true corporate monolith; no scientists ever became as famous as Sarnoff.

The CBS color system was incompatible with the RCA standard for black-and-white television. In other words, customers would need one set for black and white and one for color. Moreover, since the color system of CBS needed more spectrum space than the National Television Standards Committee black-and-white system in use, CBS was forced to request the FCC to allocate new channel space in the ultrahigh frequency (UHF) band, then not being used. In contrast, RCA scientists labored to fashion a compatible color system that required no additional spectrum space.

Not surprisingly, in the early 1940's, CBS received little encouragement from the FCC, even though one hundred scientists were trying to perfect the color system. Indeed, the leaders of CBS were not able to convince the FCC to do anything about color before the end of World War II. This meant that, although CBS had a workable color system, it faced a world lining up to purchase RCA's black-and-white television sets in 1945.

The suburbanites that populated new communities in America's cities sought television immediately; they did not want to wait for governmental bodies to decide on a color standard and then have manufacturers redesign assembly lines to make color sets. Americans, rich with savings accumulated during the prosperity of the war years, wanted to spend now, not wait as they had through the Great Depression. After the war, the FCC saw no reason to open up proceedings about color. Black and white was operational; customers were waiting in line for the new electronic marvel. To give its engineers time to create a compatible system, RCA skillfully lobbied the members of the FCC to take no action.

There were legitimate problems with the CBS mechanical color television technology. Not only was it incompatible with the millions of new black-and-white television sets being sold but also was noisy and large, and it was hard to maintain the color balance. Demonstrations often went poorly. CBS proclaimed that through further engineering work, it would improve the actual sets. RCA was able to convince other manufacturers to support it in preference to CBS principally because of its proven manufacturing track record.

In 1946, RCA demonstrated a new electronic color receiver with three picture tubes, one each for the primary colors. Color was fairly true; there was little flicker; but any movement on the screen caused color blurring. This was an all-electronic system in contrast to the mechanical system of CBS. It was compatible. Thus ended the invention phase of color television begun in 1940. The race for standardization would require seven years of corporate struggle before one system would win out.

Impact of Event

The inventions of CBS and RCA set off the race toward a standard for color television. Both companies would pour millions of dollars into convincing the FCC to select their system as the standard. The winner of the first round was RCA, when in 1946, the FCC again rejected the color technology of CBS as the standard. CBS had tried to convince the world it was time to adopt color; officials of RCA argued that black and white was here, while color was still five years away.

In 1950, the FCC reversed its decision and accepted the mechanical scanning system after a convincing demonstration. RCA countered with a lawsuit seeking to overturn their decision. In 1951, RCA lost this suit, and it seemed that the CBS color system would become the national standard. CBS began to manufacture color television sets while RCA worked to reverse official rulings. According to one source, RCA would pour about $150 million more into research and tender many more millions to Washington, D.C., lobbyists and lawyers.

The Korean war stymied the victory of CBS. Few of the company's color sets were made, for the Korean war caused CBS to cease production in October, 1951. This gave the opposing forces time to convince the National Television Standards Committee that any color system ought to be compatible with the millions of black-and-white sets Americans had purchased. That would be the system of RCA.

So lobbied, the FCC rescinded its 1950 ruling approving the CBS color television system. On December 17, 1953, it reapproved the compatible RCA system. Seeing what the delay caused by the Korean war cost CBS, RCA moved quickly. In 1954, in eighteen cities in the United States, the Pasadena Tournament of Roses New Year's

Day parade was broadcast in color on NBC. There were few viewers with color sets at that time. Owners of black and white compatible sets could receive the signal and saw the parade in black and white.

Through the 1950's, black and white television remained the order of the day. Five years after the 1953 adoption of the National Television Standards Committee, only the NBC television network was regularly airing programs in color. Full production and presentation of shows in color during prime time would not come until the mid-1960's; most industry observers date 1972 as the arrival of color television.

By 1972, more than one-half the homes in the United States owned color sets. At that point, *TV Guide* stopped tagging color program listings with a special symbol and instead tagged black-and-white shows, as it does to this day. Gradually, only cheap portable sets were made for black and white, while color sets came in all varieties from tiny hand-held pocket televisions to mammoth projection televisions.

It should be noted that specialized medical closed-circuit television sets used the high-quality color rendition of the CBS color television system for many years. Indeed, the pictures from the Moon transmitted by United States astronauts were set on CBS cameras—built by RCA.

Bibliography

Barnouw, Erik. *A History of Broadcasting in the United States.* 3 vols. New York: Oxford University Press, 1966-1970. A massive work that still stands as the standard history of broadcasting in the United States. Covers the coming of color television in the second and third volumes.

Bilby, Kenneth. *The General David Sarnoff and the Rise of the Communications Industry.* New York: Harper & Row, 1986. One of the two major book-length studies of the significant activities of RCA and its founder David Sarnoff. Presents a detailed history of the contributions of RCA in the invention and innovation of color television. A balanced account of Sarnoff's life.

Dreher, Carl. *Sarnoff: An American Success.* New York: Quadrangle, 1977. A major work on the activities of RCA and its founder. Presents a detailed history of the activities of RCA in the invention and innovation of color television. Less objective than Bilby (cited above).

Fink, Donald G., and David M. Lutyens. *The Physics of Television.* Garden City, N.Y.: Doubleday, 1960. A compact volume that gives the best explanation of how television works. Color systems are explained in the final chapter in nontechnical language that anyone with a modest science background can understand.

Goldmark, Peter C., and Lee Edson. *Maverick Inventor: My Turbulent Years at CBS.* New York: Saturday Review Press, 1973. An autobiography of the key inventor at CBS. Three chapters detail the development of color television. Goldmark was a key player, and his views represent a rare look into the world of corporate technological research and development.

Head, Sydney W., and Christopher H. Sterling. *Broadcasting in America.* 5th ed. Boston: Houghton Mifflin, 1986. The standard introduction to the institutions that make up television in the United States. Covers the invention and innovation of color television technology.

Lichty, Lawrence W., and Malachi C. Topping. *American Broadcasting: A Source Book on the History of Radio and Television*. New York: Hastings House, 1975. Contains articles and documents concerning the history of radio and television, one of which examines the introduction of color television. Other articles explain the history of all forms of television technology, as well as the changing economics and social impact of this mass entertainment industry.

Metz, Robert. *CBS: Reflections in a Bloodshot Eye*. New York: Playboy Press, 1975. One of the two significant studies of CBS. Offers a survey of the history of one of America's most important broadcasting institutions.

Smith, Sally Bedell. *In All His Glory: The Life of William S. Paley*. New York: Simon & Schuster, 1990. The most comprehensive study of the Columbia Broadcasting System. Explains why CBS developed color television technology.

Sterling, Christopher H., and John M. Kittross. *Stay Tuned: A Concise History of American Broadcasting*. Belmont, Calif.: Wadsworth, 1978. The standard, one-volume history of radio and television in the United States. The best place to start reading about the invention and innovation of color television technology.

Douglas Gomery

Cross-References

Marconi Receives the First Transatlantic Telegraphic Radio Transmission (1901), p. 128; Fleming Files a Patent for the First Vacuum Tube (1904), p. 255; Fessenden Perfects the Radio by Transmitting Music and Voice (1906), p. 361; Transatlantic Radiotelephony Is First Demonstrated (1915), p. 615; The Principles of Shortwave Radio Communication Are Discovered (1919), p. 669; Zworykin Develops an Early Type of Television (1923), p. 751; Armstrong Perfects FM Radio (1930), p. 939; Shockley, Bardeen, and Brattain Discover the Transistor (1947), p. 1304; Sony Develops the Pocket-Sized Transistor Radio (1957), p. 1528.

FLOREY AND CHAIN DEVELOP
PENICILLIN AS AN ANTIBIOTIC

Category of event: Medicine
Time: May, 1940
Locale: Oxford, England

Florey and Chain concentrated and clinically tested the antibiotic penicillin, which saves millions of lives as the twentieth century's greatest wonder drug

Principal personages:
BARON FLOREY (1898-1968), an Australian pathologist who won the 1945 Nobel Prize in Physiology or Medicine (with Sir Alexander Fleming and Chain) for his work with the antibiotic penicillin
ERNST BORIS CHAIN (1906-1979), an émigré German biochemist who played a pivotal role in the purification of penicillin

Summary of Event

During the early twentieth century, scientists were aware of antibacterial substances, but these substances had not realized their full potential for treatment of diseases in the human body. Sir Alexander Fleming discovered the antibiotic penicillin in 1928 but was unable to duplicate his laboratory results in clinical tests and, as a result, did not recognize the medical potential of penicillin as an antibiotic. Between 1935 and 1940, penicillin was purified, concentrated, and clinically tested by pathologist Baron Florey, biochemist Ernst Boris Chain, and members of their Oxford research group. Their achievement has since been regarded as one of the greatest medical discoveries of the twentieth century.

Florey decided to pursue a career in medicine at an early age rather than entering the family business. His father was a wealthy boot manufacturer. Florey received his degree at the University of Adelaide in 1922 and, with the help of a Rhodes Scholarship, continued his education at Oxford, England, where he studied under the neurophysiologist Sir Charles Sherrington. Florey later completed his doctorate at the University of Cambridge and in 1935 returned to the University of Oxford as professor in charge of the Sir William Dunn School of Pathology. Chain was the son of a wealthy chemist whose ownership of several large plants ensured that his son would attend college. Chain attended the Friedrich-Wilhelm University in Berlin, where in 1930 he received his doctorate in chemistry. In 1933, Chain left Germany for England, where he worked for two years at Cambridge in the laboratory of Frederick Gowland Hopkins, an eminent chemist and discoverer of vitamins. Hopkins recommended Chain to Florey, who was searching for a candidate to lead a new biochemical unit in the Dunn School of Pathology.

In 1938, Florey and Chain formed a research group to investigate the phenomenon of antibiosis. The union of Florey's medical knowledge and Chain's biochemical expertise proved to be an ideal combination for exploring the antibiotic potential of penicillin. Florey and Chain were not unique in their interest; many other scientists were also studying potential antibiotics. Among these was Samuel Waksman, a soil microbiologist at Rutgers University, who in 1936 began a systematic study of antibiosis. Waksman eventually isolated four antibiotics, the most famous of which— streptomycin—is used in the treatment of tuberculosis. He received the 1952 Nobel Prize in Physiology or Medicine for his contributions.

Florey and Chain began their investigation with a literature search in which Chain came across Fleming's work and added penicillin to their list of potential antibiotics. Research funds in England were hard to come by, and after receiving a small donation from the Medical Research Council, Florey submitted a proposal to the Rockefeller Foundation. On March 12, 1940, the foundation approved a grant of five thousand dollars over a period of five years.

Their first task was to isolate pure penicillin from the crude liquid extract. A culture of Fleming's original *Penicillium notatum* was maintained at Oxford and was used by the Oxford group for penicillin production. Extracting large quantities of penicillin from the medium was a painstaking task, as the solution contained only one part of the antibiotic in ten million. When enough of the raw juice was collected, the Oxford group used a back-extraction method for eliminating impurities and concentrating the penicillin. The concentrated liquid was then freeze-dried, leaving a soluble brown powder. Florey's assistant, biochemist Norman G. Heatley, made an enormous contribution to the project by developing methods for measuring and producing penicillin. Heatley's efforts ensured that enough penicillin was available to conduct chemical and clinical experiments.

In May, 1940, Florey's clinical tests of the crude penicillin proved its value as an antibiotic. Following extensive controlled experiments with mice, the Oxford group concluded that they had discovered an antibiotic that was nontoxic and far more effective against pathogenic bacteria than any of the known sulfa drugs. Furthermore, penicillin was not inactivated after injection into the bloodstream, but was excreted unchanged in the urine. Continued tests showed that penicillin did not interfere with white blood cells and had no adverse effect on living cells. Bacteria susceptible to the antibiotic included those responsible for gas gangrene, pneumonia, meningitis, diphtheria, and gonorrhea. American researchers later proved that penicillin was also effective against syphilis.

In January, 1941, Florey injected a volunteer with penicillin and found that there were no side effects to treatment with the antibiotic. In February, the group began treatment of Albert Alexander, a forty-three-year-old policeman with a serious staphylococci and streptococci infection that was resisting massive doses of sulfa drugs. Alexander was hospitalized for two months after an infection on the corner of his mouth spread to his face, shoulder, and lungs. After injection of 200 milligrams of penicillin, Alexander showed remarkable progress, and for the next ten days his condition improved. Unfortunately, the Oxford production facility was unable to generate enough penicillin to overcome Alexander's advanced infection completely, and he died on March 15. A later case involving a fourteen-year-old boy with staphylococcal septicemia and osteomyelitis had a more spectacular result: The patient made a complete recovery in two months. In all of the early clinical treatments, patients showed vast improvement and most recovered completely from infections that resisted all other treatment.

Florey hoped that his spectacular clinical successes would convince English pharmaceutical companies to begin large-scale penicillin production. He was particularly hopeful that penicillin would be used in the treatment of gangrenous and infected wounds. Unfortunately, World War II placed English industry in a position where it could not afford to embark on new business ventures. Florey, therefore, resolved to take his idea to the United States. After obtaining travel funds from the Rockefeller Foundation, Florey and Heatley visited several private and government laboratories in the United States. The United States responded quickly to their discovery and immediately began research on improved penicillin production methods at the Department of Agriculture's Northern Regional Research Laboratory in Peoria, Illinois. By 1943 to 1944, American pharmaceutical companies were mass-producing penicillin for use in World War II.

Impact of Event

Penicillin is among the greatest medical discoveries of the twentieth century. Florey and Chain's chemical and clinical research brought about a revolution in the treatment of infectious disease. Almost every organ in the body is vulnerable to bacteria. Before penicillin the only antimicrobial drugs available were quinine, arsenic, and sulfa drugs. Of these, only the sulfa drugs were useful for treatment of bacterial infection, but in many cases, high toxicity precluded their use. With this limited arsenal, doctors were helpless as thousands died in epidemics caused by bacteria.

The work of Florey and Chain achieved particular notoriety because of World War II and the need for treatments of such scourges as gas gangrene, which infected the wounds of numerous World War I soldiers. With the help of Florey and Chain's Oxford group, scientists at the U.S. Department of Agriculture's Northern Regional Research Laboratory developed a highly efficient method for producing penicillin using fermentation. An excellent cornstarch medium was developed for both surface and submerged culture of penicillium molds. After an extended search, scientists were also able to isolate a more productive penicillium strain (*Penicillium chrysogenum*). By 1945, a strain was developed that produced five hundred times more penicillin than Fleming's original mold.

American pharmaceutical companies were galvanized by the development of an efficient production technique and positive clinical tests. Corporations such as Merck, Pfizer, Squibb, and many others built large factories, which mass-produced penicillin for use by the U.S. armed forces. Penicillin prevented many of the horrendous casualties normally associated with warfare. At the conclusion of World War II, penicillin production increased to a point where the antibiotic could be distributed worldwide.

Penicillin was the first of the "wonder drugs" and is still the most powerful antibiotic in existence. Diseases such as pneumonia, meningitis, and syphilis are now treated with penicillin. Penicillin and other antibiotics also had a broad impact on medicine as major operations such as heart surgery, organ transplants, and management of severe burns became possible once the threat of bacterial infection was minimized.

Florey and Chain received numerous awards for their achievement, the greatest of which was the 1945 Nobel Prize in Physiology or Medicine. Florey was among the most effective medical scientists of his generation, and Chain earned similar accolades in the science of biochemistry. This combination of outstanding medical and chemical expertise made possible one of the greatest discoveries in human history.

Bibliography

Clark, Ronald W. *The Life of Ernst Chain: Penicillin and Beyond*. New York: St. Martin's Press, 1985. Clark's biography is a complete examination of Chain's career and includes four chapters on his penicillin work. The author makes use of Chain's papers, which are located at the Contemporary Medical Archives Center, Wellcome Institute for the History of Medicine, London.

Hare, Ronald. *The Birth of Penicillin, and the Disarming of Microbes*. London: George Allen & Unwin, 1970. An excellent firsthand description of Alexander Fleming's work. The author worked at St. Mary's at the time of Fleming's discovery and was among those who witnessed Fleming's early work with penicillin. Hare's book is a short but very informative account of Fleming's work and provides the reader with a perspective on the state of penicillin research before Florey and Chain.

Hobby, Gladys L. *Penicillin: Meeting the Challenge*. New Haven, Conn.: Yale University Press, 1985. Hobby's book is the best overall description of the roles played by Fleming, Florey, Chain, and numerous other scientists in the discovery, development, and eventual mass production of penicillin. Hobby benefits from extensive personal work with penicillin as a scientist employed by the Pfizer Corporation. Includes extensive footnotes and is the most complete overall history of penicillin available.

Macfarlane, Gwyn. *Howard Florey: The Making of a Great Scientist*. Oxford: Oxford University Press, 1979. Macfarlane's account is the best biography of Florey. She worked at Oxford and was an acquaintance of Florey's for twenty years. Makes extensive use of the Florey archives at the Royal Society and is an excellent blend of both personal and archival data.

Williams, Trevor I. *Howard Florey: Penicillin and After*. New York: Oxford University Press, 1984. Williams' book is a well-documented examination of Florey's entire scientific career, including both penicillin and his postwar work.

Peter Neushul

Cross-References

Fleming Discovers Penicillin in Molds (1928), p. 873; Waksman Discovers the Antibiotic Streptomycin (1943), p. 1224; Hodgkin Solves the Structure of Penicillin (1944), p. 1240; Duggar Discovers Aureomycin, the First of the Tetracyclines (1945), p. 1255.

SEVENTEEN-THOUSAND-YEAR-OLD PAINTINGS ARE DISCOVERED IN LASCAUX CAVE

Category of event: Archaeology
Time: September 12, 1940
Locale: Near Montignac, in the Dordogne Department of Southwestern France

Discovery of the cave paintings at Lascaux enabled archaeologists to elaborate on the historical evolution of prehistoric art techniques and to place their origins further back in the chronological record of human cultures

Principal personages:
HENRI-ÉDOUARD-PROSPER BREUIL (1877-1961), an archaeologist who confirmed the chronological stages in techniques of prehistoric paintings
MONSIEUR RAVIDAT, the seventeen-year-old youth who was the first to enter the Lascaux cave

Summary of Event

For several generations after its discovery in 1868, the cavern at Altamira in Spain, along with a few discoveries made in the Levantine (southeastern) regions of Spain and in southwestern France, represented the richest archaeological remains of paintings by prehistoric man in Europe. Then, quite by accident, a new, exceptionally rich find in the region of Dordogne in France occurred shortly after the outbreak of World War II.

On September 12, 1940, five boys—three local youths named Ravidat, Marsal, and Queroy, accompanied by two refugees, Coencas and Estréguil, who had fled the German occupied northwestern zone of France—were roaming through fields belonging to the ruins of a dwelling referred to locally as the Chateau Lascaux. The muffled yelping of their lost dog, who had fallen into a narrow opening at the base of an upturned tree, drew their attention to what appeared to be the mouth of a large cavern or grotto. Ravidat entered the hole. After sliding down 7.6 meters to a sandy floor, and lighting matches to illuminate a vaulted oval subterranean hall 18 meters by 9 meters, he became the first person (for fifteen thousand years) to gaze upon the wondrous prehistoric polychromatic cave paintings of Lascaux.

Although they had no way of realizing it, what they had discovered resembled the famous Altamira paintings in Northern Spain. The latter had been discovered seventy years before. The Lascaux cavern walls were covered with paintings of wild beasts: horses and stags, oxenlike creatures with strangely elongated bodies, and especially prominent and dominating, bulls with strange spotted patterns covering portions of their bodies. Scattered among the animals in this prehistoric scene were a series of symbols or emblems: checkers and swathelike marks resembling sprigs of grass or leaves. The first graphic impressions of what the cave contained were drawn by Estréguil.

The second, more technically perfected set of sketches came a few days later, when the youths had informed the local schoolmaster of their discovery. Qualified archaeologists were brought to view the site. Abbé Bouyssonie was one of the archaeologists who was notified; he had discovered the famous Neanderthal man skeleton in 1908. Bouyssonie was aware that Henri-Édouard-Prosper Breuil of the College of France, a well-known archaeologist who had been involved in a number of excavations connected with Neanderthal remains and Mousterian period prehistoric cultures, had come to Dordogne in June, 1940. Together with M. Peyrony, director of the famous local museum of prehistoric cultures at Les Eyzies, the two archaeologists undertook a more systematic exploration of the Lascaux cavern. For Breuil, the opportunity was particularly important, since, as a specialist interested in establishing a general theory covering the chronological evolution of prehistoric art, Lascaux held a great potential for a new archaeological breakthrough.

The first survey revealed more than eighty pictures, both in the main hall and in a side gallery attached to it. Most of these were found on blocks of stone that had fallen from the cavern roof above. It would take some time before more complex theories concerning the age and content of the paintings would emerge. Almost immediately, however, a preliminary report on the findings was written by Breuil and sent to the prestigious English scientific journal, *Nature*.

The size of the primitive paintings varied from small proportions (about 30 centimeters) to very large drawings (some 5 meters long). It was evident immediately that a number of different techniques had been used to create artistic effects, and that many paintings had been retouched or restored. Breuil noticed something that would play an important role in attempts to recreate the cultural conditions of human existence in prehistoric times: the presence of a drawing of what Breuil called a "half-conventionalized man" lying beside what were obviously his hunting tools (a javelin and a throwing stick). This human figure, presumed to be fatally wounded, faces the prominently outlined figure of a bison. The latter, his entrails disemboweled by the hunter's spear, appears to be gazing at its stalker.

Those who first entered Lascaux cave were astounded to find a number of other unique forms of artistic expression. Perhaps the most impressive was an outline of a child's hand and forearm. Although such primitive techniques of representing the "artists" themselves were not uncommon in prehistoric cave sites, archaeologists were impressed particularly by this tiny reminder of the community of painters who executed the frescos at Lascaux, simply because it was the only such hand to be found among such a large number and variety of representations of animals.

Indeed, it was not only the number and variety of animals found at Lascaux that impressed those who found them but also the uniqueness of (apparent) symbolism that was equally striking. Some paintings contain simple symbols to tell a "practical" story. This is the case of what later came to be called the "falling horses," who are depicted in chaotic disorder, often upside down, to represent primitive man's common method of hunting such prey by driving them off the edges of precipices. Other scenes contain elements that were much too complex for the first observers of the paintings to pass beyond a mere state of wonder. This is the case of the so-called Apocalyptic beast that appears prominently in the main hall of the cavern. This animal figure may have represented an ox or a prehistoric rhinoceros. The body is massive and sagging, as if in a late state of pregnancy, and spotted with curious oval-shaped rings. Other features appeared to be grossly distorted, such as the tiny head and neck on an otherwise massive beast. Most perplexing for the first observers, who could not even begin to interpret the meaning of what they had found, were the "horns" of the unidentifiable Apocalyptic beast. These were like straight rigid sticks capped by peculiar "tufts" that bore no resemblance even to now-extinct animals known to have existed in this prehistoric period.

In addition to these visually impressive features of the Lascaux paintings, an announcement came from Breuil immediately after his first viewing of the site that would alter the theoretical bases for scientific observation of prehistoric cave paintings. Drawing on his previous experience nearby at Font de Gaume (Les Eyzies), where he had identified partial remains of paintings that had been painted over in the Magdalenian archaeological period (ca. 15,000 B.C. to 10,000 B.C.), Breuil hypothesized that the Lascaux paintings were considerably older than the Magdalenian period. Although the archaeologists who found the Lascaux paintings retained full respect for the hitherto unequaled paintings at Altamira, Spain, which many called the "Sistine Chapel of Magdalenian art," specialists looking at this new discovery in 1940 were nearly certain that they would be able to push the origins of prehistoric art back to a much earlier age, christened by Breuil with the name "Perigordian."

Impact of Event

Although archaeologists had studied, since the first half of the nineteenth century, a fairly wide range of artifacts left behind in Paleolithic human settlements in various areas of Western Europe, it was the discovery, in 1868, of the now famous Cantabrian site at Altamira that provided the first evidence that prehistoric Aurignacian and Magdalenian human cultures (dating from about 25,000 to 15,000, and 15,000 to 10,000 years ago, respectively) practiced painting on the interior walls of subterranean caverns. On the ceiling of the caverns at Altamira was an extraordinary panorama of polychrome paintings of animals, mainly gigantic bisons, together with pictographs that some thought represented huts and roofs, or, possibly symbolic figures. Some were made up of checkers, squares, and dots. There were also some engraved (not painted) "semihuman" forms. Later, specialists studying the Altamira site would suggest that such pictographs held a key to ritual practices carried out by late Paleolithic human communities.

The main disappointments associated with the Altamira site, somewhat in contrast to several other important, if less spectacular discoveries made a few years later in the Gironde and Dordogne departments of France (specifically at Pair-non-Pair and at La Mouthe, respectively), involved chronological dating. If archaeologists were in general agreement that the first forms of human art as archaeologists understand it appeared in the Aurignacian period (ca. 25,000 B.C. to 15,000 B.C.), they seemed to be at a loss for making any finer distinctions concerning stages of artistic development leading to a "crossover" into the relatively sophisticated Magdalenian period (15,000 B.C. to 10,000 B.C.).

Both the Pair-non-Pair and La Mouthe sites, partially because of the more primitive techniques used to paint much less finished figures, but also because of archaeological artifacts found in them, were considered to be of Aurignacian origin. Yet, for some time, no one knew how to tie these earliest known paintings to the very considerable number of more "advanced" works associated with the Magdalenian period.

In 1900, Breuil began to build a chronological scheme at La Mouthe to evaluate cave art that would establish a major reputation for him. Breuil's theory for dating cave art was based on comparative techniques, more than on styles (which seemed to change very little over several millenia). Between his first publication on the subject in 1902 and 1934, when he published *L'Evolution de l'art pariétal dans les cavernes et abris ornées de France*, Breuil worked out a scheme that would be retained in its major essentials in his capstone monograph *Quatre cents siècles d'art pariétal* (1952; four hundred centuries of cave art), published ten years after the Lascaux discoveries. This scheme held that the passage from the primitive technique of the earliest human artists (hand prints and finger meanders, sometimes referred to as "macaroni style") to the "classical" style of the "high" Magdalenian was marked by a "two-cycle" or a "repeat development" system. The crux of this view was that Aurignacian artists, the work of some of whom he would be able to identify at Lascaux, had already mastered a series of technical methods of painting that would be "remastered" and altered during the period of passage from Aurignacian to Magdalenian times. The complete first cycle, which Breuil claimed could be detected in different Aurignacian sites, included use of the following techniques: introduction of color pigments, first yellow, then red; use of fine lines of color, then bolder lines, with flat shading, usually in red; and finally, black linear drawings. These characteristic methods could be expected in cave paintings predating ca. 15,000 B.C.

For later, "classical" Magdalenian period painting, Breuil posited the following cycle of techniques: use of simple black line drawings, some hatched and then stumped; plain flat brown paintings followed by polychromes, partially, then entirely outlined in black; and finally, red linear drawings.

Although professional archaeologists would continue to debate the "final" accuracy of Breuil's method of dating primitive cave art according to evolutionary stages in techniques employed, the fact that many Lascaux paintings were composed of superimposed "layers" (reflecting the application of a later technique to an existing "base" painting) lent considerable weight to Breuil's thesis that they were much older than Altamira's "classical Magdalenian" compositions. His "proof" of this thesis was important not only in terms of establishing the relative age of different examples of primitive cave art but also that prehistoric cultural landmarks—represented mainly in the symbolism that seemed to be mixed together in complex scenes, particularly at Lascaux—could be "unscrambled" by referring to the techniques employed by their prehistoric creators.

Bibliography

Breuil, Henri. *Four Hundred Centuries of Cave Art.* Translated by Mary E. Boyle. Montignac, France: Centre d'études et de documentation préhistoriques, 1952. Breuil's general work includes important references to the place of the Lascaux paintings in the overall framework of prehistoric art.

_____. "A Remarkable Painted Cave on the Estate of Lescaux [*sic*] (Montignac, Dordogne)." *Nature* 147 (1941): 12-13. This is the earliest written description of the Lascaux paintings prepared by a well-known professor at the College of France who was among the first people to enter the caverns in 1940.

Conkey, Margaret W. "On the Origins of Paleolithic Art: A Review and Some Critical Thoughts." In *The Mousterian Legacy: Human Biocultural Change in the Upper Pleistocene,* edited by Erik Trinkhaus. BAR International Series, Number 164. Oxford, England: British Archaeological Reports, 1983. This specialized article concentrates on prehistoric artistic products recovered by archaeologists in the southwestern regions of Europe. Reviews theories that have been put forth by a number of prominent commentators and discusses the "school" represented particularly by Breuil, whose theories hinged on early interpretations of the Lascaux paintings. Early interpretations are compared to more recent approaches.

Laming-Emperaire, Annette. *Lascaux: Paintings and Engravings.* Translated by Eleanore Frances Armstrong. Harmondsworth, England: Penguin, 1959. A comprehensive work on Lascaux only, written by a well-known French archaeologist. Draws on the wide variety of literature on the Dordogne cave paintings that accumulated over the first two decades since their discovery. Discusses methods used to date the paintings and especially to interpret the possible meanings behind the prehistoric artists' work.

Sieveking, Ann. *The Cave Artists.* London: Thames and Hudson, 1979. This is a beautifully illustrated volume covering the southwestern region of Europe, concentrating on the Franco-Cantabrian zone (spanning southwestern France and northeastern Spain). Breuil's view on prehistoric cultural stages reflected in cave paintings is reviewed objectively, pointing out both its still recognized strengths and apparent weaknesses.

Byron Cannon

Cross-References

Boule Reconstructs the First Neanderthal Skeleton (1908), p. 428; Boyd Defines Human Races by Blood Groups (1950), p. 1373; Anthropologists Claim That Ecuadorian Pottery Shows Transpacific Contact in 3000 B.C. (1960's), p. 1624; Scientists Date a *Homo sapiens* Fossil at Ninety-Two Thousand Years (1987), p. 2341.

SEABORG AND McMILLAN MAKE
ELEMENT 94, PLUTONIUM

Categories of event: Chemistry and physics
Time: February 23, 1941
Locale: Berkeley, California

McMillan and Seaborg discovered the first elements heavier than uranium in the periodic table (the so-called transuranium elements), of which plutonium is the most important

Principal personages:

EDWIN MATTISON MCMILLAN (1907-   ), an American nuclear physicist, cowinner with Seaborg of the 1951 Nobel Prize in Chemistry, who discovered neptunium and did pioneering work toward the discovery of plutonium

GLENN THEODORE SEABORG (1912-   ), an American chemist who, with his collaborators, produced, isolated, and identified plutonium and eight additional transuranium elements

PHILIP ABELSON (1913-   ), an American physical chemist who assisted McMillan in the chemical separation of neptunium

ARTHUR C. WAHL (1917-   ), an American chemist who participated both in the discovery of plutonium and in the Manhattan Project to develop the atomic bomb

EMILIO GINO SEGRÈ (1905-1989), an Italian physicist who participated in the discovery of the elements technetium, astatine, and plutonium

Summary of Event

Plutonium's story has fission at its beginning and at its end. The discovery of fission in 1938 was the stimulus for scientists to discover neptunium and plutonium, and the discovery of a fissionable isotope of plutonium led to the atomic bomb that was dropped on Nagasaki in 1945. Ironically, the discovery of nuclear fission by Otto Hahn and Fritz Strassmann was a side effect of their search for a transuranium element. They had not intended to split the uranium nucleus; they were simply trying to add a neutron to this nucleus to make a heavier element. The splitting of the nucleus into such smaller nuclei as barium and lanthanum came as a surprise, as did the production of large amounts of energy. The news of the discovery of fission in January, 1939, excited Edwin Mattison McMillan tremendously. He had worked with Ernest Orlando Lawrence on the development of the cyclotron, and this new discovery stimulated him to think of various experiments that could be done with the cyclotron to investigate this new phenomenon.

The fissioning of the uranium nucleus created fragments, and McMillan decided to measure how far these fragments would penetrate into various kinds of matter. He first studied their range in a stack of thin aluminum foils and then in a stack of cigarette papers. In the latter case, he smeared a layer of uranium oxide onto the top piece of paper, and then exposed the stack to a beam of neutrons from the cyclotron. As expected, some of the fission fragments bored into the pile of thin papers and stopped at various depths. By taking the papers apart and measuring their radioactivity with a Geiger counter, he was able to determine the range of particular fragments. He also found that the top paper, containing the uranium, had radioactivities with different properties from the radioactivities in the other pieces of paper. In particular, he found a radioactive product that had a twenty-three-minute half-life (the time for half the nuclei of an isotope to undergo radioactive decay) and another with a half-life of a little more than two days.

In 1934, Enrico Fermi had tried to create elements heavier than uranium by adding neutrons to uranium; Hahn and Strassmann had begun their experiments with the same intent. McMillan knew that the twenty-three-minute half-life was caused by uranium 239, an isotope known since 1936, whose nucleus contains 92 protons and 147 neutrons. In the spring of 1940, he concluded that the two-day activity was caused by the transformation of this twenty-three-minute uranium-239 isotope into a new element by means of electron (or beta) emission (electron emission is accompanied by a neutron changing into a proton, thus increasing the atomic number by one). For McMillan to prove that he had actually found element 93 required painstaking chemical work on an extremely minute quantity of material.

McMillan was assisted by Philip Abelson, a chemist at the Carnegie Institution in Washington. Using "carrier" techniques, they were able to separate the new element from uranium and characterize it chemically (a carrier is a substance, available in bulk amounts, chemically analogous to the radioelement obtainable only in minuscule amounts). At the start, McMillan suspected that element 93 would be chemically like rhenium, since element 93 was directly below rhenium in the periodic table; but, much to their amazement, they found that element 93's properties made it a close relative of uranium. In their paper "Radioactive Element 93," published in *Physical Review* in 1940, they suggested that this element might be part of a second "rare earth" group of related elements beginning with uranium. In the lanthanide, or first rare earth family, the elements increase their atomic numbers by electrons being added to inner atomic orbits, and so their chemical properties—dependent on the electronic configuration of the outermost orbit—are similar. McMillan decided to call element 93 neptunium, after the planet Neptune.

During the summer and fall of 1940, McMillan began looking for the product of the two-day activity, now known to be neptunium 239. Since this radioisotope emitted electrons, he reasoned that the product of the decay must be a new element with atomic number 94 and mass number 239. To make adequate amounts of this element, he bombarded uranium with deuterons in the 152-centimeter Berkeley cyclotron (the hydrogen nucleus with a proton and a neutron is called a deuteron). McMillan believed that a new element was present, but the problem was to prove it. He suspected that this new element would decay by emitting an alpha particle (a helium nucleus, with two protons and two neutrons), which was then more difficult to detect than a beta particle. Unfortunately, he had to leave Berkeley in November, 1940, to take part in the development of radar at the Massachusetts Institute of Technology.

Following academic protocol, Glenn Theodore Seaborg, who had received his doctorate at the University of California, Berkeley, in 1937, asked McMillan if he could continue his studies of element 94. McMillan agreed. Seaborg, whose post-doctoral work with Gilbert Newton Lewis was on the effects of isotopic variations on the chemistry of elements, was well prepared to work out the chemistry of the new element. In the fall of 1940, he assigned his graduate student Arthur C. Wahl the thesis problem of investigating the chemical properties of element 93. Joseph W. Kennedy, an instructor in the chemistry department with Seaborg, was also interested in the transuranium elements; therefore, Seaborg, Wahl, and Kennedy formed a team to establish the chemical properties of element 94.

On December 14, 1940, Seaborg and his colleagues bombarded uranium oxide with deuterons from the 152-centimeter cyclotron. They believed that this bombardment formed neptunium 238, an isotope with a short half-life and therefore a high radioactivity. After losing an electron, this isotope turned into element 94 with mass number 238 (and a very long half-life). During the weeks following this experiment, they were able to separate the longer-lived isotope from its short-lived precursor. The chemically separated fraction with the new element, which exhibited the alpha radioactivity that McMillan had predicted, presented the researchers with the problem of isolating the new element from its nearest neighbors, in particular, uranium and neptunium.

The chemical key to the isolation of element 94 was that it had two oxidation states; that is, it could form two different compounds with oxygen. To put it in its higher-oxidation state required a stronger oxidizing agent than for neptunium. Since different chemical properties mean a different element, the discovery of element 94's particular oxidative properties constituted the proof of its individuality. Seaborg's team first successfully oxidized element 94 on February 23 to 24, 1941. Their paper describing the oxidation experiment was sent to Washington on March 7, 1941, but it was not published until 1946 because this new element's potential military importance had become obvious.

While experiments leading to the discovery of element 94 were occurring, Seaborg's team, augmented by Emilio Gino Sergrè, was searching for the 239 isotope of this element. They suspected that this isotope would be fissionable; that is, it would split when bombarded with slow neutrons and simultaneously produce huge amounts of energy. In the spring of 1941, Seaborg and his collaborators made this new isotope by bombarding uranium 238 with neutrons. This resulted in neptunium 239, which soon decayed into the 239 isotope of element 94. This isotope turned out to be very stable, with a half-life of twenty-four thousand years. When they bombarded isotope 239 with slow neutrons from the 94-centimeter Berkeley cyclotron, its nucleus fissioned with a release of energy greater than what scientists had obtained with uranium 235 (the fissionable isotope of uranium).

The researchers recognized immediately that the 239 isotope of element 94 had the potential to make up the highly explosive ingredient of a nuclear bomb. Therefore, as with the 238 isotope, Seaborg's team decided to withhold public announcement of isotope 239's fissionability until 1946. Throughout 1941, Seaborg and his colleagues, as they studied the chemical properties of the new element, used the code name "copper" for element 94, which meant that whenever the actual element copper was involved in their experiments, they had to call it "honest-to-God copper." Finally, in March 1942, when they were preparing detailed reports about their studies of the new element, they named it "plutonium." They had decided to follow McMillan's rationale, naming their new element after Pluto. After discussions about Pl and Pu for the element's symbol, they chose Pu, an appropriate designation for this highly poisonous substance.

Impact of Event

In the spring of 1942, Seaborg took a leave of absence from the University of California to join the operation to make material for an atomic bomb. He moved to the Metallurgical Laboratory of the University of Chicago to continue research on plutonium 239. He became head of the division whose goal was to develop chemical techniques that could be scaled up to the factory-level manufacture of massive quantities of plutonium from uranium. Up to 1941, Seaborg and his collaborators had worked, using carrier techniques, with invisible amounts of transuranium elements. In Chicago, they began to work in microgram amounts (a microgram is one-millionth of a gram). In the course of their work, his team developed new techniques for handling minuscule amounts of radioactive material, transforming such common apparatus as test tubes, flasks, and balances into devices that could handle adeptly pinhead quantities of material. These ultramicrochemical techniques enabled his group to work out the chemistry of plutonium. In an important early experiment, they succeeded, on September 10, 1942, in weighing the first visible amount of plutonium 239 (about one ten-millionth of an ounce).

The Metallurgical Laboratory's mission of chemically separating plutonium and manufacturing it on a large scale was helped by Fermi's development of the first nuclear pile. On December 2, 1942, in a squash court under the University of Chicago's Stagg Field, the first self-sustaining but controlled nuclear chain reaction was put into operation in a pile of six tons of uranium oxide arranged among numerous graphite bricks. The nuclear pile turned out to be an excellent way of producing plutonium, since uranium 238, which constitutes almost all the uranium nuclei in nature, can absorb neutrons to produce neptunium 239, which in turn decays into plutonium 239. The nuclear pile brought the physicists together who had been working on the development of self-sustaining chain reactions and the chemists who had been working on the development of separation processes for plutonium.

In the course of their work at the Metallurgical Laboratory, Seaborg and his colleagues discovered in nature minute quantities of neptunium and plutonium, the products of natural radioactive processes in such uranium ores as pitchblende and carnotite. In the summer of 1944, as a result of their recognition that neptunium and plutonium form part of a new series in the periodic table, Seaborg and his collaborators were able to discover two new elements, 95 and 96. They made the transplutonium element 96 by the bombardment of plutonium 239 with helium ions (and named it curium after Marie Curie). In late 1944 and early 1945, they chemically characterized element 95 (which they named americium). The discovery of these new transuranium elements confirmed Seaborg's view that these elements were part of a whole new family. He called this family the actinides, since all its elements were like actinium, element 89, the first in the series (consequently, the earlier view that these elements were "uranides," chemically similar to uranium, had to be modified).

The successful solutions to the problems of the chemical separation of plutonium led to the construction, in Hanford, Washington, of large plutonium-producing nuclear reactors and a massive plant designed for the chemical separation of plutonium. A ratio of about one to a billion was involved in the scale-up from the minute quantities used by Seaborg's team to the huge amounts used in the Hanford plant. As is well known, the labors of these and many other scientists and technicians eventually produced enough pure plutonium for use in two bombs, one that was successfully tested at Alamogordo, New Mexico, on July 16, 1945 (the world's first detonation of an atomic bomb) and the other bomb that was dropped on Nagasaki, Japan, on August 9, 1945.

Seaborg and McMillan, the two scientists most responsible for the discovery of plutonium, believed that its use was justified in the Nagasaki bomb to bring a swift end to World War II. Since then, they have been made aware that many people associate their discovery with myriad deaths and destruction. With the development of fast breeder reactors, based on the production and recycling of plutonium, the insidious properties of plutonium have become well known to the public, especially through the efforts of various groups in the environmental movement. Seaborg, in particular, has fought against the association of plutonium with the horrors of nuclear war and the poisoning of the planet. In many of his speeches and writings, he has expressed the hope that plutonium will be used in peaceful ways to raise standards of living. For Seaborg, plutonium confronts humanity with the choice that several previous scientific discoveries have presented. Plutonium can, like them, be used destructively, but Seaborg believes that human beings, with deepened wisdom and understanding, can learn to use this element constructively to build a world of lasting peace and shared abundance.

Bibliography

Heilbron, J. L., and Robert W. Seidel. *Lawrence and His Laboratory: A History of the Lawrence Berkeley Laboratory.* Berkeley, Calif.: University of California Press, 1989. Ernest Orlando Lawrence was the guiding spirit behind Berkeley's Radiation Laboratory, in which bigger and better atom-smashing machines were built and used to do research. Uses material from the Lawrence papers and other sources to recount the early history of Lawrence's laboratory.

Rhodes, Richard. *The Making of the Atomic Bomb.* New York: Simon & Schuster, 1986. Well researched and clearly written. Has become the principal account of how the atomic and hydrogen bombs were developed. Narrates, in graphic human, scientific, and technical detail, how the bombs evolved from basic discoveries in chemistry and physics. Illustrated with diagrams and photographs. Detailed index.

Seaborg, Glenn T. *Man-Made Transuranium Elements.* Englewood Cliffs, N.J.: Prentice-Hall, 1963. Part of the Foundations of Modern General Chemistry Series, intended for use by high school students beginning their study of chemistry. Makes the discovery of the transuranium elements exciting and understandable for readers with a minimum of knowledge of chemistry and physics. List of suggested further readings, an appendix of the transuranium nuclides, and a good index.

_____. *The Transuranium Elements.* New Haven, Conn.: Yale University Press, 1958. Based on the Silliman lectures delivered at Yale University in 1957. Intended for the nonspecialist; uses a historical approach to describe the discovery of the transuranium elements, in which Seaborg played a pivotal role. Profusely illustrated with charts, diagrams, and photographs. An appendix of radionuclides and a bibliography. Subject and name indexes.

Weeks, Mary Elvira. *Discovery of the Elements.* 7th ed. Easton, Pa.: Journal of Chemical Education, 1968. Classic account of the discovery of all the elements in the periodic table, revised and updated, by Henry M. Leicester, a distinguished historian of chemistry. Good treatment of the discovery of the transuranium elements with many citations to the primary and secondary literature. Copiously illustrated with photographs and diagrams. Both name and subject indexes.

Robert J. Paradowski

Cross-References

Becquerel Wins the Nobel Prize for the Discovery of Natural Radioactivity (1903), p. 199; Thomson Confirms the Possibility of Isotopes (1910), p. 471; Lawrence Develops the Cyclotron (1931), p. 953; Cockcroft and Walton Split the Atom with a Particle Accelerator (1932), p. 978; Segrè Identifies the First Artificial Element, Technetium (1937), p. 1101; Hahn Splits an Atom of Uranium (1938), p. 1135; Fermi Creates the First Controlled Nuclear Fission Chain Reaction (1942), p. 1198; The World's First Nuclear Reactor Is Activated (1943), p. 1230; The First Atomic Bomb Is Successfully Detonated (1945), p. 1265; Teller and Ulam Develop the First H-Bomb (1951), p. 1401; The World's First Breeder Reactor Produces Electricity While Generating New Fuel (1951), p. 1419.

THE FIRST JET PLANE USING WHITTLE'S ENGINE IS FLOWN

Category of event: Space and aviation
Time: May 15, 1941
Locale: Cranwell, Lincolnshire, England

Whittle developed one of the earliest turbojet engines, making this event very critical for the future of the Allied war effort

Principal personages:

HENRY HARLEY ARNOLD (1886-1950), a chief of staff of the U.S. Army Air Corps in 1941 responsible for bringing a model of the experimental turbojet engine to the United States for further development

GERRY SAYER, a chief test pilot for Gloster Aircraft Limited who carried out the first two test flights of the Gloster/Whittle jet in May, 1941

HANS PABST VON OHAIN (1911-   ), a German engineer who developed the turbojet engine that powered a Heinkel aircraft in the first jet-powered flight

SIR FRANK WHITTLE (1907-   ), an English Royal Air Force officer and engineer who developed the first functional turbojet engine

Summary of Event

On the morning of May 15, 1941, some eleven months after the fall of France to Adolf Hitler's advancing German army, the experimental jet-propelled aircraft bearing the official name Gloster/Whittle E.28/39 was successfully tested in the air by test pilot Gerry Sayer. The airplane had been developed in a little more than two years by Gloster Aircraft Company after England's Air Ministry Overseer, Wing Commander J. H. McC. Reynolds, introduced Sir Frank Whittle—inventor of England's first jet engine—to the person in charge of aircraft design functions, George Carter, in April, 1939. Since March, 1936, Whittle had been the main organizer of a joint stock company called Power Jets, Ltd. The entire venture depended on Whittle's contribution of technical skills.

The plane that was tested in May, 1941, like the jet engine that powered it, had a number of predecessors. In fact, the May, 1941, flight was not the first jet-powered test flight: That event occurred on August 27, 1939, when a Heinkel aircraft powered by a jet engine developed by Hans Pabst von Ohain accomplished a successful test flight in Germany. During this period, Italian airplane builders were also engaged in jet aircraft testing, with lesser degrees of success.

Without the knowledge that had been gained from Whittle's experience in experimental aviation, the test flight at the Royal Air Force's Cranwell airfield might never have been possible. It was Whittle's repeated efforts to develop turbojet propulsion engines that guaranteed the success of the flight. Whittle's contribution to the development of turbojet engines began in 1928, when, as a twenty-one-year-old Royal Air Force (RAF) flight cadet at Cranwell Academy, he wrote a thesis entitled "Future Developments in Aircraft Design." One of the principal conclusions of Whittle's earliest research was that if future aircraft were eventually to achieve very high speeds over long distances, they would have to fly at very high altitudes, benefiting from reduced resistance in lower-density atmospheric conditions. Although Whittle later stated that the speeds he had in mind at that time were about 805 kilometers per hour—close to those of the first jet-powered aircraft—his earliest idea of the engines that would be necessary for such planes focused on rocket propulsion. (That is, "jets" in which the fuel and oxygen required to produce the explosion needed to propulse an air vehicle forward are entirely self-contained in the engine, or, alternatively, gas turbines driving propellers at very high speeds.) Later, it occurred to him that gas turbines could be used to provide forward thrust by what would become "ordinary" jet propulsion (that is, "thermal air" engines that take the oxygen they need to ignite their fuel from the surrounding atmosphere). Eventually, such ordinary jet engines would function following one of four possible systems: the so-called athodyd, or continuous-firing duct; the pulsejet, or intermittent-firing duct; the turbojet, or gas-turbine jet; or the propjet, which uses a gas-turbine jet to rotate a conventional propeller at very high speeds.

The principle of jet propulsion, the turbojet, tested successfully in flight in May, 1941. Turbojets involve a fairly straightforward technical improvement over the simplest form of jet propulsion, the continuous-firing duct jet. The latter consists of an open-ended tube that receives an inflow of air that is heated by burning fuel passing through holes located midway along the duct. The heated air expands, instantly creating increased pressure inside the tube. The resulting phenomenon, forward thrust, comes as the heated air passes out of the back of the duct under pressure, at the same time sucking more air in through the front, thus reinforcing thrust process continuously. In the next stage, the turbojet, increased levels of pressure, and therefore increased thrust, are obtained by placing an air compressor near the front of the engine duct ahead of the combustion chamber. This compressor gains its energy by tapping, out of the rear section of the jet duct into a gas turbine mounted around its outer circumference, only a carefully calculated amount of pressure from the thrust force leaving the combustion chamber. Turbojet turbines do not contribute in any direct way to the thrust of the overall engine. Their sole purpose is to drive the compressors that—as a result of their key function—literally push a greater mass of heat-expandable air into the combustion chamber, creating the increased force of jet propulsion characteristic of this engine design.

When Whittle demonstrated his interest in designing a workable combination of turbojet-propulsive engines and an airplane most aerodynamically capable of utilizing the power produced by such jets, he did not receive enthusiastic support. In fact, many aspects of technical progress that were incorporated eventually into the airplane tested in 1941 were finished and patented in the early 1930's, well before a viable economic market existed for their practical use. One example is that of Bristol

Aircraft Manufacturing Limited and its persistent emphasis on costly research and development of what became standard features of standard performance aircraft by World War II—the so-called sleeve valve radial air cooling system for ordinary piston engines. When Whittle approached Bristol Aircraft in the mid-1930's with a scheme to perfect his plans for jet engine technology and faster-flying aircraft, the company's directors indicated that all available research funding was committed to projects such as the sleeve valve cooling system. Such decisions would be regretted a few years later, when the prospects for a European war involving competition with more advanced German aviation technology loomed closer.

The first sign of developments that would appear increasingly logical only in 1938 and 1939, when clouds of war were forming, occurred in January, 1936, when the founders of Jet Power Limited supported financially by a London venture capital investment firm (O. T. Falk and Partners), signed an agreement with two other parties that allowed serious development of Whittle's turbojet engine to proceed. The Air Ministry granted to Whittle the special privilege of serving semiofficially in the newly formed research and development alliance among investors, civilian manufacturers, and inventor-engineers.

As the project proceeded between 1936 and 1941, several essential liaisons would develop. By the time of the May, 1941, flight, this meant that Rover and Gloster Aircraft would share in the complicated construction and testing phases that preceded plans for the flight. Because the two big manufacturing concerns, BTH and Rover, needed exact specifications, particularly concerning power thrust, of the engines that would be mounted on the aircraft, "wholesale" communication of Power Jets' detailed plans created some difficulties. These problems concerned not so much security of information as the aircraft manufacturers' disagreements with what Power Jets insisted should be incorporated into the test aircraft's design. Such disagreements delayed progress on the plane. The Air Ministry's insistence that work not be suspended, however, prevented any actual stop. In fact, once it became apparent that England's declaration of war would lead to an extension of hostilities from Eastern to Western Europe, completion of the first jet aircraft's testing process immediately became urgent.

By the time of the 1941 flight, several different engine and aircraft models had been developed as candidates for the first test experience. Such diversity of prospective engine models stemmed in part from an interchanging process. This meant incorporating either technical principles or actual parts (such as engine mounts) that had been tested in earlier design models, both of engines and aircraft, into a chain of later versions. The static power thrust of the engine in question was between 1,600 and 1,800 pounds. (To estimate the significance of this technical point, note that one pound of thrust is equal to one horsepower at an airspeed of 603 kilometers per hour.)

The aircraft that was to be used to test the flight performance was completed by April, 1941. On April 7, tests were conducted on the ground at Gloster Aircraft's landing strip at Brockworth by Gloster's chief test pilot, Sayer. At this point, all parties concerned tried to estimate if the jet engine's revolution-per-minute capacity would be sufficient to push the aircraft forward with enough speed to make it airborne. Sayer dared to take the plane off the ground for a limited distance of between 183 meters and 273 meters, despite the technical staff's warnings against trying to fly in the first tests.

On May 15, the real first flight test was conducted at Cranwell. During that test, Sayer flew the plane, now called the Pioneer, for seventeen minutes at altitudes exceeding 305 meters and at a conservative test speed exceeding 595 kilometers per hour, which was equivalent to the top speed then possible in the RAF's most versatile fighterplane, the Spitfire.

Once it was clear that the tests undertaken at Cranwell were not only successful but also highly promising in terms of even better performance, a second, more extensive test date was set for May 21, 1941. It was this latter demonstration that induced the Ministry for Air Production (MAP) to initiate the first steps to produce what would be called the Meteor jet fighter aircraft on a full industrial scale in barely more than a year after the Cranwell test flight.

Impact of Event

At the time activities that would lead to the flight were taking form in England (specifically, in July, 1936), the Junkers engine and aircraft companies in Hitler's Germany created a new secret branch dedicated to the development, under the highly qualified engineer Herbert Wagner, of a turbojet-driven aircraft. In the same period, Junkers' rival in the German aircraft industry, Heinkel, Inc., engaged von Ohain, who was far enough along in his work on the turbojet principle to have patented a device very similar to Whittle's in 1935. A later model of this jet engine would power a test flight aircraft in August, 1939, shortly before the outbreak of World War II. In order to measure the potential impact of what Whittle's project accomplished by 1941, however, it is essential to realize that as each year went by between 1936 and 1941, the critical nature of competition obviously would be magnified. In the last stages before testing the Gloster/Whittle jet—specifically during November and December, 1940—the staff of Power Jets was increased by fifty-three skilled personnel. This was a major expansion when one compares the modest number of jet propulsion experts available only four years earlier.

Ironically, what Whittle's effort to develop the turbojet accomplished by the first successful test flight in 1941 was far from adequate to assure the Allied cause that if jet propulsion technology was to assume a key role in running the war, a balance could be held between England and Germany.

On one hand, the British Ministry for Aircraft Production reacted immediately to the prospect of using jet-propulsed aircraft against the German air raid threat in the so-called Battle for Britain. This was done despite signals in the second half of 1941 from Whittle and others that a number of technical complications still needed to be worked out before considering the original jet engine used for testing to be fully operational in the air. In fact, plans were laid as early as the summer of 1941 by Sir

Henry Tizard, chairman of the Aeronautical Research Committee of the Ministry for Aircraft Production, to begin production of five hundred Meteor fighter planes and twelve hundred turbojet engines. It was estimated that operational Meteors could begin flying by June or July of 1942, and that the full contingent of Meteors could be manufactured by the spring of 1943. On the other hand, the English defense establishment had to consider what had to be done immediately to carry on an air war over Europe against Hitler's *Luftwaffe*. The course of aircraft production over the next few years after the Meteor's May, 1941, test flight indicates that because of the high number of aircraft losses inflicted on the RAF during 1940 and the first half of 1941, the most immediate practical need was a life-or-death issue: replacement of English Spitfire propeller-driven fighters. This meant that the RAF's demand for conventional aircraft remained a priority over the next few years.

In the meantime, the wider impact of the flight was the result of decisions made by General Henry Harley Arnold, chief of staff of the U.S. Army Air Corps. Arnold had visited the Power Jets testing site in March of 1941. Even before learning of the successful flight in May, he made arrangements to have one of Whittle's engines shipped to the United States to be used by General Electric Corporation as a model for separate U.S. production. The engine arrived in October, 1941, and within one year, a General Electric-built engine powered a Bell Aircraft plane, the XP-59 A Airacomet in its maiden flight. This was six months prior to the formal inauguration of the first English Meteor aircraft. The October, 1942, inauguration of the XP-59 A was not witnessed by Whittle, but he visited the United States in May, 1942, to confer with American engineers working on the project.

Meanwhile, German engineers had scored even more impressive advances, as their research and development projects did not depend (as General Electric's did) on borrowed technology. One result of German technology, the V-1 unmanned jet propelled bomb, would become notorious when it began flying against English targets at a fairly early stage in the war. Less effective than the V-1 or its promised successor, the (rocket-propelled) V-2 was the only jet aircraft that was actually used in the war: the Messerschmidt Model 262. It appeared late in 1944 and far surpassed any possible rival that the Allied powers had been developing. It could achieve speeds of more than 805 kilometers per hour. Although this aircraft was conceived as a fighter plane, it ended its brief career (still the only operational jet aircraft used during World War II) in a series of bombing attacks.

All of the wartime experimental jet aircraft developments that were either sparked by the flight in 1941 or preceded it essentially prepared the way for the research and development projects that would leave a permanent revolutionary mark on aviation history in the early 1950's.

Bibliography

Constant, Edward W., II. *The Origins of the Turbojet Revolution*. Baltimore: The Johns Hopkins University Press, 1980. This book covers a wide variety of technical questions of turbojet functioning, but it devotes more space than any other technically oriented publication to the evolution of what became the Gloster/Whittle experimental jet plane tested in 1941.

Golley, John, and William Gunston. *Whittle: The True Story.* Washington, D.C.: Smithsonian Institution Press, 1987. Aside from Whittle's autobiography (cited below), this is the most complete account of his experiences developing the plane.

Griffith, A. A. "Report on the Whittle Jet Propulsion System." Report No. E 3545 (ARC 2897). Farnborough, England: Royal Aircraft Establishment, February, 1937. Although compiled before World War II, this official report on the development of the Whittle engine was kept closed until several years after the war.

Whittle, Frank. "The Early History of the Whittle Jet-Propulsion Gas Turbine-1." In *The Aeroplane.* [London], October 19, 1945. Written for the layperson, this account of how the Whittle turbojet worked is one of the earliest descriptions made available to the general public.

_____. *Gas Turbine Aero-Thermodynamics: With Special Reference to Aircraft Propulsion.* New York: Pergamon Press, 1981. This textbook contains technical material on subjects such as dealing with shock waves in the air, effect of height and speed on performance, and Whittle's ideas on designing a "Super-Thrust Engine" in the 1980's, "regardless of fuel consumption."

_____. *Jet: The Story of a Pioneer.* London: Frederick Muller, 1953. Whittle's autobiographical account of his pre-World War II experiences in the Royal Air Force and Power Jets, as well as his immediate postwar career as a paramount representative of a struggling new area of aviation technology.

Byron Cannon

Cross-References

The Wright Brothers Launch the First Successful Airplane (1903), p. 203; The Fokker Aircraft Are the First Airplanes Equipped with Machine Guns (1915), p. 600; Goddard Launches the First Liquid Fuel Propelled Rocket (1926), p. 810; The Germans Use the V-1 Flying Bomb and the V-2 Goes into Production (1944), p. 1235; The First Jumbo Jet Service Is Introduced (1969), p. 1897; Rutan and Yeager Pilot the *Voyager* Around the World Without Refueling (1986), p. 2336.

REBER MAKES THE FIRST
RADIO MAPS OF THE UNIVERSE

Category of event: Astronomy
Time: 1942-1947
Locale: Wheaton, Illinois

Reber built the first intentional radio telescope and used it to record the first radio contour maps of the Milky Way in two complete sky surveys, establishing the foundations of radio astronomy

Principal personages:
GROTE REBER (1911-   ), an American radio engineer and amateur astronomer who built the first reflecting radio telescope and pioneered for nearly ten years as the world's only radio astronomer
KARL JANSKY (1905-1950), an American radio engineer who first made the accidental discovery of radio emissions from space and showed that they were coming from the Milky Way
SIR WILLIAM HERSCHEL (1738-1822), a German-English musician and first astronomer to map the structure of the Milky Way
HARLOW SHAPLEY (1885-1972), an American astronomer whose study of the distribution of star clusters led to an estimate of the size of the Milky Way galaxy and Earth's location to it
EDWIN POWELL HUBBLE (1889-1953), an American astronomer who studied galaxies and their motions to reveal an expanding universe

Summary of Event

Grote Reber's work in recording the first radio contour maps of the universe was a new and unexpected application of the technology of radio to the understanding of our Milky Way galaxy and the galaxies beyond. The discovery of radio waves by Heinrich Hertz only fifty years before Reber built his radio telescope in 1937 confirmed James Clerk Maxwell's electromagnetic theory of light and demonstrated that electromagnetic waves consist of many different wavelengths. These extend from the longer waves of radio and infrared down to the shorter waves of visible light, ultraviolet, and X rays at increasingly higher frequencies, but all traveling at the speed of light. Reber's work opened up the invisible window of radio frequencies in the electromagnetic spectrum for observing new features of the universe.

Sir William Herschel was one of the first astronomers to recognize the true nature of the dense band of stars across the sky called the Milky Way. From counting stars in various directions in the Milky Way, he concluded in 1785 that the vast majority of stars are contained within a flattened disk shape, forming an island universe or galaxy in space, with the solar system reduced to a tiny speck in the vast universe of stars. Early in the twentieth century, Harlow Shapley was able to use the 2.5-meter

Mount Wilson telescope to study star clusters and estimate their distances. He showed that the Milky Way galaxy is far larger than any previous estimate, and that the sun was far out from the galactic center, which he located in the direction of the constellation Sagittarius.

Much of the modern understanding of the Milky Way and other galaxies comes from the work of Edwin Powell Hubble. (Coincidentally, Reber was graduated from the same high school as Hubble in Wheaton, Illinois, and Hubble's seventh and eighth grade teacher was Reber's mother, Harriet Grote, who interested her son in astronomy by giving him a book by the famous astronomer.) Hubble used the Mount Wilson telescope to discover variable stars in the Andromeda nebula (a fuzzy patch of light in the night sky) that made it possible to calculate its distance and size. In 1924, he showed that it was an independent galaxy of stars far outside the Milky Way. By 1929, he had identified several galaxies and measured their velocities from the shift in their spectra lines, most of which were toward the red end of the spectra. This indicated recession speeds proportional to their distances, thus leading to the concept of an expanding universe.

In 1932, Karl Jansky reported his accidental discovery of radio waves from space. Using a rotating array of dipole antennas sensitive to 15-meter radio waves, he detected a steady hiss that appeared four minutes earlier every day. This corresponded to the daily motion of the stars, so he concluded that he was receiving cosmic radio waves from beyond the solar system. He was able to identify the source of the most intense radiation in the direction of Sagittarius, suggesting that it came from the center of the Milky Way galaxy. He also showed that weaker radio waves came from all directions in the Milky Way and suggested that their source is in the stars or in the interstellar matter between the stars.

Jansky's work was so unrelated to traditional astronomy that no professional astronomer followed it up. As a young radio engineer at the Stewart-Warner Company in Chicago, Reber read Jansky's papers and began to plan how he could measure the detailed distribution of the radiation intensity throughout the sky at different wavelengths. In 1937, he built a 9.5-meter parabolic reflecting dish in his side yard, mounted so that its elevation could be changed in a north-south direction (declination) while scanning east and west (right ascension) would result from the earth's rotation. He placed a dipole antenna at the focus and designed a receiver sensitive to the shortest wavelengths possible at the time. For ten years, he operated this radio telescope in Wheaton as the only active radio astronomer in the world.

After trying unsuccessfully to detect radiation at wavelengths of 9 centimeters and 33 centimeters, Reber finally changed his receiver to a new operating wavelength of 1.87 meters and began to get positive results by the spring of 1939. He did most of his work from midnight to dawn to avoid interference from automobile ignitions. As the Milky Way crossed the meridian late at night, Reber measured the increasing intensity of the cosmic radio waves by reading a microammeter at one-minute intervals. He published his initial results in the February, 1940, *Proceedings of the Institute of Radio Engineers*, where he noted an intensity too low to be caused by thermal emission, but suggested the possibility of "free-free" radiation from electrons interacting with positive ions (charged atoms) in interstellar gases.

In 1941, Reber began a complete sky survey with an automatic chart recorder and more sensitive receiving equipment. At 1.87 meters, his operating frequency was 160 megahertz (million vibrations per second) and his radio telescope had a beamwidth of about 12 Kelvins, making it possible to resolve some structure in the radio emissions from our galaxy. The pen would slowly rise and fall as the reflecting dish rotated with the earth under the Milky Way. After collecting approximately two hundred chart recordings at increasing angles of elevation, he plotted the resulting radio contours as lines of constant intensity on the two hemispheres of the sky. The resulting radio maps, published in the *Astrophysical Journal* in November, 1944, revealed interesting details: The peak intensity was at the center of our galaxy in Sagittarius, with secondary maxima clearly evident in Cygnus and Cassiopeia. More important was his recognition that radio waves could penetrate the interstellar dust that obscures much visible light in the Milky Way.

Reber's last observations in Wheaton were made from 1945 to 1947 at a wavelength of 62.5 centimeters and a frequency of 480 megahertz, giving a beamwidth of about 4 Kelvins, an improvement of nearly three times better resolution of details in the Milky Way. The resulting radio maps, published in the *Proceedings of the Institute of Radio Engineers* in October, 1948, now revealed two noise peaks in the Cygnus region, later identified as a radio galaxy (Cygnus A) and a source associated with a spiral arm in the Milky Way (Cygnus X). An intensity peak in Taurus was later identified with the eleventh century supernova remnant in the Crab nebula, and another in Cassiopeia matches the position of a seventeenth century supernova explosion. These results were the beginning of many important discoveries in the field of radio astronomy.

Impact of Event

Reber's pioneering work and resulting radio maps led to growing interest in radio astronomy and many unexpected discoveries with radio telescopes of increasing sophistication and size. After Reber's 1944 radio maps were published, the Dutch astronomer Jan Hendrik Oort asked a graduate student at the University of Leiden, Hendrik van de Hulst, to study the theory of interstellar radiation. In 1945, van de Hulst predicted that neutral hydrogen should emit 21-centimeter radio waves when its electron spin reverses in relation to its proton spin. By 1949, the Harvard physicist Edward Mills Purcell began a search for these radio waves with Harold Irving Ewen, a graduate student who was sent to confer with Reber on techniques in radio astronomy. Ewen and Purcell developed special equipment and by 1951 succeeded in detecting the predicted 21-centimeter radio waves. Oort's group then began a seven-year collaboration with Australian radio astronomers to map the spiral arms of the Milky Way galaxy, using the fact that 21-centimeter radiation could penetrate the interstellar dust that absorbed visible light.

In 1960, two radio sources were identified with what appeared to be stars, but each emitted much more radio energy than our Sun or any other known star. Four of these so-called quasars (quasi-stellar radio sources) had been discovered by 1963, when Maarten Schmidt at Mount Palomar Observatory recognized that their unusual spectra lines were caused by large redshifts that could be interpreted as rapid recession velocities, and thus at extremely great distances. At distances of billions of light years, these objects would have to be more than one hundred times brighter than entire galaxies and would appear to be some kind of highly energetic stage in the early formation of a galaxy.

Another dramatic event in radio astronomy occurred in 1967, when Jocelyn Bell discovered pulsars. She found rapidly recurring signals on recording charts from a huge array of 2,048 dipole antennas spread over four acres at the University of Cambridge. After she discussed this with the project leader Antony Hewish, they installed high-speed recorders and found sharp pulses at precise intervals of just over a second. More of these objects were soon found, some having even more rapid pulsations. They are believed to be fast-spinning neutron stars with high magnetic fields that produce a rotating beam of radio emission. A pulsar in the Crab nebula was later identified with the collapsed core of the supernova remnant that had appeared on Reber's radio maps.

Perhaps the most important discovery in radio astronomy was the 1965 detection of microwave background radiation by Arno Penzias and Robert Woodrow Wilson. Using a 6-meter horn antenna tuned to 7-centimeter waves at the Bell Telephone Laboratories in Holmdel, New Jersey, they found an unexpected excess of steady radiation with no directional variation, corresponding to about 3 Kelvins of thermal noise. This matched the predicted temperature of cosmic radiation from a primeval fireball in the "big bang" theory. Thus, radio astronomy provided confirmation of the creation and expansion of the universe.

Bibliography

Hey, J. S. *The Evolution of Radio Astronomy.* New York: Science History Publications, 1973. A good history of radio astronomy by one of the pioneers in its development. The first chapter describes the work of Jansky and Reber, followed by chapters on the growth of radio astronomy after World War II. A good discussion of radio mapping of the Milky Way, radio galaxies, quasars, and the microwave background radiation is included with many good diagrams, photographs, and radio contour maps.

Lang, Kenneth R., and Owen Gingerich, eds. *A Source Book in Astronomy and Astrophysics, 1900-1975.* Cambridge, Mass.: Harvard University Press, 1979. Reproductions are given of many of the most important journal articles on radio astronomy, including the early papers of Jansky and Reber, and later papers on quasars, pulsars, and microwave background radiation. Introductory essays help to explain the context and importance of these articles.

Spradley, Joseph L. "The First True Radio Telescope." *Sky and Telescope* 76 (July, 1988): 28-30. An introductory article in a popular astronomy magazine on Reber's background and work. Photographs of the first reflecting radio telescope and the original model used in its design are given, and Reber's early results are discussed with reproductions of the radio contour maps he obtained.

Sullivan, W. T., III, ed. *The Early Years of Radio Astronomy*. Cambridge, England: Cambridge University Press, 1984. A series of articles by the pioneers of radio astronomy on its early development. A 1958 article by Grote Reber entitled "Early Radio Astronomy at Wheaton, Illinois" includes about a dozen early photographs not in the original article. Other chapters describe the influence of radio astronomy on science and cosmology.

Verschuur, Gerrit L. *The Invisible Universe Revealed*. New York: Springer-Verlag, 1987. This book, subtitled "The Story of Radio Astronomy," gives a good description of the results of radio astronomy with more than one hundred photographs and radio contour maps. Concluding chapters give a brief history of radio astronomy.

Zeilik, Michael, and John Gaustad. *Astronomy: The Cosmic Perspective*. New York: John Wiley & Sons, 1990. A standard college textbook on astronomy with a good section on radio telescopes and results obtained with them. One of Reber's radio contour maps is shown, and the meaning of such maps is discussed with good diagrams.

Joseph L. Spradley

Cross-References

Shapley Proves the Sun Is Distant from the Center of Our Galaxy (1918), p. 655; Hubble Demonstrates That Other Galaxies Are Independent Systems (1924), p. 790; Hubble Confirms the Expanding Universe (1929), p. 878; Jansky's Experiments Lead to the Founding of Radio Astronomy (1930), p. 934; Reber Builds the First Intentional Radio Telescope (1937), p. 1113; Oort and Associates Construct a Map of the Milky Way (1951), p. 1414; Ryle Constructs the First Radio Interferometer (1955), p. 1496; Schmidt Makes What Constitutes the First Recognition of a Quasar (1963), p. 1757; Bell Discovers Pulsars, the Key to Neutron Stars (1967), p. 1862.

FERMI CREATES THE FIRST CONTROLLED NUCLEAR FISSION CHAIN REACTION

Category of event: Physics
Time: December 2, 1942
Locale: University of Chicago, Chicago, Illinois

Fermi's team demonstrated that nuclear energy could be released in a sustained chain reaction, leading to the development of the atomic bomb and nuclear fission electric power plants

Principal personages:

ENRICO FERMI (1901-1954), an Italian nuclear physicist who won the 1938 Nobel Prize in Physics and designed the atomic pile which produced the first nuclear chain reaction

WALTER HENRY ZINN (1906-   ), a Canadian physicist in charge of procuring and machining materials for the construction of the atomic pile and leader of the day construction crew

HERBERT L. ANDERSON (1914-   ), an American physicist who headed the night construction crew on the atomic pile

ARTHUR HOLLY COMPTON (1892-1962), an American Nobel prize laureate in physics who was director of the Chicago Metallurgical Atomic Project

LEO SZILARD (1898-1964), a Hungarian physicist who initially conceived the idea of a chain reaction, patented it, and encouraged the United States government to pursue its research

Summary of Event

In December, 1938, Enrico Fermi, a professor of physics in Rome, took advantage of his 1938 Nobel Prize in Physics to leave his native Italy and escape Adolf Hitler's increasing domination of Benito Mussolini's Italy. With his family, Fermi arrived in New York City and settled down to continue his research at Columbia University.

Fermi and his associates in Rome had been studying the new nuclei produced when various chemical elements were bombarded by neutrons. In 1934, experiments on uranium produced a new radioactive isotope. Fermi and his collaborators demonstrated chemically that the new isotope did not belong to any of the elements immediately below uranium on the periodic table. They concluded that they had produced the first element ever found that was heavier than uranium. The idea of a "transuranic" element caught the imagination of the scientific community and the popular press. When the German chemist Ida Noddack published an article suggesting that Fermi had not ruled out the possibility that their new radioactivity came from a lighter chemical element produced when a uranium nucleus split into two parts, she was ignored.

Fermi and other groups, including Irène Joliot-Curie and Paul Savitch in Paris, and Otto Hahn, Lise Meitner, and Fritz Strassmann in Berlin, continued to study the effects of irradiating uranium with neutrons. Fermi's group demonstrated that neutrons, which had been slowed down by passing them through a material containing hydrogen such as paraffin, were more effective in producing radioactivity than more energetic neutrons. All the experimenters gradually compiled a list of several different radioactive species which were produced when uranium was bombarded.

In December, 1938, Hahn wrote to Meitner and informed her that he and Strassmann had incontrovertible evidence that bombardment of uranium with neutrons produced lighter elements and not transuranic elements. Meitner, who was Jewish, had been forced to leave Berlin for Sweden. She and her nephew, Otto Robert Frisch, a young physicist working with Niels Bohr in Copenhagen, concluded that when a uranium nucleus absorbed a neutron, it split or fissioned into two lighter nuclei and some extra neutrons releasing a hundred million times as much energy as was released in a typical chemical reaction between two atoms.

Frisch reported the discovery of nuclear fission to Bohr. Bohr was leaving Denmark for the United States and announced the discovery to the Fifth Washington Conference on Theoretical Physics on January 26, 1939. Within days, Fermi and other American physicists had confirmed the discovery of nuclear fission. Fermi and Leo Szilard, a Hungarian physicist also driven into exile by Hitler's advance in Europe, realized immediately that if the neutrons from one fission could be used to trigger a second fission, the resulting chain reaction could be used to produce energy. If the multiplication could be made geometric, the chain reaction would be a powerful explosive. Szilard feared that Hitler's Germany would construct a super weapon based on these principles. He persuaded his American colleagues, including Fermi, to delay publication of their experimental results on fission.

Meanwhile, the physics community measured the energy released in uranium fission, the new nuclei produced, and the number of neutrons released during each fission. In August of 1939, Szilard and fellow Hungarian émigré Eugene Paul Wigner persuaded Albert Einstein to send a letter to President Franklin D. Roosevelt urging a research program into the possibility of a super weapon. The government hesitated while the physicists determined that only the rare isotope of uranium—uranium 235—underwent fission, while the isotope uranium 238, which was composed of 99.3 percent of naturally occurring uranium, did not.

Fermi and his colleagues calculated that it should be possible to sustain a chain reaction in a matrix of pure uranium oxide with graphite between blocks of uranium to slow down the neutrons. Both the graphite and the uranium would have to be free of chemical impurities which would absorb neutrons and cut off the chain reaction. In July, 1941, Fermi and his group were funded to begin experiments in constructing a graphite-uranium "pile" designed to sustain a chain reaction. In December, 1941, Arthur Holly Compton, the American Nobel laureate in physics, was placed in charge of the project and moved the experiments to Chicago in early 1942.

By July, 1942, the Chicago group had completed sufficient preliminary work to design a pile which would sustain a chain reaction and to begin its construction. Thirty preliminary atomic piles of graphite and uranium had been built before the pile which sustained the first chain reaction was started. Construction of the pile began in November in a squash court since this was the only area available that was large enough to hold the 771,000 pounds of graphite, 80,590 pounds of uranium oxide, and the 12,400 pounds of uranium metal that were to compose the pile. The uranium metal packed uranium nuclei closer together increasing the likelihood that a neutron would be captured by a uranium nucleus and cause a fission. Since Fermi could not obtain enough metal, the available supply was to be built into the center of the pile.

The pile was constructed inside an enormous balloon because Fermi feared he might have to evacuate the pile to reduce neutron absorption by air. Construction crews headed by Walter Henry Zinn and Herbert L. Anderson worked around the clock machining and stacking the graphite and uranium blocks. All the scientists slid on the graphite dust which permanently blackened their faces and hands. Control rods which absorbed neutrons were built into the pile to be withdrawn in order to start the chain reaction. Each day the control rods were withdrawn and measurements were taken to see how close the system was to sustaining a chain reaction.

On the evening of December 1, 1942, Anderson and Zinn realized that the layer of uranium and graphite which the night crew had placed on the pile should be sufficient to sustain a chain reaction. The crew went home for a few hours of sleep and reassembled at 8:30 the following morning. Fermi ordered the main control rods withdrawn, and the final control rod was moved foot by foot out of the pile as the assembled physicists, including Compton, who had fought bureaucratic battles for them, gathered to watch the neutron counters. If a chain reaction had been initiated, the counters were expected to spin as the neutron counting rate increased without sign of leveling off. At 11:35 A.M., the automatic safety control rods slammed back into the pile because they were set to operate on too low a neutron flux. According to his invariable custom, Fermi announced a lunch break.

At 2:00 P.M., the group gathered around the pile, and the withdrawal of the rods continued. At 3:25 P.M. (Anderson claims 3:36 P.M.), the control rod was removed the final foot. The counting rate climbed exponentially. A controlled fission chain reaction had been achieved and was sustained until Fermi ordered the control rods back into the pile at 3:53 P.M. As the group celebrated, they realized that the success of their experiment had inaugurated a new age.

Impact of Event

The successful operation of the atomic pile provided physicists with a tool for studying the behavior of nuclear fission chain reactions. These studies were essential for the design and construction of an atomic bomb, since details of critical mass and neutron absorption by materials could be easily measured using atomic piles. Secondly, atomic piles produced a second fissionable isotope, plutonium 239, and the design of large-scale piles for the production of plutonium was soon under way.

Plutonium was to prove more efficient as a fuel for bombs than highly enriched uranium 235. Finally, the first atomic pile demonstrated that it was possible to produce a sustained energy source from nuclear fission, the basic result that leads to the construction of nuclear electric generating plants. Compton reported the successful initiation of a chain reaction to a colleague in Washington with the famous words, ". . . the Italian navigator has just landed in the new world."

In 1942, Fermi's success produced surprisingly little excitement. The scientists were elated that their experiments had worked as planned and used the result to demonstrate that they were able to produce the technologies they promised. On the other hand, preliminary results for the thirty piles built before the first chain reaction was achieved had been so encouraging that the establishment of the Manhattan Project to construct an atomic bomb were already well under way. It was important that Compton had brought the representative of DuPont Corporation, Crawford Greenewalt, to witness the start up of the pile. The success of the pile may have been instrumental in persuading Greenewalt and DuPont to undertake the large-scale production of plutonium for nuclear weapons at reactors in Hanford, Washington. Certainly, the success of the pile removed the remaining uncertainties in anyone's mind that nuclear fission existed and could produce a chain reaction. Fermi's success gave the military confidence in the predictions of civilian scientists that they could produce a working nuclear fission weapon, even when the experimental work on the Manhattan Project went badly.

After 1942, the major work on the atomic bomb shifted to the materials production centers at Oak Ridge, Tennessee, and Hanford, Washington, and to the weapons design center at Los Alamos, New Mexico. Fermi's success in sustaining a chain reaction in the atomic pile in Chicago was the final step in the preliminary physics experiments before the actual design of an atomic weapon began. It served as a technological benchmark in the march toward peaceful energy and the beginning of the final stages of construction of an atomic weapon.

The public remained ignorant of Fermi's work until the end of World War II. When classification was lifted, the experiments leading to the bomb became scientific legend. Fermi's atomic pile in the center of Chicago has become a major element of that story.

Bibliography

Fermi, Laura. *Atoms in the Family: My Life with Enrico Fermi*. Chicago: University of Chicago Press, 1954. A very readable account, by Fermi's wife, of the events surrounding the development of the first sustained chain reaction from a nontechnical point of view.

Graetzer, Hans G., and David L. Anderson. "From Nuclear Fission to Chain Reaction (1939-1942)." In *The Discovery of Nuclear Fission: A Documentary History*. New York: Van Nostrand Reinhold, 1971. This history uses original documents to describe the discoveries in nuclear fission surrounded by careful explanations for the layperson and a clear historical narrative.

Libby, Leona Marshall. *The Uranium People.* New York: Crane, Russak, 1979. The autobiography of the only female physicist working on the atomic pile experiment, this volume provides a very readable eyewitness account of the work on the first nuclear reactor.

Rhodes, Richard. "The New World." In *The Making of the Atomic Bomb.* New York: Simon & Schuster, 1986. This excellent history of nuclear fission provides a detailed description of the Chicago pile experiment in the context of other work on nuclear physics taking place at the time.

Segrè, Emilio. *Enrico Fermi: Physicist.* Chicago: University of Chicago Press, 1970. A biography of Fermi written by a physicist who worked with him in Rome and the United States which provides insight into the way Fermi developed his physical ideas and conducted experiments.

United States Office of the Assistant Secretary for Nuclear Energy. *The First Reactor.* Springfield, Va.: National Technical Information Service, 1982. Reissued for the fortieth anniversary of the first chain reaction, this slim volume contains a reprint of Fermi's account of the experiment and a concise summary of the work that led up to it.

Ruth H. Howes

Cross-References

Chadwick Discovers the Neutron (1932), p. 973; Cockcroft and Walton Split the Atom with a Particle Accelerator (1932), p. 978; Frédéric Joliot and Irène Joliot-Curie Develop the First Artificial Radioactive Element (1933), p. 987; Hahn Splits an Atom of Uranium (1938), p. 1135; The World's First Nuclear Reactor Is Activated (1943), p. 1230; The World's First Breeder Reactor Produces Electricity While Generating New Fuel (1951), p. 1419.

AVERY, MacLEOD, AND McCARTY DETERMINE THAT DNA CARRIES HEREDITARY INFORMATION

Category of event: Biology
Time: 1943-1944
Locale: The Rockefeller Institute, New York

Avery and coworkers demonstrated that the genetic transformation of bacteria is caused by deoxyribonucleic acid (DNA), providing direct evidence about the chemical nature of hereditary information

Principal personages:
OSWALD AVERY (1877-1955), an American bacteriologist, in whose laboratory the first demonstration that DNA is the genetic material took place
FREDERICK GRIFFITH (1881-1941), a microbiologist who was the first to demonstrate genetic transformation of bacteria
COLIN MUNRO MACLEOD (1909-1972), an American microbiologist who, while working in Avery's laboratory, refined the transformation assay and coauthored the seminal paper on the transforming principle
MACLYN MCCARTY (1911-), an American microbiologist and co-author with Avery and MacLeod of subsequent supporting papers

Summary of Event

In the 1920's, the field of genetics had progressed to the point of locating hereditary information within the cell. Genes, which were uncharacterized elements responsible for the inheritable traits of organisms, had been localized to the chromosomes of cells. In the cells of higher organisms, multiple chromosomes are found within the membrane-bounded compartment called the nucleus; within the simpler cells of bacteria, a single chromosome is found without a specialized compartment. In both cases, these chromosomes were known to be made up of two major chemical components: protein and a form of nucleic acid (an acid named for its nuclear location). Protein and DNA were in chromosomes, and chromosomes had something to do with the characteristic traits of organisms, but beyond that nothing was known about the physical nature of genetic information.

Oswald Avery was a bacteriologist at the hospital of the Rockefeller Institute in New York City. He was studying pneumonia, a disease caused by bacteria and a major cause of death in the late nineteenth and early twentieth centuries. Several different strains of pneumococci, the class of bacteria causing pneumonia, were known to exist; some strains in this class were nonpathogenic (did not cause disease). Avery had demonstrated in 1917 that the blood and urine of patients infected by different pathogenic strains contained distinct soluble substances, specific for each strain. Later, experiments suggested that these specific substances were polysaccharides, starchlike molecules derived from the distinct cell coatings or capsules of these bacteria. Nonvirulent pneumococci were unencapsulated, and the differences in the coats of the encapsulated forms reflected the strain differences among the virulent pneumococci. Avery's early work helped form the foundation of the scientific study of immunology.

In 1928, Frederick Griffith, an English public health officer, reported the results of experiments using different strains of pneumococci to infect mice. Griffith had observed the following: Mice injected with a nonpathogenic (unencapsulated) strain of pneumococci did not contract pneumonia; mice injected with encapsulated pathogenic bacteria that had first been killed by heating also did not contract pneumonia. So far, there were no surprises for bacteriologists. Griffith also inoculated mice with a combination of nonpathogenic bacteria and heat-killed pathogenic pneumococci; unfortunately, many of those mice contracted pneumonia and died. Moreover, live bacteria recovered from these animals were encapsulated. The virulence and capsule-forming traits of one strain of bacteria had been transferred to a formerly nonvirulent, unencapsulated strain, thereby transforming it. This acquired pathogenicity was maintained in subsequent generations of these bacteria, and the phenomenon was dubbed "genetic transformation." Soon after they were reported, Griffith's experiments were repeated with similar findings in several laboratories. One of the scientists who confirmed Griffith's work was Martin Dawson, a Canadian scientist then working in Avery's laboratory at the Rockefeller Institute. Dawson took Griffith's finding a step further and demonstrated that genetic transformation did not require the infection of a host animal—unencapsulated bacteria mixed with killed encapsulated forms gave rise to encapsulated, virulent colonies in bacterial cultures in the laboratory. Avery's name did not appear on Dawson's paper confirming Griffith's findings; he was skeptical about transformation. This is perhaps not surprising, considering that Avery's main contribution up to that time had been in establishing the existence of distinct, stable forms of pneumococci, recognizable by just such characteristics as Griffith's work suggested could be transferred from strain to strain.

James Lionel Alloway, another scientist in Avery's laboratory, later produced cell-free extracts of broken encapsulated bacteria and showed that such extracts were as effective as heat-killed cells in transforming nonvirulent strains. Alloway's descriptions of the precipitation observed in his extracts upon the addition of alcohol would in a few years be easily recognized as the behavior of nucleic acids. At that time, however, the identity of the transforming agent in these extracts was unknown, and Alloway—like a substantial number of biologists—believed it was most likely to be protein.

Avery's interest in the pursuit of the transforming principle appears to have been engaged at this point. The combined weight of evidence, much of it from his own laboratory, was irresistible. Together with two new collaborators in his laboratory, Colin Munro MacLeod and Maclyn McCarty, he performed the key experiments that first identified DNA as the active transforming material. They exhaustively fractionated transforming extracts, removing polysaccharides, lipids, and proteins by physical, chemical, and enzymatic treatments without removing the ability to transform. Enzymes that degraded ribonucleic acid (RNA) were also unable to interfere with transformation, but even trace amounts of DNA-degrading enzymes destroyed the transforming principle. They tested and retested their extracts, using different methods of measurement and different sources of enzymes; their results continued to show that the transforming principle behaved like DNA. Furthermore, their extract was extraordinarily potent: It continued to transform even when diluted to exceedingly low concentrations, down to "1 part in 600,000,000" from the starting material.

In a well-known letter to his brother (also a bacteriologist), Avery revealed his own excitement and surprise at his discovery:

> . . . But at last *perhaps* we have it . . . the substance . . . conforms very closely to the theoretical values of pure deoxyribose *nucleic acid* . . . Who could have guessed it? . . . If we are right, & of course that's not yet proven, then . . . by means of a known chemical substance it is possible to induce *predictable* and *hereditary* changes in cells. This is something that has long been the dream of geneticists. . . .

In 1944, Avery, MacLeod, and McCarty's classic paper entitled "Studies on the Chemical Transformation of Pneumococcal Types" appeared in the *Journal of Experimental Medicine*, presenting their evidence that DNA was responsible for the transfer of genetic information.

Impact of Event

Far from being accepted as an elegant proof of DNA's role, Avery's paper met with resistance and disbelief (that DNA should be the carrier of complex heredity appeared highly unlikely to many scientists) for several reasons. One reason was the presumed simplicity (if not monotony) of DNA structure. It was thought to be a polymer of identical repeating units, similar to some starch molecules. Such a structure for DNA was incompatible with the variety and specificity of genetic information. This presumed uniformity was even more striking in comparison with the immense diversity that had been observed among protein molecules, which were known to be associated—like DNA—with chromosomes. The prevailing view held that proteins, not DNA, were probably the vectors of genetic information.

Even though Avery, MacLeod, and McCarty had demonstrated that the transforming ability of their extract was highest in the most pure, most protein-free preparations, DNA's role seemed implausible still. Many thought that even traces of contaminating proteins could be responsible for transformation. Alternatively, some suggested that transformation of pneumococci was a special case: DNA might be having some other affect on these cells that caused them to begin making capsules and become virulent.

It took several years and two other studies to resolve the doubt about DNA. In 1949, Rollin Hotchkiss, who had begun work in Avery's laboratory in 1935, demonstrated DNA-mediated transfer of an entirely different set of characteristics, related to antibiotic resistance, to a formerly nonresistant strain of pneumococci. This showed conclusively that capsule formation was not a special case. Then, in 1952, Alfred Hershey and Martha Chase grew virus cultures in the presence of two different radioactive compounds, one that would be incorporated into the proteins of the viral particles and another that would be incorporated primarily into viral DNA. These viruses infected bacteria, reproduced themselves inside, then burst the bacterial cells to release many progeny viruses. Hershey and Chase showed that, in these viral infections, virus proteins (identified by the specific radioactive tag) remained outside the bacterial cell, while the viral DNA was injected into each bacterium. That this DNA alone was responsible for the subsequent production of progeny demonstrated that viral genetic information resided in the same chemical substance that carried the genes of pneumococci. The case for DNA was now irrefutable.

In April 1953, James D. Watson and Francis Crick published their model of the double, helical structure of DNA, a model that explained how complex genetic information could be carried by a polymer built from simple subunits and how this polymer could be replicated over and over in generation after generation. Watson and others, whose work formed the basis for the new field of molecular biology, traced their interest in nucleic acids to Avery's experiments.

Bibliography

Dubos, Rene J. *The Professor, the Institute, and DNA*. New York: Rockefeller University Press, 1976. A biography of Oswald Avery. Illustrated, with bibliography and index.

Hotchkiss, Rollin D. "Gene, Transforming Principle, and DNA." In *Phage and the Origins of Molecular Biology*, edited by John Cairns, Gunther S. Stent, and James D. Watson. Cold Spring Harbor, N.Y.: Cold Spring Harbor Laboratory, 1966. A collection of essays on their work by the principal players in the early days of molecular biology. Illustrated, with bibliographies.

Judson, Horace Freeland. *The Eighth Day of Creation: Makers of the Revolution in Biology*. New York: Simon & Schuster, 1979. A historical account of the development of ideas about the chemical nature of genes. A journalist, Freeland writes with a fascination for both the science and the scientists involved. Illustrated, with bibliography and index.

Portugal, Franklin H., and Jack S. Cohen. "Genetic Transformation by DNA" and "The Mechanism of Gene Expression." In *A Century of DNA: A History of the Discovery of the Structure and Function of the Genetic Substance*. Cambridge, Mass.: MIT Press, 1977. A discussion for the general scientific reader, with extensive treatment of Avery's contributions. Illustrated, with bibliography and index.

Watson, James D. *The Double Helix: A Personal Account of the Discovery of the Structure of DNA*. New York: Atheneum, 1968. This recollection by the Nobel laureate created many ill feelings by its chronicling of jealousy, infighting, and less-than-noble competition among flawed characters—quite a contrast to the scientific cooperation and dignified pursuit of truth usually presumed in research. An eccentric book by an eccentric man, the science is presented in a fairly approachable manner, and the larger story is accessible to anyone interested in a view from the inside. Illustrated.

Jennifer L. Cruise

Cross-References

De Vries and Associates Discover Mendel's Ignored Studies of Inheritance (1900), p. 61; Sutton States That Chromosomes Are Paired and Could Be Carriers of Hereditary Traits (1902), p. 153; Morgan Develops the Gene-Chromosome Theory (1908), p. 407; Johannsen Coins the Terms "Gene," "Genotype," and "Phenotype" (1909), p. 433; Watson and Crick Develop the Double-Helix Model for DNA (1951), p. 1406; Nirenberg Invents an Experimental Technique That Cracks the Genetic Code (1961), p. 1687; Kornberg and Coworkers Synthesize Biologically Active DNA (1967), p. 1857; Cohen and Boyer Develop Recombinant DNA Technology (1973), p. 1987; A Human Growth Hormone Gene Transferred to a Mouse Creates Giant Mice (1981), p. 2154; Murray and Szostak Create the First Artificial Chromosome (1983), p. 2251.

VON WEIZSÄCKER FINALIZES HIS QUANTITATIVE THEORY OF PLANETARY FORMATION

Category of event: Astronomy
Time: 1943-1944
Locale: University of Strassburg, Germany

Von Weizsäcker finalized a quantitative theory of planetary formation, based on contemporary theories of high-temperature turbulence and stellar formation

Principal personage:
CARL FRIEDRICH VON WEIZSÄCKER (1912-   ), a German nuclear scientist and astrophysicist

Summary of Event

In contrast to many theories proposing the sudden "catastrophic" creation of Earth, the earliest scientific ("evolutionary") hypotheses of planetary formation were those of René Descartes (1644), Immanuel Kant (1755), and Pierre-Simon Laplace (1796). All these nebular (gas cloud) theories postulated that the universe, then not known beyond the Sun and five planets, was filled by gas and dustlike particles of matter. Descartes pictured a large primary gas vortex of circular shape, surrounded by still smaller eddies, from which, respectively the Sun, major planets, and their satellites were to have formed by an unspecified process of turbulent collision and condensation. Likewise, Kant, in his *Allgemeine Naturgeschichte und Theorie des Himmels* (1755); *Universal Natural History and Theories of the Heavens,* (1900), proposed a large rotating gas and dust cloud, which increased rotational speed and flattened to a disk as it progressively contracted because of gravitational attraction. From this disk, the remaining matter was supposed to condense to form the sun and planets. Laplace modified Kant's theory by assuming that as the disk-shaped cloud's rotation increased, centrifugal force at its edge also increased until it exceeded gravity forces toward the center, thereafter separating into concentric rings, each subsequently condensing to form a planet.

Nebular hypotheses for the next sixty years essentially remained fallow, resulting from the absence of both observational evidence and a more quantitative basis in physics. Only after the 1870's were significant observations of the solar system and stellar nebulas obtained that could begin to confirm or constrain further development of planetary theories. As a result, a number of particular problems with extant nebular hypotheses were examined by several English scientists. A major objection was that nebular hypotheses did not explain the skewed distribution of angular momentum observed between the sun (2 percent) and the planets having the most momentum. If the nebula increased rotational speed as it contracted, the sun should be rotating much faster than it does, and thereby have the bulk of the solar systems' angular momentum. James Clerk Maxwell further argued that Laplace's rings would not coalesce directly into planets but would first have to be collected into rings of smaller planetoids, or planetesimals. In a series of papers around 1900, American geologist and astronomer T. C. Chamberlain and F. R. Moulton argued strenuously against the nebular hypothesis and reviving Comte de Buffon's (1745) idea of a catastrophic star-sun encounter, presented their tidal-collisional planetesimal model. The solar system was said to have developed from material ejected by huge solar tides raised in a glancing collision of another star or comet. English physicist and geophysicist Sir James Jeans and Sir Harold Jeffreys later proposed a similar theory, where a close encounter withdrew solar gas filaments, coalescing into beadlike strings of protoplanets.

Within two decades, several problems arose with collision accounts of planetary origins. For one, the statistical frequency of interstellar encounters was far too low to make this a probable mechanism. Also, no collision hypothesis could ensure the current angular momentum distribution. In 1939, American astrophysicist Lyman Spitzer showed that gases torn from the sun or passing star/comet would disperse before being able to cool sufficiently for condensation. During the 1930's and early 1940's, a new group of neonebular hypotheses were proposed, as a consequence of the developments in atomic, nuclear, and plasma physics, and of quantitive physical-chemical observations of the sun and nearby stars. Kristian Birkeland (1912) and Hannes Alvén (1942) suggested that the sun acquired a nebular gas cloud, the electrically charged atoms of which condensed into gas rings, grains, globules, and planets, controlled not only by the sun's gravity but also by its electromagnetic fields. Stanley Jaki's *Planets and Planetarians* (1977) revived nebular theories. In mid-1943, at the University of Strassburg in Germany, nuclear astrophysicist Carl Friedrich von Weizsäcker was completing his own more detailed and comprehensive nebular theory. Associated with aspects of the German nuclear fission project, his paper "On the Formation of Planetary Systems" was prepared as a primary technical contribution to the memorial volume of the *Zeitschrift für Astrophysik* for the seventy-fifth birthday of German atomic physicist Arnold Sommerfeld. Sommerfeld had long insisted on real connections between quantified angular momenta of electrons in atomic structure and the planetary-solar system.

After initially synopsizing the history of prior nebular hypotheses, the first technical question addressed whether and how the sun's original mass was distributed within the boundaries of the present solar system. This reraised the old question of an apparent hundred-fold decrease in solar mass needed to account for its presently low angular momentum. Von Weizsäcker reintroduced the circumsolar gas envelope (nebula) as the earliest common origin of both the sun and planets. He assumed that by the laws of momentum and energy conservation, a portion of the original gas nebula would fall into the cloud's center, the liberated energy carrying off most of the sun's angular momentum. Von Weizsäcker next discussed whether and how it was possible for particles in the rotating disk to form systematic and stable patterns. This was feasible in his view if one assumed that the predominant interparticle interactions were almost exclusively gravitational. The next stage, his theory's core, derived a set of five concentric lenticular-shaped rings around the sun, each ring, in turn, encompassing five internal vortices of similar shape. The corresponding diagram of this system was eventually reprinted in many textbooks and publications. This nebula figure was ingeniously derived from particle dynamics, wherein particle trajectories moving in elliptical orbits of small eccentricity viewed from a rotating solar reference would appear increasingly lenticular with increasing eccentricity. More important, the plasma physics of developing mutually stable vortices demanded a vortex upper size limit. A major consequence of this quintic arrangement was that ratios of the radii of successive preplanetary rings is approximately defined by the well-known Titius-Bode law of 1772, an empirical formula. The result was seen as a major internal consistency check and plausibility argument.

An eddy is a transient thermodynamic condition generally sustained only long enough for its gas to travel a distance roughly equaling its own diameter. Turbulence, or turbulent fluid flow, has a high complex velocity and pressure distribution typically characterized by random spatial and temporal fluctuations. The location of planetary formation within this turbulent system was therefore proposed to be the low-friction "roller bearing" areas formed by three touching adjacent vortices. From theoretical considerations, turbulence at these locations seemed sufficiently high to facilitate formation of planetesimals from disk gas and dust, by way of intermediate-sized globules sufficiently large that their rate of accretional build up by gravity exceeded their volatilization rate through collision. As von Weizsäcker explicitly noted, these thermohydrodynamic assumptions were the most uncertain aspects of his theory. Specifically, strong analogies exist between hierarchical spatial relations in the preplanetary disk and gas particle patterns; these analogies were not yet a definite physical-causal connection.

Impact of Event

Although most immediate discussions of von Weizsäcker's theory were delayed by World War II, almost all initial published reactions to his theory were positive. Noted nuclear physicist and cosmologist George Gamow and J. A. Hynek in the spring of 1945 published a short review ("A New Theory by C. F. von Weizsäcker on the Origin of the Planetary System") in the *Astrophysical Journal*. In their estimate, the theory "allowed an interpretation of the Bode-Titus law of planetary distances" and explained "all the principal features of the solar system," notably the common revolution plane, small orbital eccentricities, common rotational direction, and lower material densities of the larger planets. The single criticism was difficulty in visualizing the details of a single planet forming from five planetesimals, an issue von Weizsäcker subsequently addressed. Several astronomers have argued that one reason for von Weizsäcker's theory's popularity was its extraterrestrialist implication for universal planetary formation.

The theory received further attention when in 1946 noted astrophysicist Subrahmanyan Chandrasekhar published a favorable account in the *Reviews of Modern Physics*. Nevertheless, German astronomer Friedrich Nölke and Dutch astrophysicist

D. ter Haar in 1948 independently published detailed criticisms of von Weizsäcker's theory, based on rigorous and extensive hydrodynamic considerations of energy transport by nebular eddies. Nölke showed that serious difficulties remained in the angular momentum problem. According to ter Haar, if the Sun's presently slow rate of rotation was caused by absorption of material from the nebular disk, there still existed a discrepancy of a factor of one thousand between actual and predicted solar mass. Dutch-American astronomer Gerhard Peter Kuiper from 1949 to 1951 likewise rejected von Weizsäcker's regular vortices, but redeveloped the nebular theory, proposing formation of random turbulent eddies in the nebular disk as a natural consequence of binary star formation. Kuiper argued that vortex stability required high-mass density in the cloud, such that the resulting gravitational attraction equals or exceeds the Sun's gravity.

Later theories incorporated the ideas of turbulence, magnetic fields, and planetesimals, maintaining that supersonically turbulent nebular clouds break up into chaotic swarms of "floccules," continually dispersing and reforming according to statistical laws governing plasma interaction. Despite increases in empirical and theoretical astrophysics, von Weizsäcker's theory of planetary formation remains, among some scientists, a partial source and exemplary model for future planetesimal theories.

Bibliography

Beatty, J. Kelly, and Andrew Chaikin, eds. *The New Solar System*. 3d rev. ed. New York: Cambridge University Press, 1990. Reviews most planetary theories.

Bohren, Craig F. *Clouds in a Glass of Beer: Simple Experiments in Atmospheric Physics*. New York: Wiley Press, 1987. Gives a general audience introduction to hydrodynamics.

Christianson, Gale E. *The Wild Abyss: The Story of the Men Who Made Modern Astronomy*. New York: Free Press, 1978. A valuable source. A twentieth century astronomical biography for a wide audience.

Glass, Billy. *Introduction to Planetary Geology*. New York: Cambridge University Press, 1982. One of the best introductions and reviews of early planetary theory.

Peter, Gerhard, and Barbara M. Middlehurst, eds. *The Solar System*. 4 vols. Chicago: University of Chicago Press, 1953. Details Kuiper's extensions of von Weizsäcker's theory.

Urey, Harold C. *The Planets: Their Origin and Development*. New Haven, Conn.: Yale University Press, 1952. A classic examination of geochemical data for planetary formation.

Gerardo G. Tango

Cross-References

Hartmann Discovers the First Evidence of Interstellar Matter (1904), p. 213; Russell Announces His Theory of Stellar Evolution (1913), p. 585; Eddington Publishes

ECKERT AND MAUCHLY DEVELOP THE ENIAC

Category of event: Applied science
Time: 1943-1946
Locale: Moore School of Electrical Engineering, University of Pennsylvania, Philadelphia

Eckert and Mauchly developed the first general-purpose electronic digital computer, leading directly to modern methods of computation

Principal personages:
JOHN PRESPER ECKERT (1919-   ), an electrical engineer who was the lead engineer on the ENIAC
JOHN WILLIAM MAUCHLY (1907-1980), a physicist, engineer, and professor who was the lead designer of the ENIAC
JOHN VON NEUMANN (1903-1957), a Hungarian-American mathematician, physicist, and logician who was a consultant to the ENIAC team
HERMAN HEINE GOLDSTINE (1913-   ), an Army mathematician who acted as liaison for U.S. Army Ordnance to the ENIAC team
ARTHUR WALTER BURKS (1915-   ), a philosopher, engineer, and professor who was a senior engineer on the ENIAC team
JOHN VINCENT ATANASOFF (1903-   ), a mathematician and physicist who first used digital electronics in a working prototype computer

Summary of Event

The ENIAC (Electronic Numerical Integrator and Computer) was the first general-purpose electronic digital computer. By demonstrating the feasibility and value of electronic digital computation, it initiated the computer revolution. The ENIAC was developed during World War II at the Moore School of Electrical Engineering by a team headed by John William Mauchly and John Presper Eckert, who were working on behalf of the U.S. Ordnance Ballistic Research Laboratory (BRL) at the Aberdeen Proving Ground. Early in the war, the BRL's needs for generating ballistic firing tables already far outstripped the combined abilities of the available differential analyzers (Vannevar Bush's analog computer) and teams of human computers. In 1941, Mauchly had seen the special-purpose electronic computer developed by John Vincent Atanasoff for solving sets of linear equations. Atanasoff's computer was severely limited in scope and was never fully completed. The functioning prototype, however, helped convince Mauchly of the feasibility of electronic digital computation and so led to Mauchly's formal proposal in April, 1943, to develop the general-purpose ENIAC. The BRL, in desperate need for computational help, agreed to fund the project, with Lieutenant Herman Heine Goldstine overseeing it for the United States Army.

This first substantial electronic computer was designed, built, and debugged within two and one-half years. Even given the highly talented team, it could be done only by taking as few design risks as possible. The ENIAC ended up as an electronic version of prior computers: Its functional organization was similar to that of Bush's differential analyzer, while it was programmed via a plugboard (similar to a telephone switchboard), much as were IBM's earlier electromechanical calculators. Another consequence was that the internal representation of numbers was decimal, rather than the now standard binary, since the familiar electromechanical computers used decimal digits.

Although the ENIAC was completed only after the end of the war, its primary use remained military. In fact, the first production run on the system was a two-month calculation needed for the design of the hydrogen bomb. John von Neumann, working as a consultant both to the Los Alamos Scientific Laboratory and to the ENIAC project, arranged for the production run immediately prior to ENIAC's formal dedication in 1946.

The ENIAC was an impressive machine: It contained eighteen thousand vacuum tubes, weighed 27 metric tons, and occupied a 9 by 15 meter room. The final cost to the U.S. Army was about $486,000. For this, they received a machine that computed up to a thousand times faster than its electromechanical precursors; for example, addition and subtraction required only 200 microseconds (millionths of a second). The basic cycle time was a remarkably fast ten microseconds—100,000 cycles per second. Arithmetic would have been even faster except that the decimal implementation required multiple pulses per digit; therefore, addition took 20 cycles to complete. Nevertheless, at its dedication ceremony, the ENIAC was fast enough to calculate a fired shell's trajectory faster than the shell itself took to reach its target.

The machine also was orders of magnitude more complex than any predecessor and employed a risky, new technology in vacuum tubes; this caused much concern about its potential reliability. In response to this concern, Eckert, as the lead engineer, imposed strict safety factors on all components, requiring the design to use components at a level well below the manufacturers' specified limits. The result was a machine that ran for as long as three days without a hardware malfunction.

Vacuum tubes perform most reliably when they are warm, so, once running, the machine was kept on. A historical oddity is that for some months after delivery, the BRL continued their normal practice of shutting off all of their equipment at night. As a consequence, much of the following day was wasted getting the ENIAC operational again. The new electronic speed created a new problem: the high-speed availability of both programs and data. Data were held in twenty accumulators, each capable of holding ten digits (plus a sign); in modern terms, this is only about one hundred bytes of storage. This posed a severe difficulty for performing complex calculations. In many cases, intermediate results were actually punched on IBM cards and fed to later program stages via the card reader—a process that hardly took advantage of the underlying machine speed.

The master control unit supported a variety of useful programming functions, including iterative loops, conditional branches, and subroutines. Programming the ENIAC was effected by setting switches and physically connecting accumulators, function tables (a kind of manually set read-only memory), and control units. Connections were made via cables running between plugboards. This was a laborious and error-prone process, often requiring a one-day setup time. The team recognized this problem, and in early 1945, Eckert, Mauchly, and Neumann worked on the design of a new machine. Their basic idea was to treat both program and data as the same kind of object, and in particular to store them in the same high-speed memory; in other words, they planned to produce a stored-program computer. Neumann described and explained this design in his "First Draft of a Report on the EDVAC" (EDVAC stood for Electronic Discrete Variable Automatic Computer).

Although Eckert had introduced the concept of a stored-program computer even before Neumann joined the ENIAC project, Neumann contributed new design techniques and provided the first general, comprehensive description of the stored-program architecture. Since the Moore School was constrained by the Official Secrets Act, the report on the EDVAC was distributed under Neumann's name alone. This report had a decisive influence in spreading a practical design for digital computation—so much so that machines of this type (including almost all modern commercial computers) have come to be called Neumann machines. One consequence has been a bitter dispute about who "really" invented the concept of stored-program computers. The answer appears to be that the invention was a joint effort. Special claims to intellectual priority are undercut by the fact that Alan Turing's concept of a universal machine (invented in 1935) would have been incoherent without the theoretical ability to store programs, however impractical it would have been to produce such a machine.

After delivery of the ENIAC, Neumann suggested that it could be wired up so that a set of instructions would be permanently available and could be selected by entries in the function tables. Adele Goldstine (wife of Herman) and Richard Clippinger (head of the BRL Computing Laboratory) implemented the idea, providing sixty instructions that could be invoked from the programs stored into the function tables. Despite slowing down the computer's calculations, this technique was so superior to plugboard programming that it was used exclusively thereafter. In this way, the ENIAC was converted into a kind of primitive stored-program computer.

Impact of Event

The ENIAC's electronic speed and the stored-program design of the EDVAC posed a serious engineering challenge: to produce a computer memory store that would be simultaneously large, inexpensive, and fast. Without such fast memories, the electronic control logic would spend most of its time idling. Vacuum tubes themselves (used in the control) were not an effective answer because of their large power requirements and heat generation.

The EDVAC design draft proposed using mercury delay lines, which were used earlier in radars. These delay lines converted an electronic signal into a slower acoustic signal in a mercury solution; for continuous storage, the signal picked up at the other end was regenerated and sent back into the mercury. Maurice Vincent Wilkes at the University of Cambridge was the first to complete such a system, in May, 1949 (called the EDSAC). One month earlier, Frederick Calland Williams and Tom Kilburn at Manchester University brought their prototype computer into operation, which instead used cathode-ray tubes (CRTs) for their main storage. Thus, England took an early lead in developing computing systems, largely because of a more immediate practical design approach. Neumann, together with Arthur Walter Burks and Goldstine, started a computer research group at the Institute for Advanced Study (IAS). The IAS group decided upon a new kind of parallel memory—unlike EDSAC's sequential memory—using a new kind of CRT, called the Selectron. The new design introduced a variety of synchronization problems; also, the Selectron was not ready on time. The IAS machine was finally built using the Williams CRT. While late (it was completed in 1952), the IAS computer nevertheless was very successful, very fast, and was copied at a variety of institutions, giving birth to the MANIAC, JOHNNIAC, ILLIAC, SILLIAC, and the like.

In the meantime, Eckert and Mauchly, in a dispute with the Moore School of Electrical Engineering over the ENIAC patent, had quit and formed the Electronic Control Company (later the Eckert-Mauchly Computer Corporation). They managed to keep the patent rights. In 1949, they produced the BINAC computer (at a loss) and the UNIVAC I in 1951, with both machines using mercury storage. They sold out to Remington Rand when they had financial problems, and Eckert ultimately became a vice president of Sperry Rand. The patent issue, however, was not over. After Sperry Rand tried to enforce patent rights, Honeywell sued. In 1973, the patent was invalidated, largely for technical legal reasons, but also because Atanasoff had demonstrated previously the viability of some of the innovations the patent attributed to the ENIAC.

The memory problem that the ENIAC introduced was resolved finally with the invention of magnetic core in the early 1950's. Core memory was installed on the ENIAC and soon on all new machines. The ENIAC continued in operation until October, 1955, when parts of it were retired to the Smithsonian Institution. Having proved the viability of digital electronics, and having led directly to stored-program computers, its impact can be recognized in every digital computer today.

Bibliography

Burks, Arthur W., and Alice R. Burks. "The ENIAC: First General-Purpose Electronic Computer." *Annals of the History of Computing* 3 (October, 1981): 310-399. A technical examination of the origin and design of the ENIAC, with particular consideration of the related patent dispute. Incorporates commentary by other principals and responses by the authors. Usefully illustrated.

Campbell-Kelly, Martin, and Michael R. Williams, eds. *The Moore School Lectures*. Cambridge, Mass.: MIT Press, 1985. Lecture notes from a special course held at the Moore School in the summer of 1946. Lecturers included all the major designers involved in the ENIAC and many others. This course greatly aided the dissemination of the stored-program concept. Papers range from introductory to highly technical.

Fleck, Glen, ed. *A Computer Perspective*. Cambridge, Mass.: Harvard University Press, 1973. An entertaining, pictorial survey of the history of computing machinery from 1890 through the 1940's, based on an IBM-sponsored exhibition. Contains photographs of many pioneer researchers, their machines, and various related documents.

Goldstine, Herman H. *The Computer from Pascal to von Neumann*. Princeton, N.J.: Princeton University Press, 1972. A very readable history. While incorporating earlier developments, this is especially interesting for its detailed account of the developments at the Moore School and the Institute for Advanced Study, in which Goldstine was directly involved.

Hodges, Andrew. *Alan Turing: The Enigma*. New York: Simon & Schuster, 1983. A thorough, enjoyable biography of Alan Turing. Includes a lengthy, fascinating account of England's successful cracking of Nazi Germany's encryption devices, using a variety of computational devices, including the COLOSSUS (a special-purpose electronic digital computer).

Metropolis, N., J. Howlett, and Gian-Carolo Rota, eds. *A History of Computing in the Twentieth Century*. New York: Academic Press, 1980. A collection of papers originally presented at a conference on computing history at the Los Alamos Scientific Laboratory in 1976. The authors include many of the principals involved in the early development of computers and computer software. Annotated bibliography.

Randell, Brian, comp. *The Origins of Digital Computers*. New York: Springer-Verlag, 1973. This anthology reprints historic papers from early computer development efforts. Includes a forty-page annotated bibliography.

Stern, Nancy. *From ENIAC to UNIVAC: An Appraisal of the Eckert-Mauchly Computers*. Bedford, Mass.: Digital Press, 1981. Reviews the history of Eckert and Mauchly's association and the computers they developed, concentrating on the social aspects. Issues verdicts on the priority and personal disputes in the story which cannot be assessed in isolation. Includes, as an appendix, Neumann's "First Draft of a Report on the EDVAC."

Williams, Michael R. *A History of Computing Technology*. Englewood Cliffs, N.J.: Prentice-Hall, 1985. A comprehensive and balanced presentation of the development of computer technology from the numerical systems of ancient Egypt through the first generation of electronic digital computers. Recommended for all general readers.

Kevin B. Korb

Cross-References

Fleming Files a Patent for the First Vacuum Tube (1904), p. 255; Bush Builds the First Differential Analyzer (1928), p. 846; Turing Invents the Universal Turing Machine (1935), p. 1045; A Secret English Team Develops Colossus (1940's), p. 1155; Shockley, Bardeen, and Brattain Discover the Transistor (1947), p. 1304; The First Electronic Stored-Program Computer (BINAC) Is Completed (1949), p. 1347; UNIVAC I Becomes the First Commercial Electronic Computer and the First to Use Magnetic Tape (1951), p. 1396; Teller and Ulam Develop the First H-Bomb (1951), p. 1401.

COUSTEAU AND GAGNAN DEVELOP THE AQUALUNG

Categories of event: Applied science and earth science
Time: Spring, 1943
Locale: Paris, France

Cousteau and Gagnan developed the Aqualung, a self-contained underwater breathing apparatus (scuba) that allowed divers to descend hundreds of meters below the surface of the ocean for recreation, scientific study, or treasure hunts

Principal personages:
JACQUES-YVES COUSTEAU (1910-   ), a French navy officer, undersea explorer, inventor, and author who participated in the development of the Aqualung and other diving equipment used to explore the ocean depths
ÉMILE GAGNAN, a French engineer who invented an automatic air-regulating device that, coupled with Cousteau's diving apparatus, led to the production of the Aqualung

Summary of Event

Undersea diving for the purposes of spying, to recover lost treasures from wrecks, or to obtain natural treasures (such as pearls) has been done since ancient times. The divers of antiquity, however, were able only to remain below the surface for two or three minutes, and the depth to which they could venture was very restricted. In spite of these limitations, divers are mentioned in Homer's *Iliad* (c. 800 B.C.), and Greek historians—including Herodotus of Halicarnassus (484-424 B.C.)—mention use of divers by the Greek kings in their many wars.

Clearly, once humans discovered the value of diving, many attempts were made to prolong the exposure time possible for divers. The first device, described by Aristotle in 335 B.C., was probably the progenitor of the modern snorkels. It was a bent reed placed in the mouth, with one end above the water. Such devices are useful only for spying or for swimming near the surface of a body of water. Their use is restricted because of the limit on applicable reed—or snorkel—length and to several pressure considerations.

The most serious problem associated with pressure occurs because the pressure on a diver's body increases by about one-half pound per square centimeter for every meter ventured below the surface. For this reason, it becomes impossible to inhale surface air through a snorkel after about 0.9 meter. This results from the fact that the human chest muscles are no longer strong enough to inflate the chest. In order to breathe at depths below 0.9 meter, a diver must utilize air under pressure, and the air pressure must increase continually as the depth of the dive is increased.

Few changes were made in the technology of diving until air compressors were invented during the early nineteenth century. Then, fresh, pressurized air could be supplied to divers. This compressed air could be delivered in amounts that equalized body pressure and the pressure exerted by the water that surrounded the diver. At first, the divers who utilized the method were limited to using diving suits, complete with fishbowllike helmets. This "tethered" diving made divers relatively immobile. Such diving rigs, however, were very useful when a diver was searching for sunken treasure or doing other complex jobs at a great depth. Tethered diving was especially valuable if a diver needed to remain under water for a long time.

Shallow-water work, diving efforts of shorter duration, underwater espionage, and recreational diving required less cumbersome outfits and more mobility. Scuba evolved in this manner. Its development occurred in several jumps. In one of the first of these, in 1880, Henry Fleuss of England developed an outfit that used a compartmented belt that contained pure oxygen. Belt and diver were connected, and the diver breathed the oxygen over and over.

A modification of Fleuss's rebreathing system was used by the American Navy in World War II espionage. Nevertheless, it had three serious drawbacks: The deepest dives it allowed were 7.6 to 9 meters, pure oxygen was toxic to divers at depths greater than 9 meters, and divers could carry only enough oxygen to allow them to remain submerged for a relatively short time. It did have an advantage for spies, namely, that the oxygen—breathed over and over in a closed system—did not reach the surface in the form of telltale bubbles.

The next stage of scuba development occurred when metal tanks, able to hold high-pressure compressed air, were designed. This enabled divers to use air rather than the potentially toxic oxygen. More important, the much increased amount of usable oxygen that a diver could carry greatly lengthened the duration of underwater endeavors that could be carried out. Initially, the main problem with the system was the fact that the air flowed continuously through a mask that covered the diver's entire face. This process wasted oxygen, and the scuba divers expelled a continual stream of air bubbles that precluded clandestine efforts. As a team, Jacques-Yves Cousteau and Émile Gagnan developed an underwater oxygen regulator that conserved oxygen by releasing only the amount of compressed air that the diver required to breathe. Among the advantages of the Cousteau-Gagnan apparatus was the fact that a mobile diver could stay below the surface for a prolonged time period.

As pointed out by Axel Madsen in *Cousteau* (1986), the problem solved by Cousteau and Gagnan occurred because humans breathe in and out, requiring the discovery of a way to prevent exhaling spent air back into the oxygen supply. The solution was "a valve that would allow inhaling and exhaling through the same mouthpiece."

It was fortunate for Cousteau that his father-in-law, an executive for Air Liquide—France's main producer of industrial gases—directed him to Gagnan, an engineer at the company's Paris laboratory. Gagnan had been developing an automatic gas shutoff valve for Air Liquide, and this valve became the Cousteau-Gagnan regulator.

With the valve in hand—and funding from Air Liquide—they designed a first approximation of the system. Cousteau tested this apparatus in 1943 in the Marne

River, but it did not work. Additional experimentation led to an acceptable device that they patented as the Aqualung. Soon, exhaustive study showed that Aqualungs were suitable for use at depths up to 68.5 meters.

This study identified several perils associated with Aqualung diving. For example, unless divers ascended and descended in slow stages, it was likely that they would get the bends (decompression sickness), the feared disease of earlier, tethered deep-sea divers. Another problem was that, below 42.6 meters, divers encounter nitrogen narcosis. This leads to impaired judgment that may cause fatal actions, including removing a mouthpiece or developing an overpowering desire to continue diving downward, to dangerous depths.

Cousteau believed that the Aqualung had tremendous military potential. To get it to the Allies, he traveled to London soon after the Normandy invasion. Unfortunately, self-contained underwater breathing apparatus (scuba), as the English named the Aqualung, did not seem overly important to them. So Cousteau returned to Paris and convinced France's new government to use Aqualungs to locate and neutralize underwater mines laid along the French coast by the Wehrmacht.

Cousteau was commissioned to combine minesweeping with the study of the physiology of scuba diving. Amid this work, he and his colleagues discovered that the use of helium-oxygen mixtures increased the depth to which a scuba diver could go without narcosis (76 meters instead of the 42.6 meters obtainable with air). This work also led to the sport of recreational scuba diving.

Impact of Event

The work of Cousteau and Gagnan that developed the Aqualung made humans more comfortable under the ocean and sparked a wave of undersea exploration and recreational diving that has enriched the knowledge of the world. Today, millions of people engage in scuba diving for the purposes of recreation and business.

One way to describe the effects of development of the Aqualung is to summarize Cousteau's continued efforts to the present. In 1946, he and Philippe Tailliez established the Undersea Research Group of Toulon to study diving techniques and various aspects of life in the oceans. They studied marine life in the Red Sea from 1951 to 1952, and aspects of their endeavors were described by Cousteau and Frédéric Dumas in *The Silent World* (1953). From 1952 to 1956, they engaged in an expedition supported by the National Geographic Society. By that time, the Research Group had developed many techniques that enabled them to identify life forms and conditions at great depths.

Throughout their undersea studies, Cousteau and coworkers continued to develop better techniques for scuba diving, for recording observations by still and television photography, and for collecting plant and animal specimens. In addition, Cousteau participated (with Swiss physicist Auguste Piccard) in the construction of the deep-submergence research vehicle (or bathyscaphe) and its use for undersea exploration. In the 1960's, he directed a program called Conshelf, which examined prolonged human survival in underwater stations. He also wrote and produced films on underwater exploration that attracted, entertained, and educated millions of people, both in theaters and on television.

Between 1946 and 1985, Cousteau wrote more than fifty books, including a twenty-volume encyclopedia on the oceans, several *National Geographic* articles, and more than sixty telefilms. A list of these works can be found in Axel Madsen's *Cousteau* (1986). As a consequence of his endeavors, Cousteau has won numerous medals and scientific distinctions. These include the Gold Medal of the National Geographic Society (1963), the United Nations International Environment Prize (1977), Membership in the American and Indian Academies of Science (1968 and 1978, respectively), and honorary doctor of science degrees from the University of California, Berkeley (1970), Harvard University (1979), and Rensselaer Polytechnical Institute (1979).

Bibliography

Cousteau, Jacques-Yves. "Fish Men Discover a New World." *National Geographic* 102 (October, 1952): 431-472. An interesting, illustrated article that details collaboration with Gagnan in the development of the Aqualung and some of its uses in underwater exploration. Of particular interest to those wishing to learn about the beginnings of scuba diving from Cousteau.

_____. "The Ocean, a Perspective." *National Geographic* 160 (December, 1981): 780-833. Describes many important aspects of ocean exploration and utilization (for example, mining the sea) using modern tools and methods, including those Cousteau and his collaborators helped to develop.

Cousteau, J. Y., with Frédéric Dumas. *The Silent World*. New York: Harper & Brothers, 1953. An engaging book, made into a motion picture in 1956. Recounts many of the underwater adventures and explorations of Cousteau and his colleagues from 1938, including postwar efforts at minesweeping along the French coast and development of Aqualung methodology.

Fergussen, J. Homer. "Diving." *McGraw-Hill Encyclopedia of Science and Technology*. 6th ed. New York: McGraw-Hill, 1987. A brief article on diving that touches many bases succinctly. Topics explored include techniques used in scuba and saturation diving; aspects of diving physiology such as the effects of pressure, nitrogen, oxygen, and carbon dioxide gases; and treatment of the bends.

Iverson, Genie. *Jacques Cousteau*. New York: G. P. Putnam's Sons, 1976. Contains much information on the life and career of Cousteau, including his trials and victories during World War II, his development of the Aqualung, and his later explorations and endeavors. Insight is given into his personality and activities.

Lee, Owen S. *The Complete Illustrated Guide to Snorkel and Deep Diving*. Garden City, N.Y.: Doubleday, 1963. Contains a wealth of information on many aspects of diving for sport and business. Chapters 6 (diving physics and physiology) and 7 (Aqualung equipment and how it works) are most relevant. Informative and well illustrated.

Madsen, Axel. *Cousteau: An Unauthorized Biography*. New York: Beaufort, 1986.

Covers many aspects of Cousteau's experiences as a naval officer, as a coninventor of the Aqualung, and an underwater explorer. Chapter 4, on development of the Aqualung, is particularly interesting and enlightening. Useful insight into Cousteau's personality and endeavors.

Smith, Robert W. *The New Science of Skin and Scuba Diving*. Piscataway, N.J.: New Century, 1985. A compendium of information developed by the Council for National Cooperation in Aquatics. Designed to educate those interested in the sport and technology of skin/scuba diving. Topics covered include snorkeling, skin and scuba diving, dive planning, lifesaving, and first aid. Coverage is simple, clear, and informative.

Sanford S. Singer

Cross-References

The First German U-Boat Is Launched (1906), p. 350; Haldane Develops Stage Decompression for Deep Sea Divers (1907), p. 365; Beebe and Barton Set a Diving Record in a Bathysphere (1934), p. 1018; The Sealab 2 Expedition Concludes (1965), p. 1792.

WAKSMAN DISCOVERS THE ANTIBIOTIC STREPTOMYCIN

Category of event: Medicine
Time: September, 1943-March, 1944
Locale: New Brunswick, New Jersey

Waksman searched for antibacterial substances in soil microorganisms, discovering eighteen antibiotics, including streptomycin, the first effective drug against tuberculosis

Principal personages:

SELMAN ABRAHAM WAKSMAN (1888-1973), a Soviet-born American soil microbiologist and winner of the 1952 Nobel Prize in Physiology or Medicine

RENÉ DUBOS (1901-1982), a French-born American who was the first to demonstrate the feasibility of obtaining antibiotics from microorganisms

WILLIAM HUGH FELDMAN (1892-1974), an American pathologist who developed, with Hinshaw, the first effective chemotherapy of tuberculosis

H. CORWIN HINSHAW (1902-   ), an American bacteriologist who studied the antitubercular effects of sulfa drugs, sulfones, and antibiotics on animals

Summary of Event

The discovery of streptomycin was not a matter of chance as was penicillin; it was the result of a well-planned program of research. Some microbiologists in the late nineteenth century believed in a struggle for existence in the microbial world, and in 1889 Paul Vuillemin used the word "antibiosis" in reference to this natural antagonism between species. Some microbiologists also believed microbes contained substances that inhibited the growth of other microbes. There were attempts to isolate chemotherapeutic agents from molds and bacteria, but the field was abandoned in the early twentieth century as barren until the reawakening of interest in such agents by René Dubos in the 1930's.

Dubos was a student of Selman Abraham Waksman. Both men emigrated to the United States in their twenties. Waksman spent his entire career at Rutgers University, becoming the leading figure in American soil microbiology. He was extraordinarily prolific, producing more than five hundred articles and twenty-eight books. His expertise was the population of microorganisms that inhabit the soil. He elaborated the ecology, taxonomy, and physiology of thousands of species. He specialized in one type of soil microbe, the actinomycetes, organisms intermediate between bacteria and fungi. His research included a study funded by the National Tuberculosis Association on the fate of the tubercle bacillus when introduced into soil. From 1932 to 1935, Waksman established that the germ could not survive because of the antagonism of soil microbes. This finding substantiated the fact already known that pathogenic germs introduced to soil disappeared. At the time, his finding did not seem to lead to anything new; it was only another example of microbes inhibiting other microbes.

Dubos obtained his doctorate under Waksman in 1927 and then worked at the Rockefeller Institute in New York. He wondered what would happen if soil were enriched with pathogenic germs. He pondered if perhaps their introduction would encourage soil microbes antagonistic to them to flourish. In February, 1939, Dubos announced that he had tracked down such an antagonistic microorganism, *Bacillus brevis*, and from it isolated two antibacterial substances, tyrocidine and gramicidin. The latter proved to be the first true antibiotic drug, attacking pneumococcus, staphylococcus, and streptococcus germs. Too toxic for human therapy, it came into use in treating animals, arousing public interest when at the 1939 New York World's Fair, sixteen of the Borden cow herd developed a streptococcal udder infection, and gramicidin cured twelve of the cows of the bacteria.

Dubos's discovery alerted scientists to the possibility of finding other powerful drugs in microorganisms. When Baron Florey and Ernst Boris Chain in England, who were then preparing a purely academic survey of microbial antagonisms, learned of gramicidin, they became aware immediately of the chemotherapeutic potential of penicillin, an antibacterial mold substance found by Sir Alexander Fleming in 1928, but never regarded as anything more than a laboratory curiosity for more than ten years. As a result, Florey and Chain began their classic investigation of penicillin.

The central figure in exploiting this field, however, was Waksman. He seized on Dubos's work and converted his research on soil actinomycetes into a search for antibacterial substances in them. The actinomycetes proved to be the most fertile source for antibiotics. Waksman coined and defined the word "antibiotic" in 1941 for the novel drugs found in microbes. He developed soil enrichment methods and discovered eighteen antibiotics between 1940 and 1958. He cultured thousands of soil microbes in artificial media and screened them for activity. The promising ones were then chemically processed to isolate antibiotics.

Streptomycin was the most important of Waksman's discoveries. In September, 1943, with his students Elizabeth Bugie and Albert Schatz, he isolated a soil actinomycetes, *Streptomyces griseus*, which contained an antibiotic he named "streptomycin." It was antagonistic to gram-negative bacteria. His report appeared in January, 1944 and two months later, another article claimed that streptomycin was active against the deadly tubercle germ, *Mycobacterium tuberculosis*.

Waksman wondered if streptomycin would be active against laboratory cultures of pathogenic germs, as well as in the living animal. He established an arrangement with the drug manufacturer Merck. Merck would support his research and do extensive animal testing. In return, Merck had the right to apply for patents on any processes it developed. Rutgers University would receive royalties from the sale of prod ucts. The Waksman group and Merck tests indicated streptomycin activity on germs against which penicillin was useless. Above all, streptomycin had activity against the tubercle bacillus, which raised the possibility of therapy against the most resistant, irreversible of all common infectious diseases. In the 1940's, tuberculosis was not fully under control. There was no cure, only prolonged bed rest and a regimen of nutritious food. The tubercle germ could invade any organ of the body, and in its various forms, the disease took a horrifying toll. A diagnosis of tuberculosis entailed lifelong invalidism, and patients died because the available treatment was so limited.

The medical world took notice of the clinical tests conducted by William Hugh Feldman and H. Corwin Hinshaw at the Mayo Clinic. They had been investigating the chemotherapy of tuberculosis in the 1930's. Many scientists believed that such therapy was unattainable, but they refused to accept this verdict. They worked with sulfa drugs and sulfones and found some effect in suppressing the growth of tubercle bacilli, but not their eradication. Feldman visited Waksman before his discovery of streptomycin and indicated his desire to try any promising antibiotics. When Waksman found antitubercular effects in 1944, he wrote at once to Feldman to offer streptomycin for his studies. Feldman and Hinshaw had developed a practical system to determine the ability of a drug to slow the course of tuberculosis in guinea pigs. They used streptomycin on guinea pigs inoculated with the tubercle germ. In December, 1944, they issued their first report. The tests revealed streptomycin's ability to reverse the lethal course of the inoculations, and they concluded that it was highly effective in inhibiting the germ, exerting a striking suppressive effect, and was well tolerated by the animals.

Feldman and Hinshaw were now ready to test human patients. Merck agreed to supply the streptomycin for the tests. Hinshaw enlisted two physicians from a nearby sanitarium. On November 20, 1944, and for the next six months, a twenty-one-year-old woman with far-advanced pulmonary tuberculosis (one of her lungs already subjected to surgery, the other being eaten away) received streptomycin. In June of 1945, she was discharged, her tuberculosis arrested; she married eventually and reared three children. This happy ending was followed by many more. Hinshaw and his associates made a preliminary report on thirty-four patients in 1945 and a fuller evaluation of one hundred cases in 1946. Streptomycin succeeded in the treatment of tuberculosis of the lungs, skin, bones, joints, meninges, and genito-urinary organs. The antibiotic brought humans back from the edge of death.

Toxic effects also emerged in the form of injury to the organ of equilibrium in the ear and deafness in some cases. These were sometimes transitory, sometimes permanent, and related to the dose and duration of therapy. By carefully using streptomycin between a range of too little and too much of the drug, the damage could be minimized.

Feldman and Hinshaw deserve the credit for the revelation of the efficacy of streptomycin against tuberculosis. They demonstrated its value in carefully constructed trials. Some observers believe that they should have shared the 1952 Nobel Prize with Waksman.

Impact of Event

With the realization that streptomycin was the first effective chemotherapeutic remedy for tuberculosis, Waksman and Merck agreed that no company should have a monopoly on its commercial production. Merck agreed to transfer its rights to Rutgers, which would license companies to produce it. By 1948, eight firms were manufacturers. With the increased availability of the drug, the most extensive study of a single drug ever undertaken took place as the manufacturers donated streptomycin at an estimated value of $1 million for a large-scale cooperative series of clinical trials involving several thousand tubercular patients. Major testing took place at the Cornell Medical School, which studied the most acute forms of tuberculosis—tubercular meningitis and miliary tuberculosis—hitherto 100 percent fatal. The most chronic form was pulmonary, and the National Tuberculosis Association sponsored studies of this form. The Veterans Administration organized a third major trial at its hospitals to test thousands of World War II veterans discharged with tuberculosis. The Public Health Service sponsored another clinical trial. These trials established streptomycin's effectiveness. One result was a remarkable decline in tuberculosis mortality, especially among children. By 1950, streptomycin found use against seventy different germs against which penicillin was useless. In addition to tuberculosis, these included several gram-negative infections of the abdomen, pelvis, urinary tract, and meninges.

Waksman did more than discover a major antibiotic; his work encouraged others to attempt to isolate them by means of screening programs similar to those he devised. The 1950's witnessed a large increase in the number of antibiotics, and antibiotics became a large industry with total production of more than 9 million pounds in 1955.

Streptomycin was not perfect. As early as 1946, reports appeared on the resistance of bacilli. Such resistant strains could be responsible for the failure of therapy. New drugs came to the rescue of streptomycin. In the 1940's, Swedish investigators found para-aminosalicyclic acid to inhibit the tubercle bacillus, although not as effectively as streptomycin. In 1949, the Veterans Administration combined the two drugs.

Combination therapy proved the key to the future of chemotherapy, as the combination delayed the appearance of resistant strains. Better drugs soon appeared, the most potent being isoniazid. Known to chemists since 1912 but of no value until 1952, three pharmaceutical companies independently found isoniazid to be as effective as streptomycin. The two drugs in combination became the standard initial therapy against tuberculosis. By 1970, there were eleven drugs in all, and by the judicious use of combinations, physicians could achieve recovery in nearly all cases of pulmonary tuberculosis.

By the end of the 1950's, new cases of tuberculosis had diminished to the extent that the disease seemed on the way to extinction, at least in the developed countries of the world. The enthusiasm for the chemotherapy of tuberculosis, however, was not always matched by the recipients. A combination of indifference, refusal of treatment, lack of access to adequate medical care, especially among lower socioeconomic groups, kept tuberculosis alive.

In the United States, tuberculosis strikes those who are homeless or live in crowded, unsanitary conditions; have inadequate diets; or are drug addicts, alcoholics, or AIDS (acquired immune deficiency syndrome) victims, whose immune system has been weakened. Drug therapy can control and cure tuberculosis, but the patient must continue a medication of two or more drugs daily from a minimum of nine months to two years or more. Once patients feel well again, they abandon the treatment before completion. By stopping before completion, they are not cured, the disease returns, and they can infect others, thereby producing new cases. Tuberculosis remains the leading cause of death in the world among infectious diseases.

Bibliography

Dowling, Harry F. *Fighting Infection: Conquests of the Twentieth Century.* Cambridge, Mass.: Harvard University Press, 1977. Dowling considers the antibiotics, sulfa drugs, vaccines, and serums that have played a noteworthy role in combating and preventing infectious disease. This is the finest book available on the control of diseases in the twentieth century and includes an expert account of streptomycin and its many clinical trials.

Epstein, Samuel, and Beryl Williams. *Miracles from Microbes: The Road to Streptomycin.* New Brunswick, N.J.: Rutgers University Press, 1946. This is a straightforward record of the research of Waksman that produced streptomycin. The authors include a chapter on Dubos and his discovery of gramicidin.

Lappé, Marc. *Germs That Won't Die.* Garden City, N.Y.: Doubleday, 1982. A book important for the documentation and discussion of the overuse and misuse of antibiotics, the rise of antibiotic-resistant microorganisms, and the danger they represent to human health.

Lechevalier, Hubert A., and Morris Solotorovsky. *Three Centuries of Microbiology.* New York: McGraw-Hill, 1965. The authors reconstruct the main lines of development of microbiology. The longest section is on chemotherapy with a fine narrative on Waksman and on the work of Feldman and Hinshaw at the Mayo Clinic.

Waksman, Selman A. *The Conquest of Tuberculosis.* Berkeley: University of California Press, 1964. Discusses tuberculosis, including its long history, spread, diagnosis, discovery of the tubercle microbe, treatments, tests, preventive measures, and the development of the chemotherapy of tuberculosis. For a wide audience.

_____. *My Life with the Microbes.* New Brunswick, N.J.: Rutgers University Press, 1954. A solid, straightforward, and accessible narrative of his life and work. The reader can learn the details of Waksman's career, his relations with other scientists, and how people responded to his antibiotic discoveries.

Albert B. Costa

Cross-References

Ehrlich Introduces Salvarsan as a Cure for Syphilis (1910), p. 476; Calmette and Guérin Develop the Tuberculosis Vaccine BCG (1921), p. 705; Fleming Discovers Penicillin in Molds (1928), p. 873; Domagk Discovers That a Sulfonamide Can Save Lives (1932), p. 968; Florey and Chain Develop Penicillin as an Antibiotic (1940), p. 1171; Duggar Discovers Aureomycin, the First of the Tetracyclines (1945), p. 1255.

THE WORLD'S FIRST NUCLEAR REACTOR IS ACTIVATED

Category of event: Physics
Time: November 4, 1943
Locale: Oak Ridge, Tennessee

The reactor at Oak Ridge National Laboratory produced the first substantial quantities of plutonium, making the production of usable amounts of energy from a chain reaction practical

> *Principal personages:*
> ENRICO FERMI (1901-1954), an American physicist who directed the first controlled nuclear chain reaction at the University of Chicago
> MARTIN D. WHITAKER (1902-1960), the first director of Oak Ridge National Laboratory
> EUGENE PAUL WIGNER (1902-   ), the director of research and development of Oak Ridge

Summary of Event

The construction of the nuclear reactor at Oak Ridge National Laboratory in 1943 was a vital part of the Manhattan Project, the effort by the United States during World War II to develop an atomic bomb. The successful operation of that reactor was a major achievement not only for the project itself but also for the general development and application of nuclear technology. The first director of the Oak Ridge National Laboratory was Martin D. Whitaker; the director of research and development was Eugene Paul Wigner.

The nucleus of an atom is made up of protons and neutrons. A nuclear reaction for any purpose involves the fissioning, or splitting, of the nucleus of a fissionable atom by hitting it with a neutron from a material that emits an occasional neutron naturally. When an atom splits, two things happen: A tremendous amount of thermal energy is released and two or three neutrons, on the average, escape from the nucleus. If all the atoms in a kilogram of U-235 uranium were to fission, they would produce as much heat energy as the burning of 3,000,000 kilograms of coal.

The benefit of the energy released during fission is obvious, but the extra neutrons also are important, because if at least one of them hits another atom and causes it to fission (and thus release more energy and more neutrons), the process will continue. It will become a self-sustaining chain reaction that will produce a continuing supply of heat.

Inside a reactor, a nuclear chain reaction is controlled so that it proceeds relatively slowly. The most familiar use for the heat thus released is to boil water and make steam to turn the turbine generators that produce electricity to serve industrial, commercial, and residential needs. On the other hand, the fissioning process in a weapon proceeds very rapidly so that all of the energy in the atoms is produced and released virtually at once. Therefore, the first application of nuclear technology was to produce the two atomic bombs that ended World War II.

The work that began at Oak Ridge in 1943, however, had to be preceded by a major event that took place in 1942. At the University of Chicago, Enrico Fermi had demonstrated for the first time that it was possible to achieve a self-sustaining atomic chain reaction. More important, the reaction could be controlled: It could be started up, it could generate heat and sufficient neutrons to keep itself going, and it could be turned off. That first chain reaction was very slow, and it generated very little heat; but it demonstrated and proved the principle that controlled fission was possible.

Slow or fast, however, a heat-producing nuclear reaction is an energy conversion process, and it requires fuel. There is only one readily fissionable element that occurs naturally and can be used as fuel. It is a form of uranium called U-235. It is, however, a rare form. Only 0.7 percent, one part in 140, of all naturally occurring uranium is U-235. The remainder is U-238, which does not fission readily. Therefore, the concentration of the "active ingredient," U-235, is not high enough to achieve a "critical mass" of a reasonable size. The critical mass is the amount of fissionable material needed for a chain reaction. One way around this problem is the process of enrichment, which increases the concentration of U-235 sufficiently for a chain reaction to occur. Enriched uranium is used to fuel the reactors used by electric utilities. Also, the much more plentiful U-238 can be converted into Pu-239, a form of the man-made element plutonium, which does fission readily. That conversion process is the way fuel is produced for a nuclear weapon, and was, thus, the major objective of the Oak Ridge effort: to develop a pilot operation for separating plutonium from the uranium in which it was produced. Large-scale plutonium production, which had never been attempted before, eventually would be done at the Hanford Engineer Works in Washington. First, however, it had to be proved on a small scale at Oak Ridge.

Four rural eastern Tennessee communities—Wheat, Elza, Robertsville, and Scarboro—lay not far from Knoxville in the valley beside the Clinch River where the United States government acquired 24,000 hectares needed for the Oak Ridge facility. On its first visit to the area, the site selection committee was pleased with what it saw and made the following report: "The topography is such that a number of operations could find reasonably flat areas divided by protective hills. The driving distance to Knoxville is less than 20 miles, and service from two important railroads is immediately available. . . . Water from the Clinch River is regulated . . . and because of the nearby Norris Dam is relatively free of silt. A relatively small part of the land is under cultivation, indicating that a small number of families would have to be moved."

One thousand families were paid a total of $2.6 million for their property by the government, which relocated the former residents and agreed to care for the sixty-five cemeteries that also were purchased. Ground was broken for the construction of the Oak Ridge reactor on February 1, 1943, only two months after Fermi's success in Chicago. In fact, the basic data for the design of the Oak Ridge facility came from the original Chicago reactor. Oak Ridge was the world's first operating nuclear reactor to produce substantial amounts of heat, and it was built in only nine months. The reactor was started up on November 4 under Fermi's supervision and was flawless.

The Oak Ridge laboratory (originally called Clinton Laboratories) was constructed by the DuPont Chemical Company and operated by the Metallurgical Laboratory of the University of Chicago. The facility produced several grams of plutonium by March 1, 1944. The material was sent to the Los Alamos laboratory in New Mexico for testing. By July, 1944, the reactor operated at four times its original power level. By the end of that year, however, plutonium production at Oak Ridge had ceased, and the reactor thereafter was used principally to produce radioisotopes for physical and biological research and for medical treatment. Ultimately, the Hanford Engineer Works' reactors produced the plutonium for the bomb that was dropped on Nagasaki on August 9, 1945.

At first, Oak Ridge was essentially a "company town" built and run by the United States government. A planned community for laboratory employees and their families, it was complete with grocery stores, schools, and all the standard features of any other separate community. It was, however, completely fenced in and secured by armed guards. In two and a half years, Oak Ridge became the fifth largest city in Tennessee, with a population that peaked at seventy-five thousand. When the war was over, however, the population fell to thirty-six thousand.

In July, 1945, Monsanto Chemical Company took over operating responsibility for Oak Ridge. The production of radioisotopes was expanded, and work began on designing two additional reactors.

The original objectives for which Oak Ridge had been built had been achieved, and subsequent activity at the facility was directed toward peacetime missions that included basic studies of the structure of matter.

Impact of Event

When the bombs were dropped, the war stopped. Reduced to simplest terms, the most immediate impact of the work done at Oak Ridge was its contribution to ending World War II, with the United States emerging intact to remain the principal preserver of freedom in the world. History since 1945 undeniably would have been much different if the United States' victory in the Pacific had not been decisive.

Nuclear technology, like any other technology, is neutral and can be developed for and applied to a variety of purposes. Interestingly enough, the great advances in nuclear technology since 1945 have not been for military uses. Delivery systems have changed dramatically, but the real advances in and new applications of nuclear technology have been in nonmilitary areas: terrestrial electric power generation, nuclear medicine, space power, and ship propulsion (even though it is principally for naval vessels). All those areas have profited from the pioneering efforts at the Oak Ridge National Laboratory.

Although a prediction in the late 1950's of energy from the atom as being "too cheap to meter" will never materialize, today technology exists to produce an inexhaustible supply of electricity. An example is the Integral Fast Reactor (IFR), a breeder reactor developed and proved in prototype form by Argonne National Laboratory in Idaho. The term "breeder" is applied to reactors that convert U-238 to Pu-239, thus breeding new fuel. The IFR is one form of breeder reactor, although it is quite different from the original plutonium-producing facility at Oak Ridge. In addition, the IFR solves the particularly difficult problem of disposing of radioactive waste by recycling and consuming it within the reactor.

Nuclear power also is needed in space, because of considerations involving the limits of the only other feasible alternative: solar, or photovoltaic, power. For example, a power system for a lunar base, if photovoltaic, would need to be greatly oversized not only to meet normal activity demands when sunlight is available but also to collect energy for storage and eventual use during the fourteen-day eclipse that occurs during each twenty-eight day orbit. Nuclear technology can be applied reliably for exploration of Mars and for other deep space activities. Unlike photovoltaic systems, there is no falloff in energy production as the distance from the sun increases.

The leading effort by the United States to apply nuclear technology in space is the SP-100 program, a joint project of the Department of Defense, the Department of Energy, and National Aeronautics and Space Administration (NASA). Among the many potential applications for SP-100 technology are propulsion power for interplanetary transport, power for manned and robotic extraterrestrial outposts and resource exploitation, and power for solar system exploration.

Bibliography

Faulkner, Peter, ed. *The Silent Bomb: A Guide to the Nuclear Energy Controversy.* New York: Vintage Books, 1977. Sponsored by Friends of the Earth, this book deals with the controversies of "safe" radiation levels, potential disasters at nuclear plants, and the economics of nuclear power.

Glasstone, Samuel. *Sourcebook on Atomic Energy.* 3d ed. New York: Van Nostrand Reinhold, 1967. A balanced presentation of all aspects of atomic energy, it requires only a rudimentary knowledge of science or mathematics to understand its narrative. An excellent sourcebook for the laboratory or library.

Hewlett, R. G., and O. E. Anderson, Jr. *The New World 1939/1946, Volume 1: A History of the United States Atomic Energy Commission.* University Park: Pennsylvania State University Press, 1962. The first in a series, this volume discusses the discovery of atomic fission, the race to produce the first bomb, and the problems of control and of harnessing the energy.

Inglis, David Rittenhouse. *Nuclear Energy: Its Physics and Its Social Challenge.* Reading, Mass.: Addison-Wesley, 1973. A basic primer for the person interested in nuclear energy and its history, applications, and control. Presents the social challenges inherent in this energy source.

Kaku, Michio, and Jennifer Trainer, eds. *Nuclear Power, Both Sides: The Best Arguments For and Against the Most Controversial Technology.* New York: W. W. Norton, 1982. The articles in this volume present both sides of issues such as radiation, safety, and waste disposal. Encourages readers to draw their own conclusion on whether to be for or against nuclear energy.

Murphy, Dervla. *Nuclear Stakes: Race to the Finish.* New York: Ticknor & Fields, 1981. Written by a travel writer in the vicinity of Three Mile Island at the time of the incident, this is easy reading for the layperson, yet presents the issues facing all: the safety or nonsafety of nuclear energy plants.

Seaborg, Glenn T. *Nuclear Milestones: A Collection of Speeches.* San Francisco: W. H. Freeman, 1972. A series of speeches and reminiscences by a man who was part of the growth of nuclear energy and knew the major personalities of the new discipline. Lavishly illustrated with photographs of then and now.

Wilson, Jane, ed. *All in Our Time: The Reminiscences of Twelve Nuclear Pioneers.* Chicago: Bulletin of the Atomic Scientists, 1975. These twelve pioneers depicted assisted in the long labor and birth of nuclear energy, nursing it through wartime, and watching it grow to maturity in a world of peace. Easy, readable, and chatty, it provides glimpses, occasionally humorous, into the thoughts and feelings of modern-day pioneers.

John M. Shaw

Cross-References

Rutherford Presents His Theory of the Atom (1912), p. 527; Hahn Splits an Atom of Uranium (1938), p. 1135; Fermi Creates the First Controlled Nuclear Fission Chain Reaction (1942), p. 1198; The First Atomic Bomb Is Successfully Detonated (1945), p. 1265; Teller and Ulam Develop the First H-Bomb (1951), p. 1401; The World's First Breeder Reactor Produces Electricity While Generating New Fuel (1951), p. 1419; The United States Opens the First Commercial Nuclear Power Plant (1957), p. 1557.

THE GERMANS USE THE V-1 FLYING BOMB AND THE V-2 GOES INTO PRODUCTION

Category of event: Space and aviation
Time: 1944
Locale: Peenemünde Rocket Research Institute, Germany

The world's first operational flying bomb was put into use against the Allies in World War II, while the V-2, the world's first long-range, liquid-fueled rocket went into production

Principal personages:
WERNHER VON BRAUN (1912-1977), the chief engineer and prime motivator of rocket research in Germany during the 1930's and 1940's
WALTER ROBERT DORNBERGER (1895-1980), the former commander of the Peenemünde Rocket Research Institute
ING FRITZ GOSSLAU, the head of the V-1 developmental team
PAUL SCHMIDT, the designer of the impulse jet motor

Summary of Event

On May 26, 1943, key German military officials were briefed by two teams of scientists, one representing the Air Force, and the other representing the Army. Each team had launched two experimental war craft. The German Air Force experiment, the *Fiesler 103*, failed on both trials. The German Army's *Aggregat-4* (Assembly-4, or A-4) worked beautifully. The military chiefs, who were to decide which project merited further funding and development to suit the war needs, decided to pursue both projects. Each experimental craft had both advantages and disadvantages, which counterbalanced the pros and cons of the other. Therefore, both the *Fiesler* 103 and the Army's A-4 were developed. They were to become the V-1 and the V-2 aircraft.

The concept of the V-1 motor existed in the late 1800's. In 1907, a French patent was taken on the concept, and in 1919, René Lorin published a description of this type of motor that was inexpensive and expendable. Development of the impulse jet motor continued after World War I. After the work of Munich engineer Paul Schmidt drew the attention of the German *Luftwaffe* (air force), the *Argus Motorenwerk* was authorized production, which culminated in the Argus AS 109-014. The V-1, code named *Kirschkern* (Cherry Stone), had begun.

On April 30, 1941, the motor was used to assist power on a biplane trainer. On June 10, 1942, Field Marshall Erhard Milch foresaw the future for the flying bomb, when he chaired a review of the development. The developmental team was headed by Ing Fritz Gosslau; the aircraft was designed by Robert Lusser. On December 24, 1942, the first powered missile launch took place. It was planned that by December 15, 1943, sixty-four main launch sites and thirty-two secondary sites would be in place, and operations could begin. As a result of many factors, however, including the rivalry between the V-2 and V-1 development teams and the competition for manufacturing labor and materials, the V-1 bombing campaign began on June 13, 1944.

The V-1 was a pulse-jet powered aircraft, which was capable of delivering a 1-ton payload. It was launched, under Adolf Hitler's orders, while still in a late developmental stage, to terrorize inhabited areas of London for the damage that had been wreaked in Germany during the war. An average of 102 V-1's were launched daily between June 13 and early September, 1944. On June 11, 1944, Allied sources predicted the first bombing raid within forty-eight hours, judging by the photographs of the 45.7-meter railed ramps. Early launch sites included as many as twelve support buildings that took weeks to build. Later sites, built during the latter part of 1944, were constructed in a day. Allied bombing did significant damage to the supply lines, no matter how fast the sites were built, thus making restocking of supplies and hardware difficult and slowing down the rate of firings.

Two innovative systems made the V-1 unique: the drive operation and the guidance system. In the motor, oxygen entered the grid valves through many small flaps. Fuel oil was introduced and the mixture ignited. After ignition, the expanded gases produced the reaction propulsion. When the expanded gases had vacated, the reduced internal pressure allowed the valve flaps to reopen, admitting more air for the next cycle.

The guidance system included a small propeller with a capability to preset a revolution counter. The number of revolutions accomplished at a set speed and height was calculated. By setting the counter to cover the desired distance to target, the propeller would activate the elevators on the aircraft, causing it to dive at the chosen target. Understandably, accuracy was not at the desired level. The V-1 had a wing span of slightly more than 7.6 meters. Because it used low-grade fuel oil and oxygen from the atmosphere, it was inexpensive to operate. It was restricted, however, to one speed only, about 590.4 kilometers per hour, and depended upon a certain air density to get the oxygen needed during flight. Therefore, it could not fly at a high altitude. Because it also flew in a straight line and at a constant speed, Allied aircraft could intercept more easily this "buzz-bomb" than it could the V-2.

The development of the V-2 can be traced to an organization called the *Verein für Raumschiffahrt*, or VfR (society for space travel), founded in 1927. In 1930, the group leased an area on the outskirts of Berlin for experimental rocketry development. The civilian research accomplished at the *Raketenflugplatz* (rocket flying place), interested the military authorities. According to the Treaty of Versailles, world military forces were restricted to 100,000 men and a certain level of weaponry. The German military powers realized very early, however, that the Treaty had neglected to restrict rocket-powered weaponry, not even dreaming of their possibility at the end of World War I. Captain Walter Robert Dornberger (later Major General) visited the scientists at the *Raketenflugplatz* in 1932, hired Wernher von Braun, and moved the research to the Kummersdorf Artillery Range, also called Experimental Station west, an old artillery field 27 kilometers south of Berlin. At Kummersdorf, the research grew to such an extent that an entirely new area, from which long-range test flights could be run, was needed.

Peenemünde Rocket Research Institute was established in 1939. Eventually, the research area was split. Peenemünde West was run by the German *Luftwaffe*, which was responsible for development of the V-1. Peenemünde East was under the control of Dornberger and the Germany Army, who had developed the V-2.

The V-2 had a lift-off thrust of 11,550.6 newtons and was propelled by a combustion of liquid oxygen and alcohol. The propellants were pumped into the combustion chamber by a steam-powered turboprop. The steam was generated by the decomposition of hydrogen peroxide, using sodium permanganate as catalyst. An innovation, still in use in modern technology, was regenerative cooling, with alcohol used to cool the double-walled combustion chamber.

The guidance system included two phases: powered and ballistic. Four seconds after launch, a preprogrammed tilt to 17 degrees was begun, then acceleration was continued to achieve the desired trajectory. At the desired velocity, the engine power was cut off via one of two systems. In the automatic system, a device shut off the engine at the velocity desired; under this method, accuracy was not optimal. The second system entailed a radio signal to the rocket's receiver, which cut off the power. This was a far more accurate method, but because of the extra equipment required at the launch site, Allied bombers were much more likely to strike. This system was more often employed toward the end of the war. Engine cut-off involved a two-stage process. The first stage shut down the 11,235.9 newton nozzle, leaving open the 3,595.5 newton nozzle. The second stage shut down all power.

Even the 907 kilogram warhead of the V-2 was a carefully researched and tested device. The detonators had to be able to withstand 6 g's (acceleration of gravity) of force during lift-off and reentry, as well as the vibrations inherent in a rocket flight. Yet, they also had to be sensitive enough to detonate upon impact before the explosive became buried in the target and lost power through diffusion of force.

The V-2 was a much more complex craft, having thousands of parts and flying at more than twice the speed of sound. Its first successful test was in October of 1942, but it continued under development until August of 1944. During the next eight months, more than three thousand were launched against England and the Continent, causing immense devastation and fulfilling its purpose of becoming the *Vergeltungwaffe zwei* (vengeance weapon 2). Unfortunately, the weapon that took fourteen years of research and testing entered the war too late to make an impact upon the outcome of World War II.

Impact of Event

The V-1 and V-2, although having a strong negative connotation with the destruction and terror they wrought during World War II, made a tremendous impact upon the history and development of space technology. Even during the war, captured V-2's were studied by Allied scientists. American rocket scientists were especially interested in the technology, as they were working in the same direction, with liquid-fueled rockets. After the war, military personnel were sent to the United States, where they signed contracts to work with the U.S. Army. This program was known as "Operation Paperclip." Testing of the captured V-2's was undertaken at White Sands Missile Range near Alamogordo, New Mexico. The JB-2 Loon Navy jet-propelled bomb was developed following the study of the captured German craft.

The Soviet Union also benefited from captured V-2's and from the German factories dismantled following the war. With these resources, the Soviet Union also had a boost toward development of their own rocket technology, culminating in the launch of Sputnik 1, the world's first man-made satellite, on October 4, 1957. The United States was not far behind, however, when it launched its first satellite, Explorer 1, on January 31, 1958. On April 12, 1961, the world's first human space traveler, Soviet cosmonaut Yuri A. Gagarin, was launched.

Although the same technology has allowed for the development of bigger and more lethal weapons, the liquid-fuel technology has allowed for the development for research rockets. These sounding rockets tested the atmosphere and led the way for the launching of satellite payloads, literally opening the doors to the sky. The vast array of satellites include communications, meteorological, orbiting observatories, radiation and energy measuring devices, remote sensing, and biosatellites. Satellite technology assists humankind in managing the effects of weather and climate, in researching the solar system, and in testing the effects of space travel upon the human body.

The continued development and building onto the V-2 technology gave scientists the opportunity to walk on the Moon with the aid of the massive Saturn 5 launch vehicle. Some of the "Paperclip" team members contributed to the Skylab space station project and to the development of the Space Transportation System with the reusable space shuttle Orbiter. These projects are still active and contemplate such programs as colonization of other planets, solar collecting stations, and space manufacturing facilities.

Indeed, the effect of the V-1 and V-2 may not end in the foreseeable future. As von Braun stated in his foreword to *The Rocket Team* (1979): "It [the rocket team] always has been characterized by enthusiasm, professionalism, skill, imagination, a sense of perfectionism, and dedication to rocketry and space exploration. How can the story of such people and of the exciting programs with which they are involved ever end?"

Bibliography

Cooksley, Peter G. *Flying Bomb: The Story of Hitler's V-Weapons in World War II*. New York: Charles Scribner's Sons, 1979. This is an immensely readable book, that consists more of a history from the English viewpoint, than from a technological source.

Dornberger, Walter R. *V-2*. Translated by James Cleugh and Geoffrey Halliday. New York: Viking Press, 1954. This is a fascinating, eyewitness account of the development of the V-2, including the political and financial maneuvering Dornberger had to handle during the project.

Goodwin, Harold L. *All About Rockets and Space Flight*. New York: Random House, 1964. This is a book of late elementary-level reading, with good basic material and a dictionary of terminology. Recommended for an early overview.

Kennedy, Gregory P. *Vengeance Weapon 2*. Washington, D.C.: Smithsonian Institution Press, 1983. This book is a very readable and pleasant combination of history and technology. Some passages discussing the actual mechanics of the V-2 are technical. Includes beautiful black-and-white archival photographs.

Ley, Willy. *Rockets, Missiles, and Space Travel*. Rev. ed. New York: Viking Press, 1961. Willey Ley is known as probably the most prolific writer of space history. His style is on a very readable college level, yet dense with information. This volume details history from early conceptions through the V-2. Contains a technical table.

Ordway, Frederick J., III, and Mitchell R. Sharpe. *The Rocket Team*. New York: Thomas Y. Crowell, 1979. Detailed history of the V-2, with many references to the V-1. It is college-level reading, with fascinating black-and-white photographs. Excellent resource.

Young, Richard Anthony. *The Flying Bomb*. London: I. Allan, 1978. This book is richly laden with photographs, diagrams, and the complete story of the V-1 development and deployment. Includes appendices, with all the launch sites and procedures. Easily understood technology for the college-level reader.

Ellen F. Mitchum

Cross-References

Tsiolkovsky Proposes That Liquid Oxygen Be Used for Space Travel (1903), p. 189; Goddard Launches the First Liquid Fuel Propelled Rocket (1926), p. 810; The First Jet Plane Using Whittle's Engine Is Flown (1941), p. 1187; The First Rocket with More than One Stage Is Created (1949), p. 1342; Sputnik 1, the First Artificial Satellite, Is Launched (1957), p. 1545; The United States Launches Its First Orbiting Satellite, Explorer 1 (1958), p. 1583; Echo, the First Passive Communications Satellite, Is Launched (1960), p. 1677; Gagarin Becomes the First Human to Orbit Earth (1961), p. 1693; Shepard Is the First United States Astronaut in Space (1961), p. 1698; Telstar, the First Commercial Communications Satellite, Relays Live Transatlantic Television Pictures (1962), p. 1728.

HODGKIN SOLVES THE STRUCTURE OF PENICILLIN

Category of event: Chemistry
Time: 1944-1949
Locale: Oxford, England

Hodgkin used an electronic computer to work out the X-ray data of penicillin, becoming the first to use a computer in direct application to a biochemical problem

Principal personages:
DOROTHY CROWFOOT HODGKIN (1910-   ), an English crystallographer who won the 1964 Nobel Prize in Chemistry
BARBARA WHARTON LOW (1920-   ), an English chemist who assisted in the penicillin project
C. W. BUNN and A. TURNER-JONES, the English crystallographers who collaborated on the penicillin project with Hodgkin
L. D. COMRIE and G. B. HEY, the English engineers who worked out the computing methods used in the penicillin determination

Summary of Event

The method Dorothy Crowfoot Hodgkin used to solve the problem of the molecular structure of the antibiotic penicillin consisted of three scientific disciplines that had, to that time, little common ground: synthetic organic chemistry, X-ray crystallography, and the new field of computer technology.

Penicillin was discovered in 1928 by Sir Alexander Fleming at St. Mary's Hospital in London. Fleming's original paper on penicillin, published in 1929, described potential uses of the antibiotic as well as toxicity tests performed on animals and on some sensitive human tissue. Ernst Chain and Baron Florey at the University of Oxford began working with penicillin in 1935, with Chain attempting to extract and purify sufficient penicillin for Florey's clinical testing. They published the results of a series of successful treatments in 1941. *Time* brought worldwide attention to the new wonder drug in 1941, but noted that because penicillin was difficult to extract, it had limited usefulness until it could be prepared with less expense or synthesized.

Because of the potential antibiotic activity of penicillin and its low toxicity, it was invaluable on the battlefields of World War II. An enormous effort that involved scientists in academia, industry, and government was undertaken by the English and American governments in 1942 to increase the supply of penicillin. The research effort moved in two directions: improved means of producing natural penicillins and the synthesis of an artificial penicillin.

The development of a synthetic route to penicillin required a knowledge not only of the chemical formula of penicillin but also of its molecular structure. The usual method of structure determination by organic chemists at that time was to subject the compound to harsh treatment and then study the degradation products. The analysis of these fragments would allow reconstruction of the original molecule, a jigsaw puzzle approach.

Among the proposed structures for the penicillin molecule, two were considered leading contenders by the end of 1942. The favorite of Sir Robert Robinson, a well-known organic chemist of the University of Oxford, was a combination of two rings known as oxazolone-thiazolidine. Nevertheless, the structure had a serious problem: The formula predicted that the molecule should contain a basic group that was never found by titration. A second possible structure was suggested, a different assembly of rings known as a beta-lactam-thiazolidine structure. This was an unfamiliar structure that had never been found in natural products. No known reactions could explain how the observed degradation fragments could fit to give the beta-lactam structure. It seemed that the traditional organic method of structure determination was incapable of resolving the problem. To settle the dispute, a sample of penicillin was sent to Dorothy Hodgkin at the end of 1944 for a single-crystal X-ray study of penicillin.

The discipline of X-ray crystallography, in which Hodgkin spent her scientific career, had its beginning in Munich in 1912, when Max von Laue showed that X rays behaved as electromagnetic waves with short wavelengths and that X rays scattered by a row of atoms in a crystal could produce interference patterns. The intensity of the various spots in the pattern and their spacing depended on the arrangement of the atoms in the crystal. Sir Lawrence Bragg in England formulated a simple law by which he was able to explain successfully all the spots from Laue's patterns. This development provided a new tool for examining the internal arrangements of atoms in crystals and provided solutions, almost immediately, for many inorganic structural questions.

The general method involved in crystallographic study is repeated comparison of experiments and calculation of reflections from various planes of the crystal. If the structure of the crystal and the wavelength of the X rays are known, it is easy to predict the diffraction pattern. It is much more difficult to deduce the crystal structure from the observed pattern. For very simple structures, a trial-and-error method is appropriate, but as more complex structures are studied, the calculations involved become extremely tedious and time-consuming.

The object of a crystal-structure determination is to ascertain the positions of all atoms in the basic unit of the crystal. The process involves collection of data, solution of the phase relations among the scattered X rays (determination of a trial structure), and refinement of this structure. In the 1940's and 1950's, the time involved in the difficult task of collecting three-dimensional data (the first step), was short in comparison with the time required to solve the phase problems (the second step). This depended on the complexity of the problem and on the luck, perseverance, and intuition of the investigator. The third step required such a large number of calculations that it was ignored, except for the simplest of structures.

Hodgkin applied her particular qualities of precision, astute mathematical analysis, and special imagination to the penicillin problem as soon as crystals were prepared for photographing. Three crystals were prepared for study: sodium benzylpenicillin and the isomorphous potassium and rubidium salts of benzylpenicillin. Potassium and rubidium benzylpenicillin were chosen for the X-ray analysis in the hope that their crystal structures would be amenable to direct Fourier analysis. If this were true, the analysis could be completed without any detailed chemical information. The salts were, in fact, isomorphous (same crystal structure), but the location of the cation in the crystal was such that they affected only some of the X-ray intensities. A number of phase angles were obtained, which allowed incomplete electron density maps to be derived, but did not permit a choice to be made among the possible proposed structures. The sodium benzylpenicillin analysis was carried out differently because its crystal structure, although related to that of the other salts, was not isomorphous with theirs. After some initial work at the University of Oxford, the data on the sodium salt were sent to C. W. Bunn and A. Turner-Jones at Imperial Chemical Industries, Ltd., where the analysis was completed.

The early electron density projections, based on the phase angles obtained from the isomorphous salts, indicated the presence of a heavy scattering center, identified as sulfur, in the crystal structure. Armed with these few clues and the tentative structures, Hodgkin and Barbara Wharton Low proceeded with a trial-and-error analysis. They constructed scale models using heavy wire, and by studying the shadows made by illuminating the model with parallel light beams, they were able to record new atomic coordinates. Further calculations followed for the original reflections used in the first Fourier density projections and some additional reflections. Hodgkin and Low frequently compared their results with those of Bunn and Turner-Jones, who were using an optical diffraction method in studying the sodium salt of benzylpenicillin. Eventually, the two groups agreed on the beta-lactam structure as the correct one for the penicillin molecule.

Hodgkin then proceeded to attempt refinement of the crystal structure in three dimensions following the same scheme as for the two-dimensional projections: calculating structure factors, followed by three-dimensional Fourier series. Although the calculations involve no theoretical difficulty, there is considerable practical difficulty because of the cumbersome nature of the formulas involved. L. D. Comrie and G. B. Hey of the Scientific Computing Service, Ltd., devised methods of executing the necessary calculations. These were performed on a Pierce Alpha calculating machine, which was borrowed for the project. The use of these large-scale computing methods allowed the analysis to be carried much farther than was usual in such a structure analysis.

Impact of Event

X-ray crystallographic analysis of even the simplest molecules requires many mathematical computations. When the work on penicillin began, the computing equipment available was grossly inadequate. By the mid-1940's, Hodgkin was able to borrow an old IBM card-punch machine, without which the refinement of the penicillin structure would have been almost impossible.

Hodgkin continued to make use of computers of varying degrees of complexity to solve even larger molecules. It was becoming clear that understanding the chemistry of life processes required a detailed stereochemical knowledge of the compounds involved. By 1956, Hodgkin had shown by the penicillin work and by solving the structure of vitamin B_{12} that it was possible to use X-ray crystallography alone to determine even very complex structures. As the size and complexity of the molecules to be analyzed increased, the need for more advanced computers increased also. Fortunately, computer technology kept pace with the demands of other fields of science.

During the 1960's, many organic chemists worried about the gradual encroachment of X-ray crystallography into what had been an important preserve of organic chemistry: the elucidation of structure. It was becoming evident by that time that natural product structures, especially those that contained new features, could be determined more quickly by X-ray analysis than by traditional degradative methods. The chemists feared the loss of new discoveries frequently brought about by the process of classical structural analysis, particularly in the area of chemical synthesis. In fact, organic chemistry has survived its crisis rather well. Freed from the responsibility of structural determination, organic chemists have turned, with great success, to other endeavors. As interest among organic chemists in degradation studies waned, their energy was channeled into other areas, particularly synthetic and mechanistic studies. Various types of bonds were studied during this period, especially those formed in organic molecules and their influence on geometry: angles, bonding and nonbonding distances, and planarity of certain groups. The hydrogen bond also received much attention after crystal X-ray analysis showed that some pairs of electronegative atoms (oxygen, nitrogen, fluorine), at least one of which was bonded to a hydrogen, approached closer than expected. The importance of the hydrogen bond was recognized at this time, particularly its influence in determining secondary structures of biological molecules.

The use of the computer in modeling chemical compounds has gone far beyond the computational stage. The development of graphics capability allows models of molecules to be viewed on screen and manipulated in many ways. New drugs are frequently computer-designed to mimic natural molecules and to act as positive or negative inhibitors of many body processes. The introduction of the computer truly has revolutionized chemistry.

Bibliography

Burke, John G. *Origins of the Science of Crystals.* Berkeley: University of California Press, 1966. A short history of the science of crystallography. Burke clearly explains the terms used in crystallography, as well as the basic theories.

Crowfoot, D., C.W. Bunn, B. W. Rogers-Low, and A. Turner-Jones. "The X-Ray Crystallographic Investigation of the Structure of Penicillin." In *The Chemistry of Penicillin*, edited by Hans T. Clarke, John R. Johnson, and Sir Robert Robinson. Princeton, N.J.: Princeton University Press, 1949. A rather technical article by

Hodgkin and her coworkers that describes the tedious process by which the structure of penicillin was determined. For readers with an average background in mathematics and general science.

Dodson, Guy, Jenny P. Glusker, and David Sayre, eds. *Structural Studies on Molecules of Biological Interest*. Oxford, England: Clarendon Press, 1981. Published in honor of Hodgkin's seventieth birthday. Contains technical articles and articles about the early work of Hodgkin and her importance to organic structural analysis. Many of the latter are the reminiscences of friends and coworkers.

Ewald, P. P., ed. *Fifty Years of X-Ray Diffraction*. Utrecht, The Netherlands: Oosthoek's Uitgeversmij, 1962. A detailed description of the development of X-ray crystallography written for the fiftieth anniversary of the discovery of X-ray diffraction by crystals.

Sheehan, John C. *The Enchanted Ring*. Cambridge, Mass.: MIT Press, 1982. An interesting and readable book on the history of the attempt to synthesize penicillin by the person who eventually accomplished the feat. Discusses the many conflicts that arose along the way, from the crediting of the original discovery by Fleming to the disagreements over the structures proposed by organic chemists before Hodgkin's solution.

Grace A. Banks

Cross-References

Bush Builds the First Differential Analyzer (1928), p. 846; Fleming Discovers Penicillin in Molds (1928), p. 873; Florey and Chain Develop Penicillin as an Antibiotic (1940), p. 1171; Eckert and Mauchly Develop the ENIAC (1943), p. 1213; The First Electronic Stored-Program Computer (BINAC) Is Completed (1949), p. 1347; UNIVAC I Becomes the First Commercial Electronic Computer and the First to Use Magnetic Tape (1951), p. 1396; Barton and Hassel Share the Nobel Prize for Determining the Three-Dimensional Shapes of Organic Compounds (1969), p. 1918.

KUIPER DISCOVERS THAT TITAN HAS AN ATMOSPHERE

Category of event: Astronomy
Time: January, 1944
Locale: McDonald Observatory, Fort Davis, Texas

Kuiper discovered evidence of a methane atmosphere in the spectrum of Titan, the largest satellite of Saturn

Principal personages:
GERARD PETER KUIPER (1905-1973), a Dutch-American scholar who throughout the 1950's and 1960's was the premier planetary astronomer
CHRISTIAAN HUYGENS (1629-1695), a Dutch astronomer and physicist who discovered Titan originally with a lens he had ground himself
CARL SAGAN (1934-   ), an American astronomer who proposed significant modifications of Kuiper's early studies of Titan

Summary of Event

Surprising progress occurred in observational astronomy during World War II, despite the calling of many astronomers for service in the war effort. In the midst of assignments from the Office of Scientific Research and Development and consulting for the Eighth Air Force in England, Gerard Peter Kuiper found time for research. The January, 1944, *Science News Letter* published a summary of the evidence that caused him to believe that Titan had an atmosphere: methane (marsh gas) and possibly ammonia had been discovered in its spectrum. Thus, Titan became the first satellite demonstrated to have an atmosphere, a primacy that lasted thirty years until space probes gave information about the thin atmospheres of Ganymede, Callisto, and Io, Jupiter's large satellites.

After brief stays at Lick Observatory and Harvard University, Kuiper was appointed to the faculty of the University of Chicago in 1935, becoming a full professor in 1943. The long-term relationship of Kuiper with the University of Chicago was fruitful for both, for Kuiper became the leading solar system astronomer during the 1950's and 1960's. Kuiper served as the director of both the Yerkes Observatory at Williams Bay, Wisconsin, and the McDonald Observatory at Fort Davis, Texas. In 1960, he moved to the University of Arizona where he founded the Lunar and Planetary Laboratory. Following his discovery of Titan's atmosphere, Kuiper conducted extensive studies of the atmosphere of Mars with an eye toward the popularly held hope that life existed there, discovered satellites of Uranus and Neptune, revitalized a nebular hypothesis of planetary formation, studied Pluto extensively, and was one of the leading analysts of the first Lunar surveys.

Kuiper's doctoral dissertation was a study of the spectra of binary stars. His work with stellar spectra prepared him for studies involving galactic nebulas, from which he moved to planetary spectra when he decided to settle into the study of the solar system. Titan was a natural subject for Kuiper to explore, for almost nothing was known about it, even though it was the largest satellite of Saturn, and a close competitor with Ganymede, Jupiter's largest, for status as the largest satellite in the solar system. Titan was discovered in 1655 by Christiaan Huygens while testing a new lens he had configured and polished. Four additional satellites of Saturn were discovered during the 1600's, but since Titan was the brightest, it was assumed to be the largest, a position confirmed as observations advanced and the system of defining magnitudes of light sources developed. Since Titan was magnitude 8.3 and the next brightest was magnitude 10 (the higher the magnitude, the dimmer the object), there seemed no doubt that it was the largest satellite.

In the decades prior to Kuiper's discovery, additional physical information was established with difficulty, however, astronomers found that Titan revolved around Saturn in a little less than sixteen days at a mean distance slightly greater than 1,200,000 kilometers from the center of the planet. Although Titan's observable disk was too small to measure accurately, estimates of size and mass were made on the basis of changes Saturn's satellites caused in one another's orbits. Estimates of a mass were about twice that of the Moon, with a density approximately two thirds of the Moon. By the 1940's, estimates based on brightness and distance led to a value of 4,200 kilometers for the diameter of Titan, thus projecting Titan as a Mercury-sized object much larger than Earth's moon (3,476 kilometers in diameter). By the early 1970's, estimates of Titan's size had grown to 4,880 kilometers. Voyager 2 in the early 1980's established an upward revision to about 5,150 kilometers in diameter, second only to Ganymede, which has a diameter of 5,262 kilometers. Voyager 2 also verified the mass by establishing that Titan is about 52 percent rock and about 48 percent ice. Measurements of light prior to Kuiper's discovery provided estimates of the albedo (reflectivity) of Titan. Some astronomers suggested that it was an ice ball, possibly ices of the same gases that had been found on the surface of the mother planet. That suggestion was uncertain because Titan was beyond the reach of the spectroscopes available before the early 1940's.

Despite the failure of spectroscopic evidence, the suspicion existed still that Titan had an atmosphere. As early as 1908, the Spanish astronomer Jose Comas Sola of Barcelona observed a darkening around the periphery of the disk of Titan, an indication that it could have an atmosphere. In 1916, Sir James Jeans pointed out that the kinetic theory of gases indicated that the lighter gases moved more rapidly and thus would easily escape the gravitational pull of small planetary bodies. Thus, the lightest gases such as hydrogen remained in an atmosphere only when combined with heavier gases, as with oxygen on Earth to form water. Since the Moon has only 16 percent of Earth's gravity, all the gases escaped into space. In the beginning of the twentieth century, Titan was estimated to have only 14 percent the gravity of Earth, but unlike the Moon, Titan receives only one hundredth of the light from the sun, and thus its temperature is much colder. The gases move more slowly and are more easily retained by the attenuated gravity. Jeans reasoned that Jupiter's satellites were too warm to retain atmospheres, but Titan and Neptune's large moon Triton were candidates to have atmospheres.

Kuiper was able to gather superior equipment (the 208-centimeter telescope at McDonald Observatory and infrared spectroscopes that worked well with the cool gases) experience in the observation of dim spectra from his studies of binary stars, and good observational technique to obtain the first useful spectra of a satellite. He determined that methane (consisting of one atom of carbon and four of hydrogen) was present and that ammonia (consisting of one atom of nitrogen and three of hydrogen) probably was present. This fit the expectations, for if Jeans' estimate of temperature was accurate, all but methane would be frozen on the surface.

The presence of ammonia was uncertain, although it was theoretically possible for droplets of ammonia to be suspended in the methane. The possible lines of ammonia in the spectrum were mere traces of the element and at the very limits of the equipment. Kuiper thus verified that at least one of the constituent elements of the atmosphere of Saturn itself was present on Titan, although the methane bands for Titan were much weaker than for the planet, indicating a more attenuated atmosphere. This finding supported the earlier expectations. Kuiper noted also that the color of Titan was orange, which he presumed was the result of action of the atmosphere with the surface. He reasoned analogously with speculations about Mars, whose reddish hue was presumed to result from oxidation. Dissociation of methane by the sun would leave hydrogen and an orange-colored organic precipitate, as laboratory experiments had shown; it was presumed to be either in the atmosphere or on the surface of the planet.

Impact of Event

Kuiper enjoyed the astronomical acclaim that went with establishing the first atmosphere on a satellite of a planet. For nearly three decades, Titan remained the only satellite with an observed atmosphere; finally, Pioneer 10 found a thin atmosphere around Io, a moon of Jupiter, on December 4, 1973, a clear indication of the quality of Kuiper's work. By the early 1970's, observations of the occultation of a star indicated that Ganymede probably had a very thin atmosphere because the light of the star was gradually extinguished as it passed behind the satellite. These discoveries verified the earlier calculations that had presumed that the other large satellites contained too little mass to retain a dense atmosphere of the light gases at their temperatures which were warmer than Titan's. It was clear that had Titan been significantly closer to the sun and its surface temperature higher, the methane would have long since been driven into space beyond the reach of Titan's limited gravity.

During the 1960's, various measurements of Titan's brightness at different wavelengths gave inconsistent measurements of the surface temperature, but all the theories led to higher temperatures than expected. In 1973, Carl Sagan, a former student of Kuiper, and Joseph Veverka of Cornell University proposed a greenhouse effect, which required the presence of more than methane in the atmosphere. There seemed insufficient hydrogen to trap the infrared radiation, so Sagan proposed a cloud cover of neon, argon, and nitrogen that would enhance retention of hydrogen below the cover. Sagan proposed further a solid surface with a liquid core composed of methane, ammonia, and water, which were emitted by volcanic-style eruptions into the atmosphere. Methane would dissociate in the upper atmosphere, with the neon gradually coming to predominate over the last 4.5 billion years since the beginning of the solar system. In 1973, it was impossible to verify this theory by detecting the neon, but this proposal became suspect as the conflicting temperatures implied a warmer layer above the surface of Titan.

Other probes in the early 1980's revealed more detail concerning Titan, which was closely approached by Voyager 2. Sagan's proposal of another gas was correct, but it was nitrogen, not argon or neon. A cloud cover—an orange hydrocarbon (methane/ethane) smog—combined with a predominantly molecular nitrogen atmosphere, was discovered which prevented sighting of the surface. The nitrogen-rich atmosphere results from chemical processes in the upper atmosphere as well as from earlier bombardment by meteoritic material which left tracks of nitrogen and complex hydrocarbons such as hydrogen cyanide, methylacetylene, and propane. Data indicated that Titan had surface seas of liquid ethane containing absorbed methane gas, an atmosphere at least 1.3 to 1.6 times as dense at the surface level as Earth's, and a greenhouse effect on the surface that raised the temperature from only 86 to 93 Kelvins. Radar studies culminating in published summaries in 1989 indicated that Titan is not completely covered by a hydrocarbon ocean, but shows irregular intensity of reflection, implying some solid surface and some seas of hydrocarbons. Titan is thus an exotic place that may hold clues to the development of the solar system, including Earth's early atmosphere and the first steps toward the evolution of life.

The length of time required before Kuiper's work could be superseded implies the care exercised in the research and the quality of the equipment that was used in this particular astronomical effort. Kuiper's first notable accomplishment was an enduring one.

Bibliography

Atreya, Sushil K. *Atmospheres and Ionospheres of the Outer Planets and Their Satellites.* New York: Springer-Verlag, 1986. Section 4 of chapter 7 relates to Titan and focuses exclusively on the atmosphere. While technical, the opening and concluding paragraphs are helpful.

Federer, Charles A., Jr. "Titan." *Science News* 99 (January 28, 1944): 10. A brief five-paragraph first announcement of Kuiper's discovery. The significance of Titan's having the first verified atmosphere was noted. The importance of the atmosphere's resemblance to that of Saturn for cosmological theory was also prominent.

——————. "Titan's Atmosphere." *Science News Letter* 45 (January 29, 1944): 67. A more extensive early summary of the significance of Kuiper's discovery. Focuses on the importance of verification of the first satellite atmosphere and the possible implications for cosmology.

Gehrels, Tom, and Mildred Shapley Matthews, eds. *Saturn.* Tucson: University of

Arizona Press, 1984. Part 6 discusses Titan. While this book is very technical, there are descriptive passages and conclusions that are clear and helpful. Contains a summary of the discoveries from the satellite flybys.

Hartmann, William K. "The Smaller Bodies of the Solar System." *Scientific American* 233 (September, 1975): 143-159. An extensive summary of the known information concerning the satellites in 1975. The thrust of the article is the implications for cosmogony. Titan is mentioned with the views of the Cornell astronomers receiving prominence.

Owens, Tobias. "Titan." *Scientific American* 246 (February, 1982): 98-109. A comprehensive summary of the results of the Voyager 1 and 2 passages near Saturn. Presents a clear summary of the historical development of the understanding of Titan's atmosphere.

Ivan L. Zabilka

Cross-References

Astronomers Discover the Rings of the Planet Uranus (1977), p. 2068; Voyager 1 and 2 Explore the Planets (1977), p. 2082; The First Ring Around Jupiter Is Discovered (1979), p. 2104; Pluto Is Found to Possess a Thin Atmosphere (1980), p. 2141; Astronomers Discover an Unusual Ring System of Planet Neptune (1982), p. 2211.

BLALOCK PERFORMS THE FIRST "BLUE BABY" OPERATION

Category of event: Medicine
Time: November, 1944
Locale: The Johns Hopkins University Hospital, Baltimore

Blalock developed the first surgical treatment of infants born with certain heart defects, paving the way for complete correction of these defects

Principal personages:
ALFRED BLALOCK (1899-1964), an American surgeon and physiologist who pioneered the surgical treatment of congenital heart disease
HELEN BROOKE TAUSSIG (1898-1986), an American physician, recognized as the founder of pediatric cardiology, who studied and corrected heart disease in children
SANFORD EDGAR LEVY (LEEDS) (1909-   ), an American physician who collaborated with Blalock to develop the surgical bypass procedure later used to treat "blue babies"
VIVIEN THOMAS (1911-   ), the surgical laboratory technician who worked closely with Blalock to develop surgical procedures

Summary of Event

The "blue baby" syndrome, or cyanosis, is most often caused by congenital malformations of the heart and associated vessels such that circulation to the lungs and other parts of the body is less than normal. One such condition, known as tetralogy of Fallot, is characterized by four major abnormalities: the pulmonary artery is stenosed (narrowed), a channel exists between the right and left ventricles (ventricular septal defect), the aorta is misplaced so that blood from both the right and left ventricles flows into it, and the right ventricle is enlarged. These defects result in poor oxygenation of blood (anoxemia) which is manifested by various symptoms, including blue lips and finger tips, episodes of shortness of breath that cause the child to squat, occasional loss of consciousness, stunting of growth, eruptions on the skin, and drumstick or clubbing deformities in the fingers and toes. Before the advent of modern cardiovascular surgery in the 1940's, children born with these deformities either died at an early age or lived very limited lives with extensive pain and suffering. The incidence of congenital heart disease is about seven in one thousand live births.

Alfred Blalock was a skillful surgeon with a keen interest in the physiology of the circulatory system. His research on hemorrhagic shock led to the development of volume replacement therapy which saved numerous lives during World War II. His outstanding contributions to the fields of circulatory physiology and surgery at The Johns Hopkins University Hospital led to his election to the National Academy of

Sciences in 1945, president of the American College of Surgeons in 1954, the Passano Award received jointly with Helen Brooke Taussig in 1948, the American Medical Association Distinguished Service Award in 1953, and the Albert Lasker Medical Research Award in 1954.

While at Vanderbilt University, Blalock, his laboratory assistant Vivien Thomas, and Sanford Edgar Levy (later changed to Leeds) conducted experiments on dogs to determine the effects of high blood pressure on the lungs. In order to increase pressure in the lungs experimentally, they linked (anastomosed) the left subclavian artery, a major tributary of the aorta, to the left pulmonary artery. This was the first time that the course of the large artery was diverted to change its function. They found that the blood pressure in the lungs was not increased appreciably by this operation and that the diversion did no harm to the dogs. This operation would be the prototype of the one Blalock would perform five years later to correct "blue baby" disease.

Blalock continued vascular surgery experiments on dogs at Johns Hopkins, bypassing an artificial gap in the aorta by connection to the left subclavian artery. Although this operation, designed to treat coarctation (blockage or constriction) of the aorta, was successful, Blalock was hesitant to attempt it on humans, because clamping the vessels during the operation would cut off circulation to the brain and other organs of the body for too long. His fears were somewhat allayed when the Swedish surgeon Clarence Crafoord reported in 1942 that clamping the aorta for twenty-eight minutes during a patent ductus operation resulted in no ill effects. Unfortunately, the application of his work to this problem was conceived by another physician.

During a pediatric conference at Johns Hopkins, Taussig, head of the Children's Heart Clinic, reviewed Blalock's report on blood vessel bypasses for correction of coarctation and inquired if a surgical procedure could be developed to improve pulmonary circulation in children with congenital heart defects. She had spent several years studying cardiac defects in children and was a pioneer in the use of X-ray techniques to diagnose and describe these defects. She developed the theory that narrowing of the pulmonary valve and artery in children suffering from tetralogy of Fallot resulted in poor pulmonary circulation and consequent oxygen deprivation. When Blalock agreed to consider the problem, Taussig began working with him to devise a method for joining the left subclavian artery to the pulmonary artery in children to increase the flow of blood to the lungs. With the help of Thomas, they conducted numerous experiments on dogs to prove Taussig's theory and to perfect the corrective procedure.

On November 29, 1944, Blalock performed the first "blue baby" operation on a fifteen-month-old girl suffering from tetralogy of Fallot. He was assisted by William P. Longmire, resident surgeon, Merel Harmel, anesthesiologist, Taussig, and Thomas. During the three hour operation, he clamped the left subclavian artery, cut through it several centimeters away from where it emerged from the aorta, and tied off the useless upper end. He then pulled the lower end down toward the left pulmonary artery which had also been clamped. He attached the free end of the subclavian to an opening he had made in the wall of the pulmonary artery and stitched it into place. Upon releasing the clamps, blood flowed out of the aorta through the left subclavian and into the left pulmonary artery. The net result was increased blood-flow to the lungs. The child's condition improved greatly after she surmounted a few postoperative complications. (Unfortunately, she died nine months later.) Within nine weeks, Blalock and Taussig performed two more operations and reported their results in the May 19, 1945, issue of the *Journal of the American Medical Association*.

By December, 1945, Blalock had performed sixty-five such operations with an 80 percent success rate. During this time, he was acclaimed as a hero in the press with many reports about how he had saved these doomed children brought to him from all over the country by hopeful parents. Physicians, too, came from all around the world to learn how to perform the new surgery. In the years following, Blalock traveled to London, Paris, and Stockholm to teach others how to perform the operation.

Impact of Event

The Blalock-Taussig Shunt, as the operation is now called, has saved thousands of lives and allowed numerous children to lead normal lives. That the operation is still in use today is testimony to its impact on medical science. Marc R. de Lavel states in the book *Surgery for Congenital Heart Defects* (1983) that "the Blalock-Taussig operation continues to be the shunt of choice." Although open heart procedures are now commonly used to correct tetralogy of Fallot and other heart deformities, the Blalock-Taussig Shunt continues to be used as a palliative measure in small children as an initial step in a series of corrective operations.

The only operation performed to correct a congenital cardiovascular disorder prior to the Blalock-Taussig Shunt was closure of a persistent (patent) ductus arteriosus by Robert Gross of Boston in 1939. The ductus arteriosus, a short vessel between the aorta and the pulmonary artery in the fetus, normally closes soon after birth. If it fails to close, the result is an overworked heart ultimately leading to cardiac failure and early death. The success of Blalock's operation led others to attempt similar operations. In 1946, shortly after visiting Alfred Blalock, Willis Potts of Chicago connected the descending aorta directly to the left pulmonary artery in order to increase the blood flow to the lungs of the "blue baby." A similar operation connecting the ascending aorta to the right pulmonary aorta was performed by the British surgeon David Waterston in 1962. Both of these operations were designed for use on very young children where the subclavian artery is too small to use as a shunt. Nevertheless, these two operations are not used frequently today, because there is a risk of creating too big a shunt and thus overtaxing the heart; they are also too difficult to close later when the child receives intracardiac repair. The modified Blalock-Taussig Shunt, which uses man-made material for the shunt, was first performed by Frank Redo and Roger Ecker in 1963.

The Blalock-Taussig Shunt is still widely used today, because it can be performed on very young children, too small for open-heart surgery. It provides a bridge of life for these patients until they are old enough to receive intracardiac repair. Until 1952, repair of internal heart defects had to be done blindly because there was no way to stop the heart and oxygenate the blood during the operation. Among the methods used to try to overcome this problem was body cooling (hypothermia). Robert Lewis, at the University of Minnesota in 1952, used hypothermia to reduce damage to the body tissues while he stopped circulation through the heart for a few minutes to correct an atrial septal defect. In 1934, John Gibbon, while at Harvard, developed an apparatus for extracorporeal oxygenation of blood (heart-lung machine) and perfected it over a period of years so that in 1953 he was able to use it while successfully performing open-heart surgery on an eighteen-year-old girl to repair an atrial septal defect. The first open-heart surgery to correct tetralogy of Fallot was performed by H. William Scott of Vanderbilt University in March, 1954, utilizing hypothermia. Shortly after this, Walton Lillehei, at the University of Minnesota, performed the same operation but kept the patient alive during the operation by connecting the circulatory system to another person (cross circulation).

These events ushered in the modern era of open-heart surgery and the possibility of correcting most congenital heart defects. Blalock and Taussig played a pivotal role in this attack on congenital heart disease because they had the vision and courage to attempt a radical treatment for a disease affecting young children. Blalock's brilliant yet practical experiments and Taussig's keen insight and devoted concern for ailing children led to a fortuitous relationship that ultimately triumphed over a pitiful disease that had long plagued humankind.

Bibliography

Baldry, Peter E. *The Battle Against Heart Disease.* New York: Cambridge University Press, 1971. A history of heart medicine designed for the general reader. Chapter 17, "Congenital Heart Disease," verbally and diagrammatically describes the various types of congenital heart defects and gives an excellent historical account of how each was discovered. Chapter 18, "The Triumphs of Surgery," describes the evolution of surgical treatment of heart disease. This chapter does an excellent job of relating the events leading up to and following the work of Blalock and Taussig.

Blalock, Alfred. *The Papers of Alfred Blalock.* Edited by Mark M. Ravitch. 2 vols. Baltimore: Johns Hopkins University Press, 1966. A comprehensive compilation of Blalock's published works divided into three phases: The Early Johns Hopkins Years, The Vanderbilt Years, and The Later Johns Hopkins Years. Ravitch's biography of Blalock is complete and includes many photographs and personal anecdotes. The volumes also include an extensive curriculum vitae and bibliography (Appendix A) and biographical vignettes of those who coauthored papers with Blalock (Appendix B).

Blalock, Alfred, and Helen B. Taussig. "The Surgical Treatment of Malformations of the Heart in Which There Is Pulmonary Stenosis or Pulmonary Atresia." *Jour-*

nal of the American Medical Association 128 (May, 1945): 189-202. The original article where Blalock and Taussig give the details of their operation and describe three case histories. The article is technical in nature but is filled with interesting details about the operations and attendant complications and outcomes. Illustrated with a bibliography of related medical reports.

'Meade, Richard H. *An Introduction to the History of General Surgery.* Philadelphia: W. B. Saunders, 1968. An easy-to-read college text that provides an organized and comprehensive history of all types of surgery. Chapter 14, "Thoracic Surgery," discusses the history of heart surgery up to and including Blalock's operation but lacks information on events that follow. Illustrated with a bibliography.

Richardson, Robert G. *Surgery: Old and New Frontiers.* New York: Charles Scribner's Sons, 1968. A popular history of surgery originally published as *The Surgeon's Tale* in 1958. Chapter 16 "Heart Surgery" gives a complete verbal description of cardiovascular surgery from the early nineteenth century up to the first heart transplant by Christiaan Barnard in 1967.

Rodney C. Mowbray

Cross-References

Carrel Develops a Technique for Rejoining Severed Blood Vessels (1902), p. 134; Bevis Describes Amniocentesis as a Method for Disclosing Fetal Genetic Traits (1952), p. 1439; Donald Is the First to Use Ultrasound to Examine Unborn Children (1958), p. 1562; Favaloro Develops the Coronary Artery Bypass Operation (1967), p. 1835; Barnard Performs the First Human Heart Transplant (1967), p. 1866; Gruentzig Uses Percutaneous Transluminal Angioplasty, via a Balloon Catheter, to Unclog Diseased Arteries (1977), p. 2088; Brown Gives Birth to the First "Test-Tube" Baby (1978), p. 2099; Clewell Corrects Hydrocephalus by Surgery on a Fetus (1981), p. 2174; DeVries Implants the First Jarvik-7 Artificial Heart (1982), p. 2195; Daffos Uses Blood Taken Through the Umbilical Cord to Diagnose Fetal Disease (1982), p. 2205.

DUGGAR DISCOVERS AUREOMYCIN, THE FIRST OF THE TETRACYCLINES

Category of event: Medicine
Time: 1945
Locale: Lederle Laboratories, Pearl River, New York

Duggar directed the research that led to the discovery, production, and application of Aureomycin (chlortetracycline), the first broad-spectrum antibiotic that was both safe and effective

> *Principal personages:*
> BENJAMIN MINGE DUGGAR (1872-1956), an American botanist, professor, and consultant in mycology (study of fungi) at Lederle Laboratories
> YELLAPRAGADA SUBBAROW (1896-1948), an Indian-American biochemist who was the director of research at Lederle
> ALBERT CARL DORNBUSH (1914-), an American microbiologist who headed Lederle's microbiological assay laboratory in the 1940's

Summary of Event

On July 21, 1948, at a conference arranged by the prestigious New York Academy of Sciences in the Museum of Natural History, the new antibiotic Aureomycin was introduced to the public. It was uncommon for a medical breakthrough to be trumpeted to the world as this drug was. About twenty clinicians were present to broadcast the spectacular results they had achieved with it. Also on hand were several scientists from Lederle Laboratories, where Aureomycin was first isolated by Benjamin Minge Duggar.

Before the auspicious debut of Aureomycin, several antibiotics had become available already to health professionals. By far the most efficacious of the new "miracle drugs" was penicillin, successful against 40 percent of bacteria-caused diseases, and streptomycin, effective against 30 percent. These therapeutic agents had given physicians the weapons they needed to conquer the terminal and disabling inflections.

Nevertheless, many dangerous infections refused to surrender to either agent, and these now stood out. Several were caused by viruses and by small viruslike bacteria, known as atypical bacteria. Among the latter were the rickettsias, chlamydias, and mycoplasmas. Some typical bacteria, including the brucellas, also defied the new drugs. Furthermore, the antibiotics available in the late 1940's were deficient in another area: Resistant strains of pathogenic microbes were growing ever more numerous. Thus, the fact that many infections were not well controlled, or even affected, provided a strong incentive to search for more germ fighters.

The discovery of penicillin, a mold-derived drug, had sent scientists back to the soil in a quest for natural substances with antibiotic properties; during World War II, this pursuit was taken over by the resource-rich, profit-seeking pharmaceutical industry. By 1945, at least six drug companies had teams of investigators seeking antibiotics. One of them was Lederle Laboratories, a division of American Cyanamid Company. Lederle had specialized in remedies for infectious diseases. The company's search for new mold-derived drugs began in 1939. Their success in developing a new multi-purpose antibiotic owed much to the biochemist Yellapragada SubbaRow, who joined Lederle in 1940. As director of research, he supervised Lederle's chemical, medicinal, and pharmaceutical research. During World War II, SubbaRow contributed to the research on penicillin and streptomycin in large quantities. He was also responsible for bringing Duggar to Lederle. Mindful of Duggar's extensive knowledge of molds, SubbaRow invited the former professor of several of Lederle's scientists to take a position with the company as a consultant in mycological research and production.

Although Duggar's name did not become familiar outside his field until 1948, his work had been known to botanists for a long time. For several decades, he had been recognized internationally as an authority on molds and fungi. Nevertheless, upon reaching the age of seventy, he was forced to retire from teaching. Still quite active physically and mentally, Duggar was not content to live in retirement, especially in the midst of a devastating world war. Hence, in 1944, he accepted SubbaRow's offer to join Lederle.

At first, Duggar's work at Lederle was concerned with plant sources of antimalarial drugs. He was impressed deeply by the success of penicillin, which had just come into widespread use. He perceived that the surface had only been scratched in the field of antibiotics. He soon initiated an immense soil-screening program. His objective was to discover a superior antibiotic—one that would combat diseases that completely resisted penicillin and other available antibiotics.

Duggar and his coworkers believed that one of the lesser groups of molds, known as actinomycetes, might yield a valuable antibiotic. Actinomycetes occupy an intermediate position between genuine bacteria and fungi. An expert on actinomycetes, Duggar remarked that his fellow mycologists had hitherto treated the microorganisms "with static contempt."

Because molds are denizens of the soil, Lederle scientists began their project by gathering from all over the country more than six hundred soil samples, which they screened for actinomycete strains that might have microbe-killing potential. The molds were tested by putting them in petri dishes, along with specific microorganisms, and then observing their ability to inhibit the growth of neighboring organisms. The screening was a long, tedious task. Duggar and his team suffered disappointment after disappointment. More than thirty-five hundred strains were scrutinized and rejected. Eventually, the investigators came to a petri dish labeled "A 377," which contained a golden-colored mold obtained from a soil sample taken from the campus of the University of Missouri. It was one of several samples sent to Duggar in the summer of 1945 by his former colleague, William Albert Albrecht, chairperson of Missouri's Department of Soils. Duggar was pleased to observe that A-377 exhibited antibiotic potential.

According to procedure, the promised mold was subjected next to a battery of tests to assess the extent of its antimicrobial activity and its degree of toxicity. The safety of the substance was a prime consideration; any antibiotic that was injurious to the patient would have no therapeutic value.

Test-tube experiments were conducted in September, 1945, to gauge the mold's effectiveness against some fifty pathogenic organisms. Albert Carl Dornbush, from the University of Wisconsin, was in charge of the important in vitro work. The results were astounding. The mold arrested the growth of staphylococci, streptococci, and bacilli. The fact that the mold, later named *Streptomyces aureofaciens* by Duggar, resisted bacilli signified that it was producing an antibiotic that might have a wider scope of activity than either penicillin or streptomycin. The antibiotic substance extracted from *Streptomyces aureofaciens* was christened Aureomycin, a name derived from the Latin word *aureus* (gold) and the Greek *mykes* (fungus). Both the mold and the antibiotic had a golden hue. Aureomycin was later given the generic name of chlortetracycline.

Two more years of experiments by Lederle scientists demonstrated that Aureomycin was not toxic to laboratory animals and that it had an effective range of action much greater than anyone had expected. In 1947, the new drug was isolated in a relatively pure and inexpensive form; that same year, it was used for the first time on human patients. Clinicians at several university-affiliated hospitals reported success in controlling numerous infections that had responded poorly or not at all to previously available antimicrobial agents. Furthermore, they observed that Aureomycin produced only a small number of side effects. By mid-1948, the drug was being manufactured at the rate of a pound a day. It was first offered to physicians on a wide basis on December 1, 1948. Aureomycin soon took its place among the most useful of all life-saving drugs.

Impact of Event

Antibiotics revolutionized the therapy of infectious diseases in the 1940's, and Aureomycin brought extraordinary assets to the new age of medicine. One was its versatility. Possessing a much broader application than penicillin or streptomycin, it was effective against 90 percent of bacteria-caused infections. Also, unlike the two premier antibiotics, which were usually administered by needle, Aureomycin was effective when taken by mouth. Consequently, it could be dispensed quickly and painlessly either in the physician's office or in the patient's home.

Most important, Aureomycin proved to be remarkably effective against certain infections that had failed to respond to either penicillin or streptomycin. One of these illnesses was Rocky Mountain spotted fever, endemic throughout the continental United States and recognized as one of the most severe of all infectious diseases. The tick-transmitted malady killed one out of every five victims. The number of fatalities declined sharply, however, after Aureomycin became available. In its first clinical trials, the drug dramatically restored to health a boy who was in a coma from tick fever. Numerous other diseases caused by atypical bacteria—including typhus, lymphogranuloma venereum (a disabling venereal disease), trachoma, parrot fever, and mycoplasmal pneumonia—yielded to the new microbe fighter. Aureomycin rapidly became—and remained so for several decades—the drug of choice in treating rickettsial, chlamydial, and mycoplasmal infections.

The golden antibiotic, moreover, became the preferred antimicrobial agent in combatting several diseases caused by typical bacteria. For example, it was used extensively in infections of the urinary tract because it often was effective against a broader spectrum of pathogens than streptomycin, and resistant microorganisms did not develop so quickly.

Duggar had predicted that Aureomycin would be a boon to farmers and poultry raisers. Indeed, the antibiotic has been used widely as a feed supplement to stimulate the growth of livestock. Some authorities, however, question the practice because it breeds resistant bacteria that could pose a public health problem eventually. Furthermore, prolonged low exposure to an antibiotic can sensitize individuals, making them unable to take the drug later to treat infection.

Aureomycin enjoys the distinction of being the first of the tetracyclines, a family of antibiotics that includes terramycin, achromycin, and declomycin. Tetracyclines are basically bacteriostatic, and they oppose most of the same microorganisms. They differ mainly in how readily they are absorbed by the body and in how long their effects persist. Many medical experts affirm that next to the penicillin family, the tetracycline group probably represents the most beneficial and least hazardous of the wonder drugs. The tetracyclines are relative safe antibiotics. Nevertheless, they are capable of causing a variety of reactions, chiefly nausea, vomiting, and diarrhea. In addition, tetracyclines can discolor permanently developing teeth. For this reason, they are contraindicated in the treatment of children and pregnant women.

Since 1948, Aureomycin and other tetracyclines have been widely—and often inappropriately—used to treat a wide range of diseases. This unrestricted application caused many pathogenic microorganisms, particularly streptococcus strains, to become resistant. As a result, tetracyclines are no longer the antibiotics of choice for treating most common respiratory or urinary tract infections.

Bibliography

Cowen, David L., and Alvin B. Segelman, eds. *Antibiotics in Historical Perspective.* Rahway, N.J.: Merck, 1981. A lavishly illustrated volume that traces the history of substances with antimicrobial activity from ancient Sumer and Egypt to the 1970's. Streptomycin—which the Merck Pharmaceutical Company helped to develop—and penicillin receive prime attention. One chapter is devoted to Aureomycin and the other tetracyclines. Contains chapter bibliographies, however, no index.

Dowling, Harry F. *Fighting Infection: Conquests of the Twentieth Century.* Cambridge, Mass.: Harvard University Press, 1977. Written by a former medical practitioner who participated in the early clinical trials of Aureomycin. A well-organized, fully documented, indexed history of infectious diseases and their treatment, beginning with early immunization efforts and culminating in the discovery and widespread application of sophisticated germ fighters. An excellent study; should be readily comprehensible to well-informed readers.

Lappé, Marc. *Germs That Won't Die.* Garden City, N.Y.: Anchor Press, 1982. Written by a pathologist and public health official. Presents a history of the evolution of antibiotics and laments the problems caused by their widespread application. Lappé argues that the excessive and indiscriminate prescription of these drugs by physicians and their use in animal feeds have contributed to the emergence of resistant bacteria. Glossary, chapter bibliographies, and index.

Mahoney, Tom. *The Merchants of Life.* New York: Harper & Brothers, 1959. A highly laudatory descriptive account of the American pharmaceutical industry. Tells the story of eighteen leading companies, including Lederle. Presents an abundance of factual information, especially about their founders and their notable drugs. Index, no bibliography.

Reinfeld, Fred. *Miracle Drugs and the New Age of Medicine.* Rev. ed. New York: Sterling, 1962. Brief and interesting pictorial panorama of modern medical discoveries, beginning with Louis Pasteur's germ theory of disease in the nineteenth century to the antibiotics, vaccines, and synthetic drugs of the mid-twentieth century. Appropriate for young readers. Profusely illustrated, index, no bibliography.

Walker, J. C. "Benjamin Minge Duggar." In *Biographical Memoirs.* Vol. 32. New York: Columbia University Press, 1958. Until a full-length biography of Duggar becomes available, readers will have to resort to vignettes, and this is one of the best. Includes a list of articles and books written or coauthored by Duggar.

Williams, J. H., ed. *Aureomycin—A New Antibiotic.* New York: New York Academy of Sciences, 1948. A collection of sixteen reports written by Lederle scientists and other researchers who participated in the development and/or testing of Aureomycin. Duggar's introductory report is disappointing in that it provides no information about when and how the antibiotic was discovered. The highly technical nature of the other reports will probably limit their appeal to specialists.

Ronald W. Long

Cross-References

Ehrlich Introduces Salvarsan as a Cure for Syphilis (1910), p. 476; Fleming Discovers Penicillin in Molds (1928), p. 873; Domagk Discovers That a Sulfonamide Can Save Lives (1932), p. 968; Florey and Chain Develop Penicillin as an Antibiotic (1940), p. 1171; Waksman Discovers the Antibiotic Streptomycin (1943), p. 1224.

ARTIFICIAL FLUORIDATION OF MUNICIPAL WATER SUPPLIES TO PREVENT DENTAL DECAY IS INTRODUCED

Category of event: Medicine
Time: January, 1945
Locale: Throughout the United States (and other parts of the world)

Artificial fluoridation of municipal water supplies to prevent dental decay began in 1945 and continues amid controversy to the present

Principal personages:

GREENE VARDIMAN BLACK (1836-1915), the prominent dental professional who raised the study of dental fluorosis from the level of curiosity to serious research subject

FRANCIS A. BULL, the head of the Dental Health Education Division of the Wisconsin State Board of Health who was Frisch's closest ally in promoting widespread fluoridation

H. CHURCHILL, the chief chemist who first realized that fluorine in water was the cause of dental fluorosis

H. TRENDLEY DEAN (1893-?), the United States Public Health Service employee who promoted research into dental fluorosis and tooth decay reduction

JOHN G. FRISCH (1899-?), a dentist who promoted artificial fluoridation

FREDERICK S. MCKAY (1874-?), the dentist who first began investigating mottling of teeth in Colorado Springs, Colorado

Summary of Event

Since 1945, the fluoridation of water supplies has shown how politically and socially controversial "science" can be. Proponents of fluoridation have insisted that it inhibits tooth decay with little or no health risk. They have done so in the face of opposition that has charged them with forwarding Communist designs, with removing people's freedom of choice, and with destroying the environment and endangering people's health.

Fluoridation began with the recognition as early as 1771 of mottled teeth (dental fluorosis) in human beings and the search for the cause and consequences of that condition. In 1901, Frederick S. McKay, a graduate of the University of Pennsylvania Dental School, having noticed the condition in Colorado Springs, began a lifelong quest for the reasons for fluoridation. He enlisted the aid of prominent researchers such as Greene Vardiman Black of Northwestern University Dental School and of practitioners who sent information to him that showed dental fluorosis to be a widespread problem. By 1916, McKay began to believe that something in the water of the areas where the mottling occurred was the cause. By 1928, he was convinced that mottling and absence of tooth decay were related.

McKay and other investigators finally recognized fluorine as the culprit when studying the teeth of Bauxite, Arkansas, residents who grew up after the water supply source changed in 1909. The Aluminum Company of America (ALCOA) became alarmed at possible implications after a heavy incidence of mottling was revealed in Bauxite residents. In 1931, ALCOA's chief chemist H. Churchill wrote McKay that more precise testing showed a high amount of fluorine in the water and this could be the problem substance. McKay verified this in samples sent from Colorado Springs and sites in South Dakota and Idaho. Simultaneously, a University of Arizona team of Margaret Carmack Smith and Howard Vernon Smith independently reached the same conclusion that high fluorine content in water caused the mottling.

It was left up to H. Trendley Dean of the United States Public Health Service to demonstrate a clear connection between naturally fluoridated water and the absence of tooth decay. He called for a full study of the effects of adding fluorides to water supplies, and in the early 1940's led the team that discovered that 1 part per million fluorine in water was the optimal rate at which decay was inhibited without causing mottling.

After toxicity studies indicated that levels of fluorine at 1 to 1.5 parts per million did not harm general health, field tests were instituted in Grand Rapids and Muskegon, Michigan, with sodium fluoride being added to the Grand Rapids water supply and Muskegon serving as the control. Two months later, New York public health officials designated Newburgh and Kingston as test and control cities, respectively. Both studies were scheduled to last ten years.

Conservative scientific attitudes, however, vanished in the face of a determined group of Wisconsin dentists who as early as 1941 decided that adding fluoride to water represented a great public health boon. They formed the Fluorine Study Committee, enlisted several prominent backers, and worked to promote artificial fluoridation. On March 19, 1945, two months after the Michigan study but long before the study period had elapsed, the house of delegates of the Wisconsin dental society voted unanimously that all Wisconsin water supplies be raised to the level of 1 part per million of fluorine. By April, 1945, the State Board of Health, and particularly Francis A. Bull, decided to allow experiments in Wisconsin, despite expressing caution.

Fluoridation became John G. Frisch's obsession, and he spent every spare minute promoting immediate fluoridation in conjunction with Bull and the Fluorine Study Committee. Advocates did not wait in Wisconsin for the study results before getting Madison and other communities to fluoridate their water. By January 1, 1950, they, mostly through Frisch's efforts, had convinced fifty Wisconsin communities to approve fluoridation. From 1945 to 1950, the United States Public Health Service pursued a conservative policy, choosing to await study results before encouraging artificial fluoridation treatments. Instead, the Public Health Service strongly promoted topical applications of fluorine. Bitter fighting broke out between the Wisconsin group and the United States Public Health Service on one side, with Dean and the American Dental Association on the other side. In June, 1950, however, the

Public Health Service reversed its position, bowing to rising pressures, not only from Wisconsin but also from Texas, Colorado, and New York; they strongly recommended that communities fluoridate. The American Dental Association followed in November, 1950. In December, 1951, the American Medical Association endorsed fluoridation. Moving the issue from the scientific field to the political had succeeded in circumventing the purposes of the field studies.

Once the important health organizations accepted the value of fluoridation, the process became an accepted health procedure and has remained such since 1951. Much of the initial opposition to fluoridation stemmed from its establishment position. Legitimate scientific skepticism or opposition tended to be overlooked in the heated political climate of the 1950's, and to a lesser degree, the 1960's and 1970's. Even the statistics on how many cities have accepted fluoridation are controversial. Eight states have made fluoridation mandatory, and in the other states, perhaps 40 percent of the water districts have fluoridated. A special tactic of anti-fluoridation groups has been to push for referenda to be held; and emotions often have proven more potent than science. From 1950 to 1969, 1,139 referenda were held with 473 for and 666 against fluoridation. In forty years, about 60 percent of two thousand referenda on fluoridation have failed. Since 1983, referenda in sixty-eight communities have seen forty-two voting no. In 1990, of the thirty largest cities in the United States, two have naturally fluoridated water sources, three have no fluoridation, and the remainder drink artificially fluoridated water.

The process of convincing people to fluoridate water has slowed significantly since 1970, both in the United States and in the rest of the world. About 250 million people drink artificially fluoridated water, 120 million in the United States, 50 million in Brazil (one-third of the population), 40 million in the Soviet Union (15 percent of the population), 9 percent of England, 67 percent of Australia and New Zealand, and 50 percent of Canada. Fewer than 1 percent of Continental Europeans drink fluoridated water, and the objections from Europeans have become greater in recent years. Fluoridation remains controversial, but relatively little attention is paid to the issue.

Impact of Event

Almost everything connected with fluoridation remains controversial. The average number of decayed, missing, and filled permanent teeth in American school-age children has declined from seven in 1945 to three, but foes of fluoridation cite nutrition, topical fluoridation, oral hygiene, improved dental care, and, possibly, changes in immune status as reasons rather than fluoridation of water supplies. Proponents have backed off initial claims that fluoridation produces 50 percent to 60 percent decay reductions, and now claim only 18 percent to 25 percent reductions. Even that figure is challenged by researchers who insist that no significant difference exists in tooth decay between those who drink fluoridated as opposed to nonfluoridated water. A consensus now exists that the promise of "two-thirds less tooth decay" is not the case.

Another early argument of advocates—that economic benefits to the community make fluoridation advantageous—seems to lack validity. The National Institute of Dental Research states that each dollar spent on fluoridation (and the costs are only twenty cents to fifty cents per person per year) reduces dental costs by fifty dollars. When actual costs of dental care in similar cities are compared, no benefits are apparent for drinkers of fluoridated water.

From the beginning of artificial fluoridation, some scientists have been concerned about possible health risks. Their concerns were often lost in the controversies in earlier years. In 1977, however, the National Academy of Sciences report "Drinking Water and Health" recommended research in eleven different areas where numerous concerns remained. Dental fluorosis, cancer, birth defects, skeletal fluorosis (caused by the accumulation of fluoride in bones), kidney disease, enzyme effects, genetic mutations, and hypersensitivity reactions, were described as needing additional research. Claims that fluoridation causes serious illness are not provable, but neither are claims that fluoridation reduces the incidence and severity of osteoporosis (decreased bone density in old age).

Environmentalists have begun to include fluoride in their lists of environmental pollutants. In 1986, the National Resources Defense Council sued the Environmental Protection Agency in order to block the agency's 4 parts per million maximum contaminant level for fluoride in drinking water as being unsupported scientifically. Although the levels were upheld in February, 1987, environmentalists are continuing to push for epidemiological studies.

Observers of the fluoridation controversy have reported that establishment journals in the United States have continued the fluoridation promotion by suppressing adverse scientific information about fluoridation. Edward Groth III, in writing his Ph.D. dissertation, concluded that the greatest number of reviews of the literature were designed to promote fluoridation rather than to examine evidence. That condition has not changed since 1973. The issue of fluoridation remains trapped in emotionalism, propaganda, misinformation, and unanswered questions. It demonstrates that scientific "truth" in the twentieth century is defined as much by who validates it as by any objective standard.

Bibliography

Crain, Robert L., Elihu Katz, and Donald B. Rosenthal. *The Politics of Community Conflict: The Fluoridation Decision*. Indianapolis: Bobbs-Merrill, 1969. An excellent example of how pro-fluoridationists managed the fluoridation issue in communities. Better organized and more skillful than anti-fluoridationists, pro-fluoridationists made their case on the basis of political values, not science, and by managing conflict, not by confronting it.

Dublin, Louis I. *Water Fluoridation: Facts, Not Myths*. New York: Public Affairs Committee, 1957. An example of the promotional/propagandizing literature that pro-fluoridationists wrote during the early days of the campaign. Many of the "facts" are no longer accepted as facts.

Gatzsche, Anne-Lise. *The Fluoride Question*. New York: Stein & Day, 1975. A subtle but unmistakable attack on fluoridation. Gatzsche describes the groups aligned on both sides of the question, paying careful attention to the scientific arguments but in each case weighing her argument in favor of discontinuing active efforts to fluoridate water supplies.

McNeil, Donald R. *The Fight for Fluoridation*. New York: Oxford University Press, 1957. Written early in the struggle over fluoridation; celebrates what looked to be an inevitable total victory for proponents of fluoridation. Portrays foes of fluoridation as ignorant or malicious. Historical chronicling is well done.

Waldbott, George L., Albert W. Burghstahler, and H. Lewis McKinney. *Fluoridation: The Great Dilemma*. Lawrence, Kans.: Coronado Press, 1978. A work that typifies much of the literature written in this controversy; filled with statistics, scientific language, reports of research, and scientific arguments that all seem convincing to general readers.

Wright, Charles. *Water Fluoridation*. Frankfort: Kentucky Legislative Research Commission, 1970. Typifies the type of approach used by pro-fluoridationists in campaigns to convince a state legislature to fluoridate all drinking water in the state. Describes how "backward" outsiders will consider Kentucky if fluoridation is rejected; "guarantees" no ill effects from introducing a beneficial substance into the water.

William F. Steirer, Jr.

Cross-References

Rous Discovers That Some Cancers Are Caused by Viruses (1910), p. 459; McCollum Names Vitamin D and Pioneers Its Use Against Rickets (1922), p. 725; Steenbock Discovers That Sunlight Increases Vitamin D in Food (1924), p. 771; The Artificial Sweetener Cyclamate Is Introduced (1950), p. 1368; Horsfall Announces That Cancer Results from Alterations in the DNA of Cells (1961), p. 1682; Daffos Uses Blood Taken Through the Umbilical Cord to Diagnose Fetal Disease (1982), p. 2205; The Artificial Sweetener Aspartame Is Approved for Use in Carbonated Beverages (1983), p. 2226.

THE FIRST ATOMIC BOMB
IS SUCCESSFULLY DETONATED

Categories of event: Physics and applied science
Time: July 16, 1945
Locale: Alamogordo, New Mexico

Oppenheimer directed the development and design of the atomic bomb in the Manhattan Project of World War II, culminating in the first successful nuclear explosion at Alamogordo, New Mexico

Principal personages:

J. ROBERT OPPENHEIMER (1904-1967), an American physicist who directed the Los Alamos Laboratory in New Mexico where the atomic bomb was developed during World War II

LESLIE RICHARD GROVES (1896-1970), an American engineer and army general in charge of the Manhattan District of the Corps of Engineers responsible for the atomic bomb project

ENRICO FERMI (1900-1954), an Italian-American nuclear physicist who won the 1938 Nobel Prize in Physics for his neutron work and later developed the first nuclear reactor

OTTO ROBERT FRISCH (1904-1979), an Austrian-English physicist who first calculated fission energies and requirements for a bomb

NIELS BOHR (1885-1962), a Danish physicist who won the 1922 Nobel Prize in Physics for his theory of atomic structure

Summary of Event

The successful detonation of the first atomic bomb was the dramatic conclusion of nearly fifty years of scientific research and a four-year crash program of wartime development. The discovery of radioactivity by Antoine-Henri Becquerel in 1896 revealed the enormous energy locked inside the atom. Albert Einstein's 1905 theory of relativity showed that this energy could be accounted for by a tiny loss of mass in a radioactive material. Yet, a practical method of releasing large quantities of atomic energy was not possible until after the discovery of the neutron in 1932 by James Chadwick. This led Enrico Fermi in 1934 to bombard various elements with neutrons, whose lack of electric charge allowed them to penetrate the positive nucleus and transmute them to heavier radioactive atoms. Fermi showed that neutrons slowed by water were especially effective and thought he had produced transuranic elements by bombarding uranium. He failed to recognize that he had probably split the uranium nucleus into lighter nuclei.

The first evidence of uranium fission was observed by Otto Hahn and Fritz Strassmann in Berlin at the end of 1938. When they discovered radioactive barium impurities in neutron-irradiated uranium, they wrote to their colleague Lise Meitner, a refugee in Sweden from German anti-Semitic laws. She and her nephew Otto Robert Frisch saw the possibility of fission and calculated the large release of energy in the repulsion of the nuclear fragments such as barium, which matched the resulting loss of mass. This result was reported to Niels Bohr in Copenhagen and was published in the English journal *Nature* in February, 1939.

The energy of fission fragments was soon measured by Frisch in Copenhagen, and Frédéric Joliot and his associates in Paris, who demonstrated the release of up to three additional neutrons. Soon, several researchers in American laboratories confirmed the energy and neutron yields. It was recognized immediately that if neutron-induced fission released enough additional neutrons to cause at least one more such fission, a self-sustaining chain reaction would result, yielding energy on a large scale. Leo Szilard had obtained a patent in 1934 for a similar chain reaction with neutron bombardment of beryllium, but such a process did not work because it required too much energy.

While visiting the United States from January to May of 1939, Bohr derived a theory of fission with John Wheeler of Princeton University. This theory led Bohr to predict that the common isotope uranium 238 (99.3 percent in nature) would require fast neutrons for fission, but the rarer uranium 235 would fission with neutrons of any energy. This suggested the idea of studying fission in a systematic way with a controlled chain reaction using slow neutrons.

By July of 1939, the need for government support and secrecy led Szilard and Eugene Paul Wigner to approach Einstein about writing a letter to President Franklin D. Roosevelt. The President responded by forming an Advisory Committee on Uranium, which provided six thousand dollars to Columbia University for the purchase of 50 tons of uranium oxide and 4 tons of graphite to study its ability to slow neutrons.

Meanwhile, in England, Frisch and Rudolf Peierls worked out the requirements for an atomic bomb in a paper sent to the English government in the spring of 1940. They estimated that less than 1 kilogram is required for a critical mass of pure uranium 235, in which more neutrons would cause fission than those that escaped or were absorbed. If two or more subcritical masses could be brought together rapidly enough, they would produce an explosion equivalent to several thousand tons of dynamite. They also outlined the extensive effort that would be needed to separate uranium 235 from natural uranium.

By December, 1941, when the United States entered World War II, contracts had been arranged with about twelve American universities for uranium research. Wartime research was supervised by Vannevar Bush, with James Bryant Conant as his representative for uranium research. Three major projects included the study of uranium separation methods under Harold Urey at Columbia, cyclotron studies by Ernest Orlando Lawrence at the University of California, and chain-reaction studies under Arthur Holly Compton at the University of Chicago. Uranium bombardment in the Berkeley cyclotron led to the discovery of plutonium in 1940 and the fact that plutonium 239 was fissionable. Since uranium 238 was found to absorb neutrons without fission at some high energies, it could not be used for a bomb but offered the possibility of breeding plutonium, which could then be separated from uranium by chemical methods.

In 1941 at Columbia University, Fermi began research on fission rates in a subcritical lattice of uranium oxide and graphite and showed that a chain reaction would be sustained if impurities are reduced to less than 1 percent. His group moved to Chicago in 1942, where they constructed a reactor with 40 tons of natural uranium and 385 tons of graphite, large enough for a sustained chain reaction. When neutron-absorbing cadmium control rods were partially removed on December 2, 1942, a sharp increase in neutrons indicated success. Much larger reactors would be needed to breed sufficient plutonium for a bomb.

During 1942, the Manhattan District of the Corps of Engineers was formed under General Leslie Richard Groves, who contracted with the duPont Company to construct three secret atomic cities at a total cost of $2 billion. At Oak Ridge, Tennessee, twenty-five thousand workers built a 1,000-kilowatt reactor as a pilot plant and spent two years building a 5,000-stage gaseous diffusion plant for uranium-235 separation. Huge electromagnets were built also for further uranium enrichment at a cost of $500 million. A second city of sixty thousand inhabitants was built at Hanford, Washington, where three huge reactors and remotely controlled plutonium-extraction plants were completed in early 1945.

Study of fast-neutron reactions for an atomic bomb were brought together in June of 1942 at Chicago under the leadership of J. Robert Oppenheimer. He soon became a personal adviser to Groves, who built Oppenheimer a laboratory for the design and construction of the bomb at Los Alamos, New Mexico. In 1943, Oppenheimer gathered two hundred of the best scientists of the Manhattan Project to live and work at this third secret city. Equipment was assembled, and research was begun on such problems as neutron absorption, uranium and plutonium fabrication and purification, and explosive methods for forming a critical mass.

Finally, two bomb designs were developed. A gun-type bomb called "Little Boy" used 15 kilograms of uranium 235 in a 4,500-kilogram cylinder about 2 meters long and 0.5 meter in diameter, in which a uranium bullet could be fired into three uranium target rings to form a critical mass. An implosion-type bomb called "Fat Man" had a 5-kilogram spherical core of plutonium about the size of an orange, which could be squeezed inside a 2,300-kilogram sphere about 1.5 meters in diameter by properly shaped explosives to make the mass critical in the shorter time required for the faster plutonium fission.

By early 1945, the first usable amounts of plutonium and uranium arrived from Hanford and Oak Ridge. Enough plutonium was available by the end of May to begin critical-mass studies by Frisch's group. A test date was set for July, when one uranium and two plutonium bombs would be finished. A flat scrub region 200 kilometers southeast of Alamogordo was chosen for the test site named Trinity, and observer bunkers were built about 10 kilometers from a 30-meter steel tower.

On Friday, July 13, one of the plutonium bombs was assembled at the site; the next morning, it was raised to the top of the tower. Two days later, on July 16, after a short thunderstorm delay, the bomb was detonated at 5:30 A.M. The resulting implosion initiated a chain reaction of nearly 60 fission generations in about a microsecond. It produced an intense flash of light, followed by a fireball expanding to a diameter of about 600 meters in two seconds, and then it rose to a height of more than 12 kilometers, forming its ominous mushroom shape. Forty seconds later, an air blast hit the observer bunkers, followed by a sustained and awesome roar. Measurements confirmed an explosive power of 18.6 kilotons of TNT (trinitrotoluene), nearly four times the predicted value.

Impact of Event

The successful development of the atomic bomb had an immediate impact in ending World War II and a longer-term influence on postwar weapons development and nuclear technologies. On March 9, 1945, 325 American B-29 bombers dropped 2,000 tons of incendiary bombs on Tokyo, resulting in 100,000 deaths from the fire storms that swept the city. Still, the Japanese military refused to surrender, and American military plans called for an invasion of Japan, with estimates of up to a half million American casualties, plus as many as 2 million Japanese casualties. On August 6, 1945, after authorization by President Harry S Truman, the B-29 named "Enola Gay" dropped the uranium Little-Boy bomb on Hiroshima at 8:15 A.M. On August 9, the remaining plutonium Fat-Man bomb was dropped on Nagasaki. Approximately 100,000 people died at Hiroshima (out of a population of 400,000) and about 50,000 more died at Nagasaki. Japan offered to surrender on August 10, and after a brief attempt by some Army officers to rebel, an official announcement by Emperor Hirohito was broadcast on August 15.

Early in the Manhattan Project, Edward Teller proposed the development of a thermonuclear fusion bomb, in which hydrogen isotopes would be fused together by the force of a fission explosion to produce helium nuclei and almost unlimited energy. Little effort was invested in the hydrogen bomb until after the surprise explosion of a Soviet atomic bomb in September, 1949, which was built with espionage information from the Manhattan Project. After three years of development under Teller's guidance, the first successful H-bomb was exploded on November 1, 1952, obliterating the Elugelab atoll in the Marshall Islands of the South Pacific. It used liquid hydrogen with refrigeration equipment too large for aircraft delivery, but yielded more than 10 megatons of TNT in a 5-kilogram fireball. In August, 1953, the Soviets exploded a nuclear bomb with a small amount of hydrogen in the form of lithium deuteride, a stable dry powder revealed by analysis of its radioactive fallout.

The first dry American H-bomb was tested at Bikini atoll on March 4, 1954, producing a 20-megaton explosion and fallout that exposed a number of Japanese fishermen and native islanders to dangerous levels of radioactivity. A true Soviet H-bomb was dropped from an aircraft in a test on November 23, 1955. The arms race then began to accelerate, until each side had stockpiles of thousands of H-bombs, in accordance with a deterrence policy of Mutually Assured Destruction (MAD).

The Manhattan Project contributed more than merely weapons. The development of nuclear reactors had made a major contribution to world energy resources. About 19 percent of electrical energy in the United States is generated by about 110 reactors producing about 100,000 megawatts of power. More than four hundred reactors in thirty countries provide 300,000 megawatts of the world's power without contributing to acid rain, the greenhouse effect, or fossil fuel depletion. Reactors have made possible the widespread use of radioisotopes in medical diagnosis and therapy. Much of the development of techniques for producing and using these isotopes has come from the hundreds of nuclear physicists who switched to radiation biophysics after the war, ensuring that the benefits of their wartime efforts would reach the public.

Bibliography

Glasstone, Samuel. *Sourcebook on Atomic Energy.* 3d ed. Princeton, N.J.: D. Van Nostrand, 1967. An excellent and well-organized introduction to atomic and nuclear physics, with good illustrations and historical documentation. Chapters on isotopes, the neutron, nuclear fission, and the utilization of nuclear energy provide good background on atom-bomb development

Junck, Robert. *Brighter than a Thousand Suns.* Translated by James Cleugh. New York: Harcourt Brace Jovanovich, 1958. A very readable historical account of the personal lives and political struggles of the atomic scientists who discovered nuclear fission and developed the bomb, with a particular focus on Oppenheimer.

Rhodes, Richard. *The Making of the Atomic Bomb.* New York: Simon & Schuster, 1986. The most comprehensive history of the atomic bomb available for the general reader. Rich in human, political, and scientific detail, it provides the complete story of how the bomb was developed, from the discovery of radioactivity to the development of the hydrogen bomb. Nearly eight hundred pages of text is supplemented by about seventy pages of documentation; includes a good index.

Schroeer, Dietrich. *Physics and Its Fifth Dimension: Society.* Reading, Mass.: Addison-Wesley, 1972. A good textbook on the interaction of science and society. It has readable chapters on building the bomb, the decision to drop it, the hydrogen bomb, and the fallout problem. Contains illustrations and references.

Smyth, Henry De Wolf. *Atomic Energy for Military Purposes.* Princeton, N.J.: Princeton University Press, 1945. This volume is the official report of the scientific and technical work that was done from 1940 to 1945 to develop the atomic bomb. It covers many details of both civilian and government involvement in the project. Includes several technical appendices and indexes.

Williams, Robert C., and Philip L. Cantelon, eds. *The American Atom: A Documentary History of Nuclear Policies from the Discovery of Fission to the Present, 1939-1984.* Philadelphia: University of Pennsylvania Press, 1984. This volume includes the Szilard-Einstein letter, the Frisch-Peierls memorandum, the letters of Oppenheimer, and many documents on the Manhattan Project and postwar developments related to nuclear weapons.

Joseph L. Spradley

Cross-References

Becquerel Wins the Nobel Prize for the Discovery of Natural Radioactivity (1903), p. 199; Einstein States His Theory of Special Relativity: $E = mc^2$ (1905), p. 297; Bohr Writes a Trilogy on Atomic and Molecular Structure (1912), p. 507; Rutherford Presents His Theory of the Atom (1912), p. 527; Lawrence Develops the Cyclotron (1931), p. 953; Chadwick Discovers the Neutron (1932), p. 973; Hahn Splits an Atom of Uranium (1938), p. 1135; Fermi Creates the First Controlled Nuclear Fission Chain Reaction (1942), p. 1198; The World's First Nuclear Reactor Is Activated (1943), p. 1230; Teller and Ulam Develop the First H-Bomb (1951), p. 1401; The World's First Breeder Reactor Produces Electricity While Generating New Fuel (1951), p. 1419; The United States Opens the First Commercial Nuclear Power Plant (1957), p. 1557; The Chernobyl Nuclear Reactor Explodes (1986), p. 2321.

RYLE'S RADIO TELESCOPE LOCATES THE FIRST KNOWN RADIO GALAXY

Category of event: Astronomy
Time: 1944-1952
Locale: Cambridge, England

Ryle's interferometric radio telescope detected and provided details on the structure of the first identifiable radio galaxy

Principal personages:
MARTIN RYLE (1918-1984), an English radio physicist and astronomer
E. GRAHAM SMITH (1923-), an English radio physicist and astronomer
WALTER BAADE (1893-1960), a German-American astronomer
RUDOLF MINKOWSKI (1895-1976), a German-American physicist

Summary of Event

The initial measurements of cosmic radio emission by Karl Jansky and later Grote Reber between 1932 and 1940 showed reasonably close relations between gross contours of radio intensity and overall visible light galactic structure, as seen by optical telescopes. This led many astronomers to conclude that most, if not all, celestial radio emission derived from continuously distributed sources, such as interstellar gas. Up to the immediate post-World War II period, probably the greatest weakness of the new subdiscipline of radio astronomy was the very limited accuracies it provided in determining absolute celestial position and structural detail of detected radio sources. High location accuracy was necessary to reduce sufficiently the error or uncertainty box that optical astronomers would search for the visual counterparts (if any) of a given radio source.

Immediately following World War II, J. S. Hey used receivers from the Army Operational Radar Unit to make initial experiments on some of the extraterrestrial radio emissions reported earlier by Jansky and Reber. Subsequently, in 1946, Hey and others published the first paper on apparent fluctuations in received radio noise from the direction of the constellation Cygnus. Hey and his colleagues reported on observational discovery of particular import: that the radio source in Cygnus varied significantly in strength over very short time periods. In contrast to Reber, who had concluded that interstellar hydrogen between the stars was the source of all celestial radio signals, Hey argued that the spatial localization and temporal periodicity of emissions strongly suggested a localized or starlike object.

In Australia, a similar post-World War II radio astronomy group was formed under J. L. Pawsey. In 1946, the Australian group verified Hey's observations of a localized radio source in Cygnus, using one of the earliest radio interferometers of the "Lloyd's mirror" type. An interferometer is essentially a multielement receiving array relying on receiver spacings matching the constructive interference wavelengths of the emitting source. Further "radio stars" were discovered by Pawsey's group in June, 1947, using an improved Lloyd's mirror or image-method interferometer developed by L. McCready, Pawsey, and R. Payne-Scott. This interferometer includes a multisensor aerial mounted atop a high cliff, overlooking the ocean, which specifically makes use of the Lloyd's mirror effect of optics and acoustics. The Lloyd's mirror, or image interference effect, is the constructive and destructive interference patterns resulting from interference between direct and multiply-reflected radio waves reflected at the sea surface.

Almost simultaneously, using a different type of interferometer, Sir Martin Ryle at Cambridge found another intense localized radio source in the constellation Cassiopeia. Ryle, together with J. Ratcliffe, J. Finlay, and others, brought with them extensive wartime experience in developing airborne radar detectors, radar countermeasures, underwater sonar arrays, and signal detection and localization equipment. Joined in 1946 by F. Graham Smith, Ryle's new interferometer was a multielement array whose elements could be moved horizontally to different separation distances. The receivers include two groups of four yagi-type antennas separated by 500 meters or more and operating at a receive frequency of 80 megahertz. A yagi antenna includes a dipole connected by a transmission line to a number of equispaced but unconnected dipoles mounted plane parallel to the first. Ryle's cosmic radio "pyrometer" was used successfully in July, 1946, to resolve the angular diameters of a large sunspot.

Hey and his colleagues remained unable to determine the accurate position of their radio source to better than 2 degrees because of resolution limitations of their radio telescope. J. G. Bolton and G. J. Stanley in 1948 also used the Lloyd's mirror technique to show that the Cygnus radio source was a discrete, and not distributed, source. The successful resolution of solar sunspots of small diameter suggested to Ryle additional radio telescope improvements to improve upon the Hey, Bolton, and Stanley measurements for Cygnus, and their own object in Cassiopeia.

In 1948, Ryle, Smith, and others made the first detailed radio observations of Cygnus A, using an improved version of their pyrometric radio telescope. Ryle and Smith subsequently published an improved position for Cygnus A in 1948 and showed that, unlike the sun, the Cygnus A and Cassiopeia sources were unpolarized. Ryle and Smith's measurements included the discovery of short-period radio bursts (of less than 20 seconds duration), which they (incorrectly) used to argue that the ultimate radio source must be a radiating star of some as yet unrecognized type. Eventually, it was decided that the most direct way to determine more about these radio sources would be to measure their angular size radiometrically with the greatest resolution possible: If the objects were, in fact, stars, their expected angular size would be fractions of a second of arc (and if galaxies, minutes of arc). Earlier efforts to improve position estimates for radio stars largely depended on observing a very small part of the object's celestial track after it had risen above the horizon. Almost all early measurements were affected severely by near-horizon atmospheric refraction not amenable to easy correction.

In 1949, it was proposed to carry out these measurements for Cygnus A and Cassiopeia by constructing a very large variable baseline interferometric radio telescope, with a maximum possible baseline separation of 160 kilometers receiving on 124 megahertz, the so-called long Michelson interferometer of 1950. Because of the critical importance of relative phase in determining details of the object's spatial distribution of radiated energy, in 1951, Ryle developed a new "phase-switching" receiver based on 1944 sonar detection efforts. Phase switching permits the radio receiver to discriminate accurately and reject sources with large angular size and, thus, better emphasize and locate weaker sources using larger receiver gains. After completing the prototypes and testing again on the sun, in 1951 measurements were attempted for Cygnus and Cassiopeia by R. C. Jennison and M. K. Das Gupta. Because both sources were resolved clearly with baselines of only a few thousand meters, the radio objects were clearly not stars. These same researchers shortly thereafter discovered that the Cygnus A source was actually two distinct sources. Ryle's phase-switched records were such improvements that his colleagues compiled the first radio object catalog containing more than fifty sources.

Smith recollected later that, even the confirmation of the extragalactic nature of the Cygnus radio source had little immediate effect in changing the radio "star" concept. Unable to measure a parallax for these objects, by late 1951, Smith had further localized the coordinates of Ryle's 2 radio stars to better than one minute of arc in right ascension and 101.6 centimeters in declination, reducing the original error boxes of Hey and others by a factor of 60. Smith then approached the director of the Cambridge Observatory to seek visual identification of the two radio sources. While D. Dewhirst in 1951 did, in fact, find part of the Cassiopeia supernova remnant on a photographic plate made by a 101.6 centimeter reflector telescope, the poor atmospheric observing conditions in England precluded definitive identification. Shortly thereafter, Smith sent his data and his new positions to Walter Baade and Rudolf Minkowski of the Palomar Observatory in Southern California.

Baade and Minkowski's visual objects were discovered only after many difficulties, being in a field rich in many other stars and faint galaxies. In a letter of April 29, 1952, Baade wrote to Smith that the result of the photograph was puzzling. He found a rich cluster of galaxies, and the radio position coincided closely with one of the brightest members of the cluster. In his letter dated May 26, 1952, Baade wrote to Smith that Minkowksi had obtained the spectrum of the nebula with the new spectrograph. He believed they had encountered an extragalactic object because of the large redshift of the emission lines.

Impact of Event

At first, there was notable skepticism in the optical astronomy and cosmology communities over the notion of extragalactic radio sources. This climate of disbelief was responsible for the fact that Baade and Minkowski's results could not be published until 1954. Subsequently, it required additional confirmation for these, and the other purportedly extragalactic objects, to foster the leap of the imagination necessary to place these sources in a cosmological category. Perhaps the most decisive radio data came from Ryle and Scheuer in 1955. From their 1C and recent 2C surveys, they found that the absolute radio luminosity of "normal" spiral galaxies is comparable to that radiated by the Milky Way galaxy. Plotting optical versus radio emission intensity for 1C-2C radio sources showed that most of the normal galaxies are grouped in a specific region, where optical equals radio energy. Nevertheless, there were many other galaxies—many not different in their optical appearance from normal galaxies—which are much more powerful sources (termed radio galaxies).

By the 1958 Solvay Conference on the Structure and Evolution of the Universe, the existence of at least eighteen then-confirmed extragalactic radio objects were accepted as opening a new era in cosmology. The experiment to look for parallactic motion of assumed radio stars became the identification of the first extragalactic radio sources.

Bibliography

Baade, W., and R. Minkowski. "Identification of the Radio Sources in Cassiopeia, Cygnus A, and Puppis A." *Astrophysical Journal* 119 (1954): 206-214. The final refinement of the radio position and the establishment of the optical galaxy group are discussed.

Bolton, J. G., G. J. Stanley, and O. B. Slee. "Positions of Three Discrete Sources of Galactic Radio-Frequency Radiation." *Nature* 164 (1951): 101. The first confirmation of the discrete nature of the Cygnus radio object is discussed.

Pawsey, J. L., and R. N. Bracewell. *Radio Astronomy.* Oxford, England: Clarendon Press, 1955. Contains a good introduction to key concepts and mathematics of aperture synthesis in astronomy.

Ryle, M., and F. G. Smith. "A New Intense Source of Radio Frequency Radiation in the Constellation Cassiopeia." *Nature* 162 (1948): 462. The original publication documenting the discovery of intense radio emission.

Sullivan, Woodruff T., ed. *Classics in Radio Astronomy.* Boston: D. Reidel, 1982. Contains reprints of many key journal articles on radio telescope improvements and applications.

_____. *The Early Years of Radio Astronomy: Reflections Fifty Years After Jansky's Discovery.* New York: Cambridge University Press, 1984. A comprehensive collection of the early history of radio astronomy. Contains the Smith-Baade correspondence on the discovery of the optical counterpart to Cygnus A radio source.

Verschuur, Gerrit. *The Invisible Universe: The Story of Radio Astronomy.* New York: Springer-Verlag, 1974. Although an excellent source for contemporary material on radio astronomy, its historical recounting is limited and biased.

Gerardo G. Tango

Cross-References

Slipher Obtains the Spectrum of a Distant Galaxy (1912), p. 502; Slipher Presents Evidence of Redshifts in Galactic Spectra (1920's), p. 689; Hubble Demonstrates That Other Galaxies Are Independent Systems (1924), p. 790; Jansky's Experiments Lead to the Founding of Radio Astronomy (1930), p. 934; Reber Builds the First Intentional Radio Telescope (1937), p. 1113; Baade Corrects an Error in the Cepheid Luminosity Scale (1952), p. 1449; De Vaucouleurs Identifies the Local Supercluster of Galaxies (1953), p. 1454; Ryle Constructs the First Radio Interferometer (1955), p. 1496; Very Long Baseline Interferometry (VLBI) Is Developed for High-Resolution Astronomy and Geodesy (1969), p. 1902; The Oldest Known Galaxy Is Discovered (1988); p. 2367.

SCHAEFER PERFORMS CLOUD SEEDING
BY USING DRY ICE

Category of event: Earth science
Time: July 12, 1946
Locale: General Electric Research Laboratory, near Schenectady, New York

Working alone in the General Electric Research Laboratory in New York, Schaefer created a miniature snowstorm inside his deep freezer by tossing a handful of dry ice inside, producing ice crystals

Principal personages:
VINCENT JOSEPH SCHAEFER (1906-   ), an American chemist and meteorologist who discovered the key to producing snow by forming ice crystals in supercooled air with dry ice pellets
IRVING LANGMUIR (1881-1957), an American physicist and chemist who received the 1932 Nobel Prize in Chemistry and participated in experiments in weather modification with Vonnegut and Schaefer
BERNARD VONNEGUT (1914-   ), a physical chemist and meteorologist who found a catalyst for snow and rainstorms in silver iodide crystals

Summary of Event

Beginning in 1943, an intense interest in the study of clouds grew and broadened into the practice of weather modification. Working for the General Electric Research Laboratory, Nobel laureate Irving Langmuir and his assistant researcher and technician, Vincent Joseph Schaefer, began their collaboration of discovery with the observation of the formation of rime, the thin coating of ice that covers all objects exposed to the weather. Rime formation is caused by a combination of temperature and humidity. Laboratory research following these observations was redirected, more specifically, at the ice that accumulates on airplanes after they pass through supercooled clouds. From the study of aircraft icing, the scientists moved into a more expansive study of the nature of clouds. Eventually, Schaefer refocused his research and experiments on water droplets in relation to his original interest in precipitation and its causes.

Past research and study had indicated two possible ways that clouds produce rain. The first possibility is called coalescing, a process by which tiny droplets of water vapor in a cloud merge after bumping into each other and become heavier and fatter until they drop to Earth. The second possibility is the Bergeron process of droplet growth, named after the Swedish meteorologist Tor Bergeron. Bergeron's process relates to supercooled clouds, or clouds that are at or below freezing temperatures and yet still contain both ice crystals and liquid water droplets. The size of water droplets allows them to remain liquid despite the freezing temperatures; large droplets freeze at -15 degrees Celsius, but smaller ones can remain liquid down to 4 degrees Celsius, at which point they freeze. Precipitation is caused by the ice crystals growing bigger as the water droplets become smaller until all moisture is gone and/ or the ice crystals are heavy enough to fall from the cloud. If the temperature at some point below the cloud is warm enough, it will melt the ice crystals before they reach the earth, producing rain. If the temperature remains at the freezing point, the ice crystals retain their form and it snows.

Schaefer's desire for a pure study of water droplets led him to the use of a deep freezing unit in which he could observe the water droplets in pure cloud form instead of supercooling water vapor drops on varied surfaces as he had done previously. In order to observe the droplets better, Schaefer lined the chest with black velvet, then concentrated a beam of light inside. The first agent he introduced inside the supercooled freezer was his own breath. Failing the formation of the desired ice crystals, he proceeded to try other agents. The anticipated result was the creation of a miniature snowfall when the moisture in the air would condense onto the new ice crystals.

He eventually achieved success when, in order to lower the freezer's temperature after it had been left open, he tossed a handful of dry ice inside and was rewarded with the long-awaited snow. Schaefer recorded the experiment, and when his senior partner Langmuir returned from a business trip, they successfully attempted to reproduce the laboratory results in nature. On November 13, 1946, Schaefer took to the air over Mount Greylock with several pounds of dry ice with which to sprinkle, or seed, a supercooled cloud. After he finished, he instructed the pilot to fly underneath the cloud he had just seeded. Schaefer was greeted by the sight of snow. By the time it reached Langmuir on the ground, it had evaporated into the first-ever human-made rainfall.

In the time lapse between Schaefer's discovery and the follow-up experiment over Mount Greylock, Langmuir and Schaefer spent hours reproducing the snowstorm inside the laboratory and attempting to ascertain the actual scientific mechanics and causes behind the phenomenon. Already having spent much time in the study of the nature of water vapor, the pair had an idea of what had occurred and why. Dry ice is named so because of its unusual property of passing directly from a solid to a gas when it melts, completely skipping the liquid phase under normal conditions. The reason Schaefer used the dry ice to cool down the open freezer was that it is perfect material for quick cooling, having a freezing temperature of 43 degrees Celsius. The freezer was set at the freezing point of water, 0 degrees Celsius, but not all the particles were ice crystals. As in a supercooled cloud, there was a mixture of water droplets and ice crystals, so when the dry ice was introduced to the freezer environment, all the stray water droplets froze instantly into water—ice crystals or snowflakes. When the scientists conducted the experiment on an actual cloud, the result was the same. The extra moisture in the cloud was converted into the heavier ice crystals, which fell from the cloud and melted when the temperature increased toward the earth, producing rain.

Independently of Schaefer and Langmuir, another General Electric scientist who had worked with them on the airplane icing research, Bernard Vonnegut, was also seeking a way to produce rain by trapping the excess moisture in clouds. His line of research in approaching the problem differed greatly from his colleagues. Instead of seeking a catalyst, he sought a substitute for ice crystals, a microscopic crystal with the same size and shape as ice crystals to fool water droplets into condensing on it. Vonnegut used a deep-freezing unit, as did Schaefer. He created a cloud by breathing into it, then tossed a silver-plated coin inside. A miniature snowstorm was created. The experiment failed when it was tried again later. After analyzing possible chemicals present in the freezer and the coin, Vonnegut hit upon the answer—silver iodide crystals. When a certain chemical mixture containing silver iodide is heated on a special burner called a generator, it produces silver iodide crystals in the smoke of the mixture: Although his method of experimentation leading to the discovery appeared random, he had, in fact, already observed that the structure of silver iodide closely resembled that of ice crystals. Vonnegut's discovery allowed seeding to occur in a very different way from seeding with dry ice, but with the same result. Using Vonnegut's process, the seeding is done from the ground. The generators are placed outside and the chemicals are mixed. As the smoke wafts upward, it carries the newly formed silver iodide crystals with it into the clouds.

The landmark discoveries of Schaefer, Langmuir, and Vonnegut were not greeted with overwhelming support from the scientific community. In fact, there was great resistance and open skepticism from their peers and colleagues in both private industry and government agencies, especially the Weather Bureau. Nevertheless, the recency of World War II and the great leaps in scientific discovery triggered by the war effort prompted the Department of Defense to fund research on weather modification. Langmuir was chosen to head the effort, code-named Project Cirrus, and located in New Mexico.

The results of the scientific experiments by Langmuir, Vonnegut, and Schaefer were alternately hailed and rejected as legitimate. Too many variables remain in the process of seeding to attribute rain to the addition of dry ice or silver nitrate. Furthermore, the increase in precipitation after seeding is doubted: While these and other nagging questions and speculations remain unanswered, research continues sporadically in private and government facilities, as does the practice of seeding. One of the major problems surrounding the question of weather modification by cloud seeding is the small amount of information known about the Earth's atmosphere. A journey begun about fifty years ago is still a long way from being completed.

Impact of Event

Although the actual statistical and other proofs needed to support cloud seeding are lacking, the discovery in 1946 by the General Electric employees set off a wave of interest and demand for information that far surpassed the interest generated by the discovery of nuclear fission shortly before. The possibility of ending drought and in the process, hunger, was intoxicating to many people. Their discovery also prompted both legitimate and false "rainmakers," or private entrepreneurs who used the information gathered by Schaefer, Langmuir, and Vonnegut to set up cloud-seeding businesses. Time has proven the use of weather modification, in its current stage of development, as impractical to apply to the wide-scale effort of ending drought. It does, however, have beneficial results in some cases on the crops of smaller farms that have been affected by drought. Other uses of weather modification by cloud-seeding have been postulated in the decades following its discovery, such as increasing the water supply, as a weapon or tool in war, or changing the path of hurricanes. In addition to speculation on the possible uses of weather modification, the 1946 discovery has raised further interest in unintentional weather modification by humans as well as moral dilemmas regarding the authority and possible effects and abuses of the power of humans over the weather.

The history of humankind and weather was once an unbalanced relationship with the heavier burden on humans as they attempted to adapt to the harsh blows and inconveniences of nature. Throughout the years, people have learned to protect themselves from the worst weather and sometimes, in the process, harnessed the great energies released by the atmosphere. After 1946, there was a new outlook on weather. Fueled by the possibility of actually bending weather to the will of humans, the idea of weather modification branched its way from meteorology and into numerous unrelated branches of science and life. As mentioned, some energy from the weather is tapped and used to create energy. Also, water resource managers view weather modification as a possible alternative to increase reserve levels. With the constantly growing population in the southwestern United States and other areas, traditional water reserve facilities—such as dams—are found lacking in ability to fill the ever-growing need for water. Instead of discouraging population growth in arid and semi-arid regions, or even regions with a water deficit, much energy is being directed toward finding more water to meet the new demands. Across the nation, states have been funding weather modification research to find ways of augmenting rain and/or suppressing hail. Even the Federal government allowed for weather modification in its Disaster Relief Act of 1970 to be used to add to or increase precipitation.

The attitude toward continued research and use of weather modification is varied, depending where one asks. The government is interested in modifying the weather for a variety of humanitarian reasons. Commercial enterprises are interested in earning money from producing favorable weather alterations for their customers, often farmers whose crops are threatened by drought or hail. In the field of weather and atmospheric scientists, debate continues over all aspects of weather modification to such an intensity and, often, great divergence, that the outlook of this group is one of reservation. Researchers express the desire to continue conducting projects, experiments, and study into the process to validate current knowledge, discover constants, and learn more about the weather machine in general. In order to understand the advances made in weather modification, new instruments are needed to record accurately the results of further experimentation. The storm of interest—both favorable and nonfavorable—generated by the discoveries of Schaefer, Langmuir, and Vonnegut, has had far-reaching effects on all aspects of society.

Bibliography

Battan, Louis J. *Harvesting the Clouds: Advances in Weather Modification*. Garden City, N.Y.: Doubleday, 1969. Written by an expert on the field of weather modification; a source expressly for the student and general public. Provides a glimpse into the complicated world of science. Includes history and some scientific information, as well as a discussion of pressing moral and ethical questions regarding weather control.

Bova, Ben. *Man Changes the Weather*. Reading, Mass.: Addison-Wesley, 1973. Written for amateurs and children from the fifth grade and up. Features a casual style that sometimes dips into fiction to present a scenario. Clearly promotes early scientists as heros; attempts to introduce the reader to the basics of science and weather control while answering some questions related to the practicality and uses of weather modification.

Breuer, Georg. *Weather Modification: Prospects and Problems*. Translated by Hans Morth. New York: Cambridge University Press, 1976. Focuses on the social impact weather modification has had, or could possibly have, on the world. Discusses science, yet addresses the infancy of the field and the aura of uncertainty surrounding it. Also discusses the international and personal effect the power of weather modification might have on the world. Written for the nonscientist and those interested in current affairs.

Green, Fitzhugh. *A Change in the Weather*. New York: W. W. Norton, 1977. Written by a leader in the EPA, a unique perspective. Includes a scientist's perspective of the advances in weather control, its good and bad aspects, the doubts that remain, as well as a discussion of humankind's unintentional modification of the weather. Contains alternatives to improving the damaged environment. A great source for students or anyone interested in the possibilities the future holds, as glimpsed through the work and discoveries of the past.

Halacy, D. S., Jr. *The Weather Changes*. New York: Harper & Row, 1968. Beginning in pre-Christian times, discusses humankind's historical relationship with the weather and attempts to control and predict it, and people's unintentional contribution to the change in global climate and the atmosphere. Suggests possibilities of weather control that stretch as far as altering Siberian climate to make it warmer. Questions the legal matter of who has the right to alter the weather and where air jurisdiction should end. Suitable for the college student or nonscientist.

Hess, Wilmot N., ed. *Weather and Climate Modification*. New York: John Wiley & Sons, 1974. An excellent tool for the student, scientist, and layperson alike; includes chapters contributed by outstanding experimenters in their fields on a variety of topics related to the control of the weather. Branches into other fields, such as sociology and law.

Spence, Clark C. *The Rainmakers: American "Pluviculture" to World War II*. Lincoln: University of Nebraska Press, 1980. Written by a historian; focuses on the unending battle with, against, and for the weather. Ranges from early "rainmaking quacks," to arcane and mystic native rites, to twentieth century scientific feats. Offers a general history of humans and the weather for the student or scientist interested in the underlying events and causes of attempts to control the weather.

Earl G. Hoover

Cross-References

Bjerknes Publishes the First Weather Forecast Using Computational Hydrodynamics (1897), p. 21; Fabry Quantifies Ozone in the Upper Atmosphere (1913), p. 579; Tiros 1 Becomes the First Experimental Weather Reconnaissance Satellite (1960), p. 1667; Manabe and Wetherald Warn of the Greenhouse Effect and Global Warming (1967), p. 1840; Rowland and Molina Theorize That Ozone Depletion Is Caused by Freon (1973), p. 2009; The British Antarctic Survey Confirms the First Known Hole in the Ozone Layer (1985), p. 2285.

UNIVERSITY OF CALIFORNIA PHYSICISTS DEVELOP THE FIRST SYNCHROCYCLOTRON

Category of event: Physics
Time: November, 1946
Locale: Berkeley, California

Theoretical developments by McMillan and Veksler led to the synchrocyclotron, a powerful particle accelerator that overcomes problems of its predecessor, the cyclotron

Principal personages:

EDWIN MATTISON MCMILLAN (1907-), an American physicist who derived the theoretical basis for the synchrocyclotron and was awarded the Nobel Prize in Chemistry in 1951

VLADIMIR IOSIFOVICH VEKSLER (1907-1966), the Soviet physicist who derived the theoretical basis for the synchrocyclotron simultaneously with McMillan

ERNEST ORLANDO LAWRENCE (1901-1958), the American physicist who pioneered particle accelerator technology and the synthesis of radioactive elements with his development of the cyclotron in the 1930's

HANS ALBRECHT BETHE (1906-), a German-American physicist who was among the first to derive the theoretical limitations of the Lawrence cyclotron based on Albert Einstein's theory of special relativity

Summary of Event

The synchrocyclotron is a large electromagnetic apparatus designed to accelerate atomic and subatomic particles at high energies. Therefore, it falls under the broad class of scientific apparatus known as particle accelerators. Accelerated subatomic and atomic particles occur naturally in such sources as cosmic rays and the radioactive decay of elements. Abundant as these sources may be, they allow the scientist no means of controlling the properties of the particles. By the early 1920's, the experimental work of physicists such as Ernest Rutherford and George Gamow demanded that an artificial means be developed to generate streams of atomic and subatomic particles at energies much greater than those occurring naturally. Both Gamow's and Rutherford's initial failures to bombard the nuclei of atoms with subatomic particles led Ernest Orlando Lawrence to develop the cyclotron, the prototype for most modern accelerators. The synchrocyclotron was developed in response to the limitations of the early cyclotron.

In September, 1930, Lawrence, together with a group of his graduate students at the University of California Radiation Laboratory, announced the basic principles behind the cyclotron. Ionized—that is, electrically charged—particles are admitted into the central section of a circular metal drum. The drum is actually divided into two semicircular D-shaped segments, known as "dees." A strong oscillating electrical field, known as the "rf source," is applied across the gap between the dees, while a magnetic field is applied in the vertical direction perpendicular to the electrical field. Particles are given their initial energy by the rf source, which sends them across the gap, where the magnetic field forces them into circular paths, or orbits, bringing them into the gap once again. This time, when the particles enter the gap, the rf source has been reversed. Because it is an oscillating source, it sends them into the opposite dee, increasing their energy and orbital radii. This process continues until the particles reach the desired energy and velocity and are extracted from the outer rim of the dees for use in experiments ranging from particle-to-particle collisions to the synthesis of radioactive elements.

Particle energy is measured in units called electronvolts, which are defined as the amount of energy a particle of unit charge, such as an electron, receives when it is passed through an electrical field with a strength of 1 volt. Between 1931 and 1932, the Lawrence cyclotron generated protons, which are subatomic particles, with energies in excess of 1.2 million electronvolts. By mid-1934, the Lawrence cyclotron was producing deuterons at 5 million electronvolts. Deuterons are the positive ions of deuterium, a radioactive form of hydrogen.

Although Lawrence was interested in the practical applications of his invention in medicine and biology, the cyclotron also was applied to a variety of experiments in a subfield of physics called "high-energy physics." Among the earliest applications were studies of the subatomic, or nuclear, structure of matter. The energetic particles generated by the cyclotron made possible the very type of experiment that Rutherford and Gamow had attempted earlier. These experiments, which bombarded lithium targets with streams of highly energetic accelerated protons, attempted to probe the inner structure of matter. Among other experiments was the confirmation of Sir James Chadwick's 1932 discovery of the neutron, an electrically neutral subatomic particle that, together with the proton, constitutes the atomic nucleus. These 1933 experiments were made possible by the acceleration of deuterons.

Although funding for scientific research on a large scale was scarce before World War II, Lawrence nevertheless conceived of a 467-centimeter cyclotron that would generate particles with energies approaching 100 million electronvolts. By the end of the war, increases in the public and private funding of scientific research and a demand for even higher energy particles created a situation in which this plan looked as if it would become reality, were it not for an inherent limit in the physics of cyclotron operation.

In 1937, Hans Albrecht Bethe discovered a severe theoretical limitation to the energies that could be produced in a cyclotron. Einstein's theory of special relativity had demonstrated that as any mass particle gains velocity relative to the speed of light, its mass increases. Bethe showed that this increase in mass would slow eventually the rotation of each particle. Therefore, as the rotation of each particle slows, and the rf frequency of the cyclotron remains constant, particle velocity will decrease eventually each time particles cross the gap between the cyclotron dees. This effect of "relativistic mass" set an upper limit on the energies that any cyclotron could produce.

Edwin Mattison McMillan, a colleague of Lawrence at Berkeley, proposed a solution to Bethe's problem in 1945. Simultaneously and independently, Vladimir Iosifovich Veksler of the Soviet Union proposed the same solution. They suggested that the frequency of the rf source be slowed to meet the decreasing rotational frequencies of the accelerating particles, in essence, synchronizing the rf frequency to match the particle frequency. In principle, the frequency of the rf source is to be matched to the frequency of a reference particle. This reference particle sets the rf source so that particles at either higher or lower frequencies, within a preset margin of error, are restored to the reference frequency. This process is called phase focusing. The synchrocyclotron was only one of a family of so-called synchronous accelerators developed as a result of McMillan's insight into phase focusing.

Prior to World War II, Lawrence and his colleagues had obtained the massive electromagnet for the new 100 million electronvolt cyclotron. This 467-centimeter magnet became the heart of the new Berkeley synchrocyclotron. McMillan's 1938 theory was first put to experimental test in 1945 in the older 94-centimeter cyclotron. The new synchronous rf source overcame the relativistic mass effect. With this test deemed a success, the Berkeley team decided that it would be reasonable to convert the cyclotron magnet to one in a new synchrocyclotron. The apparatus was operational in November of 1946 and produced deuterons at 190 million electronvolts and helium ions, or alpha particles, at 380 million electronvolts.

These high energies combined with economic factors to make the synchrocyclotron a major achievement for the Berkeley Radiation Laboratory. The synchrocyclotron required less voltage to produce higher energies than the cyclotron because the relativistic mass effects were virtually nonexistent. In essence, the energies produced by synchrocyclotrons are limited only by the economics of building them. These factors led to the planning and construction of other synchrocyclotrons in the United States and Europe. In 1957, the Berkeley apparatus was redesigned in order to achieve energies of 720 million electronvolts, at that time the record for cyclotrons of any kind.

The economic and scientific benefits of the synchrocyclotron were not without problems. When the change was made from cyclotrons to synchrocyclotrons, an important property of the generated particle beams was lost: intensity. Beam intensity is directly related to the number of particles leaving the accelerator. Particles leave the synchrocyclotron at a much lower rate than the cyclotron because particles are essentially "held up" until the rf source comes into agreement with the reference particle, resulting in fewer particles per unit of time. Although physicists had higher energies with which to experiment, beam intensity had dropped by a factor of one hundred. This greatly limited the number of nuclear and subatomic collisions, or "events," which could be observed in one experimental run. The synchrocyclotron was, however, still a more powerful instrument than the cyclotron in terms of the energies it could produce, and the intensity problem was eventually solved in the 1950's, with the advent of the isochronous cyclotron.

Impact of Event

Previously, scientists had to rely on natural sources for highly energetic subatomic and atomic particles with which to experiment. In the mid-1920's, Robert Andrews Millikan began his experimental work in cosmic rays, one natural source of energetic particles called mesons. Mesons are charged particles that have a mass in excess of two hundred times that of the electron and are therefore of great benefit in high-energy physics experiments. In February of 1949, McMillan announced the first synthetically produced mesons.

The mesons were produced by exploiting the high energies generated by the Berkeley synchrocyclotron. Electrons are accelerated to an energy of 300 million electronvolts. The synchrocyclotron's ability to avoid the pitfalls of its predecessor were evident in this experiment. At such a high energy, electrons weigh six hundred times more than they do before acceleration. The synchronized rf source allowed the electrons to continue to gain energy while traveling around the chamber 480,000 times, with each electron completing an average of six orbits per second.

Upon reaching this energy, the electrons are extracted and allowed to collide with a heavy metal target, which liberates a strong X-ray beam, which is responsible, in turn, for the creation of muons. The production of such particles has a wide variety of experimental applications in high-energy physics. Muons exist in both positively and negatively charged varieties. The negatively charged meson, known as the mu meson, or muon, has been linked since the late 1950's by physicists such as Luis Walter Alvarez with the possibility of attaining controlled, low-temperature nuclear fusion.

Finally, McMillan's theoretical development led not only to the development of the synchrocyclotron but also to the development of the electron synchrotron, the proton synchrotron, the microtron, and the linear accelerator. Both the proton and electron synchrotrons have been used successfully to produce precise beams of muons and another species of meson, the pi-meson, or pion.

The increased use of accelerator apparatus ushered in a new era of physics research, which has become dominated by the technical and economic magnitude of increasingly large accelerators and, subsequently, larger teams of scientists and engineers required to run individual experiments. As a rule, particle accelerators are run on the joint funding of major research universities and national governments. This joint venture has led to the generation of energies in excess of 2 trillion electronvolts at the United States' Fermi National Accelerator Laboratory, or Fermilab, in Illinois. Part of the huge Tevatron apparatus at Fermilab, which generates these particles, is a proton synchrotron, a direct descendant of McMillan and Lawrence's early efforts.

Bibliography

Burcham, W. E. *Nuclear Physics.* New York: McGraw-Hill, 1963. Primarily an undergraduate introduction to the study of nuclear physics, it assumes a background in classical and modern physics and the higher mathematics that accompany such a background, including integral and differential calculus. This should not discourage the layperson, who will find ample information on the development of particle accelerators. The author discusses the entire range of such apparatus, from the earliest direct current accelerators to the synchrocyclotron and beyond. Although somewhat outdated, it is still historically valuable.

Davis, Nuel Pharr. *Lawrence and Oppenheimer.* New York: Simon & Schuster, 1968. Much of the earliest work in twentieth century high-energy physics occurred against the background of World War II and the development of the atomic bomb. This book is a biographical account of both Lawrence and Robert Oppenheimer in the context of the war. It gives a different perspective on the field of high-energy physics. It is not overly technical and discusses the applied scientific consequences of particle accelerator technology, especially in the context of military use.

Livingston, M. Stanley. *Particle Accelerators.* Cambridge, Mass.: Harvard University Press, 1969. This small, technically concise volume presents the history of particle accelerators from their earliest conception in the early twentieth century to the 1967 Fermilab achievement of 200 to 400 billion electronvolts. It traces many of the technical and economic difficulties faced in the construction and use of particle accelerators. Livingston was involved in the early Lawrence groups at Berkeley and uses this experience to tell a well-written story that has sufficient technical detail to remain useful.

Segrè, Emilio. *From X-Rays to Quarks: Modern Physicists and Their Discoveries.* San Francisco: W. H. Freeman, 1980. Traces both the theoretical and experimental development of modern physics including relativity theory and atomic and quantum theory. Devotes an entire chapter to the development of particle accelerators. Segrè was actively involved in nuclear physics during the 1930's and 1940's and presents an excellent history of the rise of high-energy physics, which was the impetus for particle accelerator development.

_____. "Synchrotron Makes Mesons." *Science Newsletter* 55 (February, 1949): 99. This is a very brief discussion of McMillan's announcement of the production of mesons in the Berkeley synchrocyclotron. Although it is written in a journalistic style, it includes enough technical detail to make it an informative article for the layperson.

William J. McKinney

Cross-References

Millikan Names Cosmic Rays and Investigates Their Absorption (1920), p. 694; Lawrence Develops the Cyclotron (1931), p. 953; Chadwick Discovers the Neutron

GABOR DEVELOPS THE
BASIC CONCEPT OF HOLOGRAPHY

Category of event: Physics
Time: 1947
Locale: Rugby, England

Gabor created a lensless system of three-dimensional photography, which is one of the most important developments in twentieth century optical science

Principal personages:
> DENNIS GABOR (1900-1979), a Hungarian-born inventor and physicist, champion of responsible science and technology, and winner of the 1971 Nobel Prize in Physics
> EMMETT LEITH (1927-   ) and JURIS UPATNIEKS (1936-   ), the radar researchers at the University of Michigan who produced the first laser holograms

Summary of Event

Since 1900, the recording of images using the technique of photography has been commonplace. The optical lens had been in use for several centuries and the formation of images using lenses was well understood. The development of photography in the early 1900's increased greatly the importance of the lens to the scientific community. Combining the optical lens and the process of photographic emulsion made possible the recording of events and information in a way unknown before the twentieth century: photographing star clusters, recording emission spectra of heated elements, storing data in the form of small recorded images (for example, microfilm), photographing microscopic specimens, and many others. Because of its vast importance to the scientist, the science of photography has developed steadily.

An understanding of the photography process and of the holographic process requires some clarification of the wave behavior of light. Light is an electromagnetic wave which, like a water wave, has an amplitude and a phase. The amplitude corresponds to the wave height, while the phase indicates which part of the wave is passing a given point at a given time. A cork floating in a pond bobs up and down as waves pass under it. The position of the cork at any time depends on both amplitude and phase. Waves from more than one source arriving at the cork combine in ways that depend on their relative phases. If the waves arrive in phase, they add and produce a large amplitude; if out of phase, they subtract to produce a small amplitude. The total amplitude, or intensity, depends on the phases of the combining waves.

In ordinary photography, light radiating from a point of the object being photographed is focused by a lens on a photographic film to create an image of the point. Images of each point are created similarly. A record of the intensity of the image points is stored on the film without any phase information about the combining wave fronts. The clarity of the image depends in large part on the quality of the focusing lens.

Dennis Gabor, the inventor of holography, had been intrigued by the way the photographic image of an object was stored by a photographic plate since his teenage years but had been unable to devote any consistent research effort to the question until the 1940's. At that time, Gabor was involved in the development of the electron microscope. By 1947, the electron microscope had improved the resolving power of the ordinary light microscope by a factor of 100, but was still unable to resolve objects the size of atoms and small molecules. This inability resulted from imperfections in the objective of the microscope. If the aperture of the objective was decreased to reduce the spherical aberration of the lens, then the diffraction of the electrons produced a blurred image. If the aperture was opened to reduce diffraction, then the spherical aberration of the lens blurred the image. The theoretical work of O. Scherzer indicated that the limit of the resolving power of the objective was twice that needed to "see" atoms. The practical limit at that time was about twelve times. The problem faced by Gabor seemed insurmountable.

Gabor was pondering the problem of how to improve the electron microscope while sitting beside the tennis court on Easter morning in 1947 when the solution came to him. He would attempt to take a poor electron picture and then correct it optically. The process would require coherent electron beams, that is, electron waves having definite phase. This two-stage method was inspired by Lawrence Bragg. Bragg had formed the image of a crystal lattice by means of diffraction from the photographic X-ray diffraction pattern of the original lattice. This double diffraction process is the basis of the holographic process. Bragg's method was limited because of his inability to record phase information of the X-ray photograph. So, only crystals, for which the phase relationship of the reflected waves could be predicted, could be studied.

Gabor devised a way of capturing the phase information. By adding coherent background to the wave reflected from the object, an interference pattern was produced on the photographic plate. When the phases of the two waves are identical, a maximum intensity will be recorded; where they are out of phase, a minimum intensity is found. Therefore, what is recorded in a hologram is not an image of the object but rather the interference pattern of the two coherent waves. It looks like a collection of swirls and blank spots. The hologram (or photograph) then would be illuminated by the reference beam and part of the transmitted light would be a replica of the original object wave. By viewing this object wave, one sees an exact replica of the original object.

Gabor's original intention was to improve the resolving power of the electron microscope. He intended to form the hologram with electrons and then to illuminate it with visible light. The wavelength of visible light is on the order of 100,000 times the wavelengths of electrons. The magnification achieved should be on the order of 100,000.

To demonstrate the feasibility of the concept, Gabor attempted to make a hologram using visible light. The major impediment at the time in making holograms using any form of radiation was a lack of coherent sources. For example, the coherence length of the mercury lamp used by Gabor and his assistant Ivor Williams was so short that they were able to make holograms of only about 1 centimeter in diameter. The early results were rather poor in terms of image quality and also had a double image. For this reason, there was little interest in holography and the subject lay almost untouched for more than ten years.

Interest in the field returned after the development of the laser in 1962. Emmett Leith and Juris Upatnieks, who were doing radar research at the University of Michigan, published the first laser holographs in 1963. Leith and Upatnieks used an off-axis reference beam rather than the in-line arrangement that Gabor was forced to use. Gabor actually had noted from the start that this off-axis method would allow the separation in space of the twin image. The laser was an intense light source with a much longer coherence length. Its monochromatic nature allowed the off-axis reference scheme to be used to its full potential and improved the resolution of the images greatly. Also, there was no longer any restriction on the size of the object to be photographed.

The availability of the laser allowed Leith and Upatnieks to propose another improvement in the holographic technique. Before 1964, holograms were made of only thin transparent objects. A small region of the hologram bore a one-to-one correspondence to a region of the object. Only a small portion of the image could be viewed at one time without the aid of additional optical components. Illuminating the transparency diffusely allowed the whole image to be seen at one time. This development also permitted the recording of holograms of diffusely reflecting three-dimensional objects. Gabor had seen from the beginning that this should allow the formation of three-dimensional images.

After the early 1960's, the field of holography developed very quickly. Because it is basically different from conventional photography, the two techniques often complement each other. Gabor saw his idea blossom into a very important technique in optical science.

Impact of Event

Because of the lack of intense, coherent sources of light, the early holograms produced images of rather poor quality. For this reason and because of the technical difficulties in making holograms, the new technique of holography aroused little interest for the first fifteen years after its development. The development of the laser and the publication of the first laser holograms in 1963, however, caused a blossoming of the new technique in many fields. Techniques were developed quickly that allowed holograms to be viewed with white light and also holograms that could reconstruct multicolored images.

In biology, the use of holography makes it possible to overcome a basic limit of the microscope. If the microscope has a large magnification, then it has a very small depth range over which an object is in focus. Biological specimens usually are suspended in a fluid and tend to move around, moving in and out of focus. Making a holographic snapshot stops the motion and retains the three-dimensional information. The hologram can be studied later, adjusting the instrument to focus on different layers of the sample.

If a sample changes, even microscopically, a series of holograms may be made that allow the sample to be viewed at different depths and times. Material objects subjected to stress may change minutely. Holograms taken with and without the stress can be viewed simultaneously. Where the minute changes occurred (at stress points), the two holograms will show interference fringes. Much nondestructive testing of materials is done in this manner.

Holographic techniques make it possible to store a large amount of information in a small space, two hundred times as much as microfilm. More than one image may be stored in a single area of the film. The only restriction is that the object and reference beams must make different angles with each other for each picture. The information stored, both in storage density and readout speed, exceeds present library requirements. Holographic methods have been used to map terrains with radar waves and in Earth surveillance for forestry, agriculture, and meteorology.

The advertising profession has not been slow to see the possibilities of holography. The three-dimensional image of a hand holding a diamond necklace over the entrance to a jewelry store attracts customers. At the opening of a new automobile plant, a display case contains alternately a coach and the body of a new car. From time to time, the case is illuminated with diffuse light to show that it is really empty.

Another unique feature of holography is the fact that the original source and the reconstructing source need not have the same wavelength or physical nature. Holograms made using X-rays may be viewed with visible light, increasing magnification and, therefore, depth of field.

Today, holography is a multimillion dollar industry, finding applications in advertising, as an art form, as security devices on credit cards, as well as in scientific fields. An alternate form of holography, also suggested by Gabor, uses sound waves. Acoustical imaging is useful wherever the medium around the object is opaque to light rays, for example, in medical diagnosis. Holography truly has had an impact on many areas of culture.

Bibliography

Gabor, Dennis. "Holography, 1948-1971." *Science* 177 (July 28, 1972): 299-313. This article is a revised version of Gabor's Nobel lecture. It traces the development of holography from its beginnings in a nonmathematical way. The language of the article would appeal to those who have a very general knowledge of physics.

Kasper, Joseph, and Steven Feller. *The Complete Book of Holograms.* New York: John Wiley & Sons, 1987. This book is geared for use in an introductory course at the high school or college level. Kasper and Feller explain holography using many diagrams but no mathematics. There are discussions of applications of the technique and descriptions of how to make holograms for the more adventurous.

Leith, Emmett, and Juris Upatnieks. "Photography by Laser." *Scientific American* 212 (June, 1965): 20. This is a fairly nontechnical description of the first production of holograms using laser light. There are numerous photographs and diagrams that render this article readable to most nonscientists.

Pennington, Keith S. "Advances in Holography." *Scientific American* 218 (February, 1968): 17. This article discusses the advances made in the holographic technique as well as some applications of holography in the mid-1960's. The article would be appreciated by anyone with a general knowledge of science and of the holographic process.

Williamson, Samuel J., and Herman Z. Cummins. "Holography." In *Light and Color in Nature and Art*. New York: John Wiley & Sons, 1983. This college-level introductory text is geared for those with little background in mathematics or science. The chapter describes various types of holograms and illustrates the principles of holography in a basic manner.

Grace A. Banks

Cross-References

Louis and Auguste Lumière Develop Color Photography (1907), p. 375; Carlson Invents Xerography (1934), p. 1013; The First Laser Is Developed in the United States (1960), p. 1672; Optical Disks for the Storage of Computer Data Are Introduced (1984), p. 2262.

LAMB AND RETHERFORD DISCOVER THE LAMBSHIFT

Category of event: Physics
Time: 1947
Locale: Columbia University, New York City

The discovery of the Lambshift led to the formulation of the theory of quantum electrodynamics

> *Principal personages:*
> WILLIS EUGENE LAMB, JR. (1913-   ), an American physicist whose discovery of the Lambshift inspired new theories in quantum electrodynamics; awarded the 1955 Nobel Prize in Physics
> ROBERT C. RETHERFORD, an American physicist and collaborator of Lamb at Columbia University
> PAUL ADRIEN MAURICE DIRAC (1902-1984), an English physicist who contributed much to quantum mechanics, relativity, and cosmology
> RICHARD P. FEYNMAN (1918-1988), an American physicist who formulated a mathematical technique to describe electron activity and shared the 1965 Nobel Prize in Physics with Shin'ichirō Tomonaga and Julian Seymour Schwinger
> SHIN'ICHIRŌ TOMONAGA (1906-1979), a Japanese physicist who invented the mathematical procedure called renormalization to account for mass and charge of the electron
> JULIAN SEYMOUR SCHWINGER (1918-   ), an American physicist who invented the renormalization procedure independent of Tomonaga
> MAX PLANCK (1858-1947), a German physicist who was renowned for his contribution to quantum mechanics and known for the radiation equation named after him
> ALBERT EINSTEIN (1879-1955), a German-Swiss-American physicist who is known for his work on relativity and contributed to the creation of quantum mechanics
> LOUIS DE BROGLIE (1892-1987), a French physicist who formally described the nature of wave-particle duality

Summary of Event

By the end of the nineteenth century, classical physics sought to explain the physical world as the interaction between discrete particles, or corpuscles, of matter or by wave activity. The success of classical physics prompted many scientists to predict the end of physics with answers to all the significant problems of physics. Yet, problems began to occur within this system, which led Max Planck eventually to discover bursts of energy that looked like particles rather than a continuous flow of energy. This marked the beginning of quantum mechanics, a theory that states that electromagnetic waves come in discrete units of energy rather than as one continuous flow of wave action. In terms of classical physics, quantum theory violates one of the fundamental assumptions of physics; that light, or radiation, spreads continuously and is evenly distributed through space. This difference marks the dividing line between classical physics and the modern world of quantum mechanics.

By 1905, Albert Einstein had worked out the details of the theory of special relativity and began to study the photoelectric effect, wherein light waves falling on certain metals would release electrons from the metal. His studies showed that the release of electrons from metal depended solely on the wavelength of light. Regardless of the brightness of light, shorter wavelengths of light released more electrons, while longer wavelengths of light lacked the energy to release any electrons. For Einstein, the photoelectric effect meant that specific wavelengths of light possessed "quanta" of energy.

In 1913, Niels Bohr introduced a new quantum view of physics. Bohr retained the classical model of the atom, where the electrons spun in an orbit around an atomic nucleus. As a result of this spin, the electron generated electromagnetic waves according to the laws of classical physics. Bohr used Planck's theory of quantum and constructed a model of an atom where electrons emitted radiation only when they changed orbits. To jump to a higher orbit, an electron needed to absorb a quantum of energy. In returning from that higher-energy state, the electron would release a quantum of energy. The orbits were set at specific distances from the nucleus, and it required a quantum of energy to make the jump. The differences between the Bohr model and that of classical physics lies in the fact that the Bohr atom did not radiate energy when it was in a stable orbit, whereas in classical physics, a spinning electron was required to radiate electromagnetic waves continuously, with the result that the electron lost energy until it fell into the nucleus. All the components for a new view of the physical world were now available, and in 1924, Louis de Broglie proposed the wave-particle duality: Not only could waves act like particles but also particles could act like waves. Erwin Schrödinger used this idea of the dual nature of matter to develop a theory of wave mechanics.

The wave-particle duality is one of the foundations of modern physics, and Paul Adrien Maurice Dirac provided the theoretical structure for this physics in what is often called the "Copenhagen interpretation." As the leading advocate for this point of view in the 1930's, Dirac claimed that neither a particle nor a wave aspect of matter was subordinate to each other. In 1928, Dirac published an equation that described all the properties of the electron and satisfied the requirements of both quantum mechanics and relativity. By 1930, Dirac had formulated a mathematical transformation theory that became the basis of future research programs in quantum mechanics and quantum electrodynamics (QED). The development of QED, describing electromagnetic radiation and properties of the electron, is based on the work of Dirac in conjunction with the contributions of Werner Heisenberg and Wolfgang Pauli. Although the Dirac equation was a critical discovery in physics, the mathematical description produced barriers to further development. During World

War II, the experimental use of microwave techniques prompted new explorations in QED. It is at this juncture that Willis Eugene Lamb, Jr., and his longtime collaborator Robert C. Retherford, entered the picture.

Lamb had completed his doctoral dissertation at the University of California at Berkeley in 1938 and accepted an appointment to teach physics at Columbia University in New York City. His research work centered on the metastable states of atoms. For example, as the hydrogen atom absorbs energy, called the excited state, the electrons jump to a higher orbit and quickly decay to the original state by the emission of a single photon. Metastable conditions last several million times longer because of a property called parity, where the electron must emit two photons. Lamb worked on microwave absorption and emission of atoms in order to determine the "fine-structure" of the atom. He was able to excite electrons of the hydrogen atom by microwave that were equal to the energy difference between the orbits. When the electron returns to its original orbit, it emits a photon that provides the characteristic spectrum of hydrogen. The Dirac equation predicted that in the hydrogen atom, there were two exactly equal levels of energy, with one of these levels at metastable state. In 1947, working with Retherford, Lamb demonstrated that these two energy states were not exactly equal, but separated by a small energy gap now called the Lambshift. Thus began a revision of Dirac's equation that led to the development of a theory of quantum electrodynamics. Lamb followed up his experimental discovery with contributions to the new theory. In 1955, he shared the Nobel Prize in Physics with Polykarp Kusch for their independent work on the interactions of electrons and electromagnetic radiation.

Impact of Event

The experimental discovery of the Lambshift identified a problematic area in the Dirac equation and produced both the theoretical reevaluations of the quantum effects of the electron and led to the growth of quantum electrodynamics. The most imaginative theoretical approach belongs to Richard P. Feynman. While sitting in a cafeteria at Cornell University, Feynman watched someone tossing a plate in the air. He decided to formulate a mathematical description of the spin and wobble of the plate and from this serendipitous event, produced a new view of electron dynamics. The Feynman diagrams describe the space-time path of the electron using both diagrams as well as computational rules. The space-time path follows the end points of a moving particle and summarizes the possibilities of all the interactions along the path. Not only did these diagrams predict with great precision the Lambshift but also became a powerful tool in many areas of physics.

Working independently from each other, Julian Seymour Schwinger and Shin'ichirō Tomonaga chose to work out the consequences of the Lambshift from another point of view. Earlier physicists had ignored the charge and infinite mass of the electron. Schwinger and Tomonaga decided to measure both these quantities. The mathematical technique they developed to measure both the mass and charge of the electron is called renormalization. They argued that the infinite "bare" mass of the electron is canceled out by the mass of the photon and particle cloud that surrounds the electron, except for a small residual mass. This residual mass and similar residual change are the only finite quantities that can be measured. Later experimental results agree with the predictions of the renormalization process.

In 1965, Feynman, Schwinger, and Tomonaga shared the Nobel Prize in Physics. Their work opened the door for future studies in quantum electrodynamics, such as better understanding of the fine-structure of the atom, the nature of the electromagnetic field, and the interaction between radiation and electrons. Indeed, in a brief period of time, discoveries in physics have reshaped the understanding of the nature of matter and scientists are on the verge of producing a new vision of the fundamental organization of the universe.

Bibliography

De Broglie, Louis. *The Revolution in Physics: A Non-Mathematical Survey of Quanta*, translated by Ralph W. Niemeyer. New York: Noonday Press, 1955. A highly recommended text for those seeking nontechnical information on quantum mechanics. De Broglie is one of the founders of modern physics and shares these discoveries with his reader.

Einstein, Albert, and Leopold Infeld. *The Evolution of Physics: The Growth of Ideas from Early Concepts to Relativity and Quanta*. New York: Simon & Schuster, 1938. This is probably one of the most accessible single volume histories on the development of modern physics available to the general reader. There are virtually no technical terms and no mathematics are required. The final section of this book is on quanta.

Jammer, Max. *The Conceptual Development of Quantum Mechanics*. New York: McGraw-Hill, 1966. This work traces both the physics and the conceptual framework of quantum theory. The sections discussing the formative development quantum are moderately accessible for the general reader.

Segrè, Emilio. *From X-Rays to Quarks: Modern Physicists and Their Discoveries*. San Francisco: W. H. Freeman, 1980. Segrè was one of a few physicists who both participated directly in nuclear physics (and received a Nobel Prize for his work) and wrote a number of popular accounts on the history of physics. The earlier sections of this volume cover the discoveries and theories of those who produced a coherent picture of the atom.

Trefil, James S. *From Atoms to Quarks: An Introduction to the Strange World of Particle Physics*. New York: Charles Scribner's Sons, 1980. An excellent introductory text to the world of subatomic particles. The earlier chapters describe the early explorations of the atom. Later chapters that cover antimatter, accelerators, and the discovery of particles are recommended.

Victor W. Chen

Cross-References

Planck Announces His Quantum Theory (1900), p. 83; Thomson Wins the Nobel Prize for the Discovery of the Electron (1906), p. 356; Bohr Writes a Trilogy on Atomic and Molecular Structure (1912), p. 507; Rutherford Presents His Theory of the Atom (1912), p. 527; De Broglie Introduces the Theory of Wave-Particle Duality (1923), p. 741; Pauli Formulates the Exclusion Principle (1925), p. 800.

ARCHAEOLOGISTS UNEARTH ANCIENT SCROLLS

Category of event: Archaeology
Time: Spring, 1947
Locale: Qumran, northwestern shore of the Dead Sea, Palestine

The discovery of the Dead Sea scrolls allowed investigators to understand the text to the Old Testament Scriptures, the early growth of the Christian church, and the nature of Judaism

Principal personages:

ELIEZER SUKENIK (1889-1953), a professor of archaeology at the Hebrew University who was the first to recognize the age and value of the scrolls

MAR ATHANASIUS YESHUE SAMUEL (1907-   ), an archbishop in the Syrian Orthodox church who purchased four of the first seven scrolls

ROLAND DE VAUX (1903-1971), an archaeologist who explored the caves and excavated the Qumran ruins

JOHN STRUGNELL (1930-   ), a professor of Christian origins at Harvard University Divinity School and chief editor of the scrolls since 1987

Summary of Event

Accounts of the discovery of the Dead Sea scrolls do not always agree. The number of people involved and the political upheaval at the time seem to have clouded the event, leading to both exaggeration and omission. In the spring of 1947, young Bedouin of the Ta'amireh tribe watched their goats and sheep graze among the cliffs in the wilderness near Khirbet (ruin) Qumran. Some of the flock had climbed up the cliffs by the end of the day. As Muhammad adh-Dhib and a friend climbed after the animals, they found a cave. Without much thought, one of the shepherds threw a rock inside and was surprised by the sound of breaking pottery. The lateness of the day and awkward entry prevented further exploration; but with hopes of hidden treasure, the shepherds resolved to return.

Days later, they returned and with effort lowered themselves into what would become known as Qumran Cave 1. The floor was covered with debris, but along one wall were several narrow jars. They looked into one, tore the cover from another, but found nothing. Another contained dirt. Finally, in one they pulled out three smelly, old leather scrolls wrapped like mummies. They could not read them. Hopes for hidden treasure faded.

The Bedouin could not know that the Hebrew and Aramaic scrolls were the oldest biblical book of Isaiah in Hebrew, a commentary on the biblical book of Habakkuk, and a book of guidelines belonging to a religious sect called *The Manual of Discipline.* A few weeks later, one of the young men returned with other Bedouin to find and remove four more scrolls. These included a second scroll of Isaiah; a damaged but fascinating narrative in the first person, called Genesis Apocryphon; a book of thanksgiving psalms; and a work titled *The War of the Sons of Light Against the Sons of Darkness*. The Bedouin could only hope that perhaps some scholar or collector of antiquities might want the writings on rolled-up sheepskins.

The political unrest in Palestine did not favor trade and archaeological investigation. English rule was ending, and the Jews desired to establish an independent state of Israel. The English, Jews, and Arabs turned against one another. Acts of terrorism were common, and war was pending. In the middle of this upheaval in early 1947, two of the Bedouin brought the first three scrolls and two of the jars to Bethlehem with hopes of selling them. They contacted George Isaiah and Khalil Iskander Shahin (Kando), who agreed to handle the scrolls for one-third of the eventual sale price. During Holy Week, George Isaiah mentioned the scrolls to the Syrian Orthodox archbishop, Mar Athanasius Yeshue Samuel, at St. Mark's Monastery in Jerusalem. Within the week, *The Manual of Discipline* was brought to the archbishop. Samuel could not read the language of the leather scroll but decided to buy the lot. Kando agreed and left with the sample. Weeks passed, and the clergyman began to wonder if he would hear more of the scrolls.

Despite increased violence, Kando and the Bedouin brought the scrolls to Jerusalem in July. One of the fathers at St. Mark's, however, not realizing his archbishop's interest, turned Kando away, and some of the scrolls transferred to yet another dealer. This dealer contacted Eliezer L. Sukenik, a professor of archaeology at the Hebrew University. Sukenik eventually was shown four pieces of leather inscribed in a type of Hebrew script used between 100 B.C. and A.D. 100. In November, Sukenik risked traveling to see more scrolls and two of the jars from the cave. He recorded in his diary that this was one of the greatest finds ever made in Palestine. Sukenik was able to purchase three of the seven scrolls. He correctly judged them at a time when faked documents were common.

Archbishop Samuel, in the meantime, had purchased the other four scrolls from Kando but had not been able to determine their value. In late January, 1948, Sukenik asked to see them. He recognized the scrolls as belonging with those he had already purchased. Assurance was given that he would have the first chance to purchase them. Archbishop Samuel, still not sure of the scrolls' value, called on John Trever at the American School of Oriental Research. Trever excitedly sent photographs to William Foxwell Albright of Johns Hopkins University. Albright airmailed his reaction: "incredible . . . there can happily not be the slightest doubt in the world about the genuineness." The discovery of the scrolls was confirmed and announced on April 26, 1948, by Millar Burrows.

With thoughts of similar profit, Bedouin began to comb the hills and in 1952 found a second cave at Murabbaat. By 1956, Bedouin and archaeologists had found eleven caves with approximately eight hundred scrolls. Clearly, an ancient library was being discovered. Interestingly, all books of the Hebrew Bible, or Old Testament, were represented at least in part except for Esther. Many copies of some books seem to indicate favorite writings. About one-third of the scrolls were biblical. Others included commentaries on the books of the Bible, a copper scroll that told of hidden treasure, religious writings, a marriage contract, and correspondence by Simeon ben Kozibah (a.k.a. Bar Kokhba), the leader of the second revolt against the Romans. The manuscripts were in Aramaic, Hebrew, and even Greek. Each writing was given a code that indicated the cave number, the geographical area, and the title. The "4QSam" scroll was taken from cave 4 near Qumran containing the book of Samuel.

Many scrolls were damaged and incomplete. The Bedouin were not as careful as the archaeologists. There was even evidence of deliberate destruction during ancient times. Cave 4, the main library, contained fifteen thousand postage-stamp-sized scraps of some seven hundred different writings. Professor Frank Cross rightly called the situation "the ultimate in jigsaw puzzles."

Besides physically assembling the fragments, space-age technologies have proven useful. For example, the gooey, black Genesis Apocryphon scroll looked as though coffee had been spilled all over it. Nevertheless, when heated with back lights, the carbon ink absorbed more heat than the surrounding leather, and the letters became visible on a new infrared film. Noah's words after the Flood appeared: " . . . we gathered together and went . . . to see the Lord of Heaven . . . who saved us from ruin."

Father Roland de Vaux, an archaeologist who also explored the caves, excavated the nearby ruin of Qumran. Pottery from the caves matched pottery found at Qumran. Coins found at Qumran allowed dating. Things began to fall into place. Qumran was occupied for sometime shortly before and during the life of Jesus. The *Manual of Discipline* (a book of rules for a sect) and the *Damascus Documents* (found in both Qumran and Cairo) indicated that a group of Jews had split off from the group. The ancient historians Pliny, Josephus, and Philo had recorded that a group called the Essenes lived near the Dead Sea. Many scholars concluded that the scrolls were the library of this group. Qumran evidently functioned as a religious center that emphasized baptism, a facility where scribes copied scrolls, and as a pottery center to make storage jars.

Impact of Event

The scrolls are extremely important for the understanding of the text of the Hebrew or Old Testament Scriptures, the background to early growth of the Christian church, and the nature of Judaism at that time.

Before the discovery of the scrolls, scholars had to be content with ninth century medieval texts of the Hebrew Scriptures, called Masoretic texts. Comparisons were often made, however, to an older Greek translation called the Septuagint, which dated from 285 to 246 B.C., and a third reference source was the Samaritan Pentateuch. Actual original manuscripts of the Bible are lacking. The scrolls at Qumran, however, allowed investigators to see a thousand years beyond the previous Hebrew texts and opened a new era in textual studies and comparisons.

Any discovery about the Bible that would promise more information or new insights excites many. The Hebrew Bible, or Old Testament, is the foundation of both Judaism and Christianity. Although it was formed in the ancient Mideast, it has shaped modern Western thought. For example, the growth of science in the West is thought to be tied to believing that God, as described in Scriptures, is a God of consistency and order in nature. Norman L. Geisler and William E. Nix call the Bible "the most quoted, the most published, the most translated, and the most influential book in the history of mankind."

Many questioned if the scrolls would change religious belief; however, scholars expect no change in theology or doctrine to occur. The standards for making copies were high. This scroll and others do not differ in any important aspect from today's Scriptures. Minor variant readings do excite scholars, however, and new theories that explain the relationships of the texts are expected.

Insights into the times during which Jesus lived are also being gained. The Pharisees, Sadducees, and Zealots are familiar, but not the Essenes. Ethelbert Stauffer of Erlangen University points out that the *Manual of Discipline* taught to "love all sons of light" and "hate all the sons of darkness." Jesus may have been thinking of Essene teaching when he proclaimed, "You have heard that it was said, 'Love your neighbor and hate your enemy.' But I tell you, always love your enemies and always pray for those who persecute you" (Matt. 5:43, NET).

Most have concluded that the Essenes operated the settlement and caves at Qumran, but serious questions still remain. Some Essene doctrines, such as celibacy, divorce, and monogamy, parallel teachings of the early Christian church. Publication of the *Damascus Documents*, which correlate with documents found in Egypt, promises further understanding of Qumran teachings.

Slow publication of the remaining scrolls led restless scholars to criticize the exclusive assigning of documents to one investigator. By 1990, the *Biblical Archaeological Review* urged that all the remaining manuscripts be shared without further delay. Editor John Strugnell believes that funds and war have caused delay. The full theoretical implications of the document discovery of the twentieth century are still to come.

Bibliography

Coss, Thurman L. *Secrets from the Caves: A Layman's Guide to the Dead Sea Scrolls.* New York: Abingdon Press, 1963. A question-answer approach to the subject of the scrolls provides quick, nontechnical information on various basic issues that are often raised by the discoveries. Good introduction to the scrolls.

Davies, Philip R. "How Not to Do Archaeology: The Story of Qumran." *Biblical Archaeologist* 51 (December, 1988): 203-207. Davies cites slowness in publication, lack of objectivity, jumping to conclusions, and preoccupation with dating as problems at Qumran. He objects to Qumran being called a religious center and suggests that it looks more like an agricultural settlement that was strategically placed for defensive purposes.

Gaster, Theodor H. *The Dead Sea Scriptures.* 2d ed. Garden City, N.Y.: Doubleday,

1976. Gaster furnishes English translations with notes on some of the scrolls that have not been known previously through the Bible or Apocrypha. The *Memoirs of the Patriarchs* (a.k.a. *Genesis Apocryphon*) is particularly interesting. The hymns (psalms) show strong reflections of the familiar Scriptures and are thought by Gaster to be the most original literary work found in the scrolls.

Geisler, Norman L., and William E. Nix. *From God to Us: How We Got Our Bible.* Chicago: Moody Press, 1974. Two recognized scholars review the history of both testaments of the Bible. Chapter 17 discusses the differences among the Septuagint, the Masoretic text, the Samaritan, and the Dead Sea Scrolls and how scholars have interpreted these differences. They conclude that the meaning of the passages is not affected by variants.

Golb, Norman. "The Dead Sea Scrolls: A New Perspective." *American Scholar* 58 (Spring, 1989): 177-207. Not all investigators believe that the Essene sect was involved with the Qumran artifacts. Golb calls for consideration of an alternative hypothesis that the Jews generally hid their writings because of Roman oppression. He lists his arguments. His initial objection was also reported and summarized in *Scientific American* 242 (June, 1980): 85.

Mathews, K. A. "The Paleo-Hebrew Leviticus Scroll from Qumran." *Biblical Archaeologist* 50 (March, 1987): 45-54. Shows and discusses an example of variant readings with resulting English translations among the Masoretic, Samaritan Pentateuch, Greek Septuagint, and the Leviticus (11QpaleLev) scroll. Hebrew practices such as placing dots between words, "hanging" the letters on lines made with a sharp instrument, and using different script for the name of God (which was not to be read) are explained.

Shanks, Hershel. "Dead Sea Scroll Variation on 'Show and Tell'—It's Called 'Tell, But No Show'" and "Leading Dead Sea Scroll Scholar Denounces Delay." *Biblical Archaeological Review* 16 (March/April, 1990): 18-25. Recognized scholars expressed their frustrations with the slowness of the publication of "4Q" materials and especially the lack of access they have had to the scrolls. Highly recommended to anyone with an interest in biblical archaeology. The approach is nontechnical and the illustrations are excellent.

Tushingham, A. Douglas. "The Men Who Hid the Dead Sea Scrolls." *National Geographic* 64 (December, 1958): 784-808. The illustrations by Peter V. Bianchi are very well done. Findings of the excavations by Father Roland de Vaux at Qumran are explained. Provides background on the environment of the settlement and its people. The difficult sorting of the scroll fragments at the museum is shown.

Wise, Michael. "The Dead Sea Scrolls, Part 1: Archaeology and Biblical Manuscripts." *Biblical Archaeologist* 49 (September, 1986): 140-154.

_____. "The Dead Sea Scrolls, Part 2: Nonbiblical Manuscripts." *Biblical Archaeologist* 49 (December, 1986): 228-243. This two-part article discusses the site of Qumran and reviews the biblical and nonbiblical texts found there. Details abound concerning inkwells, the long work tables for scribes, the number of copies of each book of the Bible found, pottery types, and the areas of historical research that are affected by the scrolls.

Paul R. Boehlke

Cross-References
The French Expedition at Susa Discovers the Hammurabi Code (1902), p. 169; Carter Discovers the Tomb of Tutankhamen (1922), p. 730; Libby Introduces the Carbon-14 Method of Dating Ancient Objects (1940's), p. 1160; Seventeen-Thousand-Year-Old Paintings Are Discovered in Lascaux Cave (1940), p. 1176; An Ancient Sanctuary Is Discovered in El Juyo Cave, Spain (1979), p. 2110.

SHOCKLEY, BARDEEN, AND BRATTAIN DISCOVER THE TRANSISTOR

Category of event: Applied science
Time: November-December, 1947
Locale: Bell Telephone Laboratories, Murray Hill, New Jersey

Shockley and Bardeen provided the theory, and Bardeen and Brattain performed the experiments, that led to the discovery of the point-contact transistor

Principal personages: ˏ

WILLIAM SHOCKLEY (1910-1989), a theoretical solid-state physicist and leader of the team that discovered the transistor

JOHN BARDEEN (1908-   ), a theoretician who explained an early failure in the search for an amplifying and rectifying semiconductor device and who assisted Brattain in the actual experiments demonstrating the transistor effect

WALTER H. BRATTAIN (1902-1987), an experimental physicist who, working with Bardeen, performed the experiments that led to demonstrating the transistor effect

Summary of Event

Vacuum tube technology was well established by the beginning of World War II. The tubes functioned by allowing current to flow only in one direction—from one electrode inside an evacuated tube to another. The current passing through the tube could also be controlled by inserting a metal grid between the two electrodes. By changing the voltage applied to the grid, the current between the electrodes could be increased. These two basic functions of vacuum tubes (rectification and amplification) were established by 1906. In subsequent years, additional complicated tubes were designed to operate in more and more complicated circuitry. The thriving pre-World War II electronics industry, based primarily on the increasingly sophisticated vacuum tube designs, was not seriously affected by the Great Depression. The pre-war culmination of these developments took place at the 1939 World's Fair, in which fully electronic television began regular broadcasting.

Vacuum tubes had inherent limitations that were exacerbated by technological developments spurred on by World War II. Vacuum tubes were bulky, required large amounts of power to operate, were not particularly rugged, and needed reliable cooling systems to prevent damage from overheating. Radar, developed during the war, required circuits to operate over a range of frequencies, power, and voltages which vacuum tubes could not provide. Nevertheless, vacuum tube technology was resilient enough to be incorporated into a major technological advancement of the war: the proximity fuze. A small radar unit, using vacuum tubes, placed in the nose of an artillery shell could be set to detonate at a specific distance from the target. Vacuum tube circuits were designed to survive being shot out of a gun, small enough to fit in the nose of a small shell, and rugged enough to survive long enough to complete its mission.

Although electronic computers did not play a major part in World War II, they did add another impetus to the movement toward a replacement technology. The development of bigger and better computers was limited in part by the vast arrays of vacuum tubes and cooling systems required. Designers realized that significant advances in electronic computers would require circuits based on elements other than vacuum tubes.

M. J. Kelley, vice president for research at Bell Telephone Laboratories (Bell Labs), noticed in the 1930's the limitations of vacuum tubes used for the mechanical switching of telephone calls. He, among many other engineers, wished for a suitable solid-state device, such as a semiconductor, to replace vacuum tubes. Semiconductors (so named because they do not carry current as well as conductors) were suggested as possible replacements for vacuum tubes in the decades before World War II; however, the lack of detailed knowledge of the actual operation of electrical conduction in the semiconductors and the difficulties in fabricating suitable circuit elements prevented any serious progress. Kelley set up a solid-state research group in the summer of 1945. Headed by William Shockley, the group included Walter H. Brattain, John Bardeen, Gerald Pearson, and Robert Gibney. The group members were versed in the relatively new quantum theory of solids, which held out the promise of understanding the properties of solids, but they had not kept up with progress involving semiconductors. The group set out first to review attempts to use silicon and germanium (which are semiconductors) in radar. These materials seemed the most promising place to start the search for a suitable replacement for vacuum tubes.

They studied the two types of semiconductors—the "p-type" and the "n-type"— so named because the carriers of the electrical current were either positive or negative. Wartime work indicated that a very slight amount of phosphorus added to silicon or germanium made the semiconductor an n-type, because the phosphorus gave up one electron per atom. Earlier work also had shown that other impurities take up electrons from the atoms in the semiconductor, leaving "holes" in the crystal structure where the electrons used to be. These holes then can move around, carrying current.

In the summer of 1945, Shockley theorized that amplification and rectification could be achieved by applying an external electric field to a block of quartz with a thin semiconducting film on one side and a metallic conductor on the other side. His calculations indicated that the current could be increased considerably by applying a voltage between the semiconducting film and the metallic conductor. Repeated experimental attempts to verify the amplification failed. Shockley had Bardeen check the calculations, which proved correct. By March, 1946, Bardeen came up with a theoretical explanation for their inability to see this "field effect." He postulated that electrons got trapped on the surface of the semiconductor and were thus unable to contribute to the flow of the current. Brattain assisted in experiments that demonstrated that such an effect occurred. Bardeen and Brattain believed that the problems arising from field effect could be overcome if the connection between the metallic conductor and the semiconductor were made through an electrolyte (a fluid that conducts electricity). They used a "cat's whisker" contact (a piece of fine wire) to make contact. They observed amplification, but the characteristics of the electrolyte limited the amplication to very low frequencies. Bardeen and Brattain then tried to replace the electrolyte with a layer of germanium oxide and a gold contact. They could not get the oxide layer to form properly, so they placed a cat's whisker contact close to the gold contact and performed the experiment anyway. The result of the experiment was exactly opposite from what was expected. The field effect predicted a decrease in the current to the cat's whisker when a positive voltage was applied to the contact, but the experiment showed an increase in the current. The unexpected result indicated that "holes" as well as electrons were involved in the flow of current. The effect was called "bipolar," since both positive and negative charge carriers were involved.

By December, 1947, amplification was increased to a factor of fifty by replacing the cat's whisker and the gold contact with two lines of gold foil spaced about 0.5 micrometer apart. They quickly realized that contacts in the form of a line were not necessary and replaced them with two closely spaced cat's whiskers. The device was later named the "point-contact transistor" to indicate the type of connection made to the device and the fact that it transfers current from a low-resistance input to a high-resistance output.

The operation of the point-contact transistor was not well understood theoretically. Shockley suggested using a simpler system: a single crystal of semiconducting material with a p-type region sandwiched between two n-type regions. The junction between the regions would rectify the current, and Shockley's theory predicted that amplification would also occur. After 1951, the "junction transistor" dominated the field because it proved to be useful, versatile, and fairly easy to fabricate after physicists at Bell Labs were able to develop techniques to grow the crystals.

Aware of the significance of the transistor, the staff at Bell Labs spent six months drawing up patent applications and performing additional experiments before announcing the discovery at a press conference on July 1, 1948. A paper written jointly by Bardeen and Brattain appeared in a major scientific journal two weeks later.

Impact of Event

The immediate impact of the discovery of the transistor was negligible. Other scientists recognized its potential, but formidable technical obstacles hindered the transformation of the first point-contact transistor—a rather gawky looking and crude device—into a practical, functional, economical, and useful circuit element. For years, transistors were difficult to manufacture reliably and even more difficult to keep operating within given specifications. Although they got a late start, junction transistors proved easier to mass-produce than point-contact transistors. In addition, transistors could not be directly replaced for vacuum tubes in existing electronic devices: Different designs had to be produced to incorporate transistors into the existing devices.

The United States military was interested enough in the potential of the transistor to provide Bell Telephone Laboratories with financial support and a market for transistors. Transistors began to be used in telephone equipment in 1952 and appeared in hearing aids in 1953. The first hearing aids using transistors were actually more expensive than those using vacuum tubes, but the transistorized hearing aids used less power and saved their owners money on the cost of replacement batteries. Once established, the use of transistors in hearing aids dramatically changed that market. Before two years had passed, virtually all hearing aids used only transistors, and sales of hearing aids increased considerably. The first transistorized radio appeared in 1954. In 1955, IBM marketed its model 7090 computer, which took up less space and consumed 5 percent of the power of earlier vacuum-tube-laden computers. As of 1956, transistors had not yet conquered the consumer market, but Shockley, Bardeen, and Brattain were recognized for their researches on semiconductors and their discovery of the transistor effect by winning the Nobel Prize in Physics.

In 1958, ten years after the discovery of the point-contact transistor, transistor technology leapt forward with the development of the "planar technique" to produce an integrated circuit—an entire electronic circuit on a single piece of semiconductor material. The larger and more powerful electronic devices made possible by transistors had made construction and testing of the thousands of individual components a formidable task. Integrated circuits squeezed thousands of components onto one small piece of semiconducting material. The commercial introduction of microprocessors (the "computers on a chip" which incorporated highly complicated integrated circuits in a cheap, mass-producible form) appeared in 1971. The need for additional complicated devices which cost less, took up less space, required less power, and were easy to manufacture continued the drive for miniaturization that was well under way decades before the transistor effect was discovered.

Bibliography

Bernstein, Jeremy. *Three Degrees Above Zero: Bell Labs in the Information Age.* New York: Charles Scribner's Sons, 1984. Clearly written for a general audience, this book provides an overview of the many research interests of the employees of Bell Labs. Part 2 covers the developments of the 1930's and the 1940's in more detail than most other works. Few illustrations and an inadequate index.

Bode, Hendrik Wade. *Synergy: Technological Integration and Technical Innovation in the Bell System.* Murray Hill, N.J.: Bell Laboratories, 1971. Analyzes the "technical integration" of Bell Labs. Discusses how Bell Labs has been shaped by technical and engineering problems. Provides a detailed description of technological innovation as practiced by Bell Labs.

Braun, Ernest, and Stuart Macdonald. *Revolution in Miniature: The History and Impact of Semiconductor Electronics.* Cambridge, England: Cambridge University

Press, 1978. Presents an account of the development of the primary inventions in semiconductor electronics. Recounts the development of the semiconductor industry. Written for the general reader; technical language is avoided.

Mabon, Prescott C. *Mission Communications: The Story of Bell Laboratories.* Murray Hill, N.J.: Bell Telephone Laboratories, 1975. Adds some not-so-widely-understood-facts about the discovery of the transistor in chapter 5. Written by a former vice president and assistant to the chairman of the board of AT&T, this account is aimed at a general audience, whereas most of the writing of Bell Labs employees is much more technical.

Millman, S., ed. *A History of Engineering and Science in the Bell System: The Physical Sciences (1925-1980).* Indianapolis: AT&T Customer Information Center, 1983. Moderately technical and clearly written. Describes research on semiconductors in the second chapter. Contains brief reminiscences of Walter Brattain, a Bell Labs internal memo on the discovery of the transistor, and extensive references.

Smits, F. M., ed. *A History of Engineering and Science in the Bell System: Electronics Technology (1925-1975).* Indianapolis: AT&T Customer Information Center, 1985. Describes the invention of the transistor, the public announcement and reception, and its further development. Includes reproductions of pages from the notebooks of the physicists involved.

Weaire, Denis L., and Colin G. Windsor, eds. *Solid State Science: Past, Present, and Predicted.* London: Taylor and Francis, 1987. Presents an overview and discusses the state of historical research of the field of solid-state physics in nontechnical terms in the preface, introduction, and first chapter of this book. The remaining chapters are technical.

Weart, Spencer R. "The Birth of the Solid-State Physics Community." *Physics Today* 41 (July, 1988): 38-45. Adapted from the book *History of Solid State Physics* (1990). Written by the director of the Center for the History of Physics of the American Institute of Physics. Nontechnical, this article includes a sidebar which describes the International Project in the History of Solid State Physics.

Roger Sensenbaugh

Cross-References

Fleming Files a Patent for the First Vacuum Tube (1904), p. 255; Sony Develops the Pocket-Sized Transistor Radio (1957), p. 1528; Esaki Demonstrates Electron Tunneling in Semiconductors (1957), p. 1551; The Microprocessor "Computer on a Chip" Is Introduced (1971), p. 1938; Texas Instruments Introduces the First Commercial Pocket Calculator (1972), p. 1971.

GAMOW AND ASSOCIATES DEVELOP
THE BIG BANG THEORY

Category of event: Astronomy
Time: 1948
Locale: Washington, D.C.

Gamow proposed that the observable universe resulted from the explosion of a hot, dense primordial fireball, which later expanded and condensed into galaxies and then suns

Principal personages:

GEORGE GAMOW (1904-1968), a Russian-born American nuclear physicist and cosmologist who studied the evolution of stars and developed the big bang theory

RALPH ASHER ALPHER (1921-), an American physicist and collaborator with Gamow who calculated the formation of heavy elements during the big bang

ROBERT C. HERMAN (1914-), an American physicist who worked with Alpher on the calculations of heavy element formation

GEORGES LEMAÎTRE (1894-1966), a Belgian Jesuit priest, astronomer, and cosmologist who proposed the concept that the universe expanded from an original "cosmic egg" of super dense matter

FRED HOYLE (1915-), an English astronomer who proposed a "steady state" model of the universe, which was the chief cosmological competitor of the big bang during the 1950's and 1960's

Summary of Event

After World War II, George Gamow, a professor at George Washington University in Washington, D.C., began a series of calculations demonstrating that reversing the galactic expansion pointed to a time when all the matter was confined to an extremely small space (perhaps thirty times the sun's diameter) at a temperature of thousands of trillions of degrees. He presumed that the density of the radiation was greater than the density of the matter, a condition which caused the explosion leading to the formation of the present universe, known as the big bang theory.

Gamow's big bang theory was based upon the cosmological implications of Edwin Powell Hubble's discovery in 1929 of the directly proportional relationship of distance and velocity of recession for the distant galaxies. This relationship implied that the universe was expanding, which had an immediate effect upon Albert Einstein's preferred static cosmological model, which had dominated thought since his publication of the general theory of relativity in 1916. Einstein had been forced to introduce a "constant of repulsion" to counteract the force of gravity in a static universe. Willem de Sitter found a second static solution which implied near zero density and also that the light of distant stars would be redshifted. In Russia, Aleksandr A. Friedmann discovered a dynamic solution that implied an expanding universe. Georges Lemaître, unaware of Friedmann's solution, proposed in 1927 that a homogeneous and isotropic universe originated from a "cosmic egg." Lemaître unfortunately had to retain Einstein's constant of repulsion to explain the expansion in his model since he did not envision an initial explosion.

The primary motive for Gamow's proposal was not to resolve the issue of a static versus a dynamic universe but to explain how the heavier elements could be formed in their observed relative abundances. Hydrogen and helium were presumed to constitute approximately 99 percent of the matter in the universe. The other 1 percent consisted of the heavier elements which decline in abundance through the periodic table until zinc is reached. At this point, roughly halfway down the periodic table, the abundance flattens out and approximately the same amount of all the remaining elements occur. Gamow, in these early days, reasoned that this pattern could not be the result of the stellar formation of the heavy elements. He proposed that they were formed in the first thirty minutes of the initial explosion before the temperature had cooled too much. He believed he could explain how deuterium (heavy hydrogen) could be formed in the big bang, while he was convinced that it would be destroyed only in stellar interiors. He also believed that helium was too abundant to be formed in the stars and had to result from the initial explosion. Finally, the uniform distribution of the helium implied that it was not the consequence of stellar activity. This portion of his initial ideas has stood the test of time. Gamow also devoted extensive attention to stellar dynamics in his 1940 book *The Birth and Death of the Sun*. At this time, however, he still did not have an adequate explanation for how the heavy elements could be formed during stellar evolution, so he proposed the big bang as a means of resolving that problem.

Gamow enlisted the aid of two physicists to calculate the mathematics involved in heavy element formation: Ralph Asher Alpher, a Ph.D. candidate at The Johns Hopkins University, and Robert Herman, enlisted because of his skills with the early computers in use by the Bureau of Standards. A major element of their theory came from a surprising source. During World War II, Donald Hughes at Brookhaven National Laboratory had measured the neutron-capture characteristics for several atoms and found that capture increased during the first half of the periodic table and then flattened out, the inverse of the pattern of abundance of the elements. On this basis, Alpher proposed that neutron capture explained Gamow's element formation during the first thirty minutes of the big bang.

Although Alpher and Herman devoted extensive efforts to demonstrating how the elementary particles could combine under extreme conditions, serious problems remained with the formation of the heavy elements if the temperature dropped below a billion degrees, which implied that all the heavy elements had to form during the first thirty minutes of the big bang. There were no stable elements with atomic number 5 and 8, which meant that there would be a gap in the buildup of atoms of the heavier elements between helium and lithium. Other astronomers regarded the gap as evidence that the buildup would result only in the formation of hydrogen and helium in the initial big bang, a position that has become generally accepted. While Gamow devised a theoretical means of bridging the gap, the low probability of his proposed sequence of events led to a severe time constraint in the cooling state of the early universe. He conceded eventually that the heavy elements were not created in the initial big bang. While assumption that the dynamics of self-gravitating gaseous clouds caused condensation of the cooling gases into galaxies and stars presented difficulties, Gamow believed that the outline of the theory was firm enough to present it publicly in 1948. It was popularly presented in 1952 in the book entitled *The Creation of the Universe.*

Many astronomers were troubled by Gamow's proposal, especially the implications of a beginning and an ending to the universe. By 1950, Fred Hoyle of the University of Cambridge proposed what came to be called the "steady state" universe, in which hydrogen was continuously originating in intergalactic space and then coalescing into gaseous clouds that eventually gave birth to new stars. In such a universe, there need be no beginning, but it contradicted the physical concept of the conservation of matter, namely, that matter could neither originate nor be destroyed without being converted into energy.

While Gamow's presentation of the big bang was accepted by many astronomers as a proper interpretation of the astronomical evidence, the specific proof of the theory was slower in coming. Alpher and Herman pointed out in 1948 that the level of radiation had steadily declined since the big bang to a level that they estimated to be 5 Kelvins (above absolute zero). They thought that it might still be detectable, not as light but perhaps as a low-level microwave radiation.

In 1965, Robert Henry Dicke, unaware of Alpher's and Herman's work, calculated that the residual radiation should be apparent at about 5 Kelvins and would emanate from all parts of the sky. He believed so firmly in his prediction that he began to construct equipment large enough and sophisticated enough to detect the radiation. Unknown to him, Arno Penzias and Robert Wilson of the Bell Laboratories had already discovered the microwave radiation in their efforts to study sources of background radiation causing static in radio transmission. A friend who heard a lecture about Dicke's prediction mentioned it to them, whereupon they realized they had detected the radiation and contacted Dicke for verification. With the discovery of this 3 (instead of 5) Kelvins background radiation, a major confirmation of the hot big bang was available. The big bang more aptly explained the expansion of the universe than other theories and has gradually become the accepted understanding of the origin of the universe.

Impact of Event

The expansion of the universe, combined with a reasonable explanation of the manner in which it has evolved, has changed conceptions of a static universe that prevailed in the 1920's. In that sense, the big bang cosmology has been successful as a means of stimulating cosmological theory and research. As a means of explaining the relative abundance of the elements, as Gamow originally proposed it, the theory was only partially successful. The formation of the heavier elements is now presumed to take place in the stars themselves, rather than during the big bang, where hydrogen and helium are assumed to be the result. Because of the problem with heavy elements, there was some early neglect of the success of the theory in explaining the buildup of helium and the abundance of hydrogen and helium compared with the rest of the elements. Gamow's team was also successful in identifying the process of heavy element formation through neutron capture. They merely had the wrong location, the big bang, instead of in the interiors of massive stars. One attractive feature of Gamow's theory was that the original explosion was of such force that he did not have to hypothesize a "constant of repulsion" as Einstein had done in his gravitational field equations in order to counterbalance gravitation to maintain a static universe.

The clear implication of the big bang is that the universe had a beginning and that it will die a cold and isolated death as the galaxies become farther apart, with the individual stars eventually burning out as a result of an insufficient rate of birth of new stars. Some cosmologists have proposed a coming collapse of the universe (an idea Gamow described in 1952), with perhaps an oscillation of big bangs and collapses.

Gamow's general outline has become the standard cosmology, although the level of sophistication of the theory and its mathematical foundations have dramatically changed. The principal difficulty of his theory eventually forced Gamow to accept Fred Hoyle's explanation of heavy element formation in the interior of stars. The success of this portion of Hoyle's theory explained why the rest of his steady-state cosmology enjoyed some temporary success in opposition to Gamow's proposal. Heavy element building from fundamental particles during the radiative life of massive stars, and dispersal into space through supernova explosions, is now the widely accepted view. Gamow is appropriately regarded as a far-seeing pioneer of big bang cosmology. The prediction of a basic evidence in microwave radiation is properly regarded as a brilliant insight that was inappropriately neglected, but which has established the big bang as the most reasonable explanation.

Bibliography

Gamow, George. *The Creation of the Universe.* New York: Viking Press, 1952. This cosmology is out-of-date, but it is important as a statement of Gamow's understanding of the big bang in the early 1950's. It is written for the general public and reveals the strong personality and the "broad brush" picture of the universe that Gamow could present.

_____. "The Evolution of the Universe." *Nature* 162 (October 30, 1948): 680. A short early sketch of the big bang theory at a moderately technical level for the general scientific audience. Gamow's intentions for proposing the theory are clearly evident in the first and last paragraphs of this article.

_____. "Modern Cosmology." *Scientific American* 190 (March, 1954):

55-63. This is a popular summary of Gamow's theory as developed by 1954, six years after it was proposed. Beginning with the size, scale, and expansion of the universe, Gamow then presents his perception of the big bang and discusses why it was the best explanation of the observed phenomena.

_____. *My World Line: An Informal Biography.* New York: Viking Press, 1970. The afterword contains a brief description of his scientific achievements after coming to the United States. The first half of the chapter relates to the big bang from a personal perspective.

Gribbin, John. *In Search of the Big Bang.* New York: Bantam Books, 1986. A popular, accurate, and comprehensive statement of the currently accepted cosmology, which contains an excellent summary of Gamow's contribution on pages 148 to 158. One of the most readable general books.

Harrison, Edward R. *Cosmology: The Science of the Universe.* Cambridge, England: Cambridge University Press, 1981. A portion of a chapter on pages 513 to 525 contains a compact and clear sketch of the big bang and continuous creation cosmologies. Includes their strengths and why they were accepted and abandoned. One of the best overviews with an excellent bibliography.

Hoyle, Fred. *Frontiers of Astronomy.* New York: Harper & Row, 1955. Chapters 17 through 20 contain Hoyle's presentation of the steady-state cosmology, which he believed pointed up the weaknesses of Gamow's theory and provided a more philosophically acceptable explanation of the origin of the universe.

Silk, Joseph. *The Big Bang.* San Francisco: W. H. Freeman, 1980. A modern presentation of the current state of the big bang theory. There is some historical perspective, but the work should be read with Gamow's *The Creation of the Universe* for a clear picture of how the theory has evolved and become more sophisticated over the passage of time.

Ivan L. Zabilka

Cross-References

Lemaître Proposes the Big Bang Theory (1927), p. 825; Hubble Confirms the Expanding Universe (1929), p. 878; Penzias and Wilson Discover Cosmic Microwave Background Radiation (1963), p. 1762; The Inflationary Theory Solves Long-Standing Problems with the Big Bang (1980), p. 2125.

JACOBSEN INTRODUCES A DRUG FOR THE TREATMENT OF ALCOHOLISM

Category of event: Medicine
Time: 1948
Locale: Copenhagen, Denmark

Jacobsen and Hald accidentally discovered the alcohol deterrent properties of disulfiram (Antabuse) and recognized its value in the treatment of alcoholism

> *Principal personages:*
> ERIC JACOBSEN (1903-   ), a physician and professor of pharmacology who headed the team of scientists in the early investigational work on the pharmacology and toxicology of Antabuse
> JENS HALD, a Danish physician and associate of Jacobsen
> RUTH FOX (1895-1989), a psychoanalyst who was the first American physician to use Antabuse as a treatment for alcoholism

Summary of Event

Alcoholic beverages have been used by humankind since the dawn of history. The drinking of beer, wine, and distilled liquors is an accepted custom in most societies. There is a paradox in this widespread use of alcohol. Families celebrate births and weddings with alcohol, yet many families are destroyed by it. "Demon rum" is condemned by many religious groups, yet, at the same time, wine is often used as a sacrament in religious ceremonies.

People drink alcohol for a number of reasons, but a portion of the alcohol-consuming population drink alcohol in such quantities or with such frequency that, sooner or later, they lose control over their lives—with destructive consequences. In the United States, alcoholism is a factor in 30 percent of all suicides, 55 percent of all automobile fatalities, 60 percent of all child abuse, and 85 percent of all home violence. Chronic consumption of alcohol causes organic disease of the liver, heart, and nervous system. Alcohol abuse is considered to be the number three killer of Americans, ranked behind heart disease and cancer. Alcohol is also an insidiously addictive drug. Years of moderate-to-heavy drinking are required before the addiction is manifested.

Over the centuries, society has tried to curtail the excessive use of alcohol by labeling alcoholics as sinful or weak-willed individuals who have made their own problems and by legal action prohibiting the sale or consumption of alcoholic beverages. Such approaches have failed to protect either the public or susceptible individuals from the misery and destruction of alcohol abuse. In 1985, of the 160 million Americans of drinking age, 112 million drank alcoholic beverages. More than 10 percent of these social drinkers may have serious problems with alcohol and about 6 million are identified as alcoholics.

The recognition of alcoholism as a disease rather than a moral or legal problem was pioneered by Elvin Morton Jellinek, an American biometrician who performed extensive epidemiological studies of alcoholism and classified the disease into five types based on dependence of alcohol; pattern of use; and the physiological, psychological, and social consequences of its use. In 1960, Jellinek published *The Disease Concept of Alcoholism*, in which alcoholism was presented as a chronic, fatal, progressive disease and alcohol was identified as the cause of the disease, not a symptom of underlying emotional problems. The gradual acceptance by the medical community that alcoholism is a disease caused by drinking alcohol supports the beliefs expressed by Alcoholics Anonymous (AA), a group founded in 1935 by alcoholics to help other alcoholics stop drinking. Alcoholics Anonymous believes that alcoholics must realize they are powerless over the influence of alcohol. AA maintains that alcoholics can never "recover" and return to a life of social drinking; they must abstain from alcohol for the rest of their lives.

The treatment of alcoholism has long frustrated the medical community because of the limited success in helping the alcoholic abstain from drinking. Since the 1930's, therapies used to treat alcoholics have included psychological approaches (aversion therapy and psychoanalysis) and the prescription of drugs such as tranquilizers and lithium to help alcoholics overcome their addiction. For a brief period, psychotherapy sessions aided by administration of the powerful hallucinogen lysergic acid diethylamide (LSD) were strongly advocated by some researchers in the late 1960's as a breakthrough in the treatment of alcoholism. None of these medical approaches has survived or had a lasting impact in the treatment of alcoholism.

In 1951, however, the drug Antabuse was approved by the United States Food and Drug Administration (FDA) as an effective agent in the treatment of alcoholism. For the first time, physicians had a specific drug available for use as an aid in the treatment of alcoholism. The discovery of Antabuse as an effective alcohol deterrent drug was a purely serendipitous event. In 1947, at the Royal Danish School of Pharmacy in Copenhagen, Eric Jacobsen, a professor of pharmacology, and his assistant Jens Hald, were investigating a series of compounds such as anthelmintic agents, potential medicines for treating intestinal parasitic worm infections. The chemical compound disulfiram was selected for further study, and, as was common in those times, the investigators ingested small doses of the chemical for direct observations of potential side effects. No adverse reactions were noted. Several days later, these scientists attended a cocktail party. Shortly after finishing their first drink, both men became violently ill. Because they experienced the same illness at the exact same time, Jacobsen and Hald concluded that a combination of the small dose of disulfiram ingested days earlier and drinking alcoholic beverages had triggered the illness. The concept of using disulfiram as a preventive measure in the treatment of alcoholism suggested itself. Jacobsen and Hald published their preliminary findings supporting the use of the chemical disulfiram in the treatment of alcoholism in the English medical journal *Lancet* in 1948.

There is some irony in the fact that in 1937, E. E. Williams, physician to a rubber plant in Connecticut, wrote a letter to the editor of the *Journal of the American Medical Association* stating that workers exposed to disulfiram-like compounds, used as rubber polymerization accelerators, could not drink alcohol in any form. After a glass of beer, the workers would experience a flushing of the face and hands, a rapid heartbeat, and their blood pressure would drop twenty points. Williams stated that "men have worked here for years without any complaint other than their inability to drink. . . . one wonders whether one has discovered the cure for alcoholism. . . ." In reply to the query, the editor curtly stated that it had long been known that alcohol was a provocative agent that demonstrated the toxicity of such sulfide compounds, including the related chemical carbon disulfide. Although the editor missed Williams' point about using disulfiram as an alcohol-deterring agent, his statements about the relationship between, and toxicity of, compounds such as carbon disulfide and disulfiram were correct. Twenty years later, it was discovered that in patients who received large doses of disulfiram, significant amounts of the toxic chemical carbon disulfide actually were being produced in the body as a degradation product, or metabolite, of disulfiram.

The body's marked reaction to the combination of disulfiram and alcohol is a response to disulfiram's interference with the normal metabolism (detoxification) of ethyl alcohol in the liver. In the absence of disulfiram, enzymes in the liver rapidly metabolize or convert ethyl alcohol into acetaldehyde. Acetaldehyde is further converted into the compound acetate, the final nontoxic by-product of ethyl alcohol, by the liver enzyme aldehyde dehydrogenase. Disulfiram is a potent inhibitor of the liver enzyme aldehyde dehydrogenase. Inhibition of this enzyme by disulfiram breaks the chain of reactions necessary to detoxify ethyl alcohol, resulting in a rapid five- to ten-fold increase in blood levels of acetaldehyde.

A person who has been taking disulfiram and then consumes alcohol will experience what is known as a disulfiram-ethanol reaction (DER) within minutes. This profoundly unpleasant illness is characterized by the face becoming hot and scarlet, an intense throbbing in the head and neck, and a severe headache. The person may experience difficulty in breathing, chest pain, vomiting, confusion, and blurred vision. The facial flushing is replaced later by a blanched pallor, and blood pressure may fall severely. Symptoms of the DER may last from thirty minutes to several hours, depending upon the individual and amount of alcohol consumed. The victim becomes exhausted and sleeps for several hours after the symptoms have worn off. On waking, the person is well again. In rare cases, the DER can be so severe that the victim dies from cardiovascular collapse and congestive heart failure. More than twenty such fatalities have been reported in medical literature. The threat of this frightening and severe reaction to alcohol is the basis for the use of disulfiram (Antabuse) as an adjunct in the treatment of alcoholism.

Impact of Event

In 1949, Ruth Fox, a New York City psychoanalyst who specialized in the treatment of alcoholism, obtained enough disulfiram from colleagues in Denmark to treat about fifty alcoholic patients. In keeping with the current theories of that time, Dr. Fox used disulfiram in an aversion therapy regimen, in which the patient was given alcohol in a hospital setting to induce the DER deliberately. This process was repeated several times on a weekly basis in an effort to produce a conditioned reflex against the use of alcohol by the alcoholic patient. By 1950, Fox considered discontinuing disulfiram therapy. It was apparent that aversion to alcohol was not occurring, several of her patients had almost died during a DER episode, and almost one-third of the patients complained of serious side effects (headaches, skin rash, impotence). It was quite clear that the only reason the patient remained sober was a fear of the disulfiram-ethyl alcohol reaction. Fox decided to end the alcohol challenges that initiated the feared DER. Instead, she counseled patients about the severe reaction that would occur if they drank alcohol while taking disulfiram. Furthermore, she reduced the daily dose of disulfiram to a quarter of the recommended dose. Immediately after implementing these changes, patients' complaints of side effects disappeared without the loss of the alcohol-deterring properties of daily administration of disulfiram. During her career, Fox used disulfiram to treat more than twenty-five hundred alcoholic patients; many responded with gratifying results. Antabuse—the proprietary brand name of disulfiram—is still the only drug currently approved by the FDA for specific treatment of alcoholism. Approximately 200,000 people in the United States take Antabuse every day in their personal battle against alcoholism.

Antabuse therapy is not without controversy. Some physicians are reluctant to prescribe a drug that has the potential to induce a violent illness and possibly cause death if the patient ignores the doctor's advice and drinks alcohol. Controlled studies have not shown Antabuse therapy to be more successful in helping alcoholics than conventional forms of counseling or group support programs run by AA.

All patients taking Antabuse must be cautioned to be on guard against "hidden alcohol" to avoid an accidental DER. Many medications, flavoring agents, and foods contain ethyl alcohol. Some cough syrups, mouthwashes, flavoring agents such as vanilla extract, and various desserts, sauces, and soups flavored with wines or liquors may contain enough alcohol to initiate a severe DER. Antabuse is not a panacea for treating all alcoholics or all forms of alcoholism. Antabuse does not stop or prevent the alcoholic's desire to drink. Antabuse can help the motivated alcoholic who desperately wants to stop drinking.

By choosing Antabuse therapy, the alcoholic only has to make one decision a day about drinking—whether or not to take the Antabuse pill. The alcoholic who takes the pill knows that a "chemical policeman" will keep watch over the next four or five days to help prevent the compulsive urge to drink. With this knowledge, Antabuse gives the alcoholic time during the difficult transition and adjustment from alcoholism to a life of sobriety.

Bibliography

Bowman, William C., and Michael J. Rand. "Social Pharmacology: Drug Use for Nonmedical Purposes: Drug Dependence." In *Textbook of Pharmacology*. 2d ed.

Oxford, England: Blackwell Scientific Publications, 1980. Gives treatment to the social and political aspects of ethanol use equal to that given the pharmacology and toxicology of ethanol. One of the few medical pharmacology texts that discusses the theory that metabolites of ethanol may react with endogenous neurotransmitters to form morphinelike compounds in the brain of the alcoholic.

FitzGerald, Kathleen W. *Alcoholism: the Genetic Inheritance.* New York: Doubleday, 1988. Unusual format; each chapter begins with a profile sketch or short story that puts a human face on alcoholics, their spouses and children, and the struggle they face in achieving sobriety. Argues that alcoholism is a genetic disease, and, to lessen the stigma associated with alcoholism, refers to it as Jellinek's disease. No mention of Antabuse.

Fox, Ruth, ed. "Disulfiram (Antabuse) as an Adjunct in the Treatment of Alcoholism." In *Alcoholism: Behavioral Research, Therapeutic Approaches.* New York: Springer, 1967. A collection of papers presented at several scientific conferences on alcoholism. Good but dated references. Discusses the development and refinement of Antabuse therapy in alcoholism. Downplays the adverse side effects of disulfiram and suggests that even skid-row alcoholics can recover with disulfiram treatment in a half-way house setting.

McNichol, Ronald W., John A. Ewing, and Morris D. Faiman. *Disulfiram (Antabuse): A Unique Medical Aid to Sobriety.* Springfield, Ill.: Charles C Thomas, 1987. Written by three practicing physicians who enthusiastically support the use of Antabuse in alcoholic treatment. For the reader with a background in the life sciences. Emphasizes the use of disulfiram as a deterrent to impulsive drinking. Excellent chapter on the pharmacodynamics and toxicology of disulfiram. Extensive references.

Milam, James R., and Katherine Ketcham. *Under the Influence: A Guide to the Myths and Realities of Alcoholism.* Seattle: Madrona, 1981. Uses nontechnical language while presenting a solid scientific treatise on alcoholism. Offers cautious endorsement of Antabuse as a temporary aid to the recovering alcoholic. Argues that physiology, not psychology, determines whether a drinker will become addicted to alcohol.

Nace, Edgar P. *The Treatment of Alcoholism.* New York: Brunner/Mazel, 1987. Written for medical students, psychiatry residents, and counselors in alcoholism treatment centers. Emphasizes counseling, the role of the family in therapy, and the patient-physician relationship. Good history of Alcoholics Anonymous and their crucial role in providing support for the alcoholic.

Physicians' Desk Reference. 43d ed. Oradell, N.J.: Medical Economics, 1989. Capsule summary of the action, indication, and dosage administration of Antabuse. Important summary of contraindications and adverse effects noted with disulfiram administration.

Brian L. Roberts

Cross-References

Pavlov Develops the Concept of Reinforcement (1902), p. 163; Hofmann Synthesizes the Potent Psychedelic Drug LSD-25 (1938), p. 1123; Wilkins Discovers Reserpine, the First Tranquilizer (1950's), p. 1353; Wilkins Introduces Reserpine for the Treatment of High Blood Pressure (1952), p. 1429; Janowsky Publishes a Cholinergic-Adrenergic Hypothesis of Mania and Depression (1972), p. 1976; Gruentzig Uses Percutaneous Transluminal Angioplasty, via a Balloon Catheter, to Unclog Diseased Arteries (1977), p. 2088.

THE STEADY-STATE THEORY OF THE UNIVERSE IS ADVANCED BY BONDI, GOLD, AND HOYLE

Categories of event: Astronomy and physics
Time: 1948
Locale: Cambridge University, England

Bondi, Gold, and Hoyle presented the steady-state theory in which the universe was infinite, eternal, and unchanging

Principal personages:

SIR FRED HOYLE (1915-), an English astronomer and astrophysicist who was one of the chief spokesmen for the steady-state theory

THOMAS GOLD (1920-), an Austrian-English-American astronomer who was one of the originators of the steady-state theory

HERMANN BONDI (1919-), an Austrian-English mathematician and cosmologist who was one of the originators of the steady-state theory

GEORGE GAMOW (1904-1968), a Russian-American physicist who was one of the chief spokesmen for the theory

GEORGES LEMAÎTRE (1894-1966), a Belgian astronomer and priest who proposed the big bang theory

EDWIN POWELL HUBBLE (1889-1953), an American astronomer who showed that the universe is expanding

ALBERT EINSTEIN (1879-1955), a German-Swiss-American physicist who developed the theory of general relativity

Summary of Event

Since at least the time of the ancient Greek philosophers twenty-six centuries ago, these bold questions have been asked about the universe: How was the universe made? Has it always been here? If not, where did it come from? By the first half of the twentieth century, it was known that the sun was a star, one of hundreds of billions of stars that form the Milky Way galaxy. It was known that there were billions of galaxies like the Milky Way and that the farthest ones were more than a billion light-years away. In his theory of general relativity, Albert Einstein presented a framework grand enough that theories of the universe could be formulated within it. Unfortunately, it allows one to formulate many theories without telling which of the theories, if any, is correct.

In 1929, Edwin Powell Hubble showed that only models which allowed for the expansion of the universe could be correct, for he showed that distant galaxies in all directions are receding from the Milky Way and that the more distant a galaxy is, the faster it flees from our galaxy. The mathematical expression of these facts is called the Hubble law. Science, however, has been unable to come up with a better explanation of these facts other than to suppose that the universe itself is expanding.

An analogy that is frequently used is that of dots painted on a partially inflated balloon. If the balloon is further inflated, each painted dot becomes farther away from the other dots because the space between the dots expands. One could note also that dots that were twice as far away would recede twice as fast, as Hubble's observation requires. It should be understood, however, that the expansion of space has no effect on the small scale. For example, the Rock of Gibraltar is not growing larger because the space within it is expanding. The forces that hold the Rock together also keep it from expanding with space. It is only on the largest scale—that of superclusters of galaxies—that the forces are weak enough to yield to the expansion. The distances between superclusters of galaxies do grow larger as space expands.

If the universe is expanding, it must have been smaller in the past. It seems to be a straightforward matter to use Hubble's law to calculate when the universe began. If it is known how far away the parts are and how fast they are going, one should be able to calculate how long ago they were all together. Using Hubble's original data, 2 billion years was given as the age of the universe. This was somewhat embarrassing since the accepted age of the earth was far older. The problem lies in measuring the distances to distant galaxies, a difficult and uncertain process. Using other data, the age of the universe is calculated to be between 10 and 20 billion years, which fits well with the accepted age of the earth of 4.6 billion years.

In 1927, Georges Lemaître proposed an expanding universe based upon a prediction of general relativity. He supposed that all of space, matter, and energy had been crushed together and then exploded outward. It is this explosion that Sir Fred Hoyle later named the "big bang." Attracting little attention at first, Lemaître's theory gained notice only after Hubble's discovery. A common misconception of the big bang theory is to picture the matter of the universe exploding outward into the otherwise empty space of the universe. The big bang theories of general relativity, however, allow the whole universe to begin as very small. The explosion of the big bang occurred over the whole universe—it *was* the whole universe. While common sense seems at first to demand that there be some place for the universe to expand into, mathematicians assure astronomers that that is not necessary. The universe is defined commonly to include all the space there is; to say that it grows larger does not, of necessity, require anything to lie beyond the boundaries of the universe. Here, the simple analogy with the expanding balloon fails completely, for a balloon and a universe obey different rules. Motivated by observations of radioactive decay, Lemaître supposed that at the instant of the big bang, all matter had been combined into a gigantic nucleus. This nucleus then decayed into the known elements, and thus the surrounding matter had come into being.

In 1948, George Gamow and Ralph Alpher realized that the big bang must have been incredibly hot. It followed that the universe must have been filled with a primordial fireball of such heat that any element would have been ripped asunder into its constituent protons and neutrons. Building upon a theory proposed by Hans Albrecht Bethe in 1938, they showed how elements could form in the cooling fireball.

Hydrogen would be first to form since its nucleus is a proton or sometimes a proton combined with a neutron. Nuclear reactions would then convert about 25 percent of the matter into helium and a trace of lithium. There the process stops because the matter of the fireball is no longer dense enough for the reactions to continue.

In 1948, the big bang theory seemed unable to explain the existence of heavy elements, and it gave an age for the universe that was less than that of Earth. A further difficulty was the problem of forming galaxies. It seemed unlikely that matter flung outward in the violence of the big bang would be able ever to coalesce again in clumps large enough to form galaxies. To overcome these difficulties, Hermann Bondi and Thomas Gold proposed the steady-state theory in 1948. They based this theory on what they called the perfect cosmological principle: When considering a large enough volume, the universe will appear the same everywhere and at any time. This meant that the universe is infinitely old, obviously far older than Earth. Accepting the fact that the universe is expanding, they reached the astounding conclusion that matter must be continuously created uniformly throughout space. Seeing nothing to prevent it from doing so, it was assumed that the new matter would coalesce to form new galaxies.

Since the most abundant element in the universe is hydrogen, Gold and Bondi proposed that the new mass appear as hydrogen. Using the best estimate for the rate of expansion of the universe, they calculated that if only one new hydrogen atom popped into existence in each volume of space the size of a living room over every few million years, then the average number of galaxies in a given volume of space would remain constant.

While there was no way to observe directly the creation of such a tiny amount of matter, there should still be observable consequences. In more than a billion years or so, enough matter should collect in the space between galaxies to form new galaxies, while old galaxies should become giants as they gather in new matter. Thus, the steady-state theory predicts how galaxies should be grouped: There should be a small number of old massive galaxies visible to Earth, and these should be surrounded by groups of small, younger galaxies. Later in 1948, Hoyle joined the backers of the steady-state model. He showed how continuous creation of matter might be fit possibly into the formidable framework of general relativity.

Impact of Event

The steady-state theory had both a cultural and a scientific impact. It had great philosophic appeal for many because it proclaimed a universe of order, an infinite and eternal universe, one that was fit for astronomers and always would be. Its organization was simple: Viewed on a grand enough scale, the universe was the same everywhere and for all time. The ready market for the many popular books written by Hoyle, Bondi, and others says something about the public's fascination with the steady-state theory. According to science historian Wolfgang Yourgrau, the introduction of the steady-state theory caused a tremendous sensation among cosmologists (those who study models of the universe). It stimulated much theoretical and empirical work as they sought either to prove the theory false or to find evidence to support it. Astronomers looking for the distribution of young and old galaxies predicted by the steady-state theory did not find it. Instead, they found that all galaxies close enough to be so studied have at least some old stars. It appears that all galaxies formed at approximately the same time and that there are no intrinsically young galaxies. Furthermore, the most abundant type of galaxy that is dominated by old stars is small.

Hoyle, who became the chief spokesman for the steady-state theory, worked on the problem of the origin of the heavy elements. He and others were able to show that heavy elements can form under the fantastic densities and temperatures that exist in the cores of stars and that these elements are flung back into space during supernova explosions. Eventually, heavy elements are incorporated into a new generation of stars and perhaps planets. It is interesting to contemplate that while humankind is made of the dust of the earth, that dust is stardust. At any rate, the origin of heavy elements was no longer a problem for the steady-state theory, but this was also true of the big bang theory. Another prediction of the steady-state theory was that, by and large, the universe has always been the same. Strangely enough, the universe as it was in the past is spread out. For example, the Andromeda nebula is more than 2 million light-years away; this means the light that reaches Earth now left the Andromeda nebula more than 2 million years ago. Today, one sees this galaxy as it was then. Likewise, when one looks billions of light-years out into space, the universe is seen as it was billions of years in the past. Contrary to the steady-state theory, as astronomers looked far out into space, they found increasing evidence that the universe of long ago was different. Perhaps the most spectacular difference is that quasars were once abundant in the universe, but there are scarcely any within a billion light-years of Earth. This means that there are few, if any, quasars left today.

As evidence against the steady-state theory mounted, Hoyle and his companions eventually abandoned it. It had been useful to stimulate science and to fire the imaginations of many, but its day had passed. With the discovery of the remnant primordial fireball radiation by Arno A. Penzias and Robert W. Wilson in 1965, the big bang theory reigned supreme. In its turn, however, the steady-state theory has since been displaced by a variation of the big bang theory called the inflationary theory, which holds the promise of overcoming some of the problems of the old theory. This is the fashion in which science advances.

Bibliography

Bondi, Hermann. *The Universe at Large.* Garden City, N.Y: Anchor Books, 1960. Popular-level book with chapters on stars, gravitation, and several chapters dealing with cosmology. Recommended for the general reader.

Bonnor, William. *The Mystery of the Expanding Universe.* New York: Macmillan, 1964. Covers basic observations and compares them with various cosmological theories. Includes a fine nonmathematical treatment of the cosmological models of general relativity. Good chapter on the steady-state theory. Highly recommended for the interested layperson.

Harrison, Edward R. *Cosmology, the Science of the Universe.* Cambridge, England: Cambridge University Press, 1981. This is one of the best general works on the subject. In addition to discussions of the big bang and steady-state cosmologies, there are discussions of space, time, cosmic horizons, life in the universe, and the like. There are numerous helpful diagrams. At the end of each chapter are bibliographies, along with a few pages of thought-provoking quotations. While the general reader will benefit from browsing through it, the well-prepared layperson will find it to be a gold mine.

Hoyle, Fred. *The Nature of the Universe.* Rev. ed. New York: Harper and Brothers, 1960. Popular work about the solar system, stars, and the universe. There is a fine chapter on the expanding universe that discusses both the big bang and the steady-state theories. Recommended for the layperson.

Munitz, Milton K., ed. *Theories of the Universe: From Babylonian Myth to Modern Science.* Glencoe, Ill.: Free Press, 1957. This is a marvelous historical collection of essays on the nature of the universe. Representative works by Plato, Aristotle, Copernicus, Galileo, Einstein, Lemaître, Gamow, Bondi, Hoyle, and many others are included. Almost all of the articles are nonmathematical. Highly recommended.

Yourgrau, Wolfgang, and Allen D. Breck, eds. *Cosmology, History, and Theology.* New York: Plenum Press, 1977. Cosmological models from the past to modern times are discussed with considerable emphasis on the latter. As intended, most of the articles will aid in placing cosmological theories in cultural perspective, especially as it pertains to history and theology. While a few of the articles are technical, the majority of the articles can be recommended for the interested reader.

Charles W. Rogers

Cross-References

Einstein Completes His Theory of General Relativity (1915), p. 625; Lemaître Proposes the Big Bang Theory (1927), p. 825; Hubble Confirms the Expanding Universe (1929), p. 878; Gamow and Associates Develop the Big Bang Theory (1948), p. 1309; Penzias and Wilson Discover Cosmic Microwave Background Radiation (1963), p. 1762.

HALE CONSTRUCTS THE LARGEST
TELESCOPE OF THE TIME

Category of event: Astronomy
Time: June 3, 1948
Locale: Palomar Mountain, California

Hale received funding to construct a 508-centimeter reflecting telescope atop Mount Palomar

Principal personages:
GEORGE ELLERY HALE (1868-1938), a physicist and astronomer who was director of both Yerkes and Mount Wilson observatories and was given funding to build the world's largest telescope (of the time) on Mount Palomar
ELIHU THOMSON (1853-1937), a scientist who attempted to cast the first 508-centimeter quartz disk for the Hale telescope
WALTER SYDNEY ADAMS (1876-1956), the director of Mount Wilson Observatory from 1923-1946 and a member of the Observatory Council for Mount Palomar Observatory
RAYMOND FOSDICK (1883-1972), the president of the Rockefeller Foundation who donated the money needed to construct the Hale telescope
ANDREW CARNEGIE (1835-1919), a benefactor of the Carnegie Institute who had an interest in financing Hale's work in building larger telescopes

Summary of Event

George Ellery Hale was born in Chicago on June 29, 1868. He pursued his education at the Massachusetts Institute of Technology and was graduated in 1890. During that same year, Hale founded the Kenwood Astrophysical Observatory near his Chicago home. Hale conducted research in solar spectroscopy (the analysis of the sun's light) and developed, in 1891, a device called the spectroheliograph, an instrument that photographs the sun in a narrow wavelength band. (These types of photographs reveal the structure of the sun's surface.) In 1892, Hale became the first director of the Yerkes Observatory, Williams Bay, Wisconsin, and received funding for a 102-centimeter refracting telescope. He always envisioned working in an astronomy department with state-of-the-art observational equipment. Hale was one of the original founders, in 1895, of a professional publication known as the *Astrophysical Journal*. Several years later, in 1899, he helped establish the American Astronomical Society.

Not only was Hale an inventor and astronomer but also he had the fortunate ability to be an excellent fund-raiser. He continued to dream of bigger and better astronomical equipment. Hale made presentations before members of the Carnegie

Institute of Washington to advise them of the unusual opportunity of building an observatory in the nearly cloudless mountains of Southern California. In 1904, he received a grant from Andrew Carnegie of the Carnegie Institute for construction of the Mount Wilson Observatory (near Los Angeles, California), where 152-centimeter (in 1908) and 254-centimeter (in 1917) reflecting telescopes were erected. Hale served as director of Mount Wilson Observatory until 1923.

Yet, Hale continued to dream of a larger telescope. By 1928, he had written many articles describing the benefits of constructing a giant telescope. He sent copies of his articles to representatives of the Carnegie Institute and Rockefeller Foundation, hoping to arouse financial support. Miraculously, Hale negotiated an unusual financial cooperation between these foundations for the construction and future operation of a 508-centimeter telescope. The staff from Mount Wilson Observatory (funded by the Carnegie Institute) would supply scientists to construct and operate the telescope, while the California Institute of Technology (funded by the Rockefeller Foundation) would organize the utilization of the telescope.

Raymond Fosdick, then president of the Rockefeller Foundation, appropriated $6 million for the construction of the new 508-centimeter telescope. The California Institute of Technology provided an endowment for operation of the telescope. On October 29, 1928, Hale announced construction plans for the telescope to the media.

Hale was sixty years old when he received the funds to start building his dream of a telescope. His health, however, was not good; his stressful life-style caused Hale to be hospitalized for a short time in a sanatorium. Afterward, he strove to take life at a slower pace but continued to assist with the plans for the telescope. He had to solve several problems: where to build the new observatory and how to cast a 508-centimeter mirror.

Hale had originally planned to place the new telescope at Mount Wilson Observatory. He found that light pollution (light glow from Los Angeles) had increased to the point that the skies were not as dark as when the observatory was initially built. He then considered putting the telescope in the Southern Hemisphere but believed that it would be too remote from other major observatories. Instead, he investigated sites in the Northern Hemisphere.

Hale brought small telescopes to many prospective sites and noted the quality of the star images: whether they were steady and sharp. Specialized instruments measured the amount of sunny days and wind speed and direction for approximately five years. Hale and his colleagues finally decided on Mount Palomar, an area between San Diego and Pasadena, California. Geologists from the California Institute of Technology surveyed the terrain around Mount Palomar and determined the exact location on which the telescope should be built. On September 21, 1934, the land on Mount Palomar was purchased from local ranchers. An official groundbreaking ceremony was held on August 18, 1935.

Another problem to be tackled was the feasibility of casting a 508-centimeter (diameter) mirror. This particular-sized mirror would be larger and wider than any mirror previously made. The ideal glass was thought to be quartz, as it would expand or contract very little through variations in temperature. Elihu Thomson, a scientist at the General Electric Company in Lynn, Massachusetts, was contracted to cast the 508-centimeter quartz disk. Unfortunately, each time the quartz was heated, evaporation caused bubbles to form. The possibility of using quartz was finally abandoned in 1931.

Members of the Observatory Council, including Walter Adams (director of Mount Wilson Observatory), asked the Corning Glass Works, in Corning, New York, to develop a 508-centimeter Pyrex disk. (Pyrex is a low-expansion borosilicate glass.) Although temperature variations affect Pyrex more than quartz, it is still easier to work with than ordinary glass. A special annealing oven was built, and the 508-centimeter mirror was poured successfully on December 2, 1934. The Pyrex disk was cast as a hexagonal cellular structure. Thus, the disk was only about half the weight it would have been as a solid. It remained in New York for almost two years before it was crated for its west-bound trip.

The 508-centimeter disk was packed and loaded aboard a New York Central Railway car. The cross-country trek (between Corning, New York, and Pasadena, California) began on March 26, 1936. The train moved at a speed of only 40 kilometers per hour and only during daylight hours, to avoid excessive vibrations and stress on the glass. Upon the mirror's arrival in Pasadena on April 10, it was brought to the optical shop at the California Institute of Technology for polishing.

A unique "horseshoe" mounting for the mirror was designed by physicists at the California Institute, so that the mount would remain stationary when the telescope was turned. The weight of the mount was estimated to be 600,000 pounds. A benefit of this particular mounting was that the telescope could be pointed toward high northern latitudes of the sky, a term known as "declination." The 254-centimeter telescope at Mount Wilson was built with such a restrictive mount.

The 508-centimeter telescope was also constructed to be a "prime focus" instrument. That is, the observer actually climbs into a cage within the telescope and observes light reflected from the mirror onto a photographic plate. A platform moves up and down so the astronomer can step directly into the prime focus area. This telescope is one of the few that allows the observer to view from the prime focus, rather than from an eyepiece below the body of the instrument.

On February 21, 1938, Hale died before his dream of the 508-centimeter telescope could be completed. The occurrence of World War II caused optical astronomy to come almost to a halt. Many scientists who had worked on Mount Palomar were contracted into the war effort. Finally, on June 3, 1948 (ten years after Hale's death), the 508-centimeter telescope was officially dedicated and named the Hale telescope, a monument to the man whose vision and leadership made it a reality.

Impact of Event

Hale's dream of building the largest telescope in the world was conveyed to both the private and public sector. He was a genius at acquiring financial support from private foundations, and his colleagues were intrigued by his plans. Many astronomers envied Hale, while others were unsure of the possibility of constructing such a large telescope.

The general public and press followed the progress of this new telescope with great anticipation. Headlines in major newspapers provided up-to-the-minute news on the status of the mirror and dome construction. When the telescope was finally dedicated, the astronomical community prepared with excitement for the new views of the heavens that lay ahead.

In designing the 508-centimeter telescope, Hale sought to supplement the equipment of nearby Mount Wilson Observatory and provide information to other observatories to assist in the development of new experimental technology. He also foresaw that this telescope would be capable of making detailed observations of high northerly-situated stars and galaxies. (The Mount Wilson 254-centimeter telescope was restricted from observing near the north celestial pole.)

The cross-country trek of the 508-centimeter mirror was publicly visible. The media spread the latest news of the mirror's journey. Thousand of people gathered along the train route to see the precious cargo. Children were even dismissed early from school to catch a glimpse of this historic event.

One of the first observations made with the Hale telescope led to a doubling of the distance scale between our Milky Way galaxy and the Andromeda galaxy, from 1 to 2 million light-years. The importance of a detailed investigation of neighboring galaxies is in establishing a schematic of the distribution of galaxies. In addition, a spectroscopic study of galaxies (that is, an analysis of the light given off by them) allows for measurements of their speeds and whether those galaxies are receding from or moving toward the Milky Way. In fact, observations made with the Hale telescope have suggested that the universe is still expanding (from the original big bang of about 15 billion years ago).

Observations taken on the 508-centimeter telescope are not solely the property of a selective group of scientists but are available to persons interested in studying them. It may be the astronomers who take the actual photographs or measurements, but this information is relayed through the media and toward the general public. Though the Hale telescope stimulates more questions than it answers, it is a very powerful instrument—the result of a man who had a dream and never ceased to pursue it. The name "Hale telescope" is a reminder to both the general public and scientific community of their debt to Hale. This telescope remained the largest in the world, from 1948 to 1976, until the 600-centimeter reflector was completed at Zelenchukskaya, in the Soviet Union.

Bibliography

Asimov, Isaac. *Eyes on the Universe*. Boston: Houghton Mifflin, 1975. A general history of the telescope is outlined in this useful reference. From the beginnings of its use by Galileo through the construction of Mount Palomar Observatory and the future of orbiting satellites, the telescope is seen changing through the times.
Bolton, Nancy. "Press Pilgrimage to Palomar." *Sky and Telescope* 7 (January, 1948):

59-63. The incredible journey of the 508-centimeter mirror from Pasadena to Mount Palomar is seen through the eyes of a magazine reporter. Photographs depict the actual packing and transportation of the precious mirror along the rocky dirt roads of Southern California in this nostalgic article.

Coles, Robert. "The 200-Inch Telescope." *Sky and Telescope* 7 (September, 1948): 267-269. This article was written at the time of the dedication of the Hale telescope. A photograph of the 508-centimeter dome as well as photographs of the telescope mount are highlighted. The author details the excitement between the public and the astronomical community and discusses future uses of the Hale telescope.

Di Cicco, Dennis. "The Journey of the 200-Inch Mirror." *Sky and Telescope* 17 (April, 1986): 347-348. This interesting article details the voyage of the 508-centimeter mirror aboard the New York Central Railway. A detailed diagram lists all the major stops along the route, from Corning, New York, to its final destination in Pasadena, California. Two archival photographs supplement the article.

Shapley, Harlow, ed. *Source Book in Astronomy, 1900-1950.* Cambridge, Mass.: Harvard University Press, 1960. This text is an excellent reference for many great historical moments in astronomy. Chapter 1 "The 200-Inch Reflector on Mount Palomar" is particularly relevant to the fund-raising and final construction of the Hale telescope; the remainder of the text is an outstanding general reference.

Stokley, James. "A Tribute to George Ellery Hale." *The Sky* 2 (July, 1938): 10-11. This concise eulogy was written by a planetarium director in honor of Hale, the scientist and man who never gave up on his dream to build the largest telescope in the world. His success in soliciting for funds among the large foundations is illustrated.

Woodbury, David. *The Glass Giant of Palomar.* New York: Dodd, Mead, 1953. This is the text for the reader who wants to know the details of the 508-centimeter mirror of the Hale telescope. The text is supplemented with several hand-drawn sketches as well as black-and-white photographs.

Wright, Helen. *Explorer of the Universe: A Biography of George Ellery Hale.* New York: E. P. Dutton, 1966. The entire text is a chronology of Hale's life, beginning with his childhood in Chicago, his directorship of the Yerkes and Mount Wilson observatories, and his true quest to build the world's largest reflecting telescope. The personal side of Hale is reflected through photographs of his family and colleagues.

_____. *Palomar: The World's Largest Telescope.* New York: Macmillan, 1952. This small book covers the actual planning stages through the final completion of construction. Hale's negotiations with private funding sources are covered along with his great enthusiasm to make the 508-centimeter telescope the best in the world. An extremely detailed photograph of the Hale telescope is presented in the text.

Noreen A. Grice

Cross-References

Hale Establishes Mount Wilson Observatory (1903), p. 194; Hubble Confirms the Expanding Universe (1929), p. 878; Schmidt Invents the Corrector for the Schmidt Camera and Telescope (1929), p. 884; Construction of the World's Largest Telescope Begins in Hawaii (1985), p. 2291; NASA Launches the Hubble Space Telescope (1990), p. 2377.

LAND INVENTS A CAMERA/FILM SYSTEM
THAT DEVELOPS INSTANT PICTURES

Category of event: Applied science
Time: November 26, 1948
Locale: Boston, Massachusetts

Land and coworkers invented a camera and a photographic process that produced a finished positive print directly from the camera immediately after exposure

Principal personages:
>EDWIN HERBERT LAND (1909-   ), a physicist and chemist who was the inventor of the Polaroid Land camera and film system
>HOWARD G. ROGERS (1915-   ), a senior research fellow at Polaroid and Land's collaborator who was the primary force behind the invention of the instant color process
>WILLIAM J. McCUNE (1915-   ), an engineer and head of the Polaroid team that eventually designed the original camera and the machinery that produced the camera and Land's new film
>ANSEL ADAMS (1902-1984), an American photographer and Land's technical consultant who worked on improving the quality of the instant camera's film

Summary of Event

As a chemist and physicist primarily interested in research relating to light and vision, and materials that affect them, Edwin Herbert Land's first major scientific discovery was a commercially practical, synthetic, light-polarizing material in sheet form. In order to exploit this discovery, Land founded the Polaroid Corporation in 1929. It was at Polaroid that Land became inevitably drawn into the field of photography.

During the summer of 1943, while Land and his wife were vacationing in Santa Fe, New Mexico, with their three-year-old daughter, Land stopped to take a picture of the child. After the picture was taken, his daughter asked to see it. When she was told that she could not see the picture immediately, she asked how long she would have to wait. Within an hour after his daughter's question, Land had conceived a preliminary plan for design of the camera, the film, and the physical chemistry of the instant camera. With great excitement, he rushed to a friend's house and described in detail a dry camera that would produce a picture immediately after exposure. In the standard photographic process, film must be developed, rinsed, fixed, washed, and dried; then the resulting negative must be printed on the positive paper, which goes through a similar process. At Polaroid, all that he had learned about making polarizers and plastics, the properties of viscous liquids, and the preparation of microscopic crystals smaller than the wavelengths of light, he later said, prepared him for the inspiration to create a one-step photographic process.

Within six months, Land had solved most of the essential problems of the instant photography system. He and a small group of associates at Polaroid secretly worked on the project. Howard G. Rogers was Land's collaborator in the laboratory. Land conferred the responsibility for the engineering and mechanical phase of the project on William J. McCune, who led the team that eventually designed the original camera and the machinery that produced both the camera and Land's new film.

The first Polaroid Land camera—the Model 95—produced photographs measuring 8.25 by 10.8 centimeters; there were eight pictures to a roll. In the Model 95, Land's original design had been somewhat modified in order to hold the film in the back of the camera for the minute it took for the picture to develop. The back cover was then lifted and the deckle-edged print taken out. The corresponding negative was removed immediately before the next picture on the roll was processed.

Instead of using black-and-white film, the original Polaroid prints were sepia-toned, a warm, reddish-brown color. The reasons for the sepia coloration were chemical rather than aesthetic, however, and as soon as Land's researchers could devise a workable formula for sharp black-and-white prints, they replaced the sepia film, about ten months after the camera was introduced commercially.

While the mechanical process involved in the first demonstration camera was relatively simple, this process was merely the means by which a highly sophisticated chemical reaction—the diffusion transfer process—was produced.

In the basic diffusion transfer process, when an exposed negative image is developed in an emulsion, the undeveloped portion corresponds to the opposite aspect of the image, the positive. Almost all self-processing instant photography materials operate by causing the positive-aspect filter or dye-formers to transfer by diffusion out of the negative emulsion layer(s) to a receiving layer, where the visible positive image is formed. The three phases—negative development, transfer, and positive development—occur simultaneously, so that positive image formation begins instantly. With black-and-white materials, the positive was originally completed in sixty seconds; with color material (introduced later), the process took somewhat longer.

The basic phenomenon of silver in solution diffusing from one emulsion to another was first observed in the 1850's, but no practical use of this action was made until 1939 to 1940. The photographic use of diffusion transfer for producing normal-contrast, continuous-tone images was investigated actively from the early 1940's by Land and his associates. The instant camera using this method was demonstrated in 1947 and marketed in 1948.

The fundamentals of photographic diffusion transfer are simplest in a black-and-white peel-apart film. The negative sheet is exposed in the camera in the normal way. Then it is pulled out of the camera, or film pack holder, by a paper tab. Next, it passes through a set of rollers, which press it face to face with a sheet of receiving material included in the film pack. Simultaneously, the rollers rupture a pod of viscous developing reagent (chemicals) and spread it evenly between the two emulsions in a layer about .0025 millimeter thick. The reagent contains a strong alkali and a silver halide solvent, both of which diffuse into the negative emulsion. There the alkali activates the developing agent, which immediately reduces the exposed halides to a negative image. At the same time, the solvent dissolves the unexposed halides. Although fixed in place as crystals, in a dissolved state they can diffuse to the nuclei in the receiving emulsion, which exert an attraction for them. There, the silver in the dissolved halides collects on the nuclei, forming the positive image. When the two sheets are peeled apart, the surface reagent clings to the negative, which is then discarded or, if on a transparent base, can be neutralized and washed for subsequent use in conventional printing operations. In some films, the positive image has to be protected with a coating applied with a swab. This coating contains chemicals that neutralize the emulsion as well as a plasticizer that dries to form a protective top layer. In other films, neutralizing compounds are contained in the positive emulsion, and no coating is required. The image is grainless—no structure can be seen even with a microscope—because it is formed by physical development; as a result, it has high resolving power. Contrast depends on the emulsion characteristics and in some films can be varied somewhat by alterations in processing time.

Diffusion transfer color films—commercially introduced by Land in 1963—have three silver halide negative layers individually sensitive to the primary additive colors: red, green, or blue light, and associated subtractive colors: cyan, magenta, and yellow dye-developer, or dye-releaser layers. In a peel-apart color film, dye-forming compounds are locked in place wherever the negative image is developed; in other areas, they are released to diffuse to the receiving sheet to produce a positive color image. Similar action occurs in diffusion transfer darkroom materials for color printing. The chemical action is essentially the same in single-sheet Polaroid SX-70 films, but some physical details differ. The receiving layers are on top of the negative layers; they are completely transparent, so they do not interfere with the image during exposure. The lens image is reflected onto the face of the film by a mirror so that the final image will have proper left-right margin orientation. As the film emerges from the camera, reagent is forced between the upper group of receiving layers and the lower group of negative layers. The reagent contains an opaque material to protect the negative layers from further exposure. The image processes below and the positive dye formers diffuse up through the reagent to the top. As the process progresses, the black reagent layer bleaches to a clean, white background for the color image.

Impact of Event

The Polaroid Land camera had a tremendous impact on the photographic industry as well as the amateur and professional photographer. Known for his monumental and ultrasharp black-and-white panoramas of the American West, Ansel Adams suggested to Land ways in which the tonal value of Polaroid film could be enhanced, as well as new applications for Polaroid photographic technology.

Besides improving the quality of black-and-white film, another significant photographic innovation introduced with the Model 95 was the exposure value system, which greatly reduced the complexity of calculating shutter speed and lens (aperture) opening. The basic concept of incorporating a semiautomatic exposure system, which would be based on keying certain shutter speeds to certain lens openings depending on lighting conditions, was subsequently adopted throughout the photographic industry.

In the years following Land's commercial marketing of the instant camera and print process, his techniques were improved extensively. Processing that previously took one minute was reduced to ten seconds at the same time as high-speed (ISO 3000) film was introduced. Other forms of instant materials that Land introduced include high-contrast films for line copying, transparency films for lantern slides (photographic slides for projection), an ultrafast (ISO 10,000) film for oscillography (registering oscillations of electrical currents and photographically recording the variations), ten-second X-ray packets, color print materials (available as large as 20 by 25 centimeters, and an experimental camera for full-size copying of much larger full-color originals). In addition, the SX-70 instant color camera with a film that develops outside the camera and has no paper or negative to discard was presented to the public in 1972. Besides still-camera films, an instant movie film camera and viewer have been introduced. Land has received more than 160 patents for his innovations in light and plastics, and his interest in light and color has brought about a new theory of color perception, which he revealed in a series of experiments.

Soon after it was introduced, Polaroid photography became part of the American way of life and changed the face of amateur photography forever. By the 1950's, Americans had become accustomed to the world of recorded visual information through films, magazines, and newspapers; they also had become enthusiastic practitioners of photography as a result of the growing trend for simpler and more convenient cameras. By allowing this class of photographer not only to record their perceptions but also to perceive the results almost immediately, Polaroid brought people that much more intimately into the creative process and allowed them immediate feedback.

The rapid access to finished prints has made the various camera and film systems available from Polaroid and the Eastman Kodak Company attractive to professional photographers (as well as scientists and engineers). The system provides a simple means to make test shots to previsualize arrangement, lighting, and decor in fashion and advertising work, and is also used in professional studios and field cameras.

Bibliography

Adams, Ansel, and Robert Baker. *Polaroid Land Photography*. Rev. ed. Boston: New York Graphic Society, 1978. Adams, Land's friend and technical consultant, uses his early experience with the Polaroid Land process to produce the definitive manual for the user. This book, directed at amateur and professional alike, traces the growth and development of the process. Contains graphs, photographs, appendices on film-testing procedures, chemical formulas, and film characteristics.

Land, Edwin H. "The Universe of One-Step Photography." In *Pioneers of Photogra-*

phy, edited by Eugene Ostroff. Springfield, Va.: SPSE, 1987. In this useful article, originally written in 1947, Land describes the step-by-step process by which he devised a camera and a photographic process that produced a finished positive print directly from the camera immediately after exposure. Contains numerous charts, graphs, and photographs.

Olshaker, Mark. *The Instant Image: Edwin Land and the Polaroid Experience.* New York: Stein & Day, 1978. Olshaker recounts the events leading to the discovery and marketing of the instant camera and film system. An interesting personal rather than a scientific account of the discovery. Bibliography.

Sipley, Louis Walton. *Photography's Great Inventors.* Philadelphia: American Museum of Photography, 1965. In this brief work, Sipley provides short sketches of the pioneers in the photographic industry from the earliest inventors to the development of color photography. The section devoted to Land's contributions is informative. Brief bibliography follows each entry. Contains chronology of major inventions.

Wensberg, Peter C. *Land's Polaroid: A Company and the Man Who Invented It.* Boston: Houghton Mifflin, 1987. This history of the Polaroid Corporation discusses the founding and development of Land's company and describes the major inventions he and his research team developed. Wensberg's primary interest is in Land as an entrepreneur rather than as a scientist.

Genevieve Slomski

Cross-References

Louis and Auguste Lumière Develop Color Photography (1907), p. 375; Carlson Invents Xerography (1934), p. 1013; Gabor Develops the Basic Concept of Holography (1947), p. 1288.

X RAYS FROM A SYNCHROTRON ARE FIRST USED IN MEDICAL DIAGNOSIS AND TREATMENT

Categories of event: Medicine and physics
Time: 1949
Locale: Harwell, England; Cambridge, Massachusetts; Uppsala, Sweden

Several physicists, including Cockcroft, Van de Graaff, and Svedberg, produced synchrotron X rays for radiotherapy

Principal personages:

SIR JOHN COCKCROFT (1897-1967), an English physicist and 1951 Nobel laureate in Physics for his contributions to the understanding of atomic structure and development of radar

ROBERT JEMISON VAN DE GRAAFF (1901-1967), an American physicist who developed the Van de Graaff generator and other particle accelerators that emit X rays

THEODOR SVEDBERG (1884-1971), a Swedish chemist and 1926 Nobel laureate in Chemistry who developed the ultracentrifuge plus particle accelerators for biological research

ERNEST ORLANDO LAWRENCE (1901-1958), an American physicist and 1939 Nobel laureate in Physics who developed the cyclotron and synchrocyclotron

JOHN PAUL BLEWETT (1910-   ), an American physicist who predicted X-ray generation by synchrotrons

WILHELM CONRAD RÖNTGEN (1845-1923), a German physicist and 1901 Nobel laureate in Physics who discovered X rays

SIR LAWRENCE BRAGG (1890-1971), an English biophysicist and cowinner of the 1915 Nobel Prize in Physics for the discovery of X-ray diffraction crystallography

WALTER BRADFORD CANNON (1871-1945), an American physician who developed X-ray fluoroscopy

Summary of Event

Electromagnetic radiation consists of numerous types of energy that exhibit both wavelike and particle (that is, photon) properties and that travel at the speed of light, approximately 300 million meters per second. The electromagnetic spectrum ranges from low frequency (low energy), long wavelength radiations such as radio, television, microwaves, and visible light to high frequency (high energy), short wavelength radiations such as ultraviolet, X, and gamma radiations. The high frequency, short wavelength radiations are called ionizing radiations because such radiations penetrate deep within various materials, especially living tissue, and because such radiations strip electrons from atoms, thereby damaging key life molecules (for example, DNA—deoxyribonucleic acid).

X rays were first discovered by the German physicist Wilhelm Conrad Röntgen in 1895. He generated X rays by applying an electric current to the cathode (that is, negative terminal) of a vacuum tube. The cathode became heated such that it discharged a stream of electrons, which were attracted to the positively charged anode of the vacuum tube. When the electrons contacted the tungsten anode, X rays were emitted. For this discovery, Röntgen was awarded the first Nobel Prize in Physics in 1901. His work was closely followed by another important breakthrough: the discovery of radioactivity in the elements uranium and radium by Antoine-Henri Becquerel, Marie Curie, and Pierre Curie.

Applications of X rays and radioactivity to biology and medicine became readily apparent. Röntgen's discovery of X rays and their ability to penetrate living tissue meant that a patient's internal organs could be photographed. W. D. Coolidge developed the first X-ray tube for producing patient X rays in 1913. Walter Bradford Cannon used X rays in fluoroscopy, a process by which the activities of a patient's internal organs can be observed. Thomas Alva Edison invented the first fluoroscope in 1896. Cannon applied this instrument to patient diagnoses. If a patient swallowed a dense fluid such as barium sulfate while being X rayed with the X-ray fluoroscope, the dense fluid would fluoresce and appear on the X-ray photographic plate, along with the organs containing the dense fluid. Using X-ray fluoroscopy, Cannon and other physicians could identify abnormalities within internal body organs without operating.

In 1915, Sir Lawrence Bragg and his father, Sir William Henry Bragg, received the Nobel Prize in Physics for their discovery of X-ray diffraction through crystals. X rays beamed through a crystallized material are bent in specific directions when they strike the atoms of the crystal lattice. The Braggs described the properties of X-ray diffraction with a simple mathematical equation called Bragg's law. Their discovery led to a technique for visualizing submicroscopic molecules called X-ray crystallography. In X-ray crystallography, a purified molecule such as a protein can be crystallized, followed by the beaming of X rays through the molecule's crystal lattice. The pattern of images on the resulting X-ray photograph can be measured to determine the molecule's structure. X-ray crystallography was used from the 1940's onward in biochemical research to determine the structures of proteins and other important molecules of life. Eventual Nobel Prize-winning work, which depended upon X-ray crystallography, included the structures of insulin (by Frederick Sanger), the alpha helix of proteins (by Linus Pauling), and DNA (by James D. Watson, Francis Crick, and Maurice H. F. Wilkins).

During the 1930's and 1940's, physicists began developing instruments operating at much higher voltages (for example, 1 million to 100 million electronvolts) for generating higher-frequency radiations such as deeper-penetrating X rays and mesons. These devices were called accelerators, or atom smashers. The principle behind an accelerator involves the firing of charged particles (that is, ions) from an ion gun.

The ions are guided through a tunnel surrounded by powerful electromagnets; these electromagnets accelerate and direct the ion beam toward a target material. With high-voltage accelerators, the electromagnets direct the ion beam at speeds approaching that of light (300 million meters per second). The entire process requires much less than one second at such speeds. The ion beam strikes atoms of the target material, splitting the target atoms into subatomic particles and energy, whose pathways are photographed as they rapidly move through a cloud chamber.

Accelerators can be of two types: linear accelerators and circular accelerators. Linear accelerators (for example, the Van de Graaff generator) move charged particles in a straight line to the target material; they must be many kilometers long in order to achieve high velocities. Circular accelerators move charged particles in a circular pathway and have the advantage of repeatedly circling the particles to achieve higher and higher velocities before directing them at the target. Circular accelerators include cyclotrons, synchrocyclotrons, synchrotrons, bevatrons, betatrons, and cosmotrons. The $8 billion superconducting supercollider, under construction in Texas during the 1990's, is a semicircular accelerator.

The American physicist Ernest Orlando Lawrence developed the first cyclotron with his students Niels E. Edlefsen and M. Stanley Livingston at the University of California, Berkeley, in 1932. They used this cyclotron to separate isotopes of various elements and to split atoms for the release of subatomic particles and energy. In 1939, Lawrence isolated phosphorus 32, a radioactive isotope of phosphorus containing an extra neutron per atom. He delivered some of this radioisotope to his brother John H. Lawrence, a physician at the Harvard University Medical School in Cambridge, Massachusetts. John Lawrence used phosphorus 32 to treat patients suffering from chronic leukemia and polycythemia. John Lawrence's radiotherapy experiments were repeated by a colleague, Shields Warren, also a physician at Harvard. While these experiments were controversial at the time, they were the beginning of the successful use of radioactive isotopes in treating cancer. Following World War II, Ernest Lawrence invented the synchrocyclotron, a very similar instrument that synchronizes the charged particle flow with the acceleration potential of the electromagnets. At this time, the focus had shifted to the peaceful uses of atomic energy. The invention of the synchrocyclotron, synchrotron, betatron, and other closely related particle accelerators led to the generation of radiations useful for subatomic physics research, anticancer radiotherapy, and industry. The breakthroughs in this effort were shared by several scientists and companies that made considerable investments into the construction of bigger and better particle accelerators.

In 1945, the American physicist John Paul Blewett of the Brookhaven National Laboratory predicted the emission of radiation, including X rays, from synchrotrons. This prediction was verified in 1947, when scientists at the General Electric Corporation recorded X-ray emissions from a synchrotron. These results were paralleled in other laboratories.

Robert Jemison Van de Graaff, who invented the Van de Graaff generator at Princeton University in 1929, had worked with John G. Tramp at the Massachusetts Institute of Technology to develop a 1 million electronvolt generator for producing X rays. This device was used to treat cancer patients at Huntington Memorial Hospital in Boston in 1937. Using these accelerators, they generated X rays and tested the effects of X rays upon biological molecules. They reported these results in two 1948 articles: "Irradiation of Biological Materials by High Energy Röntgen Rays and Cathode Rays" in volume 19 of the *Journal of Applied Physics* and "Thick-Target X-Ray Production in the Range from 1250 to 2350 Kilovolts" in volume 74 of the *Physical Review.*

Sir John Douglas Cockcroft, an English physicist working in the laboratory of the eminent nuclear physicist Ernest Rutherford, began building a cyclotron in the late 1930's. During World War II, he helped to develop radar. Following the war, he supervised the development of several hundred million electronvolt synchrotrons. In 1949, his research group produced synchrotron X rays and applied these X rays to the radiotherapeutic treatment of cancer patients. He reported these results in an article entitled "The Development of Linear Accelerators and Synchrotrons for Radiotherapy and for Research in Physics," which appeared in Volume 96 of the *Proceedings of the Institution of Electrical Engineers.* In Sweden, the radiologist Arne Frantzell applied these X rays to the medical imaging of internal organs, bone, and muscle. The eminent Swedish physical chemist Theodor Svedberg supervised the construction of a 700 million electronvolt synchrocyclotron at the University of Uppsala. This device was applied to radiotherapy beginning in 1951.

Impact of Event

The importance of generating X rays, gamma rays, mesons, and other forms of electromagnetic radiation from cyclotrons and synchrotrons lies in their applications to nuclear physics research, radiotherapy, and industry. Whereas these particle accelerators had been used primarily in the drive to harness atomic energy during World War II, they were redirected toward their original peaceful research objectives following the war. Particle accelerators were constructed rapidly at numerous sites worldwide, including the United States, the Soviet Union, England, France, and Sweden.

In medicine, X rays are useful in radiotherapy (that is, high-frequency "hard" X rays) as well as in photographing internal organs (lower-frequency "soft" X rays). Hard X rays are produced from high-voltage energy sources such as synchrotrons. These X rays can penetrate deep within body tissues, causing severe damage to target cells. High-frequency ionizing radiation (for example, ultraviolet, X, and gamma radiations) damage molecules they intersect. In living tissue, these molecules include proteins, lipids, carbohydrates, and especially DNA. Irradiation of DNA often produces atomic changes that alter the coding sequence of DNA. Since DNA encodes proteins in living cells, alterations in the DNA coding sequence cause the production of proteins having incorrect amino acid sequences. Such damaged proteins either will not function properly or will not function at all. These changes in DNA and encoded proteins are called mutations. Cellular mutations can be harmless (for example, the appearance of freckles), damaging (sickle-cell anemia), or cancerous. Most cancers are cellular mutations caused by radiation or chemicals. While radiation can cause cancers, it also can be used to kill cancerous cells because cancer cells are more sensitive to irradiation than are normal cells. Therefore, radiation therapy is very useful in destroying tumors and cancers. The therapy involves the firing of a beam of high-energy X rays at a targeted region of a patient's body that contains a tumor. The approach produces a shotgun effect, the radiation striking both tumorous and normal tissue. Tumor cells, however, should be killed more easily with some tolerable damage to neighboring normal cells.

With early diagnoses of cancers, radiotherapy can be extremely effective in destroying tumors and curtailing further spread of the disease. The technique is most applicable to internal cancers, especially those that are inoperable. Radiotherapy is performed in conjunction with chemotherapy (anticancer chemicals and drugs) and the ingestion of radioactive isotopes that concentrate in particular tissues where the cancer is located. Researchers have greatly improved radiotherapy instrumentation, producing devices that concentrate high-energy X rays on target cancers with very little damage to normal cells.

The work of a variety of scientists, especially Cockcroft, Van de Graaff, and Svedberg, produced X rays and other radiations from particle accelerators for saving thousands of cancer victims and extending their lives. Their work also demonstrated the tremendous peaceful uses of atomic energy for the improvement of human health and welfare.

Bibliography

Alberts, Bruce, et al. *Molecular Biology of the Cell*. New York: Garland, 1983. This lengthy introductory molecular biology textbook for undergraduate biology majors is a thorough survey of the science by several leading molecular biologists and biochemists. It is clearly written, illustrated, and referenced. Chapter 4, "How Cells are Studied," provides a strong history of cell biology with the applications of X rays to biological research.

Clark, George L. *Applied X-Rays*. 4th ed. New York: McGraw-Hill, 1955. This extensive, detailed work is a complete presentation of X rays, properties of X rays, X-ray instrumentation, history, and applications. It is well written and diagrammed, although a knowledge of algebra and chemistry is needed for some topics. Chapter 3, "High-Voltage Equipment," describes synchrotrons and other accelerators. Chapter 12, "The Biological Effects of X-Radiation," describes medical applications of X rays.

Crease, Robert P., and Charles C. Mann. *The Second Creation*. New York: Macmillan, 1985. This exciting book is a history of physics research during the twentieth century, with special emphasis upon nuclear physics and unification theories. The works of numerous physicists are described, including Albert Einstein and Niels Bohr. Chapter 14, "The Eightfold Way," describes the cyclotron work of Ernest Lawrence and Cockcroft.

Gillispie, Charles Coulston, ed. *Dictionary of Scientific Biography.* New York: Charles Scribner's Sons, 1980. This strong reference work is a collection of short, concise biographical essays on major twentieth century scientists, many of whom are Nobel Prize winners. The collection includes biographies of Cockcroft, Van de Graaff, and Svedberg. Each article includes an extensive reference list.

Halliday, David, and Robert Resnick. *Fundamentals of Physics.* 2d ed. New York: John Wiley & Sons, 1981. This introductory physics textbook for undergraduate science majors is an outstanding, popular work. It is lengthy, detailed, and requires a strong background in mathematics, particularly calculus. The book includes several chapters on subatomic physics, electromagnetism, and particle accelerator principles. It includes historical sketches of prominent physicists.

U.S. Army Medical Service. *Radiology in World War II.* Washington, D.C.: Government Printing Office, 1966. This reference work is a detailed history and methodology of X-irradiation and its applications prior to and during World War II. It is extremely well documented. The works of Ernest Lawrence with cyclotrons and John Lawrence with radioactive isotope therapy for cancer are discussed.

Winick, Herman, and Arthur Bienenstock. "Synchrotron Radiation." In *McGraw-Hill Encyclopedia of Science and Technology.* 5th ed. New York: McGraw-Hill, 1982. This article is a concise, detailed summary of particle accelerators and their radiations that is comprehensible for the layperson. Properties of synchrotrons and synchrotron radiation, research applications, and the history of accelerator research are described.

David Wason Hollar, Jr.

Cross-References

Röntgen Wins the Nobel Prize for the Discovery of X Rays (1901), p. 118; X-Ray Crystallography Is Developed by the Braggs (1912), p. 517; Berger Develops the Electroencephalogram (EEG) (1929), p. 890; Lawrence Develops the Cyclotron (1931), p. 953; Cockcroft and Walton Split the Atom with a Particle Accelerator (1932), p. 978; The Tevatron Particle Accelerator Begins Operation at Fermilab (1985), p. 2301; The Superconducting Supercollider Is Under Construction in Texas (1988), p. 2372.

THE FIRST ROCKET WITH MORE THAN
ONE STAGE IS CREATED

Category of event: Space and aviation
Time: February 24, 1949
Locale: White Sands Proving Grounds, New Mexico

In Project Bumper, the WAC Corporal, with a V-2 rocket boost, was the first successful, liquid-fuel rocket with more than one stage

Principal personages:
H. N. TOFTOY, a major general who first conceived Project Bumper
FRANK J. MALINA, the Jet Propulsion Laboratory scientist who was responsible for theoretical investigations and design of the second stage to the V-2

Summary of Event

The "Ordnance Guided Missile and Rocket Programs—HERMES" investigated nearly every aspect of rocketry, including missile structures, transonic and supersonic aerodynamics and ramjet engines, missile guidance and control, ground launch equipment and handling, instrumentation, fuels and propellants, and rocket engines. Three categories were defined in the HERMES program: the A3 missile series, the A1 and A2 missile series, and other missiles and supporting research. Project Bumper was in the third category.

The purpose of HERMES, initiated in November of 1944, was to develop long-range guided missiles for use against ground targets and high-altitude aircraft. A group of scientists was to study German missiles used in World War II, with the assistance of military intelligence, then to identify confiscated hardware and collect important pieces for shipment to the United States. Their job was complicated by the fact that almost all of the rocket components and subassemblies had been deliberately damaged by the retreating German army. After assembling and launching eight V-2s, the identified hardware was divided between England and the United States. (The factory fittings were acquired by the Soviet Union.) The result of this operation was three hundred train carloads of V-2 parts, unloaded at Las Cruces, New Mexico, at the end of July, 1945.

The second critical phase of HERMES was the acquisition of top German rocket scientists in "Operation Paperclip." At the end of World War II, four hundred scientists surrendered to the United States; of those, one hundred were selected to be sent to the United States to perform scientific research. A paperclip was placed on the folder of each of the scientists selected, from which the name "Operation Paperclip" was derived. They were sent initially to Fort Strong, near Boston, Massachusetts, but were moved later to Fort Bliss, Texas, in January of 1946. Twenty of these scientists were assigned to the White Sands Proving Grounds (WSPG), now the White

Sands Missile Range, located between Alamogordo and Las Cruces, New Mexico. These scientists deciphered drawings and specifications, and the General Electric Company built the V-2s according to their directions. Before the General Electric contract expired on June 30, 1951, sixty-seven rockets had been fired.

The V-2 had five main parts: the warhead or nose cone, the control compartment, the midsection, the thrust frame, and the tail assembly. The nose cone had been used by the German army to loft a 1 ton warhead against the Allies. The nose cones of the V-2's under research at WSPG were filled with about 0.57 cubic meter of instrumentation, including a variety of measuring devices, and with lead weights, when the proper weight could not be obtained with equipment. To achieve stability, the payload weight had to equal the German warhead weight. The control compartment contained gyroscopes, which had to be manufactured in the United States because of the few gyroscopes recovered intact. Later, this compartment also contained Doppler, telemetering, and emergency cut-off radio receivers.

The midsection of the V-2 contained liquid alcohol and liquid oxygen propellant tanks, valves, and piping. Generally, the tanks were recovered after World War II in good condition. Glass wool was used for insulation of the alcohol tanks and piping, protecting them from the extreme cold of the liquid oxygen. The thrust frame contained the propulsion equipment, including the turbopump, the steam-generating plant, the heat exchanger, the combustion unit, and pipelines. Steam was generated by combining hydrogen peroxide and sodium permanganate. Except for the heat exchangers, all of this hardware was recovered in usable condition. The tail assembly contained the fairing (structure addition to reduce aerodynamic drag) for the propulsion unit, stabilized the flight, steered the missile, and carried the vanes and vane motors. The bearing surfaces of the fins supported the V-2's upright position on the launch frame. The fins stabilized the flight to maximum altitude, then lost effectiveness in the thinner air, causing the rocket to begin its fall tail-end down. Upon reaching denser air, the fins again took over steering, and the rocket swung around to fall nose down.

Project Bumper was first conceived by Major General H. N. Toftoy, then Colonel, in the Office of the Chief of Ordnance, who suggested the V-2/WAC Corporal combination. In October, 1946, Project Bumper was instituted to investigate separation problems of two-stage liquid rockets and to set a new high-altitude record. It was hoped to gain some data on high-speed, high-altitude phenomena and to attain a velocity record as well. The WAC Corporal, a small American-made rocket, was named "Without Attitude Control" Corporal, because it followed the Privates A and F. It had a range of only 40 kilometers, was 4.88 meters long, and had a thrust of 337.8 newtons for forty-five seconds of burn. It was fueled by a mixture of aniline with 20 percent furfuryl alcohol to depress the freezing point, a mixture that combusted spontaneously with red fuming nitric acid. The WAC Corporal was fitted as deeply as possible into the V-2 booster, with enough space in the instrument compartment for the necessary guidance equipment. Guide rails and expulsion cylinders (powered by compressed air) for the WAC mid-air launch were also included. The final cut-off signal of the V-2 burn signaled the compressed air valve opening, causing the second-stage fins to slide out of the slots in the nose cone of the V-2.

The forward portion of the V-2 was modified for Bumper installation, with General Electric given overall responsibility for the eight V-2 modifications. The Jet Propulsion Laboratory (JPL), with Frank J. Malina, was responsible for theoretical investigations, the design of the second stage, and the basic design of the separation system. The Douglas Aircraft Company was responsible for the fabrication of the second stage and the detail design and fabrication of special V-2 parts.

On February 24, 1949, Bumper Five reached 410 kilometers, becoming the first true space vehicle. The WAC Corporal rocket was fully tanked, with a burn of forty-five seconds. Only thirty seconds after take-off, the V-2 hit 5,904 kilometers per hour, just prior to separation. The WAC Corporal then attained 8,446 kilometers per hour, achieving both the greatest velocity and altitude records. In this flight, instrumentation in the nose cone measured temperatures and transmitted technical data pertaining to conditions during the flight. This was the first time radio equipment had operated at extreme altitudes. Although the flight was a complete success, the crashed remains were not found for more than a year.

Of the eight Bumper flights, three were successful, two had limited success, and three were failures. During one flight, the V-2 reportedly passed the second stage. The first flight, on May 13, 1948, was of short duration, with a solid propellant motor in the WAC Corporal. The second stage attained only a little more speed and altitude than the V-2 booster. Flight two, on August 19, 1948, contained a partial propellant charge in the WAC Corporal, as in the first flight. Unfortunately, a controlling circuit failure in the V-2 prevented the success of the second-stage launch. On September 30, 1948, the third flight ended in an explosion of the second stage shortly before separation, although the V-2 was successful. The fourth flight ended with a tail section explosion, probably the result of modifications, and control was lost. Flight six was the last to launch at the WSPG, on April 21, 1949. It was fully tanked with propellant and contained cosmic radiation telemetry. Again, there was a malfunction in the control system, possibly caused by excess vibration. Flights seven and eight were launched from Cape Canaveral, partly for the inauguration of the new Florida Missile Test Center, but mostly because of the need for an extended flight range. These two flights were almost horizontal, at a 322 kilometer range. The second-stage rockets were fired after the horizontal flight configuration was attained, causing a high-speed, flat flight.

Impact of Event

Project Bumper was significant in the history of space for several reasons. First of all, Bumper's program of origin, the HERMES project, was invaluable for the immense amount of research and development attained with relatively little monetary investment, particularly after the war, when cutbacks in research were prevalent. Also, these projects encouraged organizational growth, both in governmental and private sectors, to accommodate the tremendous amount of data collected. Complex management structures, particularly with regard to the interaction among German scientists, United States Army Ordnance, and private companies, had to be constructed. The competitive nature of interservice rivalry, which began with HERMES, kept the impetus for space research and development alive.

The heritage of research data provided a strong base for future developments in space technology, especially the data concerning the many problems associated with high-altitude separations, attachments, and ignition.

An interesting and satisfying effect of Project Bumper was the proof of ideas long in existence, but unproven for lack of technology. One example is Tartaglia's rule, named for Niccolo (Fontana) Tartaglia (1505-1559), an Italian mathematician. His rule, roughly translated into rocket theory from cannonball theory, states that the second stage must be fired at the point of greatest velocity, instead of the point of greatest altitude. Had the WAC Corporal been fired at the high point in the V-2 flight, it would have gone merely 41 kilometers higher, the actual range of the second stage.

Probably the most significant impact of Project Bumper was the data base obtained from successfully launching a two-stage rocket. Following the V-2 were the Jupiter and Redstone ballistic missiles. Then followed the Saturn series of rockets, the rockets that took humankind to the Moon.

On the political scene, the end of World War II heralded the beginning of the Cold War, when the two world powers—the United States and the Soviet Union—were in heavy competition to achieve "firsts" in space. Although both nations got a head start with confiscated technology from Germany after the war, the nature of the acquisitions somewhat guided the course of the future. While the Soviets were attempting to produce V-2s from the factory fittings, the Americans were putting together rockets, with the assistance of the German rocket scientists, and were adding to the technology. Although the Soviets achieved the first events in space, such as the first man, first woman, and first extravehicular activity, the Americans were the first to produce a functional, reliable heavy-launch vehicle, capable of taking humans to the Moon and returning safely. This activity took advanced technology in the rocketry necessary to separate capsules for lunar descent, for launch from the Moon, and for reunification of the capsules prior to return to Earth.

Project Bumper, with its integration of two separate stages and the technology required to launch successfully the second stage in mid-flight, left a rich heritage of space technology and a vital base of information, without which space travel would not be possible.

Bibliography

Dornberger, Walter R. *V-2*. New York: Bantam Books, 1979. A fascinating eyewitness account of the development of the V-2; covers the political and financial maneuvering necessary for the project.

Emme, Eugene M., ed. *The History of Rocket Technology*. Detroit: Wayne State University Press, 1964. A technical history that also discusses the political and social background for rocket developments. A compilation of essays on the development, research, and use of the various launch vehicles. College level.

Goodwin, Harold L. *All About Rockets and Space Flight.* New York: Random House, 1964. An elementary level book; explains basic rocketry and spaceflight theories in easily understood terms. Good for beginning studies for any age.

Kennedy, Gregory P. *Vengeance Weapon 2: The V-2 Guided Missile.* Washington, D.C.: Smithsonian Institution Press, 1983. A pleasant combination of history and technology and very readable. Some technical passages, such as those dealing with the actual mechanics of the V-2. Beautiful black and white archival photographs.

Ley, Willy. *Rockets, Missiles, and Space Travel.* 7th ed. New York: Viking Press, 1959. Written by one of the most prolific writers of space history. Very readable, college-level materials, yet dense with information. Details history and theory from early concepts through the V-2. Contains technical tables.

Ordway, Frederick J., and Mitchell R. Sharpe. *The Rocket Team.* Cambridge, Mass.: MIT Press, 1982. A detailed history of the V-2, with many references to the V-1 as well. College-level reading, with fascinating black-and-white photographs. An excellent resource.

Ellen F. Mitchum

Cross-References

Tsiolkovsky Proposes That Liquid Oxygen Be Used for Space Travel (1903), p. 189; Goddard Launches the First Liquid Fuel Propelled Rocket (1926), p. 810; The Germans Use the V-1 Flying Bomb and the V-2 Goes into Production (1944), p. 1235; The United States Launches Its First Orbiting Satellite, Explorer 1 (1958), p. 1583; Gagarin Becomes the First Human to Orbit Earth (1961), p. 1693; Glenn Is the First American to Orbit Earth (1962), p. 1723; Lunokhod 1 Lands on the Moon (1970), p. 1928.

THE FIRST ELECTRONIC STORED-PROGRAM COMPUTER (BINAC) IS COMPLETED

Category of event: Applied science
Time: August, 1949
Locale: Philadelphia, Pennsylvania

The BINAC demonstrated the viability of several engineering innovations, most important the stored-program concept, that have become standard features of many modern computers

Principal personages:

JOHN PRESPER ECKERT (1919-   ), an American electrical engineer who, with Mauchly, designed and built the first electronic digital computers, including the BINAC

JOHN W. MAUCHLY (1907-1980), an American physicist who was a colleague of Eckert

JOHN VON NEUMANN (1903-1957), a renowned Hungarian-American mathematician who made various important contributions to computer design

ALAN MATHISON TURING (1912-1954), an English mathematician who formulated the idea of a stored-program computer in 1936

Summary of Event

The evolution of computers lies at the intersection of the inventive enthusiasm of mathematicians and engineers and the practical computational needs of various segments of society. The former have supplied the designs; the latter have supplied the funds. In the 1820's, the need for error-free mathematical and astronomical tables for use in navigation, unreliable versions of which were being produced by human "computers," stirred Charles Babbage to design and partially construct some of the earliest prototypes of modern computers, with substantial but still inadequate funding from the British government. In the 1880's, the search by the United States Bureau of the Census for a more efficient method of compiling the 1890 census led Herman Hollerith to devise a punched-card calculator, a machine that reduced by several years the time required to process the data.

The emergence of modern electronic computers began in a similar situation when, during World War II, there was an urgent need in the American military for reliable and quickly produced mathematical tables to be used in aiming various types of artillery. The calculation of very complex tables had progressed somewhat since Babbage's day, and the human computers were being assisted by mechanical calculators. The growing demand for increased accuracy and efficiency was pushing the limits of these machines, and in 1946, following three years of intense work at the University of Pennsylvania's Moore School of Engineering, John Presper Eckert and

John W. Mauchly presented their solution to the problem in the form of the Electronic Numerical Integrator and Computer (ENIAC), the world's first electronic general-purpose digital computer.

The ENIAC, built under a contract with the Army's Ballistics Research Laboratory, was a great success for Eckert and Mauchly, but even before it was completed, they were setting their sights on loftier targets. The primary drawback of the ENIAC was the great difficulty involved in programming it. Whenever the operators needed to instruct the machine to shift from one type of calculation to another, they had to reset a vast array of dials and switches, unplug and replug numerous cables, and make various other adjustments to the multiple pieces of hardware involved. Such a mode of operation was deemed acceptable for the ENIAC because, in computing firing tables, it would need reprogramming only periodically. Yet, if the instructions could be stored in a machine's memory, along with the data, it would be able to handle a wide range of calculations with ease and efficiency.

The idea of a stored-program computer first appeared in a paper written by the English mathematician Alan Mathison Turing and published in London in 1937. In this paper, Turing described a hypothetical machine of quite simple design that could be used to solve a wide range of logical and mathematical problems. A most significant aspect of this imaginary Turing machine is that the tape that would run through it would contain both information to be processed and instructions on how to process it. The tape would thus be a type of memory device, storing both the data and the program as sets of symbols that would be dealt with indifferently by the machine. Turing never attempted to construct this machine, and it was not until 1946 that he developed a design for an electronic stored-program computer, a prototype of which was built in 1950.

In the meantime, John von Neumann, a Hungarian mathematician acquainted with Turing's ideas, joined Eckert and Mauchly in 1944 and contributed to the design of ENIAC's successor, the Electronic Discrete Variable Automatic Computer (EDVAC), another project financed by the Army. The EDVAC was the first computer designed to incorporate the concept of the stored-program. It is clear, however, that Eckert and Mauchly had this concept in mind prior to von Neumann's arrival; thus, they had recognized in the context of more practical concerns the importance of the stored-program principle that Turing had presented as a theoretical exercise several years earlier.

In March of 1946, Eckert and Mauchly, frustrated by a controversy over patent rights for the ENIAC, resigned from the Moore School and several months later formed the Philadelphia-based Electronic Control Company, with a contract from the National Bureau of Standards and the Census Bureau to build a much grander computer called the Universal Automatic Computer (UNIVAC). They thus abandoned the EDVAC project, which was completed finally by the Moore School in 1952, but incorporated its main features into the design of the UNIVAC.

Building the UNIVAC, however, proved to be much more involved and expensive than anticipated, and the funds provided by the original contract were inadequate.

Eckert and Mauchly, therefore, took on several other smaller projects in an effort to raise funds. On October 9, 1947, they signed a contract with Northrop Aircraft Company of Hawthorne, California, to produce a relatively small computer to be used in the guidance system of a top-secret missile called the Snark, which Northrop was building for the Air Force. This computer, known as the Binary Automatic Computer (BINAC), turned out to be Eckert and Mauchly's first commercial sale and the first stored-program computer completed in the United States.

The BINAC was designed to be at least a preliminary version of a compact, airborne computer, and was somewhat diminutive for its time. It had two main processing units. These contained a total of fourteen hundred vacuum tubes, a drastic reduction from the eighteen thousand used in the ENIAC. There were also two memory units, as well as two power supplies, an input converter unit, and an input console, which used either a typewriter keyboard or encoded magnetic tape (the first time such tape was used for computer input). Because of its dual processing, memory, and power units, the BINAC was actually two computers, each of which would continually check its results against those of the other in an effort to identify errors. If a discrepancy was found, the computer would automatically stop. If the results matched, it would continue its calculations.

The memory units contained an important innovation: the mercury delay line. This device, conceived by Eckert several years earlier and developed for use in the EDVAC, consisted of a mercury-filled tube through which electrical impulses (transformed into sound waves) pass much more slowly than through a wire. This delay made it possible for impulses, carefully quantified to represent the binary digits "1" or "0," to be stored or maintained electronically in the tube almost indefinitely. The mercury delay line greatly increased the machine's memory efficiency and capacity and made it possible to store not only data but also instructions within the computer. It was, therefore, closely tied to the successful implementation of the stored-program concept.

Despite its much smaller size, the BINAC had an internal memory capacity many times greater than the ENIAC, and in performance could at least favorably compare with, and at best far surpass, the ENIAC. It was capable of executing thirty-five hundred additions or subtractions per second (compared to ENIAC's five thousand) and one thousand multiplications or divisions per second (exceeding ENIAC's 333 multiplications and 41 divisions).

The BINAC was originally scheduled for completion on May 15, 1948, seven months after the contract was signed. Because of a variety of administrative, financial, and engineering problems, however, it did not become operational until August of 1949. Because Eckert and Mauchly wanted to publicize the fact that their company had now produced a workable computer, public demonstrations of the BINAC were held in Philadelphia from August 18 through August 20. They took this opportunity to advertise their much larger and concurrent project, the UNIVAC, to the press and potential customers. The National Bureau of Standards and the Census Bureau had sent a delegation to these demonstrations, and the successful operation of the BINAC convinced these agencies that sufficient progress was being made and enabled Eckert and Mauchly to receive additional payments on the UNIVAC contract.

On August 22, Eckert and Mauchly held the BINAC demonstration test for representatives of Northrop Aircraft Company. It performed admirably for a period of seven hours and ten minutes, with forty minutes of downtime for repairing or replacing parts. Northrop was satisfied with the performance, although not with the late date on which it occurred, and in September shipped the computer to their headquarters in California.

The contract for the BINAC had specified a total cost of $100,000, with $80,000 being paid upon signing the contract and the remaining $20,000 due upon finishing the job. The actual cost, however, turned out to be $278,000, a discrepancy indicative of Eckert and Mauchly's inability to provide accurate cost estimates. Despite the fact that the completion of the BINAC brought much-needed capital into their company, as well as the fact that they had several UNIVAC contracts, their fledgling enterprise with more than one hundred employees was sinking deeper into debt. In February of 1950, Eckert and Mauchly agreed to sell their corporation to Remington Rand, representatives of which had attended the BINAC demonstrations. Remington Rand became Sperry Rand a few years later and produced UNIVACs, under the direction of Eckert and Mauchly, with great commercial success.

Impact of Event

Throughout its construction, the BINAC stood in the shadow of the more powerful UNIVAC. Mauchly had suggested in 1948 that the company should concentrate on producing several BINACs to sell, but Eckert and the engineering staff persuaded him to follow their preference for the UNIVAC. The importance of the BINAC for the company was seen, at least in part, in terms of how it contributed to the development of the UNIVAC. It did, indeed, contribute in significant ways.

The fact that the BINAC was relegated to a secondary status meant that it did not receive the attention of the best engineers and also that some of the parts used in its construction were not of the highest quality. These factors, as well as the fact that the machine emerged from the trip to California in a battered condition, resulted in a poor performance record at Northrop.

Nevertheless, it is the design embodied in the BINAC that is the real source of its significance. It demonstrated successfully the benefits of the dual processor design for minimizing errors, a feature adopted in many subsequent computers. It showed the suitability of magnetic tape as an input-output medium. Its most important new aspect was its ability to store programs in its relatively spacious memory, the principle that Eckert, Mauchly, and von Neumann had originally designed into the EDVAC. In this respect, the BINAC was a direct descendant of the EDVAC.

The stored-program feature of BINAC's design greatly enhanced its efficiency. It contributed to its speed, because the electronically stored instructions could be accessed as quickly as the electronically encoded information. The stored-program feature also accounted for the ease with which the BINAC could be reprogrammed, and thus for its flexibility in solving a variety of computational problems. In short, the stored-program principle gave electronic computers new powers, quickness, and automatic control that, as they have continued to grow, have contributed immensely to the aura of intelligence often associated with their operation.

The BINAC successfully demonstrated some of these impressive new powers in August of 1949 to eager observers from a number of major American corporations. It helped to convince many influential leaders of the commercial segment of society both of the engineering expertise of Eckert and Mauchly and of the promise of electronic computers in general. In doing so, it helped to ensure the further evolution of computers.

Bibliography

Augarten, Stan. *Bit by Bit: An Illustrated History of Computers.* New York: Ticknor & Fields, 1984. A well-written and pleasingly presented treatment of the development of modern computers and their predecessors from antiquity to the twentieth century. Chapter 5 is devoted to stored-program computers such as the BINAC, EDVAC, EDSAC, and UNIVAC, and describes the various contributions of Turing, von Neumann, Eckert, and Mauchly. Thoroughly illustrated, with a bibliography and index.

Goldstein, Herman H. *The Computer from Pascal to Von Neumann.* Princeton, N.J.: Princeton University Press, 1972. Goldstein worked with Eckert, Mauchly, and von Neumann on the ENIAC and EDVAC, and he discusses these machines in depth. Places particular emphasis on the contributions to electronic computing made by von Neumann. Weaves together technical details and personal reminiscences.

Shurkin, Joel N. *Engines of the Mind.* New York: W. W. Norton, 1984. Chronicles the development of computers from the ancient world to the modern age. About two-thirds of the book discusses the work of Eckert and Mauchly in the 1940's and 1950's; devotes attention to the controversy surrounding the claim that John V. Atanasoff invented the first electronic computer at Iowa State University in 1939. Includes a glossary, bibliography, and detailed index.

Stern, Nancy. *From ENIAC to UNIVAC: An Appraisal of the Eckert-Mauchly Computers.* Bedford, Mass.: Digital Press, 1981. A thorough and balanced study of the technical, financial, administrative, and intellectual aspects of Eckert and Mauchly's endeavors. Includes as an appendix the famous "First Draft of a Report on the EDVAC," written by von Neumann in 1945, which was responsible for von Neumann getting primary credit for designing the first stored-program computer.

Wulforst, Harry. *Breakthrough to the Computer Age.* New York: Charles Scribner's Sons, 1982. A popularly written, anecdotal account of the first electronic computers, primarily the ENIAC, BINAC, and UNIVAC, by a former director of public information for Sperry Univac. Emphasizes the economics, politics, and personalities involved in these projects, rather than the technical aspects. Illustrated, with a brief bibliography and index.

Gordon L. Miller

Cross-References

Turing Invents the Universal Turing Machine (1935), p. 1045; A Secret English Team Develops Colossus (1940's), p. 1155; Eckert and Mauchly Develop the ENIAC (1943), p. 1213; UNIVAC I Becomes the First Commercial Electronic Computer and the First to Use Magnetic Tape (1951), p. 1396; Bubble Memory Devices Are Created for Use in Computers (1969), p. 1886; The Floppy Disk Is Introduced for Storing Data Used by Computers (1970), p. 1923; The Microprocessor "Computer on a Chip" Is Introduced (1971), p. 1938; Optical Disks for the Storage of Computer Data Are Introduced (1984), p. 2262.

WILKINS DISCOVERS RESERPINE, THE FIRST TRANQUILIZER

Category of event: Medicine
Time: The early 1950's
Locale: Boston, Massachusetts

Wilkins recognized that reserpine had properties as an antipsychotic substance, revolutionizing psychiatry

Principal personages:
ROBERT WALLACE WILKINS (1906-), an American physician and clinical researcher who pioneered important drug therapies
NATHAN S. KLINE (1916-), the director of research at Rockland State Hospital in New York and a faculty member at Columbia University who systematically studied the potential of reserpine as a psychiatric drug
WALTER E. JUDSON (1916-), a colleague of Wilkins at Boston University who collaborated frequently in the reserpine research
J. C. GUPTA, an Indian researcher responsible for the first preliminary observations on reserpine's psychoactive properties in the 1940's

Summary of Event

Reserpine is an alkaloid (a nitrogen-containing organic chemical) extracted from the roots of *Rauwolfia serpentina*. This plant has been used in India for hundreds of years to treat numerous ailments. Although *Rauwolfia serpentina* was recognized to have medicinal properties as early as the 1560's in Europe, disbelief about its true efficacies prevented meaningful acceptance of the plant's medicinal value in Western medicine until the isolation of reserpine in the mid-twentieth century.

Reserpine's medicinal importance must be viewed in the context of the long-standing need for effective treatments of mental illnesses such as schizophrenia, a collection of disorders focused around problems with thinking patterns and unstable emotions. Primitive peoples primarily viewed the unusual behaviors that are now recognized as mental disorders in the context of mysticism. Attempts at early therapy included appeals to a higher order, exorcism, and trephining (the practice of opening holes in the skull to release evil spirits or fluids). During Grecian and Roman times, the view that unusual behavior is the result of natural phenomena gone out of balance began to replace mysticism. The Dark Ages to a very large degree, however, reversed this progressive movement. The scientific revolution and Renaissance gradually reinstated the naturalistic view with emphasis on mind and brain as the site of pathology. Classification schemes and therapies appropriately targeted at suspected etiologies began to take effect. Unfortunately, no therapeutic approach—be it psychological, physical, environmental, or drug-related—was found to be particularly effective, especially without significant side effects, in the treatment of mental disorders. By the mid-twentieth century, mental institutions throughout the world were overflowing with patients who seldom got better.

As is nearly always the case, when a plant such as *Rauwolfia serpentina* (hereafter referred to as *Rauwolfia*) has been in use since ancient times, there is uncertainty regarding its exact entry into common use. There is considerable evidence to suggest that *Rauwolfia* has been an important medicinal natural product for hundreds if not thousands of years in India. By the 1930's, *Rauwolfia* had been mentioned in modern Indian medical literature. The list of putative medicinal properties for *Rauwolfia* is rather long: Cardiovascular effects, use against snake bite, and references to various mental effects compose a condensed listing. The early 1940's produced a series of reports from India suggesting the medical usefulness of the plant. Robert Wallace Wilkins took note of these hints, particularly the work of Indian physician J. C. Gupta, who mentioned mental effects such as sedation as well as blood pressure lowering properties.

Wilkins, who headed the Massachusetts Memorial Hospital's Hypertension Clinic, initiated clinical trials in 1950 with crude *Rauwolfia* to determine its effects in hypertension, an ailment involving excessively high blood pressure. Early observations included the lowering of blood pressure, decrease in heart rate, and sedation. In addition, the drug is very slow-acting. Indeed, the blood-pressure-lowering effects may take weeks or even months. The slow onset of action made things difficult for researchers and played a key role in resistance to accepting the drug's benefits. Often, investigators gave up before enough time had elapsed to see significant effects. Nevertheless, by 1952, Wilkins and his collaborator, Walter E. Judson, were convinced that *Rauwolfia* was useful in hypertension. They conducted extensive trials, including new designs with pure reserpine, one of the constituents of *Rauwolfia*. They soon concluded that the properties of reserpine were nearly indistinguishable from *Rauwolfia*, lending strong support to the idea that reserpine is the active chemical in the plant. Wilkins and Judson noted that reserpine not only lowered blood pressure and heart rate but also caused nasal congestion, weight gain, diarrhea, and lowered libido in men. Wilkins believed that reserpine's greatest advantage was in boosting the blood-pressure-lowering effects of drugs already in use. Thus, reserpine, in combination with other drugs such as veratrum or hydralazine, was one of the best approaches to treating hypertension in the 1950's.

Wilkins repeatedly stressed the central role that changes in nervous system activity appeared to play in the blood-pressure-lowering effect. In a 1954 paper in the *Annals of the New York Academy of Sciences*, Wilkins stated: "Symptomatic improvement has been so marked in some patients as to be almost embarrassing to the physician. Many patients have become positively lyrical about their sense of well-being on the drugs. . . ." Wilkins went on to say: "I have told many psychiatrists and others interested in psychotherpy that '*Rauwolfia* is good psychotherapy in pill form.'" He also concluded that the sedative effects of *Rauwolfia* were not typical calming effects: As the dose was increased, people did not typically become sleepy.

They were perfectly able to participate in activities that interested them. This provided the seeds of revolution for reserpine's use in psychiatry. As is now known, antipsychotic drugs produce a state of tranquilization which is qualitatively different from sedation. Central nervous system depressants such as phenobarbital or valium (diazepam) produce sedation and hypnosis (sleep) at higher doses, but are relatively ineffective in countering the psychotic processes of schizophrenia.

Impressed by these reports and those of Indian workers, Nathan S. Kline of Columbia University began testing reserpine's effectiveness as a psychiatric drug. Using a test population of about seven hundred at New York's Rockland State Hospital, Kline analyzed reserpine's actions as measured by a battery of physiological and behavioral parameters. While verifying the conclusions that others had reached about blood pressure and heart rate lowering and minor side effects, Kline also observed marked anxiety reduction, relief of situational depression, a tranquilizing effect with accompanying decreased motor activity, and decreased need for shock therapy, such as that induced by insulin overdose in severely psychotic patients. He concluded, however, that reserpine did not seem to cure the underlying psychosis itself. Rather, it changed certain symptomology associated with the psychosis.

Research results since the 1950's help one to understand the effects of reserpine, as reported by Wilkins, Kline, and others. Reserpine acts in nerve endings that contain monoamines as neurotransmitters. Monoamines are substances like norepinephrine, dopamine, and serotonin, which are released from one nerve cell to contact an adjacent nerve cell in the process that moves information between cells. Reserpine depletes nerve endings of the neurotransmitter, decreasing the nerve's capacity to signal other cells. Monoamines are found in a part of the peripheral nervous system known as the sympathetic nervous system and at various locales throughout the brain. Reserpine's known actions in the cardiovascular system, gastrointestinal system, and nervous systems can be explained by this molecular mechanism.

Impact of Event

Today, reserpine is not a particularly significant clinical drug. This is especially so regarding its tranquilizing effects. In the early 1950's, a separate but parallel series of developments occurred with a group of synthetic drugs known as the phenothiazines. The original prototype of this group, chlorpromazine (Thorazine) and closely related drugs are now the standard antipsychotics. The phenothiazines show greater specificity and effectiveness in treating the psychotic symptoms of schizophrenia. It is now recognized that dopamine has a central role in the pathologies of schizophrenia and that phenothiazines are more specific toward dopamine than reserpine. Nevertheless, like reserpine, phenothiazines do not cure schizophrenia; they only alleviate schizophrenic symptomology.

Reserpine holds a unique place in pharmacology and psychiatry because its discovery established that psychosis could be treated in a relatively specific fashion with drugs. Its introduction broke a long string of failure and frustration to find effective treatment, drug or otherwise. The revolution that ensued is one of the more remarkable in modern medicine. Almost every introduction to modern psychology and pharmacology illustrates the precipitous out-migration from mental institutions in the late 1950's. This occurred because many psychiatric patients who previously could not cope with the outside world were able to function in the noninstitutional world with the help of antipsychotic drugs and occasional medical consultation. The out-migration not only relieved the terrible strain on resources at institutions by reducing patient loads but also improved the entire institutional environment as patients who could not leave the hospitals were changed by using the drugs to reduce their psychotic behavior. Although controversies continue regarding societal consequences of the outpatient movement, about the "mind control" potential of antipsychotic drugs, and unusually high occurrences of some side effects, most observers believe that the overall cost benefit analysis associated with use of antipsychotic drugs is heavily weighted toward benefits, for individuals and society.

Antipsychotic drugs such as reserpine have contributed substantially to an understanding of the brain mechanisms that are out of balance in schizophrenias. A recurring theme in the history of pharmacology is that clinically useful drugs also become tools in deciphering the nature of diseases. Reserpine's lasting legacy—perhaps even beyond its germinal role in the revolution of psychiatrically useful drugs—is its productivity as a pharmacological tool. It remains an important probe in studies of nerve cell function, both in the peripheral and central nervous systems. Drugs derived from the natural products may or may not become long-term players in therapeutics, but even if they do not, their uses as models for better drugs and as experimental tools are invaluable.

Bibliography

Katzung, Bertram G., ed. *Basic and Clinical Pharmacology*. 4th ed. Norwalk, Conn.: Appleton and Lange, 1989. This widely used general pharmacology book details present thought on reserpine's actions, both positive and negative, and describes its uses in the peripheral and central nervous systems. The broader context of drugs used to treat mental disorders is nicely described in both the historical context and in modern use.

Kline, Nathan S. "Use of *Rauwolfia serpentina* Benth in Neuropsychiatric Conditions." *Annals of the New York Academy of Sciences* 59 (1954): 107-132. Kline is frequently credited with systematically studying and introducing reserpine for psychiatric use. This article provides the rationale for using the drug in mental illness and documents carefully the use of *Rauwolfia* in India prior to its introduction in the United States.

Lickey, Marvin E., and Barbara Gordon. *Drugs for Mental Illness: A Revolution in Psychiatry*. New York: W. H. Freeman, 1983. This book cogently describes the major changes in psychiatry flowing from the introduction of antipsychotic drugs in the 1950's. It outlines current understanding of the nature and diagnosis of mental illness while discussing the types of drugs used to treat common psychoses.

Shershow, John C., ed. *Schizophrenia: Science and Practice.* Cambridge, Mass.: Harvard University Press, 1978. Using a group of influential contributors, this book discusses the main psychotic disorders in their historical, cultural, and scientific contexts. It provides exceptional opportunity for readers to analyze the similarities and differences between very different ways of viewing schizophrenia.

Tyler, Varro E., et al. *Pharmacognosy.* 9th ed. Philadelphia: Lea & Febiger, 1988. This book is one of the classics of pharmacognosy, the science that studies drugs derived from natural products. It contains an extensive section on reserpine's parent plant, *Rauwolfia serpentina.* It also provides a wealth of information on many other natural product drugs that are significant historically and in modern medicine.

Wilkins, Robert W. "Clinical Usage of *Rauwolfia* Alkaloids, Including Reserpine (Serpasil)." *Annals of the New York Academy of Sciences* 59 (1954): 36-44. An interesting primary account of Wilkins' move into research with reserpine with special emphasis on its cardiovascular effects; it also contains assertions that led to its use in psychiatric medicine. Includes an interesting segment crediting the early use of *Rauwolfia* in India.

Keith Krom Parker

Cross-References

Ramón y Cajal Establishes the Neuron as the Functional Unit of the Nervous System (1888), p. 1; Berger Develops the Electroencephalogram (EEG) (1929), p. 890; Moniz Develops Prefrontal Lobotomy (1935), p. 1060; Cerletti and Bini Develop Electroconvulsive Therapy for Treating Schizophrenia (1937), p. 1086; Wilkins Introduces Reserpine for the Treatment of High Blood Pressure (1952), p. 1429; Hounsfield Introduces a CAT Scanner That Can See Clearly into the Body (1972), p. 1961; Janowsky Publishes a Cholinergic-Adrenergic Hypothesis of Mania and Depression (1972), p. 1976.

LI ISOLATES THE HUMAN GROWTH HORMONE

Category of event: Chemistry
Time: The mid-1950's
Locale: Berkeley, California

Li purified and characterized human growth hormone, ushering in a new era of advances in clinical medicine based upon understanding of fundamental biochemistry

Principal personages:

CHOH HAO LI (1913-1987), a Chinese-American biochemist who directed the University of California's Hormone Research Laboratory, which led to the discovery of many peptide hormones

HAROLD PAPKOFF (1925-   ), an endocrinologist who collaborated with Li in the human growth hormone work and who made significant contributions to the understanding of hormone action

HERBERT MCLEAN EVANS (1882-1971), an experimental biologist at the University of California, Berkeley, who worked with Li in the early isolations of nonhuman growth hormones

Summary of Event

The pituitary is a small gland lying underneath the lower surface of the brain. Controlled by the nearby brain region known as the hypothalamus, the pituitary gland secretes into the bloodstream many hormonal substances responsible for regulation of biological function. Growth hormone, a peptide or small protein, is one of these pituitary hormones responsible for proper growth and development in young animals, including humans, and for other complex processes in adults.

In a series of classic experiments in the 1920's and 1930's, Herbert McLean Evans had demonstrated the growth-promoting potential of crude pituitary extracts from dogs. By the early 1940's, Choh Hao Li and Evans of the University of California, Berkeley, had succeeded in isolating and partially characterizing growth hormone from bovine (beef) pituitaries. This work was particularly noteworthy because of the exceedingly small amounts of the hormone present in the diminutive pituitary and because of the creative use of classical methods and emerging technologies, such as electrophoresis (a method in which molecules are separated according to differences in electrical charge), to purify the hormone effectively.

Because insufficient levels of growth hormone in human infants lead to retarded growth, availability of growth hormone supplements is important in clinical medicine. Despite the basic importance of Li and Evans' work with animal growth hormones, it had no impact on human medicine because animal growth hormones, except for those of the higher primates such as monkeys, do not stimulate growth in humans. Logically, then, it became vital to isolate the human growth hormone. The reason that human growth hormone is effective in humans, while most animal growth hormones are not, is that the different growth hormones differ from one another in composition. These hormones are all small proteins, meaning that they are made of amino acids, which are the building blocks for all proteins. There are twenty amino acids commonly used to build proteins, and the exact sequence of amino acids throughout the protein precisely determines the shape and properties of the protein. Human growth hormone differs from other growth hormones in both size (number of amino acids) and sequence of amino acids. These physical differences not only lead to differences in biological activity but also lead to great difficulty in working with the various hormones as the technology to distinguish among these types of molecular differences has been rudimentary.

In the late 1940's and early 1950's, following the successful isolation of growth hormone from beef pituitary, a number of other growth hormones from a variety of species were extracted using similar methodology to that used by Li and Evans. Availability of these growth hormones allowed for the biological testing that established the inactivity of nonprimate growth hormones in primates. In 1956, Li and Harold Papkoff summarized the state of affairs in an article published in the American journal *Science.* Growth hormone, or somatotropin, by which it is often referred, from beef is inactive in humans. Growth hormone from fish is inactive in rats but, not surprisingly, active in fish. Beef hormone is inactive in monkeys. Up to this time, none of these hormones had been thoroughly characterized, meaning that their amino acid compositions and sequences were unknown. Li's work, however, had established some physical properties of the bovine growth hormone. It appeared to have a molecular weight of about forty-six thousand (molecular weight is an indication of a molecule's size from the standpoint of a chemist). It also appeared to be a branched molecule in which the two amino acids at the outer branches were phenylalanine and alanine (two of the twenty possible amino acids), with the single amino acid at the other end being alanine. With this information in hand, Li and Papkoff began to isolate and characterize the human hormone to test the hypothesis that primate hormones, including human, differed in chemical composition from other growth hormones, thus explaining the differences in biological activities.

Both human and monkey pituitary glands are rare items, so gifts of these tissues to Li were critical to the work's success. Human tissue was provided from researchers in Stockholm, Sweden, while monkey pituitaries came from the United States pharmaceutical firm Eli Lily. These gifts suggest important points about the fundamental scientific enterprise. First, it is international in scope; and secondly, cooperation among scientists is common and widely accepted as ethical behavior. Although competition within the scientific community is also accepted as healthy to progress, cooperation and competition must coexist to provide a balance that fosters both individual accomplishment, as well as benefit for the entire scientific enterprise.

Li and Papkoff used tried techniques as well as new tools to effect the purification of growth hormone from these scarce tissues. Crude preparations were extracted from the raw tissues with calcium oxide. Treating the crude preparation with the salt, ammonium sulfate, precipitated growth hormone along with some other proteins. This process, known as salting out, takes advantage of solubility characteristics to produce partial purification of proteins. The technique, although of historical significance, is still widely used in the initial phases of protein purification. Li then used a technique that was only beginning to take hold at the time. In this technique, biochemical samples were poured over a long column of chemical material known as an ion exchange column. The sample materials adhered to the column with differing strengths and were selectively released as salt solutions of increasing strength washed the column. The appropriate fractions were then treated further chemically and centrifuged (a process involving high-speed spinning) to separate the heavier, active material. The purified product was subjected to electrophoresis to verify its extremely pure status. Using the purified material, Li and Papkoff performed physical studies showing that the human and monkey growth hormones (the monkey preparation being treated in a parallel fashion) were significantly different in amino acid composition and molecular size from the growth hormones of other animals.

The final piece of standard chemical characterization of growth hormone awaited development of efficient technology for analyzing the exact sequence of amino acids in the hormone. Li and his coworkers published the sequence data in 1966. By 1970, Li succeeded in producing human growth hormone using the sequence information and new techniques of laboratory synthesis. The synthesis brought to fruitful conclusion more than forty years of revolutionary thinking and experimentation in peptide chemistry. Li's work represents the power of scientific work that effectively utilizes the cutting edge of scientific design and method. Although many new approaches have arisen, these germinal studies were responsible for charting the way.

Impact of Event

Choh Hao Li's lifelong work with peptide hormones, and especially the work with human growth hormone, resulted in a cascade of diverse but related effects. The most obvious application of the human growth hormone work has been in clinical medicine, where availability of pure, highly characterized molecules has produced dramatic positive changes for growth hormone deficient people, usually children. Pure preparations are essential in minimizing untoward effects produced by contaminants or other pituitary hormones. The pituitary is a complex organ containing many other peptide hormones and other substances. Other peptide hormones, present in even small quantities, may yield activities such as stimulation of the genitourinary tract which are inappropriate or even dangerous. Availability of pure human growth hormone is critical because of the negligible activity of other growth hormones in humans. These species differences represent general evolutionary relationships between structures of molecules from different organisms and activity of the molecules; however, these differences are particularly pronounced in the case of growth hormone. Insulin, for example, which is likewise a peptide hormone, shows considerable cross reactivity between species. Although human insulin is preferable for human use, insulin from pigs has been a standard preparation in human medical practice.

In a scientific sense, Li's work may have even longer-ranging consequences. He, among others, pioneered the techniques now routinely used to study all proteins. Since proteins are indispensable structural and functional components of all living organisms and even entities on the edge of life such as viruses and prions, Li's work touches nearly every area of modern biological science. In a more specific sense, unraveling the structural mysteries of growth hormone has led to a greater understanding of the pituitary, its relationship to the brain, most notably to the hypothalamic region, and a better appreciation of the control and dynamics of hormone function. One of the clearest reasons for this increase in knowledge is that pure, well-understood biological molecules can be used as tools for probing the structures they come from and the structures they act upon. Better understanding of the pituitary gland has proved to be instrumental not only in exploring growth-related disorders such as acromegaly, which occurs because of growth hormone excess in adults, but also in exploring many other physiological situations, such as the control of sexual functions and reproduction and the regulation of hormone action in the adrenal glands.

Despite the availability of pure human growth hormone, supplies were never able to meet demand not only because of the lack of human pituitary tissue but also, to some extent, because of the difficulties in isolating the hormone. In the 1970's, technology to isolate the genes coding for proteins became a reality. Once the genes are known, they can be amplified (cloned) and inserted into rapidly multiplying bacteria. Expression of these genetically recombined genes then produces the wanted protein in large quantities; this is known as genetic engineering.

By the early 1980's, enough wrinkles had been worked out to bring the revolution to commercial application. Eli Lilly and Genentech now produce genetically engineered human growth hormone, vastly increasing its supply. Herein, may lie Li's most lasting contribution. Small amounts of the pure hormone to be genetically engineered must be present to act as probes. Without the probes and accompanying know-how regarding isolation of the eventual protein product, the modern technology breaks down. Li's work will have lasting consequences in this regard.

Bibliography

Ganong, William F. *Review of Medical Physiology.* 14th ed. Norwalk, Conn.: Appleton and Lange, 1989. Ganong concisely places growth hormone into its context as a vital agent of physiology. Contains a nice review of pituitary function and includes a bibliography of historical and modern importance.

Li, Choh Hao, ed. *Hormonal Proteins and Peptides.* New York: Academic Press, 1973-1984. This collection of volumes on the peptide subcategory of hormones discusses developments in growth hormone research as well as in the now large number of other related substances. It shows clearly the dramatic contributions Li's early discoveries made in paving the way for a new significant area of scientific medicine. Volume 4, 1979, is specifically devoted to growth hormone.

_____, et al. "Human Pituitary Growth Hormone, XII: The Amino Acid Sequence of the Hormone." *Journal of the American Chemical Society* 88 (May 5, 1966): 2050-2051. Chemists cannot even begin to suggest closure on the studies for a protein until its primary structure (that is, its amino acid sequence) is known. This paper provides that vital information while nicely documenting important applications of the emerging technology in protein chemistry.

Li, Choh Hao, and Herbert M. Evans. "The Isolation of Pituitary Growth Hormone." *Science* 99 (March 3, 1944): 183-184. This short, but straightforward paper has great historical significance because it represents the first "clean" preparation of bovine growth hormone. The later work with human pituitaries depended heavily on the insights and experiences gained in nonhuman tissues.

Li, Choh Hao, and Harold Papkoff. "Preparation and Properties of Growth Hormone from Human and Monkey Pituitary Glands." *Science* 124 (December 18, 1956): 1293-1294. The dramatic findings with human and primate growth hormones, both so vital to the medical applications of this work, is presented in this coherent article.

Maisel, Albert Q. *The Hormone Quest*. New York: Random House, 1965. This is one of those fun books that reads like a novel while expertly chronicling the history of hormone research, including the pituitary hormones like growth hormone. Although dated, its coverage of the early days of hormone research makes it worthwhile reading. Motivating to budding endocrinologists.

Keith Krom Parker

Cross-References

Hopkins Discovers Tryptophan, an Essential Amino Acid (1900), p. 46; Bayliss and Starling Discover Secretin and Establish the Role of Hormones (1902), p. 179; Banting and Macloed Win the Nobel Prize for the Discovery of Insulin (1921), p. 720: Du Vigneaud Synthesizes Oxytocin, the First Peptide Hormone (1953), p. 1459; Sanger Wins the Nobel Prize for the Discovery of the Structure of Insulin (1958), p. 1567; Cohen and Boyer Develop Recombinant DNA Technology (1973), p. 1987; The First Commercial Genetic Engineering Product, Humulin, Is Marketed by Eli Lilly (1982), p. 2221.

OCHOA CREATES SYNTHETIC RNA

Category of event: Biology
Time: The mid-1950's
Locale: New York, New York

Ochoa discovered a method for synthesizing the biological molecule ribonucleic acid (RNA), establishing that this process can occur outside the living cell

Principal personages:

SEVERO OCHOA (1905-   ), a Spanish biochemist who was a corecipient of the 1959 Nobel Prize in Physiology or Medicine and contributed widely in metabolic biochemistry and molecular biology

MARIANNE GRUNBERG-MANAGO, a French biochemist who worked with Ochoa in the synthetic RNA work

MARSHALL W. NIRENBERG (1927-   ), an American biochemist and recipient of the 1968 Nobel Prize in Physiology or Medicine for the decisive work leading to the discovery of the genetic code

PETER LENGYEL (1929-   ), a Hungarian-American biochemist who worked with Ochoa in studies leading to the understanding of the genetic code

Summary of Event

Transmission of parental characteristics to offspring in humans and other organisms has been assumed over the ages. Nevertheless, not until the mid-eighteenth century was a comprehensive theory put forth to outline the general biological parameters of heredity. These ideas, established by the insightful Austrian monk, Gregor Johann Mendel, are now known as classical, or Mendelian, genetics. By the early twentieth century, Mendel's ideas had been linked to cell theory (the idea that cells compose the fundamental units of life) by observations that cellular entities known as chromosomes carry Mendel's hereditary units. The hereditary units had been named genes, and the work of Thomas Hunt Morgan and his colleagues at Columbia University rooted the new science of genetics firmly within the context of hereditary units being located as well-organized arrays of genes on chromosomes.

In the early decades of the twentieth century, genetics had not been experimentally united with biochemistry. This merging soon occurred, however, with work in the mold *Neurospora crassa*. This Nobel award-winning work by Edward Lawrie Tatum and George Wells Beadle showed that genes control production of proteins, which are major functional molecules in cells. Yet, no one knew the chemical composition of genes and chromosomes, or, rather, the molecules of heredity. Oswald Avery and his colleagues at New York's Rockefeller Institute determined experimentally that the molecular basis of heredity, or the transforming principle, as they called it, was a large polymer known as deoxyribonucleic acid (DNA). DNA had been recognized as a cellular component for some seventy years; but until 1944, its functional importance, if any, was unrecognized. Avery's discovery triggered a furious worldwide search for the particular structural characteristics of DNA, which allow for the known biological characteristics of genes. One of the most famous studies in the history of science solved this problem in 1953. James D. Watson, Francis Crick, and Maurice Wilkins postulated that DNA exists as a double helix. That is, two long strands twist about each other in a predictable pattern, with each single strand held to the other by weak, reversible linkages known as hydrogen bonds. About this time, researchers recognized also that a closely related molecule to DNA, ribonucleic acid (RNA), plays an important role in transcribing the genetic information as well as in other biological functions.

Severo Ochoa was born in Spain as the science of genetics was developing. He received his medical degree from the University of Madrid in 1928, idolizing the great Spanish histologist Santiago Ramón y Cajal and finding himself deeply immersed in experimental biology by the end of his medical studies. The 1930's found him studying and researching in Madrid, Germany, and England, until a combination of professional and political factors caused Ochoa to move to St. Louis and the dynamic biochemistry studies occurring at Washington University's School of Medicine. He landed into an environment focused upon the central biochemical issues of that time—that is, those surrounding questions of how cells process energy from organic molecules like the sugar glucose to provide usable biological energy in the form of adenosine triphosphate (ATP). Ochoa made many significant discoveries in biochemical energetics, especially in studies with vitamins, with some of the reactions of what is now often called the Krebs cycle, and in oxidative phosphorylation, the final common pathway that produces most of ATP.

In 1942, Ochoa moved to New York University, where he continued his interests in oxidative phosphorylation by studying the bacterium *Azobacter vinelandii*, which was known to be extremely active metabolically. With postdoctoral fellow Marianne Grunberg-Manago, he studied enzymatic reactions capable of incorporating inorganic phosphate (a compound consisting of one atom of phosphorus and four atoms of oxygen) into adenosine diphosphate (ADP) to form ATP. One particularly interesting reaction was followed by monitoring the amount of radioactive phosphate reacting with ADP. Following separation of the reaction products, it was discovered that the main product was not ATP, but a much larger molecule. Chemical characterization demonstrated that this product was a polymer of adenosine monophosphate (AMP). When other nucleocide diphosphates, such as inosine diphosphate (IDP), were used in the reaction, the corresponding polymer of inosine monophosphate (IMP) was formed. Thus, in each case, a polymer—a long string of building-block units—was formed. The polymers formed were synthetic RNAs, and the enzyme responsible for the conversion became known as polynucleotide phosphorylase. This finding, once the early skepticism was resolved, was received by biochemists with great enthusiasm because no technique outside the cell had ever been discovered previously in which a nucleic acid similar to RNA could be synthesized.

Ochoa, Peter Lengyel, and Marshall W. Nirenberg at the National Institute of Health took advantage of this breakthrough to synthesize different RNAs useful in cracking the genetic code. Crick had postulated that the flow of information in biological systems is from DNA to RNA to protein. In other words, genetic information contained in DNA structure is transcribed into complementary RNA structures, which, in turn, are translated into protein structure by specifying the particular amino acids to be incorporated into the protein. Protein synthesis, an extremely complex process, involves bringing a type of RNA, known as message, together with amino acids and huge cellular organelles, known as ribosomes. Investigators did not know the nature of the nucleic acid alphabet—for example, how many single units of the RNA polymer code were needed for each amino acid, and the order that the units must be in to stand for a word in the nucleic acid language. In 1961, Nirenberg demonstrated that the polymer of synthetic RNA with multiple units of uracil (poly U) coded for a protein containing the amino acid phenylalanine only. Each three units (U's) gave one phenylalanine. Therefore, genetic words each contain three letters. UUU translates into phenylalanine. Poly A, the first polymer discovered with polynucleotide phosphorylase was coded for a protein containing multiple lysines. That is, AAA translates into the amino acid lysine.

The words containing combinations of letters such as AUG were not as easily studied, but Nirenberg, Ochoa, and Gobind Khorana of the University of Wisconsin uncovered eventually the exact translation for each amino acid. In RNA, there are four possible letters (A, U, G, and C) and three letters to each word. Accordingly, there are sixty-four possible words. With only twenty amino acids, it became clear that more than one RNA word can translate into a given amino acid. Yet, no given word stands for any more than one amino acid. For example, UUU specifies phenylalanine only. UUC also means phenylalanine but no other amino acid. A few RNA words do not translate into any amino acid; they are stop signals, telling the ribosome to cease translating RNA.

The questions of which direction an RNA is translated are critical. For example, CAA codes for the amino acid glutamine, but the reverse, AAC, translates to the amino acid asparagine. Such a difference is critical because the exact sequence of a protein determines its activity. To a large extent, this problem had to be solved simultaneously. Ochoa and his colleagues made great strides using polynucleotide phosphorylase to build synthetic RNAs with predictable directionality. By 1964, Khorana had developed more direct methods to analyze these questions, and the field began to move in new directions.

Impact of Event

In a 1980 autobiographical sketch in the *Annual Review of Biochemistry* Severo Ochoa stated: "I tell this story to justify the title of this essay, because in my life biochemistry has been my only and real hobby." His research pursuits covered vitamins, the central reactions of intermediary metabolism, RNA and the genetic code, and protein synthesis.

Ochoa's discovery of polynucleotide phosphorylase, leading to the laboratory synthesis of RNA, was a serendipitous side effect of studies planned in the central area of oxidative phosphorylation. Even though Ochoa's experimental productivity in a quantitative sense may have been greater in the metabolic areas, the production of synthetic RNA will likely have the longest lasting consequences. This conclusion may seem odd in the light of follow-up studies, which have shown polynucleotide phosphorylase to be a minor player in general RNA synthesis. For the most part, it is found in bacteria only, and even there, its function remains controversial. Since this enzyme catalyzes relatively reversible reactions, it is possible that RNA degradation, the opposite of synthesis, is its real biological niche. In 1960, the enzyme responsible for most of the RNA synthesis in cells, RNA polymerase, was discovered by the University of Chicago's Samuel Weiss and Jerard Hurwitz at New York University. In a related area, the enzyme catalyzing DNA synthesis, DNA polymerase, was discovered by Arthur Kornberg of Stanford University, who worked with Ochoa in the late 1940's. Ochoa and Kornberg shared the Nobel Prize in Physiology or Medicine in 1959.

The germinal nature of Ochoa's elicitation of RNA synthesis from this obscure enzyme lies in methodology. Synthetic RNAs provided the key to understanding the genetic code. The genetic code is universal; it operates in all organisms, simple or complex. It is used by viruses, which are near life, yet still not alive. Spelling out the genetic code was one of the top discoveries of the twentieth century. Nearly all work in molecular biology depends on this knowledge. Further, availability of synthetic RNAs provided hybridization tools for molecular geneticists. Hybridization is a technique in which an RNA is allowed to bind in a complementary fashion to DNA under investigation. The greater similarity between RNA and DNA, the greater the amount of binding. The differential binding allows for seeking, finding, and ultimately isolating a target DNA from a large diverse pool of DNA, in short, finding a needle in a haystack. Hybridization approaches are indispensable aids in experimental molecular genetics as well as in applied sciences, such as forensics.

Historians and philosophers of science debate the relative merits of methodological breakthrough versus conceptual revolution, of convergent thinking as opposed to the divergent, and luck compared to the rationally planned. Ochoa's work with synthetic RNA was not planned but led eventually to rigorous step-by-step experimental unraveling of the genetic code. It diverged from the expected but provided the tool to converge upon a universal principle. It made available a technique that ultimately revolutionized biochemists' ideas about life and its evolution. Ochoa's life and work embodied a creative synergy of these qualities, resulting in world-class science.

Bibliography

Grunberg-Manago, Marianne, and Severo Ochoa. "Enzymatic Synthesis and Breakdown of Polynucleotides; Polynucleotide Phosphorylase." *Journal of the American Chemical Society* 77 (June 5, 1955): 3165-3166. This article in one of the world's leading chemical journals is a short, coherent account of the key investigation with synthetic RNA. Presented in a concise and straightforward manner.

Lehninger, Albert L. *Principles of Biochemistry.* New York: Worth, 1982. This book is extremely useful for those readers who wish some knowledge of the chemistry involved in Ochoa's RNA discovery. It is very readable and provides historical perspective as well as other context for this area of biochemistry.

Ochoa, Severo. "The Pursuit of a Hobby." *Annual Review of Biochemistry* 49 (1980): 1-30. This highly personal reflection provides insight into the man, his formative years in Spain and his life in New York, and his work from developmental experiences with other biochemists to his independent forays into metabolism and molecular biology.

Recombinant DNA: Readings from Scientific American. Introductions by David Freifelder. San Francisco: W. H. Freeman, 1978. This collection of articles from *Scientific American* provides one of the best opportunities for popular reading that borders on the semitechnical. A reader seeking an introduction to molecular biology will be treated to the best possible writing, fine illustrations, and historical perspective from cell biology through gene engineering.

Watson, J. D., et al. *Molecular Biology of the Gene.* 4th ed. Menlo Park, Calif.: Benjamin/Cummings, 1987. This highly successful multiedition book by nucleic acid pioneer James Watson is for the technical reader. Yet, it goes to great lengths to bring novices to equal footing with brilliant descriptions of fundamental biochemical tenants, in conjunction with historical perspective.

Keith Krom Parker

Cross-References

Sutton States That Chromosomes Are Paired and Could Be Carriers of Hereditary Traits (1902), p. 153; Morgan Develops the Gene-Chromosome Theory (1908), p. 407; Johannsen Coins the Terms "Gene," "Genotype," and "Phenotype" (1909), p. 433; Avery, MacLeod, and McCarty Determine That DNA Carries Hereditary Information (1943), 1203; Watson and Crick Develop the Double-Helix Model for DNA (1951), p. 1406; Nirenberg Invents an Experimental Technique That Cracks the Genetic Code (1961), p. 1687; Kornberg and Coworkers Synthesize Biologically Active DNA (1967), p. 1857; Berg, Gilbert, and Sanger Develop Techniques for Genetic Engineering (1980), p. 2115.

THE ARTIFICIAL SWEETENER CYCLAMATE
IS INTRODUCED

Category of event: Chemistry
Time: 1950
Locale: Abbott Laboratories, Illinois

Abbott launched the artificial sweetener Sucaryl, which contained the sodium salt of cyclamic acid or cyclamate; Du Pont marketed a similar product, Cyclan

Principal personage:
    MICHAEL SVEDA (1912-   ), the American chemist who, while at graduate school at the University of Illinois, discovered the artificial sweetener cyclamate.

Summary of Event

The first synthetic sugar substitute, saccharin, was developed in 1879. It became commercially available in 1907 but was banned for safety reasons in 1912. Sugar shortages during World War I resulted in its reintroduction. Two other artificial sweeteners, Dulcin and P-4000, were introduced later but were banned in 1950 for causing cancer in laboratory animals.

In 1937, Michael Sveda was a young chemist working on his Ph.D. at the University of Illinois. A flood in the Ohio valley had ruined the local pipe-tobacco crop, and Sveda had been forced to smoke cigarettes. While at his laboratory bench, where he was working on fever-depressant compounds, Sveda brushed some loose tobacco from his lips and noticed that his fingers tasted sweet. Having a curious, if rather foolhardy nature, Sveda tasted the chemicals on his bench to find which one was responsible for the taste. The culprit was the forerunner of cyclohexylsulfamate, the material which came to be known as cyclamate. Sveda had time on his hands because the starting materials he needed for his fever-depressant work were out of stock, and he had the chance to work with the sweetener. Later, on reviewing his career, Sveda explained the serendipitous discovery with the comment: "God looks after damn fools, children, and chemists."

Sveda had not planned a career in industry; he intended to teach chemistry when he received his doctorate but explained, "I was married and already had a youngster, so I had to go to work." Sveda joined the Du Pont company in 1939 and assigned the patent for cyclamate to his employer. In June of 1950, after a decade of testing on animals and humans, Abbott Laboratories announced that it was launching Sveda's artificial sweetener under the trade name Sucaryl. Du Pont followed with its sweetener product, Cyclan. A *Time* magazine article in 1950 announced the new product and noted that Abbott had warned that because the product was a sodium salt, individuals with kidney problems should consult their doctors before using the additive.

Cyclamate dissolves readily in water, is very stable, and is unaffected by temperatures up to 500 degrees Celsius, certainly well beyond that to which food stuffs would be exposed. Therefore, food containing the sweetener would have a long shelf life and cyclamate could be used like sugar in cooking. It has no calorific value, but is thirty to forty times sweeter than sugar. Unlike saccharin, cyclamate is sweet, with no unpleasant aftertaste. The additive was also found to improve the flavor of some foods, such as meat, and was used extensively in curing processes. In the decade after cyclamates were introduced, their production rose to ten thousand tons a year, enough to sweeten fifty billion cups of coffee. By 1969, about 250 food products contained cyclamate, including cakes, puddings, canned fruit, ice cream, salad dressings, and, its most important use, carbonated beverages. It was estimated in the late 1960's that 175 million Americans had cyclamate as part of their diet. Some common soft drinks used cyclamate.

It was originally thought that cyclamates were harmless, excreted unmetabolized from the body. In 1959, the chemical was added to the GRAS ("generally regarded as safe") list. Materials on this list, such as sugar, salt, pepper, and vinegar, do not have to be rigorously tested before being added to food. As late as 1965, the Food and Drug Administration (FDA) reported that "there is no evidence that cyclamates at their present levels are a hazard to health." In 1964, however, publication of a report citing evidence that cyclamates and saccharin taken together provided a health hazard raised alarm in the scientific community. Numerous investigations followed. The debate surrounding this chemical became acrimonious, with claims and counterclaims between scientists, federal agencies, and the major supplier of cyclamate, Abbott Laboratories. The sugar industry was concerned that the newly developing diet food market would cut into their business. In 1967, a spokesperson from the New York Sugar Research Foundation indicated that the industry stood to lose $1 billion by its own estimate, and commented, "That's a big prize to fight to keep." This foundation alone had spent $500,000 over two years to support research into the safety of cyclamates. Abbott, for whom cyclamate provided $14 million a year in profits (4 percent of their business) insisted that their extensive tests had shown no evidence of harm at the levels usually consumed.

Initially, the claims against cyclamate had been that it causes diarrhea or interferes with drug action. By 1969, the focus had moved to cancer. Ironically, the evidence that sealed the fate of the artificial sweetener was provided by Abbott itself. A private Long Island company was commissioned by Abbott to conduct an extensive toxicity study to determine the effects of long-term exposure to the cyclamate-saccharin mixtures often found in commercial products. The team of scientists had been feeding rats doses of the mixture from 500 to 2,500 milligrams daily to study the effect on reproduction, unborn fetuses, and fertility. In each case, the rats were declared to be normal. When the rats were sacrificed at the end of the study, however, those that had been exposed to the higher doses showed evidence of bladder tumors. Abbott shared the report with investigators from the National Cancer Institute and then with the FDA. The doses required to produce the tumors were equivalent to an individual drinking 350 bottles of diet cola a day, 100 to 120 times greater than even high cyclamate users consumed. A six-person panel of scientists was convened to review the data and urged the ban of all cyclamate from foodstuffs. In October, 1969, amid enormous media coverage, Robert H. Finch, Health, Education and Welfare secretary, announced that cyclamates were to be withdrawn from the market by the beginning of 1970.

Cyclamate is absorbed into the blood through the upper intestine. If cyclamate remains in the lower intestine, it can be converted to cyclohexylamine by naturally occurring bacteria. It is this conversion to cyclohexylamine that is most often cited as the basis of the risk to public health. Between 20 and 30 percent of the population can metabolize cyclamate to cyclohexylamine. Of this group, 90 percent metabolize only 0.1 percent of their daily intake; however, 4 percent of consumers are able to metabolize larger quantities of cyclamate. It is this population that is regarded to be at risk by use of the sweetener.

In the years following the ban, the controversy continued. Doubt was cast on the results of the independent study linking sweetener use to tumors in rats, because the study was not designed to evaluate cancer risks but to develop long-term toxicity data. Bladder parasites, known as nematodes, found in the rats may have affected the outcome of the tests. In addition, an impurity, *ortho*-toluenesulfonamide, found in some of the saccharin used in the study may have led to the problems observed. When these other factors were removed, the results from the earlier tests could not be reproduced. Extensive investigations such as the three-year project conducted at the National Cancer Research Center in Heidelberg, Germany, found no basis for the widespread ban. The major concern for many researchers during this period was not the threat of cancer but the fact that large doses of cyclohexylamine, the product formed from cyclamate by a small percentage of the population, had caused the testes of rats to shrink. In 1972, rats fed high doses of saccharin alone were found to have developed bladder tumors. At that time, the sweetener was removed from the GRAS list. An outright ban was averted by labeling laws that required disclosure of information to the consumer on products containing saccharin.

Impact of Event

The introduction of cyclamate heralded the start of a new industry. For individuals who had to restrict their sugar intake for health reasons, or for those who wished to lose weight for cosmetic purposes, there was now an alternative to giving up sweet food.

The original ban of the sweetener was accompanied by something of a media circus. *The New York Times* showed pictures of concerned housewives standing next to large displays of diet drinks. *Newsweek* published a photograph of a bulldozer in Toronto crushing thousands of cans of Canada Dry. Prior to the ban, most diet drink companies had been working on cyclamate-free formulations for their products. The Pepsi-Cola company scored a coup by having a new diet drink formulation on the market almost as soon as the ban was instituted. In fact, they ran advertisements the day after the ban was announced showing the Diet Pepsi product boldly proclaiming "Sugar added—No Cyclamates" with the byline "Pepsi-Cola Company cannot in good conscience offer its customers any product about which even the remotest doubt exists."

Sveda, the discoverer of cyclamates, was not impressed with the FDA's decision on the sweetener and subsequent investigations. He accused the FDA of "a massive cover-up of elemental blunders" and claimed that the original ban was based on sugar politics and bad science. The situation was further complicated by the strenuous efforts of a number of consumer activist groups such as Ralph Nader's organization. In 1982, the FDA was sufficiently concerned over the validity of the data which promoted the ban originally that they instituted a yearlong study by the National Academy of Sciences. The report issued by this group concluded that cyclamate itself does not cause cancer but raised issues that left the safety of the sweetener in dispute. The committee stated that there was "suggestive evidence" that cyclamate was a tumor promoter, or co-carcinogen. In addition, it was noted that, used in combination with saccharin, cyclamate may cause an increased risk of bladder cancer. In the light of this report, the FDA decided not to reverse their earlier decision. The scientific community appears split on the cyclamate question. It seems unlikely that the FDA, which is sensitive to criticism leveled by the concerned public over their dealings with a number of new drugs and foodstuffs, will reverse the decision. For the manufacturers of cyclamate, the problem lies with the wording of the Delaney amendment, the legislation that regulates new food additives. The amendment states that the manufacturer must prove that its product is safe, rather than the FDA having to prove that it is unsafe. The onus was on Abbott Laboratories to deflect concerns about the safety of the product and it remained unable to do so.

Bibliography

"Bitter Battle Over Sweets." *Science News* 92 (August 26, 1967): 199-202. A nontechnical article outlining the development of the cyclamate industry. Cites research supported by the Sugar Foundation. Animal studies performed by the Wisconsin Alumni Research Foundation, which linked the sweetener to inhibited growth and infertility in some laboratory rats, are discussed.

"Cyclamates Try for a Comeback." *Business Week*, August 6, 1984, 24. A nontechnical article chronicling the continued efforts by the sweetener industry to have cyclamates reinstated as a food additive. Weighs the possibility of a comeback for the sweetener after a public hearing by the National Academy of Sciences at the end of July discussed new experimental findings.

Gardner, W. David. "Bitter News About Sweeteners." *The New Republic* 159 (September 14, 1968): 17-18. Aimed at the nonscientist, this article weighs some of the evidence supporting the harmful effects of cyclamates. Questions the policy that allowed the introduction of the sweetener in the 1950's.

Miller, William T. "The Legacy of Cyclamate." *Food Technology*, January, 1987, 116. A concise, nontechnical overview of the political and scientific history of cyclamates from their discovery in 1937 to the 1987 report by the Food and Drug Administration. Very little detail, but reports that a petition for reintroduction of the cyclamate products made by the sweetener industry in 1982 had been denied by the FDA.

Storm, Jackie. "The Sweet Truth." *Women's Sports & Fitness* 9 (December, 1987): 12-13. Aimed at the nonscientist; discusses the relative nutritional merits of various natural and synthetic sweeteners and the controversy surrounding the introduction of aspartame. Brief reference to cyclamates.

Sun, Marjorie. "Cyclamate's Safety Still Unresolved." *Science* 228 (June 28, 1985): 1514-1515. A short discussion of the National Academy's report on their year-long investigation of the experimental evidence linking cyclamates to dangerous health effects.

Turner, James T. "Cyclamates." In *The Chemical Feast*. New York: Grossman, 1970. An angry and inflammatory indictment of the Food and Drug Administration. The authors' opinions are clearly evident throughout the discussion of scientific results, on which the scientific community could not agree. A sensational chapter from a best-selling book that unfortunately provides one of the few sources of information about events that led up to the banning of cyclamates in 1969.

Susan J. Mole

Cross-References

Bayliss and Starling Discover Secretin and Establish the Role of Hormones (1902), p. 179; Rous Discovers That Some Cancers Are Caused by Viruses (1910), p. 459; Banting and Macleod Win the Nobel Prize for the Discovery of Insulin (1921), p. 720; Sanger Wins the Nobel Prize for the Discovery of the Structure of Insulin (1958), p. 1567; Horsfall Announces That Cancer Results from Alterations in the DNA of Cells (1961), p. 1682; The First Commercial Genetic Engineering Product, Humulin, Is Marketed by Eli Lilly (1982), p. 2221; The Artificial Sweetener Aspartame Is Approved for Use in Carbonated Beverages (1983), p. 2226.

BOYD DEFINES HUMAN RACES BY BLOOD GROUPS

Categories of event: Anthropology and biology
Time: 1950
Locale: Boston, Massachusetts

Boyd produced evidence based on blood groups and genetic principles that revolutionized scientific perceptions of race and refuted racist concepts of "pure" or "superior" races

Principal personage:
WILLIAM CLOUSER BOYD (1903-1983), a professor of immunochemistry and author whose most successful effort was *Genetics and the Races of Man* (1950), which clearly exposed the fallacies involved in the racist philosophies

Summary of Event

Although individual scientists and philosophers have noted the great variation in physical characteristics and culture among the members of the human race since the beginnings of recorded history, it was only after the Age of Exploration and the Enlightenment that modern concepts of race began to emerge. Toward the end of the eighteenth century, J. F. Blumenbach proposed that the human species includes five distinct "races"—the white, yellow, black, Malayan, and American Indian. Blumenbach based his classification system primarily on cranial measurements, hair texture, stature, and skin color. Therefore, the modern science of physical anthropology was born.

For the next 150 years, physical anthropologists concentrated primarily on measurements of human types in their investigations of racial diversity. This one-dimensional approach led to gross oversimplifications in understanding the evolution of modern races of humankind. During the latter part of the nineteenth century, popular accounts of the findings of physical anthropologists led to the development of modern racism.

A number of writers in the mid-1800's began to argue that some races were more "advanced" than others in technological development and in the complexity of their social institutions. The advocates of Darwinian theories of evolution argued that some races were clearly more highly evolved than others, while the champions of creation, as related in the Bible, maintained that God had created some races to be subservient to others. This latter argument was especially popular in the southern United States as a justification for slavery.

Between 1853 and 1855, Joseph-Arthur Gobineau published his four-volume essay, *Essai sur l'inégalité des races humaines* (an essay on the inequality of human races). Gobineau argued for the superiority of the "white" race over all others. He maintained further that one branch of the white race—the "Aryans"—were the only peoples capable of creating true civilization. Gobineau identified the "Teutons" (Germans) as being the purest modern representatives of the original Aryan race. Gobineau's ideas became widely popular in Europe and the United States during the latter part of the nineteenth century and found a powerfully articulate champion in Houston Stewart Chamberlain, an Englishman who spent most of his life in Germany. In 1899, Chamberlain published *Die Grundlagen des Neunzehnten Jahrhunderts* (the foundations of the nineteenth century), which elaborated and refined the ideas first put forward by Gobineau. Adolf Hitler later acknowledged that his own philosophy concerning race was shaped by Chamberlain's book.

The emergence of these doctrines of racial superiority coincided with a new wave of imperialist expansion during the two decades preceding the twentieth century. Politicians and industrialists eagerly embraced those doctrines to justify colonialism and applauded writers such as Rudyard Kipling, who argued that the superior white race had a duty to extend the blessings of its higher civilization to the poor, benighted colored races of the world. Religious leaders adopted the rhetoric of racism and imperialism in advocating that the inferior peoples of the world must be given instruction in the true faith. The popular press in Europe and the United States— newspapers, novels, and magazines—distorted, sensationalized, and bastardized the findings of physical anthropologists in justifying imperialism to the point that racism became an ingrained part of Western society by the early twentieth century.

In addition to denigrating the colored races, racists around the world singled out the Jews as not only an inferior race but also as parasites who destroyed civilizations created by Aryans. Modern anti-Semitism, or Judeophobia, may be said to have originated with the publication of *Der Sieg des Judenthums über das Germanenthum* (the victory of judaism over germanism) by Wilhelm Marr in Germany in 1873. Marr was one of the first Europeans to advance the thesis, echoed in countless subsequent works, that Jews have infected Western civilization with a spirit of materialism that has robbed it of its spirituality and humanity and will ultimately lead to its destruction. In the early part of the twentieth century, rumors began to circulate throughout the Western world concerning a Jewish plot to plunge the European nations into a general war, which would weaken them to the point that the Jews could regain control of Palestine and from there rule the world economically. Judeophobia, along with racist ideas directed against the colored peoples of the world, reached a crescendo in the 1920's and were finally translated into political action in Germany in the 1930's.

Physical anthropologists, most of whom realized the invalidity of racist doctrines, made feeble and ineffective efforts only to refute prevailing popular attitudes toward race before World War II. After Hitler came to power in 1933, anthropologists in Germany were, along with scientists in all other disciplines, forced to "coordinate" their discipline with national socialist ideology. Consequently, German anthropologists concerned themselves between 1933 and 1945 with scientifically proving the superiority of the Aryan race and the inferiority of the Jews. The German anthropologists produced a number of studies containing evidence to support the racist view.

Only a few anthropologists in the Western world made any effort to disprove the German findings. The results of this failure were a disaster and tragedy for the entire world.

It was only after the war that anthropologists developed the will and the tools to discredit earlier popular concepts of race. Although medical scientists had been aware for many years prior to 1939 that human blood may be divided into four broad types (A, B, O, and AB) and that individuals with widely varying physical characteristics may share the same type of blood, it was only after 1945 that sufficient data became available to anthropologists to begin exploring systematically the blood-group phenomenon as a key to human evolution and the nature of human races. One of the first scientific works to adopt this new methodology and redefine concepts of race was William Clouser Boyd's *Genetics and the Races of Man* (1950).

Boyd revolutionized concepts of race and provided a powerful new tool for understanding human evolution by applying the principles of genetics worked out by Gregor Johann Mendel in the nineteenth century to data concerning the distribution of human blood types. Mendel, experimenting with the hybridization of plants, discovered certain "laws" concerning the passing along of physical characteristics from one generation to the next. Using Mendel's principles, Boyd showed that the concept of a "pure" race of humankind is absurd and that the physical measurements of such characteristics as skull shape and cranial capacity used by racists to prove their contentions are meaningless. Boyd showed that although the inhabitants of some areas of the world have higher concentrations of one or the other of the major blood types, all blood types are present among the human populations of all areas of the world, regardless of color, hair texture, stature, shape or size of the skull, and the like. He showed also that there must have been an almost constant exchange of genes between all human populations since before the time that humans became sapient, despite the frequent isolation of some breeding populations for extended periods.

Based on his findings, Boyd proposed the subdivision of humanity into six races, or subtypes: Early European, modern European, African, Asiatic, American Indian, and Australoid (he later refined this to thirteen human blood types, but he stopped short of calling them races). Boyd went to great pains to emphasize that the distribution of all blood types in all these races shows clearly that there are no pure races. He also emphasized that there is no scientific test that can determine the superiority or inferiority of any race vis-à-vis the other races.

Impact of Event

Boyd's study of human blood groups and genetics had two important results. One result affected social policy and social attitudes, the other involved the advancement of science.

Perhaps the most important outcome of Boyd's data was its influence on the movement within the social sciences to discredit racial prejudice and political and social discrimination based on race. Beginning during World War II, anthropologists, sociologists, and historians started a systematic campaign to educate the public about race. Many social scientists considered it their duty to address problems of racial discord, since it had played an important role in the origins of the war. One of the first of these efforts was a pamphlet published by the Public Affairs Committee of New York City entitled *The Races of Mankind* (1943), by Ruth Benedict and Gene Weltfish, both of Columbia University. The pamphlet, which argued for the basic equality of people regardless of race, encountered a storm of controversy and was banned eventually from distribution to the armed forces by members of the United States government. Social scientists in other disciplines who published similar works met with the same sort of resistance because of the ingrained attitudes concerning race throughout society. Even in 1942, the publication of Ashley Montagu's *Man's Most Dangerous Myth: The Fallacy of Race*, which pointed out the dangers to society brought on by racism, made little impact on the general public.

Boyd's research provided the first hard evidence to support the contentions of those who found racial prejudice and discrimination unacceptable. Social scientists from many disciplines cited Boyd's study as evidence in their own books attempting to refute racial myths. A good example is historian Kenneth Stampp's *The Peculiar Institution* (1956), which attacked, in particular, stereotypes of American black people and the prejudice directed against them.

This new emphasis on racial equality in the academic community was much more palatable to officials of the United States government than similar arguments had been in the past because of the escalating Cold War and the perceived threat of communism. Communist propaganda in the nonindustrial world denouncing the racism of the United States was a powerful tool. In addition, some governmental agencies in America believed that communism was making increasing inroads in the black community of the United States because of continued discrimination and segregation. Almost certainly, the new wave toward racial equality was a major factor in the Supreme Court's rejection in 1954 of state laws that had established segregation in much of the United States for more than seventy years and in the sweeping civil rights legislation of the 1960's. Boyd's work was an integral part of that new wave.

Boyd's findings concerning human blood type distribution had another important consequence: Paleoanthropology is the science that studies early forms of humans and the evolution of the human species. Prior to studies concerning blood types, paleoanthropologists had little on which to base their investigations other than scanty fossil remains of early hominids. Boyd's application of genetic principles to human evolution provided students of the development of modern humans with a powerful new tool, which has led to a much more sophisticated understanding of human origins and evolution.

Bibliography

Benedict, Ruth. *Race: Science and Politics.* Foreword by Margaret Mead. New York: Viking Press, 1940. One of the earliest American efforts to discredit prevailing myths concerning racial superiority. Although its arguments are cogent and well reasoned, the original edition lacked any sort of hard evidence to support its claims of racial equality. Later editions contained Boyd's findings concerning human blood types. Also included is the text of the pamphlet *The Races of Mankind*, which caused considerable controversy during World War II.

Boyd, William Clouser. *Genetics and the Races of Man*. Boston: Little, Brown, 1950. Prepared and used as a textbook in physical anthropology, this book was the first presentation to a mass audience of Boyd's findings resulting from the application of Mendelian genetic principles to the study of human blood type distribution. It is written in such a way as to be understandable to the nonspecialist. Contains a wealth of maps and graphs illustrating the distribution of human blood types.

Boyd, William Clouser, and Isaac Asimov. *Races and People*. New York: Abelard-Schuman, 1955. Science-fiction writer and science populizer, Asimov collaborated with Boyd in presenting Boyd's findings concerning human blood types and their implications concerning race in such a way as to be understandable to children. Although the purpose of the book is admirable, it is probably too dull to hold the attention of children and too simplistic to interest adults.

Coon, Carleton S. *The Origin of Races*. New York: Alfred A. Knopf, 1962. Shows the ways in which blood type distribution has been used by paleoanthropologists in untangling the path of human evolution. Also demonstrates that the older methodology employed by physical anthropologists (physical measurements) has not disappeared from the field. Contains considerable technical terminology, but still understandable and enjoyable for a general audience. Contains many maps, graphs, and photographs.

Coon, Carleton S., with Edward E. Hunt, Jr. *The Living Races of Man*. New York: Alfred A. Knopf, 1965. Perhaps the most extensive and comprehensive effort to categorize the current races of humans. Makes extensive use of data concerning the distribution of human blood types and acknowledges a debt to Boyd. Although his classification system differs in many respects from that advanced by Boyd, Coon's conclusion is the same: There is no such thing as a pure race and no evidence that any race is superior to any other. Written for a wide audience. Contains numerous photographs, maps, and graphs.

Lawler, Sylvia D., and L. J. Lawler. *Human Blood Groups and Inheritance*. New York: St. Martin's Press, 1951. Written as a supplementary textbook for first-year biology students to acquaint them with the blood types known at the time Boyd produced his major work. Although technical, the book explains the nature of blood types and the mechanics of inheritance in such a way as to make them understandable to a general audience.

Mourant, A. E. *Blood Relations: Blood Groups and Anthropology*. New York: Oxford University Press, 1985. Contains a chapter on elementary genetics that will inform readers without a background in science as to the mechanics of that discipline. Contains a comprehensive examination of the distribution of human blood types in all regions of the world. Blood types among Jews and Gypsies are treated in a separate chapter. Includes many informative maps and graphs.

Snyder, Laurence H. *Blood Goups.* Minneapolis: Burgess, 1973. A very technical account of exactly how blood types are inherited and the anthropological meaning of the current distribution of blood types. Any person who wishes to understand the problems concerned with identifying and classifying human populations by blood types will profit greatly from this book.

Tills, D., Ada C. Kopeć, and Rosemary E. Tills. *The Distribution of the Human Blood Groups, and Other Polymorphisms. Supplement 1.* New York: Oxford University Press, 1983. The most comprehensive breakdown of human blood type distribution available. Designed for the professional, this book will be very difficult for the casual reader. Many tables, graphs, and maps. Contains much information not available to Boyd.

Paul Madden

Cross-References

Landsteiner Discovers Human Blood Groups (1900), p. 56; De Vries and Associates Discover Mendel's Ignored Studies of Inheritance (1900), p. 61; Punnett's *Mendelism* Contains a Diagram for Showing Heredity (1905), p. 270; Hardy and Weinberg Present a Model of Population Genetics (1908), p. 390.

OORT POSTULATES THE EXISTENCE
OF THE OORT CLOUD

Category of event: Astronomy
Time: 1950
Locale: Leiden Observatory, Holland, The Netherlands

Oort propounded the theory that comets originate in a cloud of comets one light-year from the sun and explained why short-lived comets are found

Principal personages:
JAN HENDRIK OORT (1900-   ), a Dutch astronomer who was the director of the Leiden Observatory and first described comets
FRED WHIPPLE (1906-   ), an American astronomer who was the director of the Smithsonian Astrophysical Observatory and described comets as dirty snowballs

Summary of Event

Comets have fascinated humans for millennia. For most of that time, the appearance of a comet has been considered a portent of disaster. When the great comet of A.D. 1066 made its appearance, William the Conqueror, claimant to the throne of England, shrewdly informed his troops that the comet signified defeat of the English defenders; it also implied that he would become the King of England. In the 1500's, comets became the subject of scientific inquiry. Edmond Halley, a friend of Sir Isaac Newton, noticed that comets appearing in 1456, 1531, 1607, and 1682 had similar orbits around the sun and came close to the sun every seventy-six years. He concluded that these were not several comets, but rather one comet with a period of revolution around the sun of seventy-six years. In 1705, he predicted that it would appear again in 1758. It arrived as scheduled, and was christened Halley's comet in his honor.

As technology improved, additional information about comets has been gathered: the shapes of their orbits, the directions in which they orbit the sun, why they have two tails, and why the tails always point away from the sun. Other comets are repeat visitors to the inner solar system; some comets such as Kohoutek approached the sun for the first time. Scientists have attempted to explain the comet's composition and its origin. For decades this problem has troubled scientists: There is evidence that the solar system is 4.6 billion years old, but comets exist when they should have burned out long ago. Fred Whipple first described comets as dirty snowballs in 1949. Their composition is one of ices of ammonia, methane, and other compounds. Mixed in with ices are pieces of rocky material. Each time a comet comes close to the sun, the heat from the sun melts some of the icy material. This forms a coma or atmosphere around the comet body, known as a nucleus, that may be kilometers to tens of kilometers in diameter. The solar wind, which is composed of gases expelled by the sun at high speeds, pushes these gases away from the coma to form one of the comet's tails. Light pressure forms the other tail by pushing dusty matter from the coma. This explains why the tails always point away from the sun, since it is the source of the sunlight and solar wind that form the tails.

With the melting and vaporizing of its ices, the comet loses some of its mass each time it makes a pass of the sun. Even if it loses one one-millionth of its mass per orbit, Halley's comet would disappear in 76 million years. There are objects that orbit the sun that may be burned-out comets. This is possible since once the ices melt, most of the rocky material remains. Yet, it is not known where they come from originally.

The length of their orbital period is used to classify comets. Long-period comets have a period greater than two hundred years, and short-period less than two hundred years. Short-period comets were once long-period comets, but the gravitational attraction of the outer planets, such as Jupiter, has altered their orbits. Long-period comets have greatly elongated elliptical orbits that take them far beyond the orbit of Pluto. Even the orbit of Halley's comet with a period of only seventy-six years reaches beyond the orbit of Neptune. This tendency for very elongated orbits is unique in the solar system; most other objects—the planets, their satellites, the asteroids—have a less elliptical orbit.

Another oddity of cometary orbits is that they can orbit the sun in any direction. Planets orbit the sun in a counterclockwise direction, as viewed from the direction of the earth's North Pole. The planes of these planetary orbits are close to the plane of Earth's orbit. In other words, they orbit the sun in a limited range of directions. Comets can orbit the sun at any angle. The orbital plane of Halley's comet, for example, is inclined to Earth's orbit by 18 degrees and orbits the sun in the clockwise direction.

Jan Hendrik Oort first described the source of comets in 1950. He reasoned that the comets came from a cloud of comets located a light-year from the sun. The cloud should be a spherical shell and billions of kilometers thick. The number of comets in this reservoir could be in the trillions. Although that seems to be a very large number, it represents a total mass similar to that of the sun. The individual orbits should be elliptical but not as elongated as comets that closely approach the sun. The orbital period for a comet at a distance of a light-year is 15 million years. Their temperature should be close to absolute zero, since they receive very little energy from the sun.

To verify this theory, the known facts about comets can be checked. A comet in Oort's cloud is moving around the sun at a velocity of several meters per second, compared to tens of kilometers per second for an object like Earth. If a comet comes close to another comet, they will gravitationally interact and will change their orbital direction and speed. If a comet slows down, it will move closer to the sun, and its orbit becomes elongated. More gravitational encounters with the outer planets change its orbit even more, and it moves closer to the sun. The point of its orbit farthest from the sun, its aphelion, also becomes less. Now it would be recognized as a long-period comet. Additional encounters with Jupiter alter the orbit to that of a short-period comet.

Since the comet is coming toward the sun from such a large distance, it can orbit the sun at any angle or direction and explains that aspect of the comet's orbital behavior. They should be composed of icy and rocky material, since that is the average composition of the material in the solar system. The ice is caused by the low temperature of the outer reaches of the solar system. In the inner solar system, comets burn out over time and need to be replaced by new comets from the Oort cloud. Only several per year need to start their journey toward the inner solar system to keep the solar system supplied with comets. Over the centuries, other facts about the members of the solar system have been cataloged. In describing how the solar system originated, the explanation that accounts for the most facts of the solar system is accepted as the best theory. Some of these facts include the coplanar nature of the planets orbiting the sun, the planets orbit the sun in a counterclockwise direction, the planet and the sun rotate in the counterclockwise direction, and the inner planets are rocky and metallic in nature, while the outer planets have a composition of mostly liquefied gases. The comets and their postulated Oort cloud also must fit into this scenario.

Impact of Event

The idea of Oort's cloud being the source of the solar system's comets fits in well with the accepted model for the origin of the solar system. It is believed that it arose from a slowly rotating cloud of gas and dust several light-years across and several times the mass of the present solar system. The cloud started to collapse under the gravitational attraction of its various particles. A supernova explosion near the cloud may have sent a shock wave through the cloud that helped start the process. As the cloud collapsed, it spun faster like a skater spins faster and pulls in her arms. As it spun, the collisions of the particles caused the cloud to become more disk-shaped. Some of the collisions resulted in the particles sticking together and thereby growing larger. The inner portion of the cloud grew hotter since the collisions occurred more often there. Only rocky and metallic material could form under those high-temperature conditions, while icy compounds condensed out in the outer portion of the solar system. As the particles grew, they reached a size of several kilometers in diameter. At this stage they are called planetesimals. Some of these planetesimals would collide and grow in size to become the satellites and planets. Others would interact gravitationally and would be thrown away from the sun. They could escape totally or become part of Oort's cloud.

The nebular theory is the best explanation of how the solar system came into existence. The disk shape resulted in the planets being coplanar and revolving in the counterclockwise direction. The sun, the planets, the satellites, and the asteroids rotate counterclockwise as part of the original nebular rotation. Because of the temperatures within the collapsing nebula, the inner planets of Mercury, Venus, Earth, and Mars are composed of materials that melt at high temperatures, while the outer planets are mostly liquefied gases.

Another implication of Oort's cloud is its possible involvement in the periodic mass extinctions that have occurred on Earth. Sixty-five million years ago the dinosaurs and many other creatures became extinct. The impact of a 10-kilometer-diameter asteroid or comet may be the cause. Other mass extinctions have occurred at roughly 26-million-year intervals. An unknown planet with a 26-million-year period of revolution may pass through the Oort cloud and cause many comets to start toward the inner solar system. There some could collide with Earth and cause the mass extinctions by drastically changing the climate of Earth. The idea of Oort's cloud explains many of the characteristics of comets and agrees well with the nebular theory of the solar system's origin.

Bibliography

Chapman, Robert, and John Brandt. "An Introduction to Comets and Their Origin." *Mercury* 14 (January/February, 1985): 2-8. The article contains excerpts from the authors' book *The Comet Book* (1984). Among the topics discussed are the components and compositions of comets, their paths, and their origins.

Delsemme, A. "Comets and the Origin of the Solar System." In *The Origin of the Solar System*, edited by S. F. Dermott. New York: John Wiley & Sons, 1978. This is a short article dealing with the origin of comets, their chemical composition, dust and gas amounts, and their thermal history. It is somewhat technical, but a reader with some science background should comprehend it. It also has many references including classic papers by Fred Whipple.

Kronk, Gary. "Meteor Showers." *Mercury* 17 (November/December, 1988): 162-169. The article describes the history, formation, and techniques for observing meteors and comets. It furnishes pictures and diagrams and lists of meteor organizations and publications, as well as meteor shower observation tables.

Raup, David M. *The Nemesis Affair*. New York: W. W. Norton, 1986. This book is the story of the investigations into how the mass extinctions on Earth were caused by comets from Oort's cloud hitting Earth. It is a good discussion of how science and scientists really work.

Van Flandern, Tom. "Where Do Comets Come From?" *Mercury* 11 (November/December, 1982): 189-193. Science is not static. New theories are always being developed, and this article proves that point since it proposes a new origin for comets in the solar system. The author contends that comets originated when a "planet," in or near the asteroid belt in the past, fragmented.

Whipple, Fred. "Discovering the Nature of Comets." *Mercury* 15 (January/February, 1986): 2-9. This article is an adaptation of Whipple's book *The Mystery of Comets* (1985) and provides an introduction to the latest information on comets. He also presents his personal thoughts on how he developed his model of comets.

_____. "The Nature of Comets." *Scientific American* 230 (February, 1974): 48-57. Since Whipple is the developer of the dirty-snowball description of comets, it is fitting that he write this article about comet Kohoutek and the nature of comets. Although Kohoutek was a great disappointment, it furnished scientists with a wealth of information about the primordial solar system and the origin of comets in the Oort cloud.

Stephen J. Shulik

Cross-References

Hartmann Discovers the First Evidence of Interstellar Matter (1904), p. 213; Penzias and Wilson Discover Cosmic Microwave Background Radiation (1963), p. 1762; Kibble Proposes the Theory of Cosmic Strings (1976), p. 2047.

HOFSTADTER DISCOVERS THAT PROTONS AND NEUTRONS EACH HAVE A STRUCTURE

Category of event: Physics
Time: 1951
Locale: Stanford University, Palo Alto, California

Hofstadter began to use the high-energy electrons from the Stanford Linear Accelerator to probe the structure of the nucleus and its constituents, the proton and neutron

Principal personages:

ROBERT HOFSTADTER (1915-1990), an American physicist who led an experimental group working at the Stanford high-energy electron accelerator during the 1960's

EDWARD LEONARD GINZTON (1915-), a Soviet physicist who was in charge of design, operation, and development of the linear accelerators

WILLIAM WEBSTER HANSEN (1909-1949), an American physicist who developed the technologies needed to build linear accelerators for electrons

ROBERT WALLACE MCALLISTER (1919-), an American physicist who was a graduate student at Stanford when he worked with Hofstadter to study the structure of the proton

MASON RUSSELL YEARIAN (1932-), an American physicist who was a graduate student at Stanford when he worked with Hofstadter to study the structure of the neutron

Summary of Event

At the end of World War II, physicists who had been working in industrial and national laboratories returned to the universities eager to undertake research on the basic structure of matter. The atomic nucleus offered unexplored territory amenable to many of the new experimental techniques developed to support war-related technologies, such as radar and the atomic bomb. In particular, William Webster Hansen, who had worked during the war on microwave technology for radar, returned to Stanford University and renewed his interest in accelerating electrons to high energies by using microwave frequencies. The electrons are pushed along a series of electrodes in a linear accelerator by an electric wave at microwave frequencies in phase with their motions like surfers pushed along by a water wave. By the end of 1947, he had constructed a working 3.7-meter accelerator, the Mark I, which delivered electrons with energies of 6 million electronvolts. Hansen's death might have ended work on linear accelerators for electrons, but Edward Leonard Ginzton, also a professor at Stanford, took up accelerator construction and built two other electron linear accelerators, the Mark II and the Mark III. In 1952, the Mark III stretched 24 meters and delivered electron beams of 200 million electronvolts. Since linear accelerators could be built in sections, the Mark III grew slowly as funds were available and delivered electrons at 1 billion electronvolts by 1960. The intensity of the electron beams and the reliability of the accelerator also increased, making it a powerful tool waiting for exploitation.

At the beginning of the 1950's, high-energy electrons lacked the glamor of the cyclotrons used to accelerate protons and alpha particles. Electrons could not be accelerated easily in circular machines since their small mass meant that they radiated away most of their energy. As protons from the cyclotrons and synchrotrons crashed into nuclei, they produced new nuclear species and the first of the new fundamental particles that hinted at a new layer of complexity in the structure of ordinary matter. Electrons had long been used to explore atomic structure, but they seemed crude and uninteresting tools compared to the protons.

When Robert Hofstadter moved to Stanford University from Princeton, he realized that the high-energy electron beam from the Mark III provided an ideal method for determining the structure of nuclei. The technique he decided to use is known as scattering. Because the nucleus of the atom and its constituents—the proton and neutron, known generically as nucleons—are too small to examine using visible light, they are studied using the scattering of other probe particles. These particles are projected at a target containing the nuclei of interest, where they interact with the nuclei and bounce off. If the target nuclei are small hard spheres, the probe particles generally will travel straight through the target without realizing that it is there. If they strike one of the point targets, they will bounce back at large angles. If, on the other hand, nuclei are diffuse distributions of charge, one expects the probes to be slightly deflected as they pass through but are not bounced back at large angles. Ernest Rutherford had used this technique with alpha particles to develop the original nuclear model of the atom.

Like other constituents of matter, electrons are both particles and waves. The wavelength of a particle decreases as its momentum increases. Because electrons have only one two-thousandth the mass of a proton, the momenta of electrons is normally much less than that of a proton, and the electron's wavelength is longer than that of the more massive particle. Thus, electrons at normal energy are simply too large to explore the interior of the nucleus, which is 100,000 times smaller than the atom. Electrons accelerated to the energies available from the Mark III (first 190, then 550 million electronvolts) had wavelengths smaller than the radius of typical nuclei and could be used to probe them. Experiments done in 1951 at the University of Illinois using lower-energy electrons (15 million electronvolts) showed that the technique was feasible, although the electrons used had too long a wavelength to probe nuclear details.

Electrons offer a second advantage over protons and nucleons as probes of the nucleus. Unlike the nucleons, electrons do not experience the strong nuclear force. Therefore, they interact with the nucleus only through the electric and magnetic forces that physicists understand much better than they understand the strong nuclear force. As Hofstadter and his colleagues examined the patterns formed by the high-energy electrons scattered from nuclei, they were able to determine the precise distribution of charge and magnetism within the nucleus without the confusion introduced by the relatively poorly understood nuclear forces.

Hofstadter's initial experiments probed the structure of large nuclei. He and his colleagues constructed a detector using a huge magnet mounted on a naval gun base so the magnet could be aligned accurately at different angles. This magnet was necessary because the experimenters wished to examine the nucleus in its normal state, not after it had been excited by an interaction with the incident electrons. The very large and expensive magnet was needed to bend the extremely high-energy electrons and separate them into those that had simply bounced off the nucleus (scattered elastically) and those that had interacted with the nucleus. The electrons were detected behind the magnet by a lucite counter, which flashed light when struck by an electron and whose light was collected by a photomultiplier tube.

Hofstadter and his group were able to determine that the nucleus is not a point particle. Instead, nuclei consist of a central portion of nearly constant density, which increased in size as the number of nucleons in the nucleus increased. The central portion was surrounded by a "skin" of gradually decreasing charge density. As they went to lighter and lighter nuclei, the central core disappeared leaving only a fuzzy sphere. Finally, Hofstadter and his colleagues, including graduate student Robert Wallace McAllister, extended the measurement to a target of hydrogen, which contained only protons. They found that the proton had a definite charge distribution and could not be considered a point particle.

Next, the group, now including graduate student Mason Russell Yearian, turned their attention to studying the neutron. This measurement was more difficult because free neutrons do not exist in nature. Therefore, the target had to be made of deuterium gas, a form of hydrogen whose nucleus consists of a proton and a neutron. The properties of the neutron were deduced from the scattering data by subtracting out the effect of the proton.

Hofstadter and his associates continued to use the very short wavelength electrons from the linear accelerator to make precise measurements of the distribution of charge and magnetism within both the proton and neutron. By 1961, when Hofstadter was a cowinner of the Nobel Prize in Physics, they had shown that the nucleons were complex particles concealing a new layer in the structure of matter. Any possibility that the proton and neutron might be simple point particles had been effectively laid to rest. High-energy electrons were an established tool for probing the fundamental structure of matter.

Impact of Event

Hofstadter's experimental proof that the proton and neutron were in fact complex particles provided one of the major clues that led to the modern picture of the structure of matter, the quark model. His experiments were extended to higher energies using electrons with smaller wavelengths. By the end of the 1960's, the Mark III had been replaced with the 1.6-kilometer long Stanford Linear Accelerator (SLAC), which produced electrons with energies of 20 billion electronvolts. At these energies, the scattering experiments no longer showed a continuous distribution of charge inside the proton. In 1970, scattering experiments at SLAC showed results that demonstrated electrons suddenly bouncing back from small point particles inside the proton. With the new, very small wavelengths of the extremely high-energy electrons, experimenters finally had seen the entities that combine to form protons and neutrons, the point particles called quarks.

High-energy electron scattering was not the only experimental technique to produce results leading to the discovery of the quark model. Beams of high-energy protons fired at hydrogen targets also revealed evidence of interactions between constituents of the protons in the beam and in the target. In addition, the number of known fundamental particles had continued to grow with each increase in the energy of the existing accelerators. The proliferation of particles gave rise to several theoretical approaches that sought to explain the multitude of new particles in terms of an underlying theoretical concept.

In 1963, Murray Gell-Mann and George Zweig proposed a mathematical model in which all fundamental particles were composed of three subconstituents called quarks. Neither theorist actually supposed the quarks had physical reality. They merely used them as a conceptual device to organize the rapidly expanding numbers of known fundamental particles. They were able to predict the properties and masses of undiscovered particles on the basis of their quark model. Finally, scattering experiments with both high-energy electrons and protons demonstrated clearly that the quarks were not merely a theoretician's heuristic device but were, in fact, physical particles that interacted with one another and the other family of particles—the leptons—through the major forces.

Physicists have accepted that there are six different types of quarks which, together with their antiparticles, make up all fundamental particles that experience the strong nuclear force. Five of the six have been identified uniquely in particle interactions and the sixth is expected to be discovered. The six quarks are matched by six leptons, which do not experience the strong nuclear force. Again, five of these six particles have been seen in particle interactions.

Just as Hofstadter probed the interior of the proton with high-energy electrons to understand the forces that hold nuclei together, particle physicists are probing the interior of the proton with much higher-energy beams in order to understand the force—called the color force—that binds quarks together to form nucleons. Hofstadter's pioneering scattering experiments with high-energy electrons have spawned a generation of physics experiments that continue to deepen an understanding of the fundamental nature of matter.

Bibliography

Hofstadter, Robert. "The Atomic Nucleus." *Scientific American* 194 (July, 1956):

55-68. Hofstadter's own description of his work written for the well-informed nonphysicist, this article provides a succinct introduction to the major ideas and experimental details involved in Hofstadter's work. This article is the best starting point for the reader interested in examining Hofstadter's experiments.

_____, ed. *Electron Scattering and Nuclear and Nucleon Structure*. New York: W. A. Benjamin, 1963. This volume contains technical reprints documenting the results of Hofstadter's experiments on nuclear and nucleon structure as well as an introduction to the theory of determination of nuclear structure from scattering experiments. The best introduction to the subject available, this source requires a knowledge of physics and mathematics, although the introductory material is accessible to the beginner in nuclear physics.

Jacob, Maurice, and Peter Landshoff. "The Inner Structure of the Proton." *Scientific American* 242 (March, 1980): 66-75. This article describes the eventual results of the experiments Hofstadter undertook in the 1950's. Although Hofstadter personally was not involved in most of the work described here, his techniques have been extended to provide the modern picture of the structure of the nucleons as composed of substructures called quarks.

Livingston, M. Stanley. "Linear Accelerators." In *High-Energy Accelerators*. New York: Interscience Publishers, 1954. This summary chapter presents the technology of the electron accelerator that was critical to the study of the structure of nuclei and the proton and neutron using high-energy electrons. The work is aimed at nonscientists and explains some of the complexities of building a large accelerator.

Riordan, Michael. *The Hunting of the Quark*. New York: Simon & Schuster, 1987. Written by a physicist with the unusual gift of explaining complex ideas clearly and entertainingly, this volume places Hofstadter's work in context as part of a long series of experiments that have led to the modern picture of the nucleon. The importance of Hofstadter's work is clearly presented at the beginning of chapter 5, "The Birth of a Monster."

Seth, Kamal K. "Nuclear Sizes and Density Distributions." *Physics Today* 11 (May, 1958): 24-28. As part of a report on a topical conference on nuclear structure, this brief paper presents a very readable account of the main issues in the study of the structure of the proton and neutron. Because it was written at the time of Hofstadter's work, it places his work in the context of the current physics research of that time and mentions most of the other major experimental techniques being used in similar studies of nucleons.

Ruth H. Howes

Cross-References

Rutherford Presents His Theory of the Atom (1912), p. 527; Rutherford Discovers the Proton (1914), p. 590; Chadwick Discovers the Neutron (1932), p. 973; The Liquid Bubble Chamber Is Developed (1953), p. 1470; Quarks Are Postulated by Gell-Mann and Zweig (1964), p. 1767; Friedman, Kendell, and Taylor Discover Quarks (1968), p. 1871; Gell-Mann Formulates the Theory of Quantum Chromodynamics (QCD) (1972), p. 1966; The J/psi Subatomic Particle Is Discovered (1974), p. 2031.

LIPMANN DISCOVERS ACETYL COENZYME A

Category of event: Biology
Time: 1951
Locale: Biochemistry Research Department, Massachusetts General Hospital, Boston

Lipmann discovered the molecule acetyl coenzyme A, the link between the glyco-lytic and citric acid enzyme cycles in living cells

Principal personages:
FRITZ ALBERT LIPMANN (1899-1986), a German-American biochemist and cowinner of the 1953 Nobel Prize in Physiology or Medicine for his discovery of acetyl coenzyme A
SIR HANS ADOLF KREBS (1900-1981), a German biochemist and cowinner of the 1953 Nobel Prize in Physiology or Medicine for his discovery of the energy-generating citric acid cycle
OTTO HEINRICH WARBURG (1883-1970), a German biochemist and 1931 Nobel laureate in Physiology or Medicine for his studies of respiratory enzymes in cellular respiration
OTTO MEYERHOF (1884-1951), a German biochemist and physiologist who supervised Lipmann's early work on cellular respiration

Summary of Event

All life on Earth is sustained by the constant recycling of matter and energy through the earth's environment. The energy cycle begins with the absorption of visible light by photosynthetic autotrophs, those organisms (for example, plants, phytoplankton) that can produce their own food (sugar) from sunlight, water, and carbon dioxide. These photosynthetic autotrophs make this food so that the cells of their bodies can later convert the sugar into usable energy to drive chemical reactions essential for life. Organisms that cannot make their own food must scavenge for food; they are heterotrophs. Heterotrophs need to obtain food for the same reason as autotrophs: to provide energy to drive the cellular chemical reactions necessary for life. Heterotrophs include animals, protozoa, and fungi. Herbivorous heterotrophs eat plants to obtain food which the plants made from sunlight. Carnivorous heterotrophs eat herbivores and other carnivores to obtain the food which these organisms gained by eating someone else. When organisms die, they are decomposed by bacteria and fungi until their component molecules are returned to the soil to be recycled into new plants. The energy cycle starts over again, the entire purpose being to provide energy for two very important life chemical reaction pathways: glycolysis and the citric acid cycle.

These two chemical reaction pathways were deciphered by biochemists during the first half of the twentieth century. In 1897, Eduard Buchner and Hans Buchner discovered that the process of fermentation (alcohol formation) can occur without the presence of living cells. They found that sugar solutions will decompose eventually into ethyl alcohol. Fermentation, however, can be accelerated in the presence of yeast cells. In 1905, William Young and Arthur Harden discovered that an extract of fluids from yeast cells could ferment the sugar glucose. There were certain chemical reactions occurring within the cytoplasm of yeast cells that catalyzed, or sped up, the conversion of glucose into ethyl alcohol. Furthermore, this series of reactions was anaerobic: These chemical reactions did not require oxygen. Phosphate, however, was essential. The next step was to determine what protein enzymes from yeast extract drove the fermentation reactions and to identify the various chemical intermediates in the reaction pathway.

During the 1920's and 1930's, biochemists derived most of the chemical reaction steps involved in alcoholic fermentation. The principal scientists involved in these studies were Gustav Embden, Otto Meyerhof, and Otto Heinrich Warburg. They solved the complete enzymatic pathway for the breakdown of glucose, a series of anaerobic chemical reactions called glycolysis, also called the Embden-Meyerhof Pathway. Glycolysis begins with the conversion of the sugar glucose into glucose-6-phosphate by the enzyme hexokinase. Glucose-6-phosphate is then converted to fructose-6-phosphate by another enzyme. Fructose-6-phosphate is converted to fructose-1,6-diphosphate by a third enzyme. Fructose-1,6-diphosphate is then split into two molecules of glyceraldehyde-3-phosphate. Each glyceraldehyde-3-phosphate is converted to 1,3-diphosphoglycerate, which is converted to 3-phosphoglycerate, which is converted to 2-phosphoglycerate, which is converted to phosphoenolpyruvate. The final glycolytic reaction is the conversion of phosphoenolpyruvate to pyruvic acid.

The net result of glycolysis is the conversion of one six-carbon molecule (glucose) into two three-carbon molecules (two pyruvic acids). Along the reaction pathway, the energy of two ATP (adenosine triphosphate) molecules is expended, four new ATP molecules are produced directly, and four additional ATP molecules are produced indirectly. The purpose of glycolysis in living cells is the production of ATP, a high-energy molecule, from ADP (adenosine diphosphate), a low-energy molecule. ATP is a high-energy molecule because approximately 7,300 calories of energy are released when one of ATP's phosphate bonds is broken, when ATP is converted to ADP. When a cell runs out of ATP, it has no energy, chemical reactions cease, and the cell dies. With a supply of glucose, a cell can add phosphates back to ADP to construct ATP by the process of glycolysis. The cell lives.

Pyruvic acid, the end product of glycolysis, can be converted into one of three possible molecules: ethyl alcohol, lactic acid, or acetyl coenzyme A. Acetyl coenzyme A was discovered by one of Meyerhof's students, Fritz Albert Lipmann. Lipmann, a native of Königsberg, Germany, began his biochemical research in Meyerhof's laboratory at the University of Heidelberg from 1927 to 1930. He played an important supporting role in Meyerhof's discovery of glycolysis. In 1941, Lipmann became director of the Biochemistry Research Department at Massachusetts General Hospital in Boston. He continued his studies of energy generation in living organisms, particularly animals. Animal ATP production was much higher than could be explained simply by glycolysis. Seeking other enzymatic pathways for ATP production, Lipmann concentrated his studies on fluid extract from pigeon liver. Pigeons were primary targets of energy metabolism research because of their higher metabolic rates needed for flight. A number of biochemists were studying pigeon flight muscles and liver in order to isolate the necessary enzymes for ATP production. They were attempting to derive an enzymatic pathway for aerobic energy production (that is, aerobic respiration), ATP production in the presence of oxygen. Among the key scientists in this research effort were Lipmann, Sir Hans Adolf Krebs, Warburg, Albert Szent-Györgyi, Franz Knoop, and Carl Martius.

Krebs had discovered several of the intermediate molecules (for example, citric acid, succinate, fumarate) of aerobic metabolism in the early 1930's. He had discovered these molecules because of their high reactivity with oxygen in muscles. Szent-Györgyi obtained similar results. After these and other discoveries, Krebs pieced together the various intermediates of aerobic ATP production. By 1937, he had deciphered the enzymatic pathway known as the citric acid cycle, also called the Krebs cycle or the tricarboxylic acid (TCA) cycle.

In 1945, Lipmann discovered a molecule in pigeon liver extracts that accelerated aerobic respiration without being part of Krebs' famous citric acid cycle. By 1947, he had isolated the molecule and determined its structure. The molecule, which he named coenzyme A (CoA), is a large molecule consisting of four major components: an adenine unit, a five-carbon sugar unit, a pantothenic acid unit, and a beta-mercaptoethylamine unit. Coenzyme A was important because it was highly reactive, particularly with two-carbon molecules such as acetic acid.

In 1951, Lipmann and colleagues demonstrated that coenzyme A can chemically react with pyruvic acid, the end-product of anaerobic glycolysis, to produce acetyl coenzyme A (coenzyme A plus acetic acid). Acetyl coenzyme A dumps the acetate into the Krebs cycle, thereby leaving coenzyme A free to react with another pyruvic acid. Therefore, coenzyme A is the intermediate between the two most important energy-generating reaction pathways in the cells of living organisms: anaerobic glycolysis and the aerobic Krebs cycle. Coenzyme A routes two-carbon units (acetyl groups) from glycolysis to the Krebs cycle. Once coenzyme A dumps acetate into the Krebs cycle, the two-carbon acetate combines with a four-carbon molecule called oxaloacetate to produce the six-carbon molecule citric acid. Citric acid is converted to cis-aconitate, which subsequently is converted to isocitrate. Isocitrate, a six-carbon molecule, is converted to a five-carbon molecule called alpha-ketoglutarate, with the lost carbon being carried away by inhaled oxygen, eventually being exhaled by the organism as carbon dioxide. The five-carbon alpha-ketoglutarate is converted to the four-carbon molecule succinyl-coenzyme A, with the lost carbon again being carried away by oxygen in the form of carbon dioxide. The four-carbon succinyl-coenzyme A is converted to succinate. Succinate is converted to fumarate, which is converted to malate, which is converted to oxaloacetate. Oxaloacetate picks up an acetate from coenzyme A to produce citric acid and thus the Krebs cycle begins over again. Each time through the cycle, fifteen new ATP molecules are generated from ADP.

Impact of Event

Fritz Lipmann's discovery of coenzyme A, his determination of its structure, and his deciphering of its role as acetyl coenzyme A in cellular respiration represent a great breakthrough in twentieth century biochemistry. The discovery of coenzyme A linked the anaerobic and aerobic phases of cellular respiration, helped to quantify the amount of energy production for each glucose molecule an organism consumes, and helped to link cellular respiration to other metabolic reaction pathways (for example, carbohydrate and protein metabolism). Lipmann and Krebs shared the 1953 Nobel Prize in Physiology or Medicine for their contributions to the understanding of energy metabolism in living organisms.

Cellular respiration is the core of modern biochemistry since the field was established by Krebs, Lipmann, Meyerhof, and others studying energy metabolism in the 1930's, 1940's, and 1950's. The central focus of every introductory biochemistry course is cellular respiration. Lipmann's contribution is of great value because it helped to resolve how cells stay alive.

All cells must have energy in order to survive. They need energy in order to drive the thousands of chemical reactions that occur every minute of each cell's life. These chemical reactions involve nutrient assimilation, deoxyribonucleic acid (DNA) replication, membrane recycling, intracellular movements, and the like. Energy is released when one phosphate bond is broken from ATP, thus leaving the less energetic molecule, ADP, and a free inorganic phosphate. The purpose of glycolysis and the Krebs cycle is to reunite ADP and inorganic phosphate to produce ATP so that the cell can rebreak ATP to release energy to drive more chemical reactions.

Glycolysis is an anaerobic process; it does not require the presence of oxygen. It is a series of enzyme reactions in the cell cytoplasm that converts one six-carbon molecule, glucose, into two three-carbon molecules, pyruvic acids. During the reaction pathway, there is a net gain of six ATPs (eight in bacteria). Each pyruvic acid then binds to Lipmann's coenzyme A, with one carbon dioxide released, to produce acetyl coenzyme A, the intermediate between glycolysis and the Krebs cycle. The acetyl unit (two carbons) of acetyl coenzyme A is passed along to oxaloacetate (four carbons) to form the six-carbon citric acid. The remainder of the circular Krebs cycle is the elimination of two carbons (via carbon dioxide) to make oxaloacetate and stimulate the production of fifteen ATPs. Therefore, for each sugar molecule that starts glycolysis, six ATPs are generated from glycolysis, followed by fifteen more ATPs for each of the two pyruvic acids that enter the Krebs cycle. A total of thirty-six ATPs are produced by the two cycles for each glucose molecule (thirty-eight in bacteria).

Therefore, the work of Lipmann, Krebs, and other biochemists explains why one must eat and breathe. One eats to obtain sugar and other nutrients for ATP production. Oxygen is inhaled to carry away the excess carbons of the Krebs cycle, carbons which originally came from the sugar consumed. This carbon dioxide is exhaled. If sugar or oxygen is not received, the Krebs cycle soon stops in the cells, the cells die from lack of ATP, and death occurs.

Bibliography

Alberts, Bruce, et al. *Molecular Biology of the Cell*. New York: Garland, 1983. This lengthy introductory molecular biology textbook for undergraduate biology majors is a thorough survey of the science by several leading molecular biologists and biochemists. It contains excellent photographs, diagrams, and reference lists. Chapter 9, "Energy Conversion: Mitochondria and Chloroplasts," is a clear introduction to cellular respiration.

Karp, Gerald. *Cell Biology*. New York: McGraw-Hill, 1979. This introductory cell biology textbook for undergraduate biology majors emphasizes the relationship between genetics and biochemistry. It contains excellent illustrations and reference lists. Chapter 4, "Energy, Enzymes, and Metabolism," is a detailed discussion of glycolysis and the Krebs cycle.

Lipmann, Fritz, and Nathan O. Kaplan. "Intermediary Metabolism of Phosphorus Compounds." *Annual Review of Biochemistry* 18 (1949): 267-298. This extensive review article, written by Lipmann prior to his discovery of acetyl coenzyme A, describes his research into cellular respiration. The article describes coenzyme A and points toward experiments involving coenzyme A and acetate. More than one hundred references are provided.

Nicholls, David G. *Bioenergetics: An Introduction to the Chemiosmotic Theory*. New York: Academic Press, 1982. This textbook of energy conversion in cellular respiration is intended for advanced undergraduate and graduate biology students. The book describes cellular energy production with schematic illustrations, cartoons, and mathematical derivations. It includes an extensive list of references.

Raven, Peter H., and George B. Johnson. *Biology*. 2d ed. St. Louis: Times Mirror/ Mosby, 1989. This outstanding introductory biology textbook for undergraduate biology majors is clearly written with beautiful photographs and illustrations. Chapter 8, "Cellular respiration," is a simple introduction to glycolysis and the Krebs cycle that is understandable to the layperson.

Stryer, Lubert. *Biochemistry*. 2d ed. San Francisco: W. H. Freeman, 1981. Classic introductory biochemistry textbook for undergraduate biology and premedical students. The book is clearly written, contains outstanding illustrations, and includes historical sketches. Chapter 12, "Glycolysis," and chapter 13, "Citric Acid Cycle," are very understandable presentations of cellular respiration.

Zubay, Geoffrey L. *Biochemistry*. Reading, Mass.: Addison-Wesley, 1983. This comprehensive introductory biochemistry textbook for advanced undergraduate and graduate biology students is a strong survey of the subject. The book is very detailed, but it includes excellent diagrams and illustrations. Chapter 8, "Anaerobic Production of ATP," and chapter 9, "Aerobic Production of ATP," are complete discussions of cellular respiration.

David Wason Hollar, Jr.

Cross-References

Hopkins Discovers Tryptophan, an Essential Amino Acid (1900), p. 46; Hopkins Suggests That Food Contains Vitamins Essential to Life (1906), p. 330; Szent-Györgyi Discovers Vitamin C (1928), p. 857; Krebs Describes the Citric Acid Cycle (1937), p. 1107.

UNIVAC I BECOMES THE FIRST COMMERCIAL ELECTRONIC COMPUTER AND THE FIRST TO USE MAGNETIC TAPE

Category of event: Applied science
Time: 1951
Locale: Philadelphia, Pennsylvania

Eckert and Mauchly, coinventors of the ENIAC, became the first to exploit the commercial applications of computers with the introduction of the UNIVAC I

Principal personages:
J. PRESPER ECKERT (1919-   ), an electrical engineer who was chief designer for the ENIAC, EDVAC, BINAC, and UNIVAC computers
JOHN WILLIAM MAUCHLY (1907-1980), a physicist and creative innovator who teamed up with Eckert to produce the world's first general-purpose electronic computers
JOHN VON NEUMANN (1903-1957), a mathematician who saw the potential in electronic computational assistance in the pursuit of science, briefly teamed up with Eckert and Mauchly, and later opposed them
HOWARD AIKEN (1900-1973), a Harvard physicist who constructed the Mark I, an electromechanical analog computer, and provided opposition to Eckert and Mauchly
GEORGE STIBITZ (1904-   ), a Bell Telephone Laboratories scientist who was the developer of relay-based computers that predate the ENIAC and who opposed Eckert and Mauchly

Summary of Event

On March 31, 1951, the United States Census Bureau accepted delivery of the first UNIVAC. This powerful electronic computer, far surpassing anything then available in technological features and capability, ushered in the first computer generation and pioneered the commercialization of what had previously been the domain of academia and the interest of the military. The fanfare that surrounded this historic occasion, however, masked the turbulence of the preceding five years for the young upstart Eckert-Mauchly Computer Corporation (EMCC), which by this time was a wholly-owned subsidiary of Remington Rand Corporation.

The early history of computers is a lively and controversial topic that has been the subject of countless debates with an abundance of personal antagonism, numerous articles and books (scholarly and otherwise), and landmark patent disputes and lawsuits. The relatively recent birth of the computer age and the resultant fact that many of the pioneers are still alive have sustained the conflicts and controversy. Since the late 1970's, historians have begun to unravel and document the originals of computing. Many of the articles and books available are testimonial recollections by principals who participated and molded the development of computers and thus represent an important but skewed contribution.

J. Presper Eckert and John William Mauchly met in the summer of 1941 at the University of Pennsylvania. A short time later, Mauchly, then a physics professor at Ursinus College, joined the Moore School of Engineering at the University of Pennsylvania and embarked on a crusade to convince others of the feasibility of electronic digital computers. Up to this time, the only computers available were the special-purpose, electromechanical analog computers called differential analyzers used to solve complex mathematical equations known as differential equations. Not only were these machines slow because of the need for human assistance and the operation of mechanical parts but also were good only for solving a relatively narrow range of mathematical problems, thus the label special-purpose. These computers were also analog in nature: The physical nature of the problem to be analyzed is modeled in the circuitry and the solution of a different problem requires modification of that circuitry. Analog also means that values of parameters or quantities can take on a continuous range by representing these quantities by a voltage or current. Most computers (beginning with the ENIAC) are digital in nature. The label digital means that processing is done on discrete or quantized values. Digital computers provide much more flexibility in that the simulation of the physical process is done in software (the sequence of instructions the computer executes) rather than in hardware (the physical circuitry of the computer).

Eckert and Mauchly landed a contract eventually that resulted in the development and construction of the world's first operational general-purpose electronic digital computer: the ENIAC. This computer, used eventually by the Army for the calculation of ballistics tables, was deficient in many obvious areas, but this was caused by economic rather than engineering constraints. One major deficiency was the lack of automatic program control; the ENIAC did not have stored program memory. This was addressed in the development of the EDVAC, the successor to the ENIAC.

A symbiotic relationship had developed between Eckert and Mauchly that worked to their advantage on technical matters. They worked well with each other and this, in part, contributed to their success in spite of external obstacles. They both were interested in commercial applications of computers and envisioned uses for these machines far beyond the narrow military-related solutions of mathematical equations. This interest brought them into conflict with the administration at the Moore School of Engineering as well as with the noted mathematician John von Neumann who "joined" the ENIAC/EDVAC development team in 1945. Von Neumann made significant contributions and added credibility to the Moore School group that often had to fight against the conservative scientific establishment characterized by Howard Aiken at Harvard University and George Stibitz at Bell Telephone Laboratories. Philosophical differences between von Neumann and Eckert and Mauchly, as well as patent issue disputes with the Moore School administration, eventually caused the resignation of Eckert and Mauchly on March 31, 1946.

Eckert and Mauchly, along with some of their engineering colleagues at the University of Pennsylvania, formed the Electronic Control Company and proceeded to interest potential customers in an "EDVAC-type" machine. Mauchly approached the Census Bureau and the National Bureau of Standards (NBS). He had to negotiate with the NBS since the Census Bureau was not permitted to contract on as yet unavailable equipment. A fixed-fee contract for $300,000 for an EDVAC-type computer was signed on September 25, 1946. It is interesting to note that Eckert and Mauchly had estimated a development cost of about $400,000. They were optimistic that subsequent contracts would compensate for the initial loss. Their continual optimism and lack of business acumen led eventually to the demise of their company. Other factors that contributed to the continually precarious financial condition of the company were the roadblocks set up by the review committees and consultants made up of members of the scientific elite who, because of their involvement in alternate competing technology or out of personal dislike, made decisions that negatively affected funding for the company.

On May 24, 1947, the "EDVAC-type" machine became UNIVAC, an acronym for Universal Automatic Computer. This new computer would overcome the shortfalls of ENIAC and EDVAC (which was eventually completed by the Moore School in 1951). It would be a stored program computer and would allow input to and output from the computer via magnetic tape. The prior method of input/output used "IBM" cards. This technique was extremely slow compared to the speed at which data in the computer could be processed. While Eckert concentrated on the technical side, Mauchly worked on getting more contracts and additional sources of funding. Constraints imposed upon them by the nature of their contracts forced the newly renamed Eckert-Mauchly Computer Corporation (EMCC) to find a buyer for the "intermediate" computer that could bring in funds to spur development of the UNIVAC. Mauchly interested Northrop Aircraft Corporation in this machine, which was called BINAC. Thus, during the years 1947 to 1949, EMCC worked on two computers. The engineering staff at EMCC still considered the UNIVAC its primary goal and this resulted in yet more turmoil for Eckert and Mauchly, as Northrop accepted grudgingly a late and shoddily-built BINAC that never worked to specification. Once again, Eckert and Mauchly underestimated the costs of development and incurred a loss on the BINAC contract. This series of poor business decisions and other unfortunate circumstances forced EMCC eventually to look for a buyer. They found one in Remington Rand in 1950. Remington Rand built tabulating equipment and was a competitor of IBM. IBM was approached about buying EMCC, but negotiations fell apart. EMCC became a division of Remington Rand and now had access to the resources necessary to finish UNIVAC.

In spite of all their obstacles, Eckert and Mauchly succeeded in producing the world's first commercial electronic digital computer. UNIVAC quickly became a household word.

Impact of Event

Eckert and Mauchly made a significant contribution to the advent of the computer age with the introduction of the UNIVAC I. Two visionary men, captured by the idea that the world was ready for computers, handicapped by their lack of financial resources and business acumen, and hampered by the conservative and biased scientific establishment, were able to create a landmark in computing. The words "computer" and "UNIVAC" simultaneously entered the vernacular as synonyms. Their efforts were rewarded quickly as contracts started to pour in, taking IBM by surprise and propelling the inventors into the national spotlight. This spotlight shone brightest, perhaps, on the eve of the national presidential election of 1952 pitting the war hero General Dwight D. Eisenhower against the statesman Adlai Stevenson. At the suggestion of the parent company Remington Rand, CBS was invited to use UNIVAC to predict the outcome of the election. Millions of television viewers watched as CBS anchorman Walter Cronkite "asked" UNIVAC for its predictions. A program had been written that analyzed the results of thousands of voting districts in the elections of 1944 and 1948. Based on only 7 percent of the vote, UNIVAC had Eisenhower winning by a landslide in contrast with all the prior human forecasts of a close election. Surprised by this answer and not willing to suffer the embarrassment of being wrong, the programmers quickly tweaked the program to provide an answer closer to the polls. The outcome of the election, however, matched UNIVAC's original answer. This prompted CBS commentator Edward R. Murrow's famous quote, "The trouble with machines is people."

The development of the UNIVAC I produced many technical innovations. Primary among these is the use of magnetic tape for input and output. To be useful, a computer needs a way to communicate with people. All computer systems have some arrangement for providing data (information) to the machine, that is, input, and for displaying the results of the computer's work, that is, output. All machines that preceded the UNIVAC (with the exception of BINAC) used either paper tape or cards for input and cards for output. These methods were very slow and created a bottleneck for information. The computers could add and subtract with lightning speed but had to slow down to read or write the date. In addition, these IBM cards, about the size of turnpike toll tickets, could not hold much information so that one had to use hundreds or thousands of cards to perform any task of significance. Indeed, the first test run of the ENIAC was a program written by Manhattan Project physicists to check the feasibility of a design for the hydrogen bomb that contained thousands of steps and about a million punch cards for the data.

The great advantage of magnetic tape was the ability to store thousands of cards worth of data on one 30-centimeter reel of tape. Another advantage was speed—of reading from and writing to tape. Yet, in spite of this superior technology, Eckert and Mauchly had to design and build card-to-tape and tape-to-card converters, since the industry was saturated with cards and was reluctant to risk conversion to an unproven technology.

Bibliography

Augarten, Stan. *Bit by Bit: An Illustrated History of Computers.* New York: Ticknor & Fields, 1984. A superbly illustrated text filled with wonderful pictures that takes the reader on a journey through history from mechanical calculating aids of the middle ages to the integrated circuits in the personal computers of today.

Burks, Alice R., and Arthur W. Burks. *The First Electronic Computer: The Atanasoff Story*. Ann Arbor: University of Michigan Press, 1987. Arthur Burks, a mathematician who worked on the ENIAC, is the champion of the cause of John Atanasoff. This well-written compilation presents a good case for the claim that Atanasoff created the first electronic computer and greatly influenced Mauchly.

Goldstine, Herman H. *The Computer from Pascal to von Neumann*. Princeton, N.J.: Princeton University Press, 1972. A classic of computer history literature written by a mathematician who participated in the development of the ENIAC. It is readily evident in this book that Goldstine was in awe of von Neumann and affords him a greater role in computing history than warranted.

Lundstrom, David E. *A Few Good Men from Univac*. Cambridge, Mass.: MIT Press, 1987. A fascinating tale by one of the "good men" from UNIVAC about events that occurred after 1952 and following the careers of several UNIVAC engineers, leading to the creation of Control Data Corporation.

Moreau, Rene. *The Computer Comes of Age*. Cambridge, Mass.: MIT Press, 1984. This book serves as a classic in the distortion of computer history. Written by an IBM scientist, it emphasizes IBM's early work and concentrates on subsequent IBM machines. For history buffs only.

Shurkin, Joel. *Engines of the Mind: A History of the Computer*. New York: W. W. Norton, 1984. A popular book that draws heavily from the work of Nancy Stern. Shurkin devotes considerable text defending Eckert and Mauchly on the issue of the court battle about the ENIAC patent and the Atanasoff-Berry computer.

Stern, Nancy. *From ENIAC to UNIVAC: An Appraisal of the Eckert-Mauchly Computers*. Bedford, Mass.: Digital Press, 1981. This landmark volume should be the starting point of any serious inquiry into the early history of computers. In contrast to some of the testimonial books, Stern, in this publication of her doctoral thesis, is writing clearly from an objective vantage point.

Wulforst, Harry. *Breakthrough to the Computer Age*. New York: Charles Scribner's Sons, 1982. This well-written book provides an excellent portrayal of the development of the early computers from the ENIAC to the UNIVAC. Contains some pictures and the full story of the 1952 presidential prediction by UNIVAC.

Paul G. Nyce

Cross-References

Fleming Files a Patent for the First Vacuum Tube (1904), p. 255; Bush Builds the First Differential Analyzer (1928), p. 846; A Secret English Team Develops Colossus (1940's), p. 1155; Eckert and Mauchly Develop the ENIAC (1943), p. 1213; Shockley, Bardeen, and Brattain Discover the Transistor (1947), p. 1304; The First Electronic Stored-Program Computer (BINAC) Is Completed (1949), p. 1347; The Microprocessor "Computer on a Chip" Is Introduced (1971), p. 1938.

TELLER AND ULAM DEVELOP THE FIRST H-BOMB

Categories of event: Physics and applied science
Time: 1951-1952
Locale: Los Alamos, New Mexico; Marshall Islands, South Pacific

Inspired by the work of Ulam and others, Teller proposed a workable concept for a thermonuclear device

Principal personages:
    EDWARD TELLER (1908-   ), a Hungarian-born theoretical physicist who was a principal figure in the effort by the United States to develop a thermonuclear bomb
    STANISLAW ULAM (1909-1984), a Polish-born mathematician who provided crucial analyses and critical insight that made the H-bomb concept workable

Summary of Event

A few months before the 1942 creation of the Manhattan Project, the United States-led effort to build an atomic (fission) bomb, Enrico Fermi suggested to Edward Teller that such a bomb could release more of the energy that binds atomic nuclei together by heating a mass of the hydrogen isotope deuterium and igniting the fusion of hydrogen into helium. These were also the thermonuclear reactions in stars, making them shine and radiate heat, that Hans Bethe, George Gamow, and Teller had been studying in the United States since 1934. Initially, Teller dismissed Fermi's idea, but later in 1942, in collaboration with Emil Konopinski, he concluded that a hydrogen bomb, or superbomb, could be made.

German scientists were working on an atomic bomb, and with Teller's advocacy, the superbomb received serious consideration within the Manhattan Project. To increase the probability of success for the concept then championed by Teller, Konopinski suggested that the rare heavy isotope of hydrogen—tritium—should be added also as fusion fuel. An atomic bomb had not yet been produced, and in 1944 the Los Alamos Laboratory Governing Board concluded that Teller's proposed superbomb would require more tritium than could be available for some time. J. Robert Oppenheimer, then director at Los Alamos, stated that after World War II, the United States should make every effort to determine the practical feasibility of a hydrogen bomb. In the meantime, Teller worked less on the atomic bomb, devoting his time to investigating the superbomb.

With the war over and the atomic bomb a proven reality, Teller returned to Los Alamos in 1946 to chair a secret conference on the superbomb attended by, among other Manhattan Project veterans, Stanislaw Ulam and Klaus Emil Julius Fuchs. Supporting the investigation of Teller's concept, the conferees requested a more complete mathematical analysis of his own admittedly crude calculations on the hydrodynamics of the fusion reactions. In 1947, Teller believed that these calculations might take years. Two years later, however, for Teller, with his parents in a Hungary now within the folds of the Iron Curtain, and to his supporters, the Soviet's explosion of an atomic bomb meant that America's Cold War adversary was hard at work on its own superbomb. Even when new calculations cast further doubt on his designs, Teller began a vigorous campaign for a crash development of the H-bomb.

For several reasons, Oppenheimer and the General Advisory Committee (GAC) of the Atomic Energy Commission (AEC) in 1949 did not endorse Teller's urgent demands. The GAC did not find evidence to support a high probability of success in Teller's design to warrant massive expenditures at that time. Also, the GAC was certain that with modest funding and existing facilities, the addition of fusion components to an atomic bomb would boost efficiency by several orders of magnitude, producing yields of about 200,000 tons of TNT (trinitrotoluene). A weapon above such an explosive yield, the GAC observed, would produce genocide. Teller, however, was gaining important political and military support. For him, it was a moral imperative of the United States to be the first nation to develop such a weapon.

In 1950, the same year that Fuchs admitted to passing information to the Soviet Union about United States nuclear weapons programs, the Korean War broke out, and President Harry S Truman decided to approve an all-out effort to build the H-bomb. The basic design under consideration remained Teller's classic superbomb, one that consisted of liquid deuterium and tritium configured within an atomic device. During that year and into the spring of 1951, however, Ulam, Cornelius J. Everett, Fermi, Frederick de Hoffman, and the ENIAC computer had disproven the possibility of Teller's design working. That some other design might work, however, had not been disproved.

That fusion reactions could be induced by the explosion of an atomic bomb was not in doubt. The basic problem was simple and formidable; how could fusion fuel be heated and compressed long enough to achieve significant thermonuclear burning before the expansion of the fireball from the atomic explosion blew the assembly apart? During these difficult months, the collaboration of these individuals and others, and verification provided by ENIAC, moved them closer to a practical solution of building a workable H-bomb. As a group, however, their recollections and contemporary documentation revealed that they were hoping to discover that an H-bomb could not be built by any nation. Early in 1951, however, a major part of the ultimate solution came from Ulam, who proposed using the energy from an exploding atomic bomb to induce significant thermonuclear reactions in adjacent fusion fuel components.

This arrangement of materials became known as the Teller-Ulam configuration, that is, the physical separation of the A-bomb primary from the secondary's fusion fuel; all H-bombs are cylindrical, with an atomic device at one end and the other components filling the remaining space. In Teller's unexpected approach, energy from the exploding primary could be transported by X rays at near-light speed, thus affecting the secondary before the arrival of the explosion. De Hoffman's work verified and enriched the new concept. Now, moderated X rays from the primary would in the secondary irradiate a reactive plastic medium surrounding concentric and generally cylindrical layers of fusion and fission fuel. Instantly, the plastic becomes a hot plasma that compresses and heats an inner layer of fusion fuel, which in turn compresses a central core of fissile plutonium to supercriticality. Thus compressed and bombarded by fusion-produced, high-energy neutrons, the fission element expands rapidly in chain reaction from the inside out, further compressing and heating the surrounding fusion fuel, resulting in the liberation of more energy and fast neutrons that induce fission in a fuel casing-tamper made of normally stable uranium 238.

The device to test Teller's new concept weighed more than 60 tons with its equipment to refrigerate the hydrogen isotopes. Like all the H-bomb prototypes, concepts were given workable forms by the Los Alamos Laboratory, with which Teller was no longer affiliated. During Operation Ivy, it was tested at Elugelab Island in the Eniwetok atoll on November 1, 1952. Exceeding the expectations of all concerned and vaporizing the island, the explosion equaled 10.4 million tons of TNT, or about seven hundred times greater than the atomic bomb used on Hiroshima in 1945. An emergency capability version of this device weighing about 20 tons was prepared for delivery by specially modified Air Force B-36 bombers.

In development at Los Alamos before the 1952 test was a device weighing only about 4 tons, a "dry bomb" that did not require cryogenic equipment or liquid fusion fuel; when sufficiently compressed and heated in its molded-powder form, the new fusion fuel component, lithium-6 deutride, instantly produces tritium. This concept was tested during Operation Castle at Bikini atoll in 1954 and produced a yield of 15 million tons of TNT, the largest-ever nuclear explosion by the United States. Not until 1956, in Operation Cherokee-Redwing, did the United States explode an H-bomb dropped from an aircraft, an Air Force B-52 bomber.

Impact of Event

The successful explosion of a Teller-inspired thermonuclear device in 1952 gave impetus to an ongoing global nuclear arms race. Ideas may originate in one country, but political and scientific zeal is international. One example of this phenomenon occurred in May, 1941: Months before Fermi suggested to Teller the possibility of explosive thermonuclear reactions on Earth, Japanese physicist Tokutaro Hagiwara proposed that a uranium-235 bomb could ignite significant fusion reactions in hydrogen. Another example came in 1955, when the Soviet Union tested successfully an H-bomb dropped from an airplane, the year before the United States did so. Teller was not alone in believing that the world could produce many nuclear and thermonuclear-capable nation-states and that some would threaten the United States.

During these early years of military and ideological confrontation with the Soviet Union, Teller advocated and received in 1952 a second nuclear weapons facility, the Lawrence-Livermore National Laboratory in California. For many years within the scientific community there existed disagreement over weapons development and the role that such weapons should play in national defense policy-making. Prior to the identification of Teller's name with the H-bomb, it had been Oppenheimer, Los Alamos, and the A-bomb receiving attention. Oppenheimer and others on technical and moral grounds had initially opposed building the H-bomb, seeking instead an international moratorium on its development. For many years in the future, the expression of such concerns within the weapons community would not be tolerated.

With anticommunist activity and legislation reaching a peak, Oppenheimer's loyalty was questioned. During Oppenheimer's security clearance hearing held by the AEC in 1954, Teller's testimony against his former superior at Los Alamos and consistent critic of his early H-bomb designs proved decisive. President Dwight D. Eisenhower endorsed the AEC findings, and Oppenheimer's security clearance for work in classified nuclear areas was withdrawn. Teller became the scientific adviser in the nuclear affairs of the nation to presidents, from Eisenhower to Ronald Reagan. The widespread blast and fallout effects of H-bombs assured the mutual destruction of the combatants. Teller knew that the availability of H-bombs encouraged but did not guarantee the deterrence of use.

A long-standing schism developed within the U.S. scientific community between the supporters of Teller or Oppenheimer and the combatants over the issue of nuclear test ban treaties. Teller consistently advised against U.S. participation with the Soviet Union in a moratorium on nuclear weapons testing. Largely based on Teller's advocacy of retaining the prerogative to test underground, the United States rejected a total moratorium in favor of the 1963 Atmospheric Test Ban Treaty. During the 1980's, Teller, among others, convinced President Reagan to embrace the Strategic Defense Initiative (SDI). Teller argued that SDI components, such as the space-based "Excalibur," a nuclear bomb-powered X-ray laser antiwarhead weapon proposed by the Lawrence-Livermore National Laboratory, would make thermonuclear war not so much unimaginable as theoretically impossible.

Bibliography

Bethe, Hans. "Comments on the History of the H-bomb, 1954." In *The American Atom: A Documentary History of Nuclear Policies from the Discovery of Fission to the Present, 1939-1984*, edited by Robert C. Williams and Philip L. Cantelon. Philadelphia: University of Pennsylvania Press, 1984. Nobel laureate Bethe provides critical eyewitness assessment of Teller's role in the H-bomb program, describes Teller's early designs and why they would not work, and declares Ulam's work essential. Argues that Teller's direction of the program was itself an inhibiting factor and defends the technical skepticism of Oppenheimer and the GAC in 1949.
Kevles, Daniel J. *The Physicists: The History of a Scientific Community in Modern America*. New York: Alfred A. Knopf, 1977. A valuable study for understanding the changing twentieth century relationships between academic and industrial science, and the military; extensive bibliography.
Morland, Howard. *The Secret That Exploded*. New York: Random House, 1981.

Based on information in the public domain, Morland conjectured the secret of the Teller-Ulam configuration. In 1979, the federal government sued his employer, *The Progressive* magazine, to prevent publication of his diagrams. To avoid further revelations, the government conceded the case; in 1979, the article and more accurate diagrams were published. Includes diagrams of H-bomb schemata, photographs of facilities, processes of fabrication, and H-bombs.

Rhodes, Richard. *The Making of the Atomic Bomb*. New York: Simon & Schuster, 1986. The discussion of the H-bomb draws upon and confirms the claims and observations of Bethe, Ulam, York, Morland, and others. The contributions of others, especially Ulam's, have been underestimated. Includes exhaustive bibliography, diagrams and photographs of nuclear bombs, and the original emergency-capability thermonuclear bomb.

Teller, Edward. "The Hydrogen Bomb: The Work of Many People." In *Better a Shield than a Sword: Perspectives on Defense and Technology*. New York: Free Press, 1987. Originally published in 1955, offers Teller's recollection of H-bomb development; he acknowledges his indebtedness to many others, but does not grant Ulam major status in the solution of the H-bomb problem.

Ulam, Stanislaw. "Thermonuclear Devices." In *Perspectives in Modern Physics: Essays in Honor of Hans A. Bethe*, edited by R. E. Marshak. New York: Interscience, 1966. Adds credibility to the belief that while an H-bomb was theoretically possible, until the spring of 1951, Teller had no practicable idea on how to realize it. As other sources confirm, Ulam's contributions were more than architectural.

York, Herbert F. *The Advisors: Oppenheimer, Teller, and the Superbomb*. San Francisco: W. H. Freeman, 1976. York, the first director of the Lawrence-Livermore National Laboratory, corroborates the accounts of others. York believed Ulam's contributions were critical and discusses the emergence of Teller as the authority on nuclear matters. Extensive bibliography.

Eric Howard Christianson

Cross-References

WATSON AND CRICK DEVELOP THE
DOUBLE-HELIX MODEL FOR DNA

Categories of event: Biology, chemistry, and physics
Time: 1951-1953
Locale: Cambridge and London, England

By showing precisely how two polynucleotide strands of deoxyribonucleic acid (DNA) are twisted into a double helix, Waston and Crick essentially discovered the chemical nature of the gene

Principal personages:

JAMES D. WATSON (1928-   ), an American molecular biologist who shared, with Crick and Wilkins, the 1962 Nobel Prize in Physiology or Medicine for the discovery of the three-dimensional structure of DNA

FRANCIS CRICK (1916-   ), an English physicist whose theoretical work on the X-ray diffraction studies of proteins prepared him to make significant contributions to the determination of DNA's structure

MAURICE H. F. WILKINS (1916-   ), an English biophysicist whose X-ray diffraction studies of DNA were instrumental in determining its structure

ROSALIND FRANKLIN (1920-1958), an English physical chemist and X-ray crystallographer who identified two forms of DNA and produced highly detailed X-ray pictures of both forms

LINUS PAULING (1901-   ), an American theoretical physical chemist whose determination of the alpha-helix served as a model for the work of Watson and Crick on DNA

JERRY DONOHUE (1920-1985), an American crystallographer whose knowledge of the structure of DNA's nitrogenous bases allowed Watson to pair them properly

Summary of Event

DNA, in a highly impure form called nuclein, was first isolated in 1869 from cell nuclei by Friedrich Miescher, a Swiss physiological chemist. During the latter part of the nineteenth century, Albrecht Kossel, a German biochemist, worked out the overall composition of nuclein (which, because of its acidic properties, came to be called "nucleic acid"). He found that nucleic acid was made up of three molecular groups: phosphoric acid, a sugar, and a variety of nitrogen-containing bases. These nitrogenous bases involved pyrimidines (with single rings) and purines (with two rings). The research of Phoebus Levene, a Soviet-American chemist, made it clear that nucleic acids existed in two types, one based on the sugar ribose and the other on deoxyribose. The two kinds of nucleic acid became known as deoxyribonucleic acid (DNA) and ribonucleic acid (RNA).

A pivotal discovery in DNA's history was Oswald T. Avery's demonstration that this molecule is the carrier of genetic information. Working at the Rockefeller Institute for Medical Research in New York City, Avery and his coworkers found that protein-free DNA could transform a nonvirulent bacterial strain into a virulent one. In 1943, Avery stated that his experiments showed that DNA might be the gene. He believed that DNA not only was structurally important in the nucleus but also was a functionally active material in determining a cell's specific characteristics and biochemical activity. In a paper he and his colleagues published in 1944, Avery was circumspect in his statements about DNA's genetic role (some of his colleagues were contending that minute protein impurities in his DNA samples were really the transforming principle). Most scientists then believed that protein, with its more than twenty amino acid building blocks, had a better chance of being the genetic material than nucleic acid, with its four or five nitrogenous-base building blocks. Therefore, the idea of DNA as the genetic material spread slowly, but Avery's work endured both experimental and theoretical challenges, and by the late 1940's, many scientists accepted DNA as the genetic molecule and some even began focusing attention on the details of its structure.

During the 1940's, largely through the work of the English organic chemist Alexander Todd, DNA's construction from nucleotide building blocks was understood in terms of how all its atoms are linked together. Each nucleotide consists of a base (a purine or pyrimidine derivative), a five-carbon sugar, and a phosphoric-acid group. Todd had been able to determine exactly how the deoxyribose ring is bonded to the various bases and to the phosphate group. While he was working out the detailed bonding of the nucleic acids, Erwin Chargaff, a biochemist at the College of Physicians and Surgeons in New York, was investigating the differences in the base compositions of DNA from various plants and animals. By 1950, his careful analyses had revealed that the amounts of various bases in different DNAs varied widely, but his data also yielded the significant result that the ratios of bases adenine to thymine and guanine to cytosine were always close to one.

Linus Pauling, along with many other American chemists, was slow to accept DNA as the genetic material. DNA contained only four bases, and for a long time it seemed to him that the molecule was too simple to handle the formidable task of transferring huge amounts of information from one generation of living things to the next. Proteins, with their large variety of amino acids, seemed much better adapted to this information-carrying role. While he was visiting professor at the University of Oxford in 1948, Pauling discovered one of the basic structures of proteins: the alpha-helix. This three-dimensional structure, which was based on the planarity of the group of atoms holding the amino acids together (the peptide bond), was secured in its twisting turns by hydrogen bonds (links whereby a hydrogen atom serves as a bridge between certain neighboring atoms). Pauling was initially hesitant to publish his structure because experimental evidence seemed to go against it, but in 1950, he began a series of papers detailing his views on protein structure.

In the early 1950's, James D. Watson, a young postdoctoral fellow, and Francis Crick, a graduate student, both of whom had become interested in DNA, were deeply impressed by Pauling's work. Crick believed that Pauling's method would allow biologists to build accurate three-dimensional models of the complex molecules in living things, particularly DNA. At the time Watson and Crick got together at the Cavendish Laboratory at the University of Cambridge, Crick was a physicist working on the theory of the X-ray diffraction of proteins and Watson was a biologist with a desire to determine the structure of DNA, which he believed was the key to the gene's secrets. At first, Watson and Crick seemed an odd team for this task. Neither had much knowledge of chemistry. Crick's previous training was in physics and work on mines during the war; Watson's education in ornithology and zoology did not prepare him for dealing with the daunting complexities of the DNA molecule. Nevertheless, they were determined to discover DNA's three-dimensional structure.

Watson and Crick were not the only scientists interested in this problem. At the California Institute of Technology, Pauling, who had come to accept DNA as the genetic material, was thinking of applying his model-building approach to the problem of DNA's structure. In John Randall's laboratory at King's College of the University of London, Maurice H. F. Wilkins and Rosalind Franklin were engaged in an experimental approach to the problem: They were trying to determine DNA's structure through improved X-ray diffraction photographs of carefully prepared DNA samples. Wilkins had taken X-ray photographs of DNA early in 1950, but he was not a professional crystallographer; in 1951, Franklin was hired to set up a crystallographic unit to work on the DNA problem. Unfortunately, she and Wilkins did not get along, which seriously hampered the DNA research. Despite this personality conflict, Franklin eventually was able to show that DNA exists in two forms, each of which gives a distinctive X-ray picture: a cruciform pattern characteristic of very wet DNA (the B form) and a complex array of spots characteristic of a less humid DNA (the A form). From her X-ray pictures, Franklin was able to discover that the DNA molecule had two periodicities in its B form.

Unlike Franklin and Wilkins, Watson and Crick decided to attack the problem of DNA's structure not by experimental X-ray methods but by a theoretical model-building approach. By 1951, DNA's chemical structural formula, that is, how its atoms are linked together, was well known. Many of these links involve a single electron pair, which allows free rotation around these bonds, resulting in many possible orientations for attached atoms and groups of atoms. For various physical and chemical reasons, Watson and Crick could eliminate as unlikely many of these configurations, and they hoped that the number of sensible remaining structures would be small and reducible to a single structure through new X-ray information.

In November, 1951, Watson traveled to London to attend a lecture by Franklin. She presented some insights about her DNA work, including her finding of the two different forms of DNA and her analysis of the probable helicity of the B form; Watson, however, who did not know about crystallography, returned to Cambridge with a garbled account of Franklin's points. On the basis of this faulty understanding, he and Crick began to work out the structure of DNA as if it were perfectly dry. Their misunderstanding of the molecule's density led them to construct a model with three polynucleotide strands, each coiled in a helix, somewhat like three vines winding around a cylinder. Because the nitrogenous bases were extremely bulky, Watson and Crick put them on the outside of the molecule and arranged the sugar-phosphate groups on the inside. They invited Wilkins and Franklin to see their finished model. When Franklin saw no water in the structure, she told them it was ridiculous.

Early in 1952, when Sir Lawrence Bragg, the director of the Cavendish Laboratory, became aware of the triple-helix fiasco, he advised Watson and Crick to stop their research. In the spring of 1952, Franklin, who continued her experimental studies of DNA, was able to obtain excellent X-ray pictures of DNA fibers. Although Watson and Crick were warned off DNA research, circumstances kept bringing them back to it. In the summer of 1952, for example, Erwin Chargaff visited Cambridge. After talking with Watson and Crick about DNA, he was shocked to learn that neither of them had precise knowledge about the chemical differences among the four bases. He explained to them his findings about the base ratios, but he did not see them as skilled chemists who could solve the problem of DNA's three-dimensional structure. Although Crick had not been aware of Chargaff's discovery, he had been thinking about piling complementary bases on top of one another in a DNA model, so he was fascinated by Chargaff's information. By pairing adenine with thymine, and guanine with cytosine, a rational explanation for the ratios emerged.

Peter Pauling, one of Linus Pauling's sons, went to Cambridge in the fall of 1952, and through the letters he exchanged with his father, he kept Watson and Crick apprised of his father's work. Late in 1952, relying on poor X-ray photographs of DNA and faulty data about its density, Pauling worked out a three-strand structure, with the very bulky bases on the periphery of the molecule. In some of his earlier papers and lectures, he had speculated that the genetic material in living things had to be composed of two complementary strands, but he was forced to conclude that this DNA—the product of laboratory manipulations—must be a triple helix. When Peter Pauling told Watson and Crick that his father had a structure for DNA, they became disheartened, but when Peter gave them his father's manuscript, they realized that Pauling's three-strand structure was wrong. In January of 1953, when Watson showed Pauling's manuscript to Wilkins, he, too, thought the triple helix was wrong. Wilkins showed Watson Franklin's X-ray picture of the B form, which clearly revealed in its crosslike pattern the presence of a helix. On his return to Cambridge, Watson began building models of DNA. Like Pauling, he began by arranging the phosphoric-acid groups in the center. Some of the information for Watson's model came from a report made available to him by Max Perutz, a member of a committee whose goal was to coordinate research groups working in biophysics. The data in the report proved helpful in determining some important variables of the molecule.

For example, the density of the B form clearly implied that the DNA molecule had two strands.

When Watson encountered insurmountable difficulties with his model, Crick suggested that he place the backbone of phosphates on the molecule's outside and stack the flat bases in its center. Watson believed that this tactic would create too many possibilities, but he prepared cardboard representations of the bases and made attempts to fit them together. Fortunately, Jerry Donohue, an American crystallographer and Pauling protégé, was sharing an office with Watson. He saw from Watson's cardboard cut-outs that he did not understand the proper chemical structures for the nitrogenous bases. When Watson—following Donohue's advice—put the bases into their correct forms, he was able to pair adenine and thymine as well as guanine and cytosine by means of hydrogen bonds whose locations were natural, not forced. He immediately sensed something was right about these pairings, since both pairs (adenine-thymine, guanine-cytosine) had nearly the same size and shape and could be neatly stacked, like a pile of plates, in the interior of a double helix, while the regular sugar-phosphate backbone at the molecule's exterior could account for its acidity and its interactions with water. It turned out that this pairing of bases is the pivotal feature of DNA's structure and the reason for its complementary nature.

In March of 1953, Watson and Crick constructed a detailed model of their double helix to show that all the atoms were in sensible locations. Its two strands, helically wound around an imaginary axis, were repeatedly linked together across the molecule's middle via the hydrogen-bonded bases, whose constant pairing of adenine with thymine and guanine with cytosine accounted for the ratios observed by Chargaff. The model, with the helix making a complete turn every ten base pairs, was consistent also with the X-ray data. Watson and Crick recognized that an important characteristic of their double helix was the complementariness of the strands; that is, each strand's directional orientation was opposite to the other's. Watson and Crick published their model in *Nature* on April 25, 1953. Their brief paper, which quickly achieved classic status, succinctly described their discovery and noted its implications, especially as a mechanism for copying the genetic material.

Impact of Event

Scholars have compared the discovery of the double helix with Darwin's discovery of natural selection and Mendel's discovery of the laws of heredity. The importance of the double helix also can be gauged by the proliferation of significant discoveries in molecular biology that it precipitated. Pauling stated that the double helix was "the most important discovery in the field of biology that has been made in the last hundred years." He saw it as the culmination of molecular biology, since no problem is more fundamental than the mechanism of heredity. The double helix did not disappoint scientists eager to understand this mechanism. In the years after the model was unveiled, it proved surpassingly suitable for explaining molecular details about how cells replicate. Indeed, the most obvious feature of the model was its natural explanation of how DNA could make an exact copy of itself. In this process of replication, DNA's two complementary strands unzip and separate and each uncovered base takes on a new partner. Thus, both halves of the separated double helix act as the templates or molds on which complementary strands are synthesized. When the process is completed, two identical double helices appear where one previously existed. This explanation of how, at the molecular level, genes duplicate themselves with great fidelity was not only scientifically satisfying but also aesthetically pleasing.

Although several years elapsed before this gene-replication process was confirmed experimentally, few scientists doubted the essential verity of the Watson and Crick explanation. On the other hand, more than three decades elapsed before molecular biologists overcame staggering difficulties to work out the intricate details of the cell's protein-manufacturing mechanisms. These problems were not solved directly by the double helix, but studies of information transfer from DNA to the cellular mechanisms responsible for protein construction revealed that the double helix was indirectly involved. For example, research on the interactions between DNA and RNA, and RNA and proteins, revealed that DNA's structure contained, in the sequences of its bases, an intricate code that supervised, through different kinds of RNA, the construction of the thousands of proteins used by cells. Mathematical analysis made clear that a triplet of nucleotides could code for a particular amino acid, but several years would pass before molecular biologists worked out all the details of the genetic code. In some cases, different triplets coded for the same amino acid and a few triplets were nonsense codons, standing for no amino acid. In the end, however, molecular biologists succeeded in showing how some molecular messages in DNA's bases are translated into the chemical language of such proteins as enzymes, hemoglobin, and collagen.

Watson and Crick also played important roles in its evolution. For example, they helped formulate its central dogma, which accounts for how genetic information passes from DNA to the cell's proteins. In the first part of the process (duplication), DNA serves as the template for its self-replication. Then, in transcription, RNA molecules are made on the DNA template. Finally, in translation, the RNA templates determine the construction of protein. In this process, DNA has the ability to act on itself, but transcription and translation are unidirectional; that is, RNA sequences are never made on protein templates, and DNA sequences are never made on RNA templates. In the course of many experimental investigations of these processes, some exceptions to these rules have been found, but the central dogma remains essentially valid, as does the structure of DNA. Within a short time of the discovery of the double helix, Pauling and others pointed out a few corrections in some of the details of the Watson and Crick structure, yet their model has stood the test of time. By the 1970's, many scientists believed that this model had solved most of the basic mysteries of the gene. During the 1980's, molecular biologists developed applications derived from clever manipulations of the double helix. The debate stirred up by these applications clearly demonstrates that the revolution wrought by the double helix is not yet over.

Bibliography

Crick, Francis. *What Mad Pursuit: A Personal View of Scientific Discovery*. New York: Basic Books, 1988. A memoir that focuses on Crick's experiences before, during, and after the discovery of the double helix. Crick's version of the discovery of the double helix helps to correct some of the distortions in Watson's well-known account. Photographs, two scientific appendices, and an index.

Judson, Horace Freeland. *The Eighth Day of Creation: The Makers of the Revolution in Biology*. New York: Simon & Schuster, 1979. A popular account of the making of modern molecular biology, much of which originally appeared in *The New Yorker*. Based on more than a hundred interviews of the scientists involved; Judson communicates both a sense of the intellectual curiosity and a clear grasp of the chief scientific ideas of the modern biological revolution. Contains a large number of notes, many of which have detailed bibliographical information, and an extensive index.

Olby, Robert. *The Path of the Double Helix*. Seattle: University of Washington Press, 1974. Intended for scholars and students of the life sciences. Focuses on how basic developments in biology, chemistry, physics, and medicine led to a chemical understanding of the gene. Major sections delineate how the idea of the macromolecule was developed, how nucleic acids came to be seen as the hereditary material, and how the double helix was discovered. Illustrated with figures and photographs; includes an extensive bibliography and a detailed index.

Sayre, Anne. *Rosalind Franklin and DNA*. New York: W. W. Norton, 1978. Sayre was deeply troubled by Watson's portrayal of Franklin in *The Double Helix*, and her book is an attempt to correct what she sees as Watson's distortions of Franklin as a person and as a scientist. Based on interviews, Franklin's research notes and correspondence, and published materials; Sayre maintains that Franklin's research was a major factor in the discovery of the double helix by Watson and Crick. Includes notes with references to primary and secondary sources, but no index.

Watson, James D. *The Double Helix: A Personal Account of the Discovery of the Structure of DNA*. Reprint. New York: W. W. Norton, 1980. Contains several commentaries, reviews, and relevant scientific papers. Watson's book infuriated many of his colleagues, who believed that he had been unnecessarily cruel to several individuals, especially Franklin, but others liked his revelations never before presented to the public. Index.

Robert J. Paradowski

Cross-References

Sutton States That Chromosomes Are Paired and Could be Carriers of Hereditary Traits (1902), p. 153; Morgan Develops the Gene-Chromosome Theory (1908), p. 407; Johannsen Coins the Terms "Gene," "Genotype," and "Phenotype" (1909), p. 433; Sturtevant Produces the First Chromosome Map (1911), p. 486; Avery, MacLeod, and McCarty Determine That DNA Carries Hereditary Information (1943),

p. 1203; Ochoa Creates Synthetic RNA (1950's), p. 1363; Horsfall Announces That Cancer Results from Alterations in the DNA of Cells (1961), p. 1682; Kornberg and Coworkers Synthesize Biologically Active DNA (1967), p. 1857; Cohen and Boyer Develop Recombinant DNA Technology (1973), p. 1987; Berg, Gilbert, and Sanger Develop Techniques for Genetic Engineering (1980), p. 2115; Jeffreys Discovers the Technique of Genetic Fingerprinting (1985), p. 2296; Erlich Develops DNA Fingerprinting from a Single Hair (1988), p. 2362.

OORT AND ASSOCIATES CONSTRUCT
A MAP OF THE MILKY WAY

Category of event: Astronomy
Time: May, 1951-May, 1954
Locale: Leiden, The Netherlands

Following van de Hulst's discovery of the 21-centimeter spectral line of atomic hydrogen, Oort and Muller used this radio frequency to construct a map of the Milky Way galaxy

Principal personages:

JAN HENDRIK OORT (1900-   ), a Dutch astronomer who supported the model of a large rotating Galaxy with the sun in an off-center location

ALEX MULLER (1923-   ), a Dutch electrical engineer with whom Oort and his coworkers produced the first radio map of the Galaxy

HENDRIK VAN DE HULST (1918-   ), a Dutch astronomer who predicted that neutral hydrogen in the Galaxy's spiral arms could be detected

Summary of Event

After it was established that the Milky Way was merely one of many galaxies, astronomers remained unsure of its nature and size. Earlier calculations in 1914 placed the sun near the center of the Milky Way galaxy, determined to be only about 30,000 light-years in diameter and 6,000 light-years thick (about one-third the presently accepted size). The study of globular star clusters in 1918 revised these estimates and erroneously placed the sun near the edge of the Galaxy, calculated to be ten times larger than presently believed. This latter model was not widely accepted.

Astronomers in the 1940's began to map out the spiral arms of the Milky Way by concentrating on young hot population I stars embedded in vast luminous clouds called emission nebulas, such as the Orion nebula. It was not until radio astronomy became widely used in the 1940's and 1950's that vast new areas of the sky began to open up that had previously been invisible to the most powerful optical telescopes because of high concentrations of dust.

Since atomic hydrogen is the most abundant part of interstellar matter, Jan Hendrik Oort believed it to be ideal for radio studies. Oort suggested to one of his students, Hendrik van de Hulst, that if he could detect an emission line in the radio frequency spectrum for neutral hydrogen, then the Doppler shift technique could be used to measure relative motions of the Galaxy that would otherwise be invisible. The problem, however, was knowing just what this frequency was as well as the mechanism that would cause it. After analysis of the hydrogen energy level diagram, van de Hulst determined that the ground state of hydrogen was split into two closely spaced energy levels. Research in the 1920's and 1930's had shown that the proton and electron behave like spinning miniature tops. The spinning motion of the proton and electron creates a small magnetic field that interacts with and affects the hydrogen atom's energy levels. When electrons collide with other electrons or atoms, changes occur from one energy level to another, and photons are emitted. A much rarer occurrence is a spontaneous change from the same to the opposite direction of spin. At one level, the atom's electron spins in the same direction as the proton or "parallel" and at the other slightly higher level, spins in the opposite direction or "antiparallel." If an atom in the parallel ground state happens to collide with another atom, it may absorb a small amount of energy from the collision and end up in the antiparallel ground state. When this occurs, a very low-energy photon is emitted with its wavelength of 21 centimeters in the radio part of the spectrum. This provides the hydrogen atom with another way to radiate energy. An individual hydrogen atom might undergo such a spin change only once every 10 million years, but van de Hulst believed that the huge amounts of interstellar hydrogen should collectively produce a strong enough signal to be detected.

The 21-centimeter line discovered by van de Hulst indicated the presence of neutral hydrogen that was previously difficult to study optically because it passed opaque interstellar dust. The discovery was first announced in 1944, but Europe was still at war and the pursuit of radio astronomy was not a priority because of the lack of equipment available for searching out this weak spectral line. When peace returned to Europe, however, Oort assembled a team to seek out the 21-centimeter line. The group included Alex Muller, an electrical engineer, whose expertise was instrumental in acquiring German radar antennas as well as building their own instruments. Misfortune struck the Dutch team in early 1951 when a fire destroyed important types of equipment before they could be used. Meanwhile, in the United States, astronomers who were using radio astronomy were also in search of the 21-centimeter line. A group from Harvard University first detected this line in March, 1951. When the line was detected, van de Hulst was visiting Harvard University at the time and was given a description of the receiver first used by the American team. Van de Hulst immediately relayed back to Muller in The Netherlands the details of this design; on May 11, the Dutch confirmed the discovery along with the Australians in July of the same year.

Radio astronomy allowed astronomers to "see" hydrogen directly and penetrate interstellar dust. Oort saw this as an opportunity to construct a much more refined picture of the Milky Way galaxy. By aiming a radio telescope along a specific line of sight from Earth, one could obtain a profile of the spectral line at the 21-centimeter wavelength, with peaks corresponding to various concentrations of the atoms at different velocities. Upon analyzing the Doppler shifts of these peaks, researchers could determine the distances and locations of these hydrogen concentrations relative to the sun's position. For example, two different clouds of neutral hydrogen both emit 21-centimeter radiation, but the wavelength emitted will look more intense with a higher peak if one looks along the length of a spiral arm rather than across it. Also, the component of an arm that is moving directly away from the sun will show the largest Doppler shift because it has the highest radial velocity and would be observed at a shorter wavelength than normally would be expected. Similarly, a spiral arm moving toward the sun would produce a spectral line Doppler shifted to longer wavelengths than normal.

Using these techniques, a picture could be constructed of the individual arms of the Galaxy. The Dutch were persistent in subsequent efforts to survey the Milky Way galaxy. With their war surplus antenna and two small hand cranks, the group tediously changed both the elevations and directions of the antenna every two and one-half minutes for almost two years. With Australian research in the Southern Hemisphere, combined with the data that was gathered from the Northern Hemisphere, both groups produced a joint effort: the Leiden-Sydney Map. This map described four extended spiral arms with many linked branches.

Impact of Event

The discovery of the 21-centimeter line by van de Hulst and the subsequent mapping of the Milky Way galaxy by Oort and his team by means of radio astronomy were essential to reveal the secrets of the structure of the Galaxy that interstellar dust had hidden and radio astronomy was able to penetrate. Light in conventional astronomy, however, is dimmed by some 40 percent in a direction vertical to the galactic plane to nearly total along or parallel to the plane of the Galaxy. Radio waves that are much longer in wavelength than the size of the atoms of hydrogen or even the dust particles easily pass around these obstacles. The much shorter-wavelength light waves, on the other hand, are either scattered or absorbed by these same particles.

For the radio astronomer, the significance of the Galaxy's spiral arms is the presence of great clouds of neutral hydrogen, the building blocks of bright young stars. The hydrogen gives off radio energy and the resulting Doppler shift is an indication of the relative distance and location of the clouds. As a result of the mapping, astronomers were presented a picture of the Milky Way galaxy that appeared to be older, generally larger, and far more complex than previously believed. With the radio mapping emerged a view of the Galaxy with vast dust clouds obscuring the galactic hub, with most of the gas and dust distributed along the spiral arms where new stars were thought to form. Instead of a simple pattern that most spirals exhibit, a much more complex pattern involving the spiral arms began to emerge. This mapping, when combined with Oort's earlier mapping of stellar motion, established the sun at an off-center galactic location rather than a central one as had been accepted for many years.

Another interesting result from these studies was the apparent pressure of a ring of material about 10,000 light-years from the center of the Galaxy moving outward at approximately 50 kilometers per second. Basic models of the Galaxy had no allowances for such a feature and were not able to explain it. In wedge-shaped regions of the Galaxy, radio mapping has not been possible. In these zones, the gaseous contents move parallel to the sun, allowing no observable motion toward or away from Earth and, hence, no apparent Doppler shift. Also, because of the absence of apparent relative motion, one cannot map near the galactic center. The uncertainty here is caused by individual hydrogen clouds having their own peculiar motions in a variety of directions. The Dutch and Australian map reflects this uncertainty in data collecting and shows a large pie-shaped wedge of missing information in a zone in the galactic plane opposite the solar system.

Bibliography

Berman, Louis, and John C. Evans. "Radio Mapping of Spiral Structure." In *Exploring the Cosmos*. 5th ed. Boston: Little, Brown, 1986. A clear discussion of the mapping of the Galaxy by the Dutch and Australian radio astronomers is accompanied by illustrations and diagrams. Suitable for the beginning astronomy student.

Bok, Bart J., and Priscilla F. Bok. *The Milky Way*. 5th ed. Cambridge, Mass.: Harvard University Press, 1981. A definitive discussion of the Milky Way galaxy is presented from a historical perspective, including the contributions of the Dutch radio astronomers in publishing a map of our galaxy. Ample photographs and illustrations make this a valuable resource for the astronomy student.

Chaisson, Eric. *Universe*. Englewood Cliffs, N.J.: Prentice-Hall, 1988. The text, in addition to being an excellent source of information for general astronomy, has two chapters that discuss 21-centimeter radiation and radio studies of the Milky Way. Several diagrams explain how motion of a galactic cloud can change one's perception of that cloud's Doppler shift spectrum. Suitable for the lay reader interested in general astronomy.

Oort, Jan H. "The Development of Our Insight into the Structure of the Galaxy between 1920 and 1940." *Annals of the New York Academy of Sciences* 198 (August, 1972): 255-265. An important source of galactic research during the period from 1920 to 1940 is discussed that had impact on Oort's work. Oort describes his earlier method of mapping the differential rotation of the Galaxy by plotting the motions of distant stars in the galactic plane. Suitable for a general reader of astronomical history.

Time-Life books, eds. *Galaxies*. Alexandria, Va.: Time-Life Books, 1988. The Time-Life books series on the universe will fascinate the general reader with its abundance of color diagrams, photographs, and sequential illustrations. The great astronomers who contributed to galactic structure are presented in historical context and their photographs are included. A glossary of technical terms is included in the appendix.

Michael L. Broyles

Cross-References

Jansky's Experiments Lead to the Founding of Radio Astronomy (1930), p. 934;

THE WORLD'S FIRST BREEDER REACTOR PRODUCES ELECTRICITY WHILE GENERATING NEW FUEL

Categories of event: Physics and applied science
Time: December 20, 1951
Locale: Arco, Idaho

Engineers and physicists at the Idaho National Engineering Laboratory successfully produced electricity from nuclear fission and in the process generated new fuel

Principal personage:
WALTER HENRY ZINN (1906-   ), the first director of the Argonne National Laboratory, who led a team of physicists who applied the science of nuclear fission

Summary of Event

The discovery of nuclear fission involved not only the discovery that a nucleus would split into two lighter elements but also the observation that significant amounts of energy were released at the same time. Besides the possibility that an explosive weapon could be constructed, early speculation about nuclear fission included its use in the generation of electricity. The occurrence of World War II meant that the explosive weapon was developed first. This was the first of several key decisions in the progress of nuclear science and its applications. Fear of what the enemy might be doing spurred the weapon program. Both the weapon technology and the basic physics for the electrical reactor had their beginnings in Chicago with the first nuclear chain reaction. The first self-sustaining nuclear chain reaction occurred in a laboratory at the University of Chicago on December 2, 1942. It also became apparent at that time that there was more than one way to build a bomb. At this point, two paths were taken: One was to build an atomic bomb with enough fissionable uranium in it to explode when detonated, and another path was to generate fissionable plutonium and build a bomb. In either process, energy was released, but the second method also produced another fissionable substance.

The observation that plutonium and energy could be produced together meant that it would be possible to design electric-power systems that would simultaneously produce fissionable plutonium in quantities as large as, or larger than, the amount of fissionable material consumed. This is the breeder concept, the idea that while using up fissionable uranium 235 (U 235), another fissionable element could be made. This concept was delayed until the end of World War II for its full development for electric power in the Fast Breeder Reactor (FBR) program.

On August 1, 1946, the Atomic Energy Commission (AEC) was established to control the development of nuclear energy and explore the peaceful uses of nuclear energy. The Argonne National Laboratory was assigned the major responsibilities for pioneering breeder reactor technologies; Walter Henry Zinn was its first director.

He led the team to plan a modest facility (Experimental Breeder Reactor I, EBR-I) for testing the validity of the breeding principle. Planning for this had begun in late 1944 and grew as a natural extension of the physics that developed the plutonium atomic bomb. The conceptual design details for a breeder-electric reactor were reasonably complete by late 1945. On March 1, 1949, the AEC announced the selection of a site in Idaho for the National Reactor Station (later to be named the Idaho National Engineering Laboratory, INEL). Construction at the INEL site in Arco, Idaho, began in October, 1949. Criticality was reached in August, 1951. (Criticality is the time when the nuclear fission produces a self-sustaining chain reaction—that time when some natural fission induces more fission in the neighboring nuclei.)

The system was brought to full operating power, 1.1 megawatt of thermal power, on December 19, 1951. The next day, December 20, at 11:00 A.M., steam was led to a turbine-generator. At 1:23 P.M., the generator was connected to the electrical grid at the site, and "electricity flowed from atomic energy," in the words of Zinn's console log of that day. Approximately 200 kilowatts of electric power were generated most of the time that the reactor was run. This was enough to satisfy the needs of the EBR-I facilities. The reactor was shut down in 1964 after five years of use primarily as a test facility, studying various fuel assemblies and cladding material for fuels. It also produced the first pure plutonium.

The reactor had several unique features because it was a first. It was also very different from the common light-water nuclear reactors used commercially throughout the United States to produce electricity. The key features were: Liquid metal, a sodium-potassium alloy, which is a liquid at room temperatures, was used as a coolant through the reactor, not water. The first several fuel loadings used highly enriched uranium (93 percent) metallic fuel, not 3 percent fuel that is more common in ordinary light-water reactors and not the oxide or ceramic form of the fuel. The neutrons that result from the fission and that perpetuate the chain reaction were not slowed down, or moderated, to thermal speeds. Hence, the name Fast Breeder Reactor, as distinguished from the more common thermal-neutron reactors. It is fast neutrons that allow the transmutations that produce the plutonium that is used as the new fuel.

With the first fuel loading, a conversion ratio of 1.01 was achieved, meaning that more new fuel was generated than was consumed by about 1 percent. When later fuel loadings were made with plutonium, the conversion ratios were more favorable, reaching as high as 1.27. EBR-I was the first reactor to generate its own fuel and the first power reactor to use plutonium as a fuel. The use of EBR-I also meant pioneering work on fuel recovery and reprocessing. During its five-year lifetime, EBR-I operated with four different fuel loadings, each designed to establish specific benchmarks of FBR technology. This reactor was seen as a first in a series of increasingly larger reactors in a program to develop the breeder technology fully. The reactor was replaced by EBR-II, which had been proposed in 1953 and was constructed from 1955 to 1964. EBR-II was capable of 62.5 megawatts of thermal power (20 megawatts electrical). This is approximately fifty times more powerful than EBR-I but still small compared to light water commercial reactors of 600 to 1,100 megawatts (electrical) in use during the end of the twentieth century.

The production of electricity and the lighting of a string of light bulbs is the event on December 20, 1951, that made newspaper headlines. There were less photogenic breakthroughs; among the significant engineering achievements was the use of a liquid metal coolant. The sodium-potassium alloy used in EBR-I reacts explosively with water and yet is used to turn water into steam. This system called for several engineering feats. Liquid metal was chosen for this particular reactor in Idaho because of its tremendous thermal conductivity. Liquid sodium is many times more efficient at transferring heat than water. The high efficiency of liquid metal coolant meant that the system could tolerate an intermediate loop, or secondary loop, of coolant between the reactor and the steam generators. The existence of the secondary loop served as a safety feature in the event that some of the coolant should inadvertently react with some of the water being turned into steam. Liquid metal coolants are used in the major breeder reactors in operation around the world. Its high heat transfer abilities offer other safety features, making it highly desirable and worthy of this developmental effort.

Following the completion of tests with the plutonium loading in 1964, EBR-I was shut down, placed in standby status; in 1966, it was declared a national historical landmark under the stewardship of the U.S. Department of the Interior. The facility was opened to the public in June, 1975.

Impact of Event

Some historians describe the World War II race for an atomic bomb as one that pitted the scientists of Germany against those of the United States, England, and Canada. Yet, some of those historians relate that the initial German interest in nuclear fission saw its potential for the production of electricity as more interesting than its potential as a weapon or a super bomb. The potential for peaceful uses of nuclear fission were dramatized with the start up of EBR-I in 1951. It was the first in the world to produce electricity, although it was also the pioneer in a breeder reactor program. The breeder program was not the only reactor program being developed and eventually lost out to the light-water reactor design for use in the United States. This is another of the major decision points in nuclear power development.

The full impact of the choice between breeder reactors and light-water reactors can be appreciated with a look at uranium. Nuclear fission supplies many times more energy than the combustion of fossil fuels. In doing so, it makes use of the rare form of the element uranium that undergoes fission, the isotope U 235. This isotope occurs at less than 1 percent abundance in naturally occurring uranium, and uranium is not considered to be an abundant element. Thus, while powerful, U 235 is rare. By developing a breeder reactor with fast neutrons, otherwise unfissionable uranium can be transmuted into a fissionable form of plutonium, generating new fuel. EBR-I, EBR-II, and the intended Clinch River Breeder Reactor were part of the plan to develop breeder reactor technology. It was argued that this would make the best use of limited uranium reserves. The Clinch River Breeder Reactor became a 1980 goal of President Richard Nixon in 1971; however, in 1977, President Jimmy Carter announced his plans to defer the FBR program. President Carter wanted to minimize the proliferation of fissionable material—material that could possibly make its way into a nuclear weapon. In 1983, the United States Congress terminated funding for the Clinch River Breeder Reactor. At that time, EBR-II had run continuously for nineteen years.

Breeder reactor development has been curtailed in the United States. If energy sources fall into short supply, it is likely that the technologies first developed with EBR-I will find new importance. In France and Japan, the newest commercial reactors make use of breeder reactor technology; they require extensive fuel reprocessing.

In the United States, various versions of the light-water reactor became the technology for general electrical production. The first commercial reactor, the Shippingport Atomic Power Station, near Pittsburgh, Pennsylvania, was a scaled-up version of the reactor used in the submarine USS *Nautilus*. These light-water reactors burn fissionable U 235. They do not use the reactive liquid metal coolant, and because they incorporate thermal-neutrons, they do not generate new fissionable material. They do not require fuel reprocessing.

Bibliography

Allardice, Corbin, and Edward R. Trapnell. *The Atomic Energy Commission*. New York: Praeger, 1974. A brief history of the AEC written from firsthand observations of early Atomic Energy Commission employees.

Compton, Arthur Holly. *Atomic Quest*. New York: Oxford University Press, 1956. A personal account of the research that led to the release of atomic energy by one who was an active participant in the atomic bomb work and the reactor development programs.

Dean, Gordon E. *Report on the Atom*. 2d ed. New York: Alfred A. Knopf, 1957. A description by a former Commission chairman of the major parts of the United States' atomic energy program in the 1950's.

Glasstone, Samuel. *Sourcebook on Atomic Energy*. 3d ed. Princeton, N.J.: Van Nostrand, 1967. A compilation of useful atomic energy information in a textbook format.

Holl, Jack M., Roger M. Anders, Alice L. Buck. *United States Civilian Nuclear Power Policy, 1954-1984: A Summary History*. Springfield, Va.: National Technical Information Sources, 1986. Factual and without interpretation. For the technical reader.

Little (Arthur D.) Inc. *Atoms for Peace: U.S.A. 1958*. Edited by John F. Hogerton. Cambridge, Mass., 1958. A pictorial representation of the early atomic installations in the United States.

Mazuzan, George T., and J. Samuel Walker. *Controlling the Atom: The Beginnings of Nuclear Regulation, 1946-1962*. Berkeley: University of California Press, 1985. A comprehensive study.

Murray, Raymond L. *Understanding Radioactive Waste.* 3d ed. Columbus, Ohio: Battelle Press, 1989. Easy-to-understand explanation of fuel reprocessing and waste handling.

Rhodes, Richard. *The Making of the Atomic Bomb.* New York: Simon & Schuster, 1986. A charming and very readable account of the people, the politics, and the times up to the breeder reactor technology.

Rose, David J. *Learning About Energy.* New York: Plenum Press, 1986. Although it has only one chapter on nuclear power, it places the entire breeder program in context, although rather technically.

Donald H. Williams

Cross-References

Hahn Splits an Atom of Uranium (1938), p. 1135; Fermi Creates the First Controlled Nuclear Fission Chain Reaction (1942), p. 1198; The World's First Nuclear Reactor Is Activated (1943), p. 1230; The First Atomic Bomb Is Successfully Detonated (1945), p. 1265; Teller and Ulam Develop the First H-Bomb (1951), p. 1401. The United States Opens the First Commercial Nuclear Power Plant (1957), p. 1557; The Chernobyl Nuclear Reactor Explodes (1986), p. 2321.

ASERINSKY DISCOVERS RAPID EYE MOVEMENT (REM) IN SLEEP AND DREAMS

Category of event: Medicine
Time: 1952
Locale: University of Chicago, Chicago, Illinois

Aserinsky's discovery of rapid eye movements (REMs) in normal human sleep provided the first objective method of studying neural function and behavioral patterns associated with dreaming

Principal personages:

EUGENE ASERINSKY (1921-   ), a graduate student of physiology at the University of Chicago whose investigations led to a major scientific breakthrough in sleep research

NATHANIEL KLEITMAN (1895-   ), the Russian-born professor of physiology at the University of Chicago under whom Aserinsky worked and with whom he collaborated on sleep research

WILLIAM DEMENT (1928-   ), an American physiologist who confirmed Aserinsky and Kleitman's hypothesis that REM periods of brain activity during sleep are highly correlated with dreaming

Summary of Event

As early as 1867, a German psychiatrist named Wilhelm Griesinger speculated on the occurrence of eye movements during dreams. These eye movements, he believed, occurred both during the transition from wakefulness to sleep and during dreaming. From these observations, he concluded that sleep was not a passive but rather an active state. It was another eighty-five years before Eugene Aserinsky (under the guidance of Nathaniel Kleitman) discovered that sleep is not a homogeneous process but is organized in rhythmic cycles of different stages, each of which is characterized by specific behavioral, electrophysiologic, autonomic, and endocrine changes.

After studying with a French physiologist, Kleitman had sought to provide a thorough physiological description of sleep. His 1939 book (updated in 1963), entitled *Sleep and Wakefulness*, constitutes an encyclopedic compendium on the subject; its bibliographic thoroughness has remained unsurpassed.

In 1952, Aserinsky, a graduate student working on his dissertation in the physiology laboratory of Nathaniel Kleitman at the University of Chicago, achieved a breakthrough in modern sleep research. Aserinsky turned his attention to the study of attention in children, using his young son, Armond, as one of his subjects. (According to Aserinsky, the first hint of the presence of REMs came about during the recording of Armond.) While making clinical observations of his young subject's efforts to attend, he noticed that eye closure was associated with attentional lapse, and thus decided to record these eyelid movements using the electrooculogram

(EOG). Aserinsky and Kleitman observed that a series of bursts of rapid eye movements occurred about four to six times during the night. The first such REM period took place about an hour after the onset of sleep and lasted from five to ten minutes. Succeeding REM periods occurred at intervals of about ninety minutes each and lasted progressively longer; the final period occupied approximately thirty minutes. (As was later learned, about one fifth of an adult's typical sleep is REM sleep; however, the percentage is much higher in infants. Animals of many kinds also have REM periods during their sleep.)

Suspecting a correlation of eye movements with dreaming, Aserinsky and Kleitman awakened subjects during REM periods and asked them whether they had been dreaming. In a large majority of such awakenings, the subjects acknowledged that they had been dreaming and proceeded to relate their dreams. When a subject was reawakened while his eyes were quiescent, he could rarely remember a dream. Therefore, Aserinsky and Kleitman concluded that rapid eye movements were an objective signal of dreaming. Thus, although investigators still had to rely upon the dreamer's verbal report to ascertain the content of the dream, the process of dreaming was now opened up to objective study under laboratory conditions.

In order to obtain a more complete representation of the attentional state of his subjects, Aserinsky also recorded brain-wave activity with an electroencephalograph (EEG). This combination of measures was fortuitous because, unlike adults, children often enter the REM phase immediately at sleep onset; and these sleep-onset REM periods are especially likely to occur during daytime naps. When Aserinsky's subjects lost attentional focus and fell asleep, their EEGs showed an activation pattern, and their EOGs showed rapid eye movements. Kleitman quickly deduced that this brain-activated sleep state, with its rapid eye movements, might be associated with dreaming. The two investigators immediately applied the combined EEG and EOG measures to the sleep of adult humans and were able to observe the periodic alternation of REM and non-REM sleep throughout the night. In addition, when the investigators awakened their subjects during REM sleep, these subjects related accounts of dreams.

In 1953, Aserinsky and Kleitman reported their findings in the journal *Science* in an article entitled "Regularly Occurring Periods of Eye Motility and Concomitant Phenomena During Sleep." As is the case with many breakthrough articles, this one was relatively brief (barely two pages). Yet, it included the observation that other physiological functions change with the state of the brain mind: Respiratory frequency and heart rate had both been noted as increasing, and their rhythm became irregular.

To describe Aserinsky and Kleitman's series of experiments (reported in the 1953 article) in more detail, eye movements were recorded by EOGs by employing two sets of leads on each eye, measuring horizontal and vertical changes in corneoretinal movement. The criterion for identification of eye movement was confirmed by direct observation of several subjects under both weak and gradually intensified illumination. Under the latter condition, video recordings were taken of two subjects without awakening them, thereby further confirming the validity of the investigators' methods and also the synchronicity of eye movements.

Twenty normal adult subjects were used in several series of experiments. To confirm the conjecture that this particular eye activity was associated with dreaming, ten sleeping individuals in fourteen experiments were awakened and interrogated during the occurrence of this eye movement and also after a period of at least thirty minutes to three hours of nonocular movement. After twenty-seven interrogations during periods of rapid eye movement, twenty responses involved recall of dreams full of detailed visual imagery. Of twenty-three interrogations during ocular inactivity, nineteen subjects disclosed a complete failure of recall.

In another series of experiments, periods of REM were timed during an uninterrupted seven-hour sleep; and in another series, the respiratory and heart rate were calculated during eye movement and compared with a similar period of time during ocular quiescence. Given the fact that these eye movements, EEG pattern (the EEG was used in conjunction with the EOG), and autonomic nervous system activity were significantly related and did not occur randomly, Aserinsky and Kleitman theorized that these physiological phenomena, and presumably dreaming, were very likely all manifestations of a particular level of cortical activity which is encountered normally during sleep. An eye movement period first appeared about three hours after going to sleep, recurred two hours later, and then emerged at somewhat closer intervals a third or fourth time shortly prior to awakening. This investigative method furnished the means of determining the incidence and duration of dream periods.

Aserinsky and Kleitman provided more systematic observations of this phase of ocular motility in sleep in an article entitled "Two Types of Ocular Motility Occurring in Sleep," published in the *Journal of Applied Physiology* in 1955. This classic paper first described in detail the link between dreaming and rapid eye movements, only briefly mentioned in their earlier article.

William Dement, a physiologist and subsequent collaborator of Kleitman's, later confirmed Aserinsky and Kleitman's hypothesis. Also, following Aserinsky and Kleitman's groundbreaking article on human REM sleep in 1953, and their immediate recognition of REM as the physiological basis of dreaming, Dement established that an identical phase of sleep occurs in cats; he published his results in the 1958 *EEG Journal*.

Impact of Event

Aserinsky's discovery stimulated extensive research on the physiological aspects of REM sleep. Among the earliest discoveries was that of a characteristic brain-wave pattern accompanying REM sleep. This pattern is distinguished by rapid, low-voltage waves, not unlike those that occur in the waking state but very different from the slower, high-voltage waves of non-REM sleep. During REM sleep, breathing and pulse rates are more irregular than during non-REM sleep, suggesting emotional disturbance; there is a relaxation of the head and neck muscles; and, in men, the penis becomes partially or fully erect.

Studies of the relationship of the subject matter of dreams to physiological changes during REM periods have not sufficiently established any close correlations. Although early investigations indicated that the pattern of eye movements is correlated with the directions in which the dreamer is looking in the dream, subsequent evidence raises serious doubt concerning this hypothesis. More conclusive evidence exists demonstrating the theory that dreaming can sometimes occur during non-REM periods. This possibility suggests that dreaming may be more or less continuous during sleep, but that conditions for the recall of dreams are more favorable following REM awakenings than otherwise. In any case, the prevailing view is that REMs are not an objective sign of all dreaming, but that they indicate reliably when a dream is most likely to be recalled.

Aserinsky's discovery of a stage of sleep during which most dreaming seems to occur led to experiments to investigate what would happen if a sleeping person were deprived of REM sleep. These studies concluded that there is an overwhelming demand for REM sleep. Because REM sleep usually accompanies dreaming, it was also concluded from these studies that there is a strong need to dream. Later studies with prolonged deprivation of REM sleep, however, did not confirm the degree of behavioral changes noted earlier. Thus, it can be concluded that there is definitely a need for REM sleep, but the question of whether there is also a need to dream is still open to debate.

By using an EEG to monitor sleep during the night and by awakening subjects during REM periods, it has been conclusively established that everyone normally dreams every night. Even a person who has never remembered a dream in his or her life will do so if awakened during an REM period.

New methods of collecting dreams have given rise to new methods of analyzing them. The principal method employed in analyzing reported dreams, whether collected in the laboratory or at home, is content analysis. This method consists of classifying the various elements that appear in dreams (for example, males and females, familiar persons and strangers, and objects).

The understanding of dreams has been greatly advanced in the twentieth century not only by analytic work but also by Aserinsky's discovery of REM sleep. The discovery that REM sleep is regularly recurrent, and that dreaming is its concomitant state of consciousness, opened the doors to a truly objective investigative approach to the mind-brain question. The recognition of REM sleep as a predictable phase of brain activity in the sleep of all mammals further provided animal models for in-depth exploration of the physical basis of dreaming. Consequently, explicit theories of how REM sleep is generated became possible; also, many puzzling features of the dream state could be accounted for in physiological terms.

Bibliography

Cohen, David B. *Sleeping and Dreaming.* New York: Pergamon Press, 1979. Although this thorough investigation of the origins, nature, and functions of sleeping and dreaming discusses the advances in sleep research since Aserinsky and Kleitman, Cohen discusses the work of these two scientists in its historical context. First half of book is devoted to REM sleep. Contains references, name and subject index.

Hobson, J. Allan. *The Dreaming Brain*. New York: Basic Books, 1988. This eminently readable work written for layperson and expert alike, discusses the brain-based approach to dreaming. It covers dream research from the nineteenth century to 1988. In a chapter on the discovery of REM sleep and dreaming, Hobson discusses the work of Aserinsky and Kleitman. Contains excellent bibliography.

Horne, James. *Why We Sleep*. New York: Oxford University Press, 1988. In this work, geared toward the layperson as well as the expert, the author discusses the functions of sleep in humans and other mammals. In the chapter on REM sleep, the work of Aserinsky and Kleitman is briefly mentioned.

Kleitman, Nathaniel. *Sleep and Wakefulness*. Rev. ed. Chicago: University of Chicago Press, 1963. Referred to as the "old testament of sleep research," this classic work is a scholarly and encyclopedic summary of all of the relevant research in sleep from 1939 to 1963. Contains voluminous bibliography, with more than four thousand entries.

Oswald, Ian. *Sleeping and Waking*. New York: Elsevier, 1962. This brief and somewhat technical work is devoted to the psychology and physiology of sleep and waking. It offers an account of the advances in sleep research since Kleitman's *Sleep and Wakefulness* and briefly alludes to Aserinsky's work in the section dealing with REM sleep.

Genevieve Slomski

Cross-References

Berger Develops the Electroencephalogram (EEG) (1929), p. 890; Wilkins Discovers Reserpine, the First Tranquilizer (1950's), p. 1353; Sperry Discovers That Each Side of the Brain Can Function Independently (1960's), p. 1635; Hounsfield Introduces a CAT Scanner That Can See Clearly into the Body (1972), p. 1961.

GREAT EVENTS
FROM
HISTORY II

CHRONOLOGICAL LIST OF EVENTS

VOLUME I

VOLUME II

VOLUME III

VOLUME IV

VOLUME V